VHF/UHF Handbook

Editor: Dick Biddulph, G8DPS

Radio Society of Great Britain

Published by the Radio Society of Great Britain, Cranborne Road, Potters Bar, Herts EN6 3JE.

First published 1997, reprinted digitally 2002 onwards

ISBN 1 872309 42 9

Publisher's note

The opinions expressed in this book are those of the editor and contributors and not necessarily those of the RSGB. While the information presented is believed to be correct, the editor, contributors, publisher and their agents cannot accept responsibility for consequences arising from any inaccuracies or omissions.

Cover design: Anne McVicar.

Illustrations: Derek Cole and Bob Ryan (Radio Society of Great Britain), Ray Eckersley, and Jean Faithfull.

Production: Mark Allgar RSGB Typography: Ray Eckersley, Seven Stars Publishing.

Printed in Great Britain by Page Bros Ltd, Norwich.

Acknowledgements

The principal contributors to this book were:

Chapter 1	– 'Introduction to VHF/UHF'	Dave Stockton, GM4ZNX
Chapter 2	– 'Getting started'	Dick Pascoe, G0BPS
Chapter 3	– 'Propagation'	Ray Flavell, G3LTP
Chapter 4	– 'Receivers, transmitters and transceivers'	Mike Wooding, G6IQM Steve Thompson, G8GSQ Geoff Pike, GI0GDP
Chapter 5	– 'Antennas and transmission lines'	Peter Swallow, G8EZE
Chapter 6	– 'EMC'	Dave Lauder, G0SNO
Chapter 7	– 'Data modes'	Chris Lorek, G4HCL
Chapter 8	– 'Amateur television'	Brian Kelly, GW6BWX
Chapter 9	– 'Satellite communications'	Ron Broadbent, G3AAJ
Chapter 10	– 'Repeaters'	Geoff Dover, G4AFJ
Chapter 11	– 'Test equipment, methods and accessories'	Clive Smith, G4FZH
Chapter 12	– 'General data'	Dick Biddulph, G8DPS
Appendix 2	– 'Fitting coaxial connectors'	Roger Blackwell, G4PMK

Acknowledgement is also made to the authors of articles published in *Radio Communication* and other magazines from which extracts have been made. In this connection, thanks are due to the publishers of *Ham Radio*, *Practical Wireless* and *VHF Communications* for permission to reproduce copyright material. Acknowledgement is also due to Jaybeam Engineering Ltd for permission to reproduce certain charts appearing in Chapter 5. Other acknowledgements are made in the text where appropriate.

Contents

Acknowledgements. iii

Preface vii

1   Introduction to VHF/UHF 1.1

2   Getting started 2.1

3   Propagation 3.1

4   Receivers, transmitters and transceivers 4.1

5   Antennas and transmission lines. 5.1

6   EMC 6.1

7   Data modes 7.1

8   Amateur television 8.1

9   Satellite communications. 9.1

10 Repeaters 10.1

11 Test equipment, methods and accessories. . . 11.1

12 General data. 12.1

    Appendix 1: PCB layouts A1.1

    Appendix 2: Fitting coaxial connectors. A2.1

    Index. ix

Preface

SINCE the last edition of the *VHF/UHF Manual* was published in 1983 there has been rapid progress, particularly in the hardware associated with VHF and UHF. For example, it is now possible to build a legal-limit linear amplifier using only solid-state devices. In reception, devices with very low noise levels have appeared and, furthermore, integrated circuits containing most of the 'works' of a receiver have also arrived on the scene.

There is one major departure in this book from its predecessor – no microwave chapter. This is because there is now the *Microwave Handbook* published by the RSGB. There is a little overlap as both books contain information on the 23cm (1.3GHz) band. Another area left out, apart from its operation, is mobile work since nearly everyone uses commercial equipment now.

The only disappointing trend since the *VHF/UHF Manual* was last published is the reduction in interest in home construction. One of the aims of this book is to promote that facet of amateur radio by including tried and tested circuits for receivers and transverters as well as for building blocks for receivers, transceivers and transmitters. It is the editor's belief that any amateur ought to be able, and should be encouraged, to build something, even a complete receiver, transmitter or transceiver. These should be at least as good as the commercial articles but may not be as neat or as small. By doing this, he or she can incorporate only the 'bells and whistles' that are needed.

Dick Biddulph, G8DPS

1 Introduction to VHF/UHF

WHAT IS VHF/UHF?

The electromagnetic spectrum cannot be infinite due to limitations imposed by the finite age of our universe and by there only being a finite amount of energy in it. Nevertheless, the range of frequencies at which something, somewhere, is happening is immense. The (relatively) much smaller range of frequencies used for deliberate communication is still too big to contemplate all at once.

VHF (very high frequencies) is the name given to the 30 to 300MHz part of the electromagnetic spectrum. *UHF* (ultra high frequencies) is the name given to the 300 to 3000MHz part.

The whole of the 'radio' part of the electromagnetic spectrum is divided into a series of named ranges. The boundaries between ranges are at 3, 30, 300, 3000MHz (or not quite exactly at 100, 10, 1, 0.1 metres wavelength). Fig 1.1 shows the broad picture of the electromagnetic spectrum. Fig 1.2 focuses on the part of the spectrum used for radio communications.

The boundaries were just chosen arbitrarily at nice, round, numbers. Nothing abrupt happens at them. It is well known that there are differences in the propagation characteristics of radio signals of different frequencies, but these are caused by the environment – our atmosphere and terrain – rather than being direct consequences of the frequency of the signal. As a result of changing weather and upper-atmospheric conditions, the frequencies where changes in propagation effects occur are not fixed. They can move by at least a factor of 10, and the changes may be abrupt or gradual. Without any fixed natural landmarks, any fixed divisions have to be arbitrary. Any attempt to fix boundaries based on the different technologies we use would fare no better, as they too would shift as new technologies evolve.

30 to 3000MHz is still a very large chunk of spectrum, and while someone studying propagation may be interested in the whole of it, most amateur interest naturally focuses on the bands where our licences permit us to transmit. Table 1.1 shows the worldwide VHF and UHF amateur bands.

Table 1.1. VHF/UHF amateur bands in the IARU Regions

Band (MHz)	Region 1	Region 2	Region 3
50–54	UK 50–52MHz*	Yes	Yes
144–146	Yes	Yes	Yes*
146–148	No	Yes	Yes*
220–225	No	Yes*	No
430–440	Yes*	Yes*	Yes*
902–928	No	Yes*	No
1240–1300	Yes*	Yes*	Yes*
2300–2450	Yes*	Yes*	Yes*

*Shared band

THE BORDER WITH MICROWAVES

Although the formal definition of UHF extends up to 3000MHz, traditionally some of the higher-frequency part of the range has been considered to be 'microwaves' and treated separately, with its own technologies, literature and specialists. The word 'microwave' does not feature on the HF, VHF, UHF, SHF, EHF etc scale. It's really an older name from an earlier nomenclature of the spectrum and overlays part of UHF upwards, right up to infra-red light. It doesn't have any definite frequency boundaries, but you will find that contests, specialist groups and specialist publications have drawn their own (sometimes different) arbitrary lines and class everything higher in frequency as 'microwaves'.

Historically, microwaves were treated separately from the rest of radio technology because of the very different techniques that had to be used at such frequencies. Waveguide structures, dishes, horns, klystrons, and cavity magnetrons made up the armoury of the microwave engineer. Active devices were unusual in that the dimensions of their internal components were chosen to be resonant at their intended operating frequency. Conventional radio techniques of the time were simply not capable of approaching these frequencies. Lumped components and pin-based valves worked well into the VHF region, while microwave components had an effective limit to how low a frequency they could be made for – imposed simply by what physical size could be tolerated.

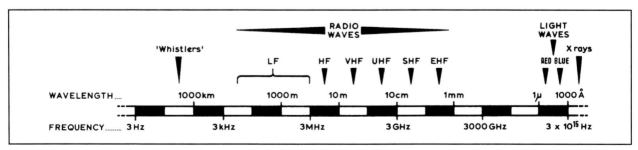

Fig 1.1. The electromagnetic spectrum

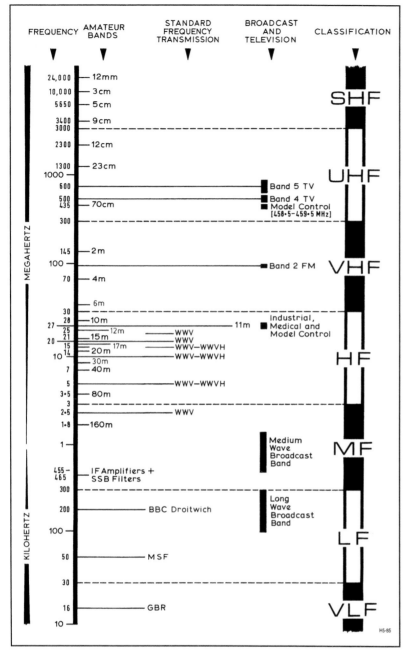

Fig 1.2. Amateur bands in relation to other services

this band has reinforced this. There is a still-higher UHF band at 2310MHz, but it is currently thought of as being a microwave band even though it's definitely in the UHF range. Technology continues to advance and the '13cm' band at 2310MHz may eventually be poached from the microwave people . . .

THE BORDER WITH HF

Radio signals do not halt obediently at national borders, so the governments of the world have long been forced to meet in order to plan the usage of the electromagnetic spectrum. The level of chaos that would result without meticulously detailed planning is a powerful incentive. Even those nations who frequently refuse to sit around the same table send their representatives, who sit down and get on with some good, pragmatic compromising. The ITU is the overall international co-ordinating body for all communications, covering wired and optical fibre systems as well as radio. The CCIR is its main committee on radio matters. The large spectrum management meetings are called the *World Administrative Radio Conferences* (WARCs), and are usually given a year number suffix. WARCs are not held regularly, but are called when there is sufficient need. The amount of information gathering and planning needed to put together proposals for such meetings mean that several years notice is normally given, though it may be less if the amount of spectrum scheduled for review is limited. WARC79 was a major one which reviewed the entire spectrum and gave us three new HF amateur bands. There have since been a number of smaller conferences but WARC97 is the next major one.

The HF-VHF boundary, at 30MHz, is the major breakpoint in this planning process. Signals below 30MHz are treated as if they could propagate over the entire planet, and thus need to be co-ordinated globally. Those above 30MHz are treated as if long-distance propagation is rare, and so need only relatively local co-ordination. This is rather simplistic and fails to take into account the large variations in propagation that occur in this area, but it has been made to work reasonably well to date. Consequently, changes to the plans above 30MHz can be made readily by more frequent and smaller meetings than the global-scale ones that have to be called to make decisions below 30MHz. Above 30MHz, the ITU regulations give a lot more freedom for individual administrations to create their own variations to suit their particular countries. In the UK, these freedoms can be seen in the existence of the 4m and 6m bands as well as the Class B licence.

PREHISTORY

Faraday, Oersted, Gauss and others had discovered that there was some sort of relationship between electric charge,

Progress is rarely smooth, and the frantic development of centimetric radar in the 'forties was a sudden jump to much higher frequencies than had ever before been used. It opened up a gap in the VHF/UHF region where available techniques were much less advanced than those used at both lower and higher frequencies. Subsequent advances have filled in the gap, and the whole of the VHF/UHF range is now fought over as prime territory for many different uses. Modern semiconductors, surface-mount components, and stripline techniques allow printed circuit type construction to be used well into microwave territory. The 1296MHz amateur band used to be considered to be a microwave band, but advancing technology has meant that techniques used at 144 and 430MHz can now be used at 1296MHz, so it is now firmly in the UHF fold. The appearance of commercially made equipment for motion and magnetism. They had performed a variety of experiments and evolved a number of theories, but there was something missing. The ideas of forces that acted at right-angles to motion and action at a distance seemed bizarre compared to classical mechanics. James Clark Maxwell set out to tidy up the theories, and produce something simpler that would collect them all together and cover all the known phenomena. Between 1864 and 1873 he published four very small equations that did just that. They were written in partial-differential form, in a dialect of mathematics he had learned at Cambridge. They were quite general and covered all conditions, but when they were used to study what would happen if an electric charge was oscillated, they predicted something new. They predicted that it would cause a pair of moving waves, one of electric field, the other of magnetic field, to radiate away from it. They also predicted that the waves would be in phase with each other, moving at the same speed, the speed of light. They showed that the two fields would be oriented at right-angles to each other, and be transverse to the direction of propagation. The concept of electromagnetic waves had been born.

Theory is fine, as far as it goes, but experimental verification does a lot to help make it believable. The first experiment looked like a disaster. Maxwell had thought of how sound waves are carried in air, and how waves of the nautical sort are carried in water, and proposed that there had to be a medium that carried electromagnetic waves. It was called the *ether*. Michelson and Morley devised a neat experiment in 1881 to prove the existence of the ether. Surprisingly, it proved that the ether did not exist. This destroyed the concept of any sort of carrier medium for electromagnetic waves, and caused a great upset that eventually resulted in the theories of relativity. It did not destroy Maxwell's equations, though. They described moving waves, irrespective of whatever they did or did not move in. Maxwell's equations similarly survived the theories of relativity, and are still believed to be generally valid today.

Heinrich Hertz set out to make some electromagnetic waves. Michelson and Morley had needed waves of extremely short wavelength to make their experiment practicable, and had chosen light (wavelength about 0.0005mm). Hertz wanted to show the relationship with electricity and used a gapped metal ring which he excited with a spark. His receiver was a second gapped ring which would spark across its gap if it was close enough when the transmitter was excited. Using amazingly simple apparatus, he showed that electromagnetic waves did indeed travel at the speed of light. He demonstrated polarisation and the fact that the electric and magnetic field components lay in orthogonal planes, transverse to the direction of motion. With different-sized rings he made signals of different wavelengths, and showed that a similar-sized receiving ring was needed to be able to detect a signal.

Many people believe that radio started on long wave, and only much later expanded into the VHF, then UHF, regions. This is completely wrong! Hertz had chosen to make his apparatus a comfortable size for bench-top experimentation. His early experiments were at UHF, about 800MHz, as a consequence. Just for fun, it could be argued that because Hertz's receiver produced light as its output, then the first-ever radio link was in fact UHF television. Admittedly, it was only of one pixel resolution, but at least its intensity could be varied!

Hertz had no interest in long-distance communication. He had been inspired by the work of Helmholtz and Maxwell, and had produced the necessary experimental support for their theories. 'Action at a distance' was no longer dubious, it was demonstrable. Hertz's work, in its turn, was the inspiration for others. Marconi saw great possibilities in developing Hertz's laboratory toys. After a start at UHF, radio technology entered a period of rapid evolution with antennas getting higher, power levels getting higher and frequencies getting far lower.

HISTORY

The history of the development of long-wave communications and broadcasting, followed by the revolutionary discovery of the capabilities of short waves is widely known and oft repeated. Comparatively unknown, perhaps simply lost in the tumult of new LF/HF developments, people were experimenting at even higher frequencies.

In 1919, Marconi was experimenting at 150MHz, pushing the limits of what valves could then do. He used dipole antennas with the oscillator and detector placed right at their centres, and used parabolic reflectors to form the emission into a narrow beam. Also in 1919, Barkhausen discovered that ordinary, cylindrical anode, triodes could be made to oscillate internally. Frequencies up to 900MHz could be created under very peculiar bias conditions, with the anode slightly negative and the grid at a high positive voltage.

In 1920, Hull applied a strong magnetic field to a simple diode valve. He could make the electrons spiral out from the cathode to the anode because their trajectories were bent by the magnetic field. With a strong enough field, the anode current cut off as the electrons went into circular orbits. With anode current flowing, useful oscillation could be achieved to several hundred megahertz. A later refinement, splitting the cylindrical anode into two pieces with separate connections, made it much easier to extract a signal from the valve, and the magnetron was born. George Jessop reported that one commercial type was capable of 50W output at 144MHz. This was before strong, compact, permanent magnets had been developed, so early magnetrons were rather unwieldy – just recall the loudspeakers of the period with their huge permanent magnets or large field-coils.

The discovery, by amateurs, that the short waves were not after all useless, but instead were dramatically better than long waves for long-distance communication, made people wonder what might be found at still higher frequencies. If a move to higher frequencies produced wonderful results, then maybe going still higher might produce still . . . people had to try it. It was not long before commercial use of the short waves started. This fuelled the development of improved valves for high-frequency use.

One proud tradition of amateur radio – give an amateur a new device and he'll soon extract more power and higher frequencies from it than the designer ever thought possible – goes right back to the beginning. HF ionospheric propagation had been explored with signals coaxed out of valves intended for LF use. Small 'short-wave' triodes with the electrode connections brought straight out of the bulb to avoid the stray capacitance and inductive coupling of conventionally-based types proved useful up to 50–70MHz.

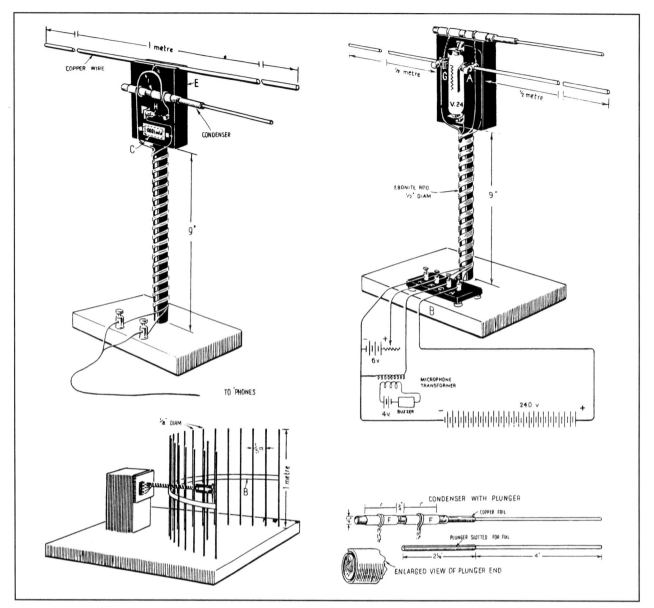

Fig 1.3. Marconi's 2m receiver and transmitter, made in 1919, which demonstrated the production of a beam using a parabolic reflector

All valves were very expensive in this period, so minimising the number needed was a very high priority. A typical transmitter would have been a pair of triodes configured as a push-pull oscillator, while super-regenerative receivers provided the necessary sensitivity with the minimum number of valves. Wire antennas were used, based on those used at lower frequencies.

In Japan, Yagi and Uda were experimenting with arrays of dipoles and had discovered the ability of non-driven dipoles to reflect or direct the signals from a driven one. From this, in the late 'twenties, they developed the *Yagi-Uda array*, much better known as the *Yagi antenna*. The ability of this new antenna to concentrate the radiated power in a narrow beam made up for the difficulty of generating appreciable power at higher frequencies, though only in the direction it was pointed. Marconi experimented with Yagi antennas and special valves at 500MHz and proved that communication beyond the visible horizon was possible. Up to this time, VHF and UHF

signals had been assumed to behave like light, and the first sign of a flaw in this belief helped to stimulate increased interest in these frequencies.

Commercial research is done with a view to eventual profit. Academic research is done with a view to the publication of new knowledge. Both have to justify their existence; there has to be some possible outcome that can be explained to the controllers of their sources of funding. We amateurs are free to explore where our interests take us. We may not have industrial-strength budgets to spend, but we do have a unique level of freedom. In the late 'twenties, SSB was invented by a telephone company as a means of multiplexing several telephone channels onto one wire. It was considered to be esoteric and rather fragile in view of the quality of cable it needed to make it work acceptably. No-one thought that a radio connection could be good enough to carry it until amateurs demonstrated reliable intercontinental SSB contacts. Earlier, it was the sheer number of amateur stations, their geographic diversity and their operation at all hours that allowed the totally unexpected propagation effects of HF to be discovered.

The amateurs exploring VHF were developing new techniques and setting new records. Almost everything that could be thought of was being tried. The small size of efficient VHF antennas must have made trials from aircraft seem natural. One VHF DX-pedition of 1935 ran an extensively equipped 5m station at the top of Snowdon and logged a 205-mile contact with Romford, Essex.

An early 2.3GHz klystron oscillator and receiver

Higher-frequency bands were tried and techniques were developed to suit them. Coaxial cavities and troughlines gave the frequency stability needed to get results on 112MHz. 'Acorn' valves like the 955 triode appeared and were pressed into service up to 500MHz. Their extremely direct electrode connections and small size made them ideal.

WAR

The 1939–1945 period saw some of the most intense development of radio and electronics ever. The skills of the radio amateurs were quickly put to work as operators, technicians, instructors and researchers. Because of the amateur's insatiable desire for long-distance contacts, much of the commercially made equipment for the amateur market represented the state of the art. The American Hallicrafters S27 receiver covered from 28 to 142MHz and proved to be the only available instrument that could be used in the hunt for the first VHF radio navigational aids that had been revealed in notes from crashed aircraft. According to an unsubstantiated legend, the entire stock of S27s at Webbs Radio, Soho, was bought up by an RAF signals officer – on credit! One lesson learned from this was that even line-of sight frequencies can be used over large distances when one station is on a high-flying aircraft, without needing any help from unusual propagation. The navigational beams were simple extensions of the Lorenz landing aid that had been developed in the mid-'thirties. The ILS system still in use today is a direct descendant.

The possibility of making directional antennas of convenient size made the VHF part of the spectrum the natural choice for beam-type navigational systems. Throughout the war a cat-and-mouse game of progressively more sophisticated navigational systems and their subsequent countermeasures was played. Perhaps we ought not to get too focused on the interesting technology of it all – we must always remember that these 'games' were literally deadly to people on both sides. As fast as new valves could be developed to make high power at higher frequencies, radar moved up in frequency to take advantage of the increased directivity of the antennas that could be made in the available space. Night fighters were larger than their daytime equivalents and had arrays of Yagi beam antennas pointing forwards from their noses. Imagine a respectable 2m or 70cm moonbounce array bolted to the front of an aircraft! Ground-based radar could detect nocturnal

bombers, and could direct fighters to their rough location, but the fighters needed their own radar to close the remaining distance.

In the late 'thirties, a system of electronically-scanned television had been developed at EMI to challenge Baird's mechanically scanned system. This had created a whole new sort of electronics: sawtooth 'timebase' oscillators, cathode-ray tubes, pulse amplifiers, synchronisation and triggering circuits. Previously the only signals that anyone had had much experience with had been sine waves, speech and modulated sine waves. Britain's lead in the strange new circuits of electronic television was a great help to the radar pioneers. Because several megahertz of bandwidth were needed to transmit what was then called 'high-definition' 405-line television, operation in the deserted parts of the VHF band was inevitable. Not only did television create the signal-processing circuits needed by radar, but it also created the high-power VHF transmitter technology. After the war, radar repaid its debts because the new valves and circuits that had been developed for it gave a flying re-start to the infant TV industry.

Ships' masts are the obvious mountings for sea-borne radar antennas, and for an uninterrupted view, the radar antenna has to go on top. This means that the size of the antenna has a large effect on the stability of the ship as well as on its visibility. Rayleigh's criterion from optics works for all wave phenomena, so the Royal Navy was able to estimate what angular resolution it needed, and what size of antenna it could tolerate, in order to decide on the minimum frequency they needed. They commissioned a team at Birmingham University to develop radar at 3000MHz. This was a huge step from the existing systems which had been in the 30, 50 and 200MHz regions. Radar requires very high peak power pulsed transmitters and the increase in frequency required a step far beyond the limits of any known technology. One group at Birmingham based their work on the klystron valve that was known to be able to oscillate at 3GHz, but they could not achieve anything like the power output needed. Instead, the klystron was to prove useful as the receiver local oscillator. In one of those jokes that Nature sometimes plays, John Randall and Harry Boot were working on the Barkhausen-Kurz oscillator (the mis-biased triode described earlier) to develop it as the receiver local oscillator. Eventually, they gave up hope of getting enough power to drive a mixer, or good enough frequency stability, and switched their attentions to the split-anode magnetron. This was at least known to be capable of moderate power, although the frequency stability was known to be poor.

Randall and Boot attacked the frequency stability issue by replacing the simple split anode with a solid block of copper, drilled to make a group of resonant chambers, sized for the wanted frequency. Their prototype had six resonator cavities, each linked to the central cavity by a slot. It was reputed to have been made by using the cylinder of a revolver as a drilling jig. It burned out their dummy load and easily produced several hundred watts, close to the intended frequency. Permanent magnets had been greatly improved by this time, and the quest for a receiver LO had produced a marvellous high-power transmitter. Small, robust, and efficient, the cavity magnetron was simply ideal, and could easily produce peak powers of many kilowatts in pulsed radar duty. Klystrons, which had started out being groomed for the power output job, made great LOs for superhet receivers. Centimetric radar had arrived, right at the upper limit of UHF.

Just after the war, many people were using beam antennas, crystal-controlled transmitters and superheterodyne receivers. The first trans-American contact had been made at 50MHz, showing that VHF was sometimes anything but 'optical'.

WAR SURPLUS

At the end of hostilities, the immense military organisations could not be dismantled instantly, and time was needed for the world's economies to change back to peacetime activities. Military service and rationing continued for several years in some countries. Huge quantities of hardware became surplus to requirements. Cryptographic equipment and other highly secret things were stockpiled or were carefully destroyed to protect their secrets, but tremendous amounts of communications equipment and components were sold off. Disposable incomes were very low before the economies recovered, so technical treasure could only be sold for a tiny fraction of its original cost.

It took until the middle of the 'sixties for the flow of war-surplus goodies to dry up – there was simply so much of it. In the space of a couple of decades we had gone from it taking many weeks worth of the average income to buy one valve, to amazing devices, being sold by the tea-chest-full, at disposal prices. Large numbers of people had been trained as makers, operators and repairers of all manner of communications and radar equipment. They, too, had become surplus to requirements. Suddenly dumping large quantities of people or things onto an open market is usually a precursor to disaster, but in this case the things and people were complementary and were just what the emerging civilian markets needed. Radar experience was very appropriate to television, and the work done in developing CRTs and wide-band valves was not wasted. Many home-brew TV receivers were founded on the VCR97 electrostatic CRT and the EF50 VHF pentode.

Most amateurs were primarily interested in HF activities, so the demand created a scale of prices, with radios like AR88s at the top, then down through the HRO, CR100, BC348, R1155 etc. The 19 set tank radio was one of the bargain-basement jobs, and although it had a crude VHF transceiver built into it, the VHF section was usually unceremoniously ripped out to make space for an audio amplifier. The period of

homebrew television construction created a market for some VHF bits and pieces, but it was relatively short lived as commercially made televisions became available. Perhaps black-and-green pictures on 5in screens just didn't fit in with the entertainment needs of other members of households? Specialised VHF or radar equipment and components went for junk prices.

No true amateur can ever turn down something for nothing or even close to nothing, so a lot of strange things wound up in the hands of people who then wondered what they could do with them. In addition to the dispersal of all this bounty, there was the dispersal of the knowledge to go with it. There was a big influx into the hobby caused by some of all those highly trained people looking for an outlet for their curiosity. Many of them had been involved with VHF/microwave technology. With advanced components and knowledge the records previously set on the VHF/UHF bands were highly vulnerable, and new frequencies with no records had become accessible. The 144 and 432MHz bands were allocated in the late 'forties, virgin territory for new explorers.

As had happened earlier on short waves, it was the creation of a large number of stations spread across the world, operating at all hours, looking for long-distance contacts, which led to new discoveries. Two American stations made the first moonbounce contact in 1953. One bunch of radio astronomers-to-be tried to use the surplus mobile radar unit they had obtained to detect their own lunar echoes. They included Bernard Lovell, and they went on to build the Jodrell Bank radio telescope. Terrestrial propagation studies got a boost in 1957, the International Geophysical Year, with the opening of GB3IGY, the first of the VHF beacons. The potential of meteor-scatter and sporadic-E propagation were beginning to be discovered. In 1959, a sporadic-E opening gave contacts between the UK and Italy. In America, 400 miles was achieved on 1.3GHz, then California and Hawaii were linked on 220MHz. Records and 'firsts' were there for the taking.

THE RISE AND RISE OF THE TRANSISTOR

Typical VHF/UHF stations of the time consisted of a crystal oscillator-multiplier-PA chain as the transmitter, with a crystal-controlled converter ahead of a standard HF receiver as the receiver. In the 'sixties, commercial VHF transceivers became commonplace in emergency services vehicles, with utilities, and with taxi firms. There had been experiments with mobile 'two-way' radio much earlier, on HF and VHF, but this was the full-scale deployment of private mobile radio (PMR). Successive generations of PMR mobiles were rapidly developed, as new types of transistors became available, capable of supplanting valves in progressively more awkward applications. Some of these earlier generations of PMR sets found their way into amateur hands when they were prematurely pensioned off to make way for each successive smaller and cooler replacement. It was not difficult to re-crystal some of them for 144MHz, though some people who acquired 'low-band' units had to put in a lot of work rebuilding their RF stages to convert them into 'high-band' units. Up to the appearance of this equipment, anyone who wanted to operate mobile had to build their entire station.

On HF, the arrival of the transistor coincided with the rapid growth of high-power short-wave broadcasting, so the

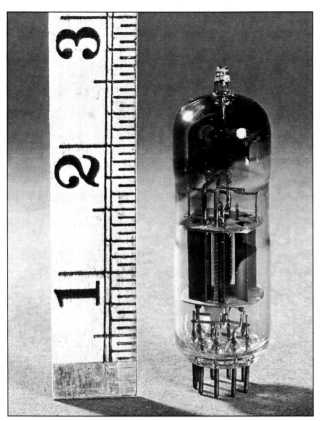

Manuafacturers introduced smaller and smaller valves for VHF mobile radio, such as this 6W double tetrode (Mullard QQV02-6), but all-transistor technology was already on the way

sudden worsening of the ability of receivers to handle nearby big signals was rather badly timed. It took over two decades to make up for this great step backwards, and to be able to make semiconductor-based HF receivers that were in no way inferior to the best of the valved units. On VHF/UHF, conditions were more favourable, receivers were not being 'tenderised' to the same extent, and semiconductors offered progressively lower noise figures, a great boon where noise limitation was far more likely than overload problems.

In 1961, just four years after the first-ever artificial satellite, Sputnik-1, the first amateur satellite, Oscar 1, was launched. It transmitted telemetry on a low-power beacon in the 144MHz band. Later amateur satellites offered communications facilities for short periods. While these were marvellous advertisements for the hobby, and a great deal was learned from them, satellite operation in the 'sixties was very much a minority interest. Many people listened to them, but only the very dedicated built the multiband stations with azimuth-elevation mounted antenna arrays needed for two-way working through something that might only last weeks, if it made orbit at all. It was Oscar 6, which was launched in 1972 and survived for four years, that broke the pattern and showed that satellite DX was a long-term proposition. Four years was more than long enough for the exploits of the pioneer users, and the details of how to follow their lead, to reach print and become general knowledge.

CLASS B LICENCES

The ITU Regulations call on member states to require proof of proficiency at Morse code from anyone to be awarded an amateur licence giving access to the bands below 30MHz. This was a simple consequence of some MF/HF amateur bands being shared with higher-priority users, who were only equipped for CW transmission and might need to request an amateur station to close down. Without this requirement, we would probably not have those bands at all. However, because signals above 30MHz were not expected to travel far, countries were left free to make their own decisions about Morse proficiency and access to these bands. The UK took advantage of this and created a new type of licence limited to 430MHz and above, and issued it without requiring the usual Morse test pass slip. Later, this 'B' licence was extended to include the 144MHz band, and more recently, to cover all bands above 30MHz. An experiment in the 'eighties to allow Class B licence holders to use Morse code on the air proved very successful, and it is now permanent.

The Class B licence (and similar licences in other countries) has had a very large effect on amateur radio. Once upon a time, the usual mode of entry to the hobby started with a period of short-wave listening with one of those war-surplus HF receivers, while reading and re-reading every book and magazine that could be found on the subject. Local amateurs offered encouragement, help, and the loan of books and magazines from their joist-threatening 'archives'. After enough of this, the beginner would be ready to attempt the Radio Amateurs' Examination, which then had a small number of questions, each requiring a mini-essay as an answer. The candidates were also expected to be able to draw circuit diagrams from memory of typical sections of transmitters and receivers. This was not as fearsome as it might sound today – radios were a lot simpler then, and there were only a few circuits that were ever called for. After plenty of listening to Morse transmissions, especially the low-speed training broadcasts, the beginner would take the dreaded Morse test at a shore station or other Post Office radio establishment. Despite a few stations that were reputed to have had at least one ogre on their staff, many amateurs have described examiners making great effort to be welcoming, encouraging and to help candidates overcome their nerves.

The freshly licensed beginner went on the air after some years of familiarisation with operating practices. The 1.8MHz band was the most popular starting point because the receiver used for the short-wave listening period could be used with a cheap and easily built low-power transmitter. On the 1.8MHz band, everyone was limited to low power, so the beginner was at little disadvantage with a simple transmitter.

The Class B licence now allows someone to go on the air after passing just the RAE, and the only extra limitation on them is the 30MHz barrier. If someone wishes to learn Morse code, either for VHF use or to gain access to the bands below 30MHz, they can now get a Class B licence, and join in one of the Morse training nets on 144–146MHz. This is a lot less lonely than just listening, and a lot more encouraging. Copy can be read back for checking, and the instructor can choose the speed to suit the progress of the group. Due to the relative price and availability of commercially made radios for the different bands available to the Class B licensee, the FM segment of the 144–145MHz band has replaced the 1.8MHz band as the 'nursery slopes' of amateur radio, where the majority of newcomers make their first contacts.

The Class B licence has now been with us for a few decades,

and, contrary to the predictions of some of its critics, the world has not ended. It has been the entry point for many good people. It can justly be called a success. The USA has recently introduced its first-ever no-Morse-required VHF-and-above licence and is still suffering the inevitable flare-up of its branch of the great Morse debate.

ENTER THE 'BIG THREE'

In Japan, amateur radio had long been practised by a much larger fraction of their population than had been the case in the West. This proved to be a fertile market for the evolution of a number of fiercely competitive manufacturers, each large enough to support mass-production methods. Once their home market approached saturation, they looked to exports for further expansion. The Western manufacturers never knew what hit them.

The radio amateurs in the West were abruptly confronted with shiny, new, feature-packed radios at much more affordable prices than ever before, and the move from home-built to purchased equipment was fully underway. The first equipment from Japan concentrated on HF SSB operation and rode the change from AM to SSB on those bands. Soon afterwards, the Japanese companies started to export their VHF models. The VHF bands had never before been served by specifically manufactured equipment, and affordable off-the-peg radios were an attractive alternative to scratch-building or modifying surplus PMR equipment. In the UK, the appearance of these radios fuelled the rise in popularity of the Class B licence.

REPEATERS

The amateur world was awash with affordable, commercially made, 2m band FM transceivers. Some were retuned, recrystalled commercial PMR sets, others were purpose made for the amateur market. The 144–146MHz band had been fairly popular for local natter using AM PMR equipment, but the switch to FM accompanied a big increase in occupancy. The majority of PMR sets had been designed for mobile or portable operation, and the Japanese manufacturers produced portable and mobile models. To enhance the coverage of all these mobiles, an extensive network of repeaters has been built. With the part of the 145–146MHz bandplan assigned to repeaters pretty much full, most new repeater development has shifted to the 430–440MHz band. Not all repeaters are FM, just the majority, so the rarer SSB and TV repeaters are especially interesting.

The repeaters have acted as magnets for a very small number of disaffected people who try to jam them. This is antisocial, illegal, and damages the reputation of the hobby. Their motivation seems to be a mixture of wanting to annoy people so that they can listen to the resulting anger, and of wanting to get attention. If you do encounter a repeater jammer, the best advice is to do nothing that acknowledges their existence in any way. Do not rise to any taunts. Any sign whatsoever that they have been noticed seems to encourage them. Quietly log the times, the signal strength on the input frequency (and direction, if possible) as this may later help. Never discuss such things on the air as this may either encourage them or tip them off. Ultimately, the Radiocommunications Agency has the power to prosecute, leading to confiscation of equipment and fines. Finding the perpetrator is

only part of the problem; sufficient evidence has to be collected in a way that is admissible in court. All this work goes on behind the scenes, and all that is ever seen is a small piece in the news columns of *Radio Communication* magazine announcing the result of a court case. The number of jammers is very small indeed (though they try to make as much nuisance as possible), and the number of prosecutions indicates an excellent clean-up rate. Some have tried jamming while mobile, but now their vehicles are at risk of confiscation.

Based on the number of QSOs and the number of users, the repeater network is very successful. Very few of the QSOs may contain matters of direct importance to amateur radio, but they are useful indirect tools that allow the communities around them to organise various activities.

THE 6m BAND

The creation of a 6m band in the UK came as a large surprise, and was solid evidence that the DTI looks favourably on the Amateur Service. This part of the spectrum was freed up when the 405-line TV broadcast system was closed down and, although it is assigned as an amateur band in the Americas, in our region it is not. The first amateur use was by a few stations with special licence variations as an experiment. Part of the experiment was to investigate the effect on French TV which was still active on low VHF. As the French TV service had coped with our old 405-line TV transmitters, each blasting out many kilowatts across the same band, some care over our power output and antenna configurations ensured a satisfactory demonstration of co-existence. The experiment turned into a permanent new band. It is ideally situated, with interesting propagation effects to be explored and a heavily equipped continent just an ocean away to form the other end of long-range contacts.

DATA MODES

The radio-teleprinter techniques used on HF have always been directly applicable on VHF, but the appearance of mass-market home computers in the 'eighties prompted widespread exploration of new possibilities. Just using the computer to simulate the function of a classic electro-mechanical teleprinter may not look like a bold step forward, but the reduction of size, noise and weight in a domestic environment did a lot to increase the numbers of people prepared to try RTTY.

The X.25 protocol of the packet-switched data technology, used in some parts of the public telephone network, was modified for use on the air (AX.25) and grew into the packet radio network. The originators of X.25 never considered it suitable to be deployed over links made out of simple speech-type radios, but amateurs love making the unexpected work. To the basic packet radio network, bulletin board servers have been added, offering news and electronic mail facilities. Specialised bulletin board servers have been linked to make the DX clusters which rapidly distribute news of interesting band openings or the appearance of rare stations. They may be a mixed blessing, for while the news of a band opening can stir up activity on that band, the 'spots' of rare stations do tend to create beautifully synchronised pile-ups – though mostly on HF! The packet format is well suited to VHF/UHF conditions, and does not work anywhere near as well when tried on HF.

Here Belgian and Dutch radio amateurs are exchanging TV pictures via the British TV repeater GB3LO

IMAGE MODES

Slow-scan TV works well on VHF/UHF and, compared to HF, the clearer channels give less interference on the pictures. Once again home computers have made things much easier and have replaced the long-persistence CRTs, photographic drum printers and scanners that were once the only way of handling slow-scan and facsimile images. The UHF and microwave bands offer the space needed to carry a conventional TV signal. TV repeaters have also been built. Digitised images can be treated just as any other data files and sent by the normal data modes.

SPACE

There are amateur satellites acting as very-wide-area repeaters for SSB, while some provide images of the Earth and others carry packet mailboxes. Send your long-distance email up when the satellite is over you, and the recipient can read it when the satellite passes over him or her. Astronauts and cosmonauts have taken out amateur licences, and taken up amateur transceivers. There have been many contacts with Mir and the Space Shuttle. One group onboard Mir actually did their exam in space to get their licences before the end of their mission, and had equipment sent up on a routine supply rocket. Amateur radio has become a popular hobby with spacemen and spacewomen everywhere. It is probable that most future missions will have some amateur radio content. As part of the first-ever amateur operation from orbit, Owen Garriott also sent slow-scan TV images of the interior of the Space Shuttle in the 2m band. Average VHF stations were sufficient to receive these. Few of us will get the chance to try radio actually *in* orbit, but we can all be Earth stations if we wish and join in the funding, design and development of future amateur satellites.

THE PRESENT AND THE FUTURE

History is not 'bunk', it is simply inaccessible, and we can neither visit it nor change it. Living in the present, we can see the past clearly, yet our influence is over a future that we cannot see. This seems like a recipe for disaster. Given the unfair advantage of the certainty of the past over the uncertainty of the future, it is easy to believe that most of the wonderful things have already been done, and that there is little left worth doing. This is very probably not so – such things

The Phase 3C amateur radio satellite being packed for transit to the launch site

have been said for centuries by people who ought to have known better.

Amateur radio is now quite a mature interest and, with the advances in communications in general, it must now look not at all magical to the layman. One of the greatest challenges of the future must be the attraction of new people.

The future holds great threats to the survival of the hobby, especially on VHF/UHF. In the 'eighties, the liberalisation and privatisation of telephone companies in various countries has led to a boom in radio-based communications services that is still continuing. The analogue cellphone networks may be close to their peak, but the digital networks will replace them and grow much larger still. Public appreciation of the relative security of their conversations on different types of telephones can only increase. Some companies are trying to sell cellphones not just as mobile devices, but also as alternatives to wired phones in homes. The network of wires leading from the telephone exchanges to their subscribers is something that cannot be duplicated to allow free-market choice without astronomical cost, so there are plans for competitive phone networks using fixed radio links to homes and businesses. Add in the growth of cordless telephones, cordless burglar alarms, remote control devices, and car key-fob transmitters, and it can be seen that the demand for space in the RF spectrum is accelerating dramatically. Proposals for global spectrum allocations for use by low-orbit satellite-to-person communications have included requests for the reassignment of all of our prime VHF and UHF bands. The idea of a wristwatch phone that will work anywhere on Earth (or in nearby space) with everyone having a single personal telephone number, without geographic codes, is now very close to being achieved. Such progress cannot and should not be stopped, but nor should it be allowed to simply destroy other services.

Amateur radio above 30MHz is facing the most severe threats ever. To fight these pressures we need to be able to demonstrate large numbers of people regularly using all the bands, and we need to be able to make good presentations of the value of the continued existence of these amateur bands.

THINGS TO DO

There are plenty of things waiting to be done that will advance the individual and/or the hobby.

On 2m or 70cm FM, there are new people to be welcomed and encouraged. This could range from informal help when requested, to organised on-air RAE tuition for novices in your area. The voice repeater network is still expanding but it is fairly mature now. The receiver sections of many repeaters are suffering from overload from adjacent paging transmitters, so a high-dynamic-range receiver design would solve many problems. Some groups are experimenting with solar or wind powered repeaters to take advantage of low-cost isolated sites, and also with linking groups of repeaters. A few TV repeaters already exist, but more of them would stimulate TV evening nets.

DXing can be done via sporadic-E openings, meteor-scatter or moonbounce. The moonbounce station at GM4JJJ is a typical medium-sized installation for the 144MHz band, with four long-boom Yagis driven by a pair of 4CX250B valves at about 900W, allowed by a special experimental licence. A small moonbounce station might have a single long-boom Yagi fed from a 100W solid-state amplifier. There are big-league stations with monster antenna arrays that can make CW contact with small stations, or SSB contacts with medium stations. Occasionally some amateurs get the temporary use of a really big dish and moonbounce contacts become possible for quite modest stations.

The packet network is there to be explored, but it is now bound by two limitations. Our licence conditions covering message content and purpose prevent it becoming open to full Internet traffic, because of the wide-open nature of that network. More open to being fixed is the speed limitation forced by channel bandwidths originally planned for narrowband FM speech. The progressive replacement of the network with high data-rate microwave links could yield a great improvement in network capacity and response speed.

There is very little activity on the higher and microwave bands other than during contests. On the use it or lose it principle, we need to devise attractive new uses for these bands. TV and fast data links are obviously suited to the great bandwidth available, but what other possibilities are there?

In a market flooded with commercially made equipment, there is still a place for home construction. Much of the commercial gear tries to do everything at the cost of doing nothing particularly well. If you want a competition-grade system, think in terms of masthead pre-amps and home-made transverters into HF transceivers, if not entirely home-built transceivers. Much commercial equipment has been compromised – the current fashion for wide receiver coverage has made the receiver sections of many transceivers resemble scanners, with a subsequently increased likelihood of intermodulation and overload problems from out-of-band signals. Hand-held transceivers have responded to market

The moonbounce antenna at GM4JJJ

demands for smaller size, longer battery operation, as well as wide range scanning. The tiny 'rubber duck' broad-band antennas are very inefficient, but the receivers have been compromised by their wide range and low power consumption design goals, such that the use of any better antenna risks overload problems. Much better performance can be got from a radio specifically optimised for amateur-band-only use. One approach would be to convert one of the cheap ex-PMR handhelds that appear at all rallies. It would be unfashionably big, but it would also be tough enough to knock nails in with and would also maintain a QSO under conditions that would overload something more fashionable. Kitchen-table construction can still produce things that can outdo the big firms if the constructor targets his specific needs and tolerates a less 'consumer' appearance.

WELCOME

Well, that's a brief introduction to the VHF/UHF bands, a place of threat and opportunity. It offers wide open spaces in which to try out things that no-one has yet thought of, and it offers many known activities that may still be adventurous for the individual. The Brendan Trophy still awaits the first transatlantic 2m QSO.

Anyone fancy a QSO with the first manned mission to Mars?

2 Getting started

OK, you've done it! The pass certificate for the Radio Amateurs' Examination is in your hand and perhaps the Morse test on the way – you are ready to post off for your licence but while you wait for that anticipated 'M' callsign you will be thinking of where to start and what with.

You may have spent some time listening to the bands as a short-wave listener and have a pretty good idea of where your interests lie but there are those who do not have this preconceived idea of their immediate future.

The best place for your first stop is your local club – if you are not sure where your nearest club is located then a phone call to the RSGB will give the required details of dates, times and contacts. Most clubs give newcomers a hearty welcome and this will be your chance to talk to other amateurs about what they prefer. Many clubs have a club station where you can get 'hands on' experience of some of the available transceivers and get some answers to those difficult questions. Many of the local amateur radio retail outlets will also offer advice but remember that they may be tempted to push the higher-profit radios your way.

TRANSCEIVERS

The first real decision is which transceiver to obtain. There are many on the market but which one is best for you? Should you go for a hand-portable one ('hand-held'), or a more expensive base unit to sit on the table at home? Would a mobile unit be preferable and should it be just for FM or for SSB and CW use too? Which bands do you want?

The questions are easy to ask but much more difficult to answer, and of course the answers will be constrained by the money you have available for the hobby or the units you are willing and able to build. Let's take a look at each in turn – it should be noted that all comments made here refer to the 2m band but are also applicable to all VHF and UHF bands too, from 6m upwards to the microwave bands.

A great percentage of radio amateurs own a 'hand-held' transceiver – most are on the 2m (144MHz band), some are only for the 70cm (432MHz) band and some are dual-banders for 2m and 70cm together. They are typically FM only and will only give an output power of about 1W when run from the supplied battery. (Some may give higher power when run from 12V, though.)

These hand-helds can be used while walking the dog, while you are strolling around the local rally or even while mobile or sitting in the armchair at home. When in use out walking, the 'rubber duck' antenna supplied with the transceiver will be used – these are helically wound in most cases and will radiate a signal (of sorts). For base use or in an mobile environment some form of outside antenna will be beneficial. It must be remembered that the 1W output of these rigs will be heavily attenuated if poor-quality coaxial cable is used. Even in short lengths a good proportion of the signal can be wasted. Having said that, a good antenna can make all the difference to any radiated signal, but more of that later.

So, we have our hand-held radio clipped to our belts or in a pocket. It will prove very useful, but not so good for longer-distance contacts except perhaps through a repeater or when standing on the top of a hill. Many of these repeaters also require slightly more power than the typical hand-held can deliver.

There are many, many hand-helds available on the market, both new and used. It all depends on what you require of your rig, how much you can afford or more importantly how much you are willing to spend. If this is your main interest than a call into the local shop or a browse through the adverts in a few magazines will point you in the right direction.

The older type of thumbwheel-tuned type such as the IC2E has been used by many amateurs over the years. There are even a few modern look-a-likes available too. They are simple, easy to use and above all cheap. The more modern type of hand-held with its built-in processor may at times make you feel that you need a degree in programming to understand the way they work.

If your interest lies more further afield you may wish to consider something a little different. While FM is a good chat mode for stations fairly close to each other it is not as efficient as single sideband working for longer-distance contacts. In this mode the carrier is removed and thus more of the available power is used to concentrate the voice into a narrower bandwidth than FM.

Single sideband is a much more efficient way of using the available spectrum when conducting a contact – the FM signal is typically 12kHz wide, while the SSB signal is typically only 2.5kHz. Thus the output power of the transmitter is more efficiently used. It is because of this that an SSB signal will be heard over a greater distance and stations that would be impossible to work when using FM can be contacted with ease when using SSB.

So, which transceivers are available for SSB and FM working? Without doubt the most famous of all the simple, low-power transceivers ever built were the FT290R and the FT790R from Yaesu. This is not meant as an adverse comment about all the other manufacturers, but these rigs stand out. Throughout the late 'seventies, the 'eighties and the early 'nineties almost every amateur owned one of these at one time or another. They were used mobile, portable, at home, and on planes and ships – truly versatile rigs. It is true that they only gave 2.5W out on 2m or 1W on 70cm but they worked and worked very well.

These radios gave the newly licensed amateurs their first

taste of longer-distance working (DX) on VHF/UHF and the addition of a small linear amplifier made the chance of those 200km-or-more contacts a distinct possibility. Like all good things the early FT290R was superseded by a Mk 2 version which in many people's opinion never came up to the standard of its elder brother.

So, in the case of the hand-held transceiver, the advantages are: portability, low weight, ease of use (mainly), and low power consumption. The disadvantages are: low power output, the need to recharge the batteries, and the ease of losing the set if you are not careful.

The trusty hand-held with its 1W of power may seem very basic, but under certain conditions can work very long distances – the chapter on propagation should be studied in detail to give more information on this. Suffice it to say that I have worked from my house in Folkestone, Kent to Paris, France on FM with 'flea power' – just 2W into a vertical antenna. On VHF you should be able to work all over Europe with a couple of watts of CW.

Let's look a little more closely at the larger transceivers available for base use. These typically run off a mains supply but after the introduction of the EMC regulations in 1996 most of the big manufacturers changed over to transceivers that required an external 12V supply.

During the late 'seventies and the early 'eighties the champion VHF rig was the FT221R. This transceiver was used by most of the big contest groups and when fitted with the famous replacement muTek front-end became the 'be-all and end-all' of contest rigs. These transceivers changed hands at huge amounts of money. Because of trends they have become less popular. These rigs didn't have too many bells and whistles but did work extremely well. They had analogue tuning too – no digital frequency readout here. The advantage for us now is that because of these supposed disadvantages the transceiver is considered 'old hat'. The value has dropped considerably but they still work very well when compared with modern equipment. The later contest radios didn't become classics like the FT221R did, but some became firm favourites. The Icom IC251E and the later IC271E were also very good and the later IC275E was used by many contest groups.

The moral of this story is that even some of the older rigs have good receivers and that is what is important. Remember that 10W of RF from an cheap old transceiver will sound much the same as that from its multi-thousand-pound rival. It's the receiver that counts!

For those who wish to have only a simple, inexpensive FM rig for VHF/UHF the ex-PMR (private mobile radio) types are an invaluable source of cheap rigs. Most will require some work to get them onto the amateur frequencies but many of these modifications have been published in the amateur press. Chris Lorek, G4HCL, has published a profusion of them. His *PMR Conversion Handbook* (and its predecessor, *Surplus 2-Way Conversion Handbook*) gives many. These transceivers may be found at silly prices at your local rally. There are always a selection available if you look around.

These days, there is a profusion of rigs that can be used by the newly licensed, the only proviso being whether your interests lie in only FM local contacts and/or SSB with longer-distance contacts, packet use with the radio connected to your computer or even the receiving and transmitting of ATV (amateur television). There is of course a world of difference

in the way the various modes are operated. There is usually a huge difference in cost, too. The multitude of transceivers available will baffle most, but eventually one will stand out above the rest. Listen to what the locals say about it and try to listen to other owners of the same model. See what they think about it. Are they happy with their purchase?

Reviews of current and older transceivers are always available. Finding which magazine did the review will not be difficult as they generally all do a review of each one. Read the reviews and see what they say. Be careful and read between the lines – sometimes a lot can be said by what is *not* written about a radio.

So, we have discussed

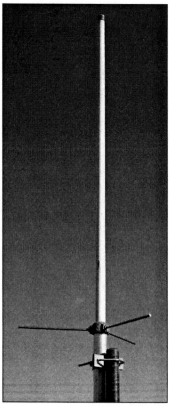

Fig 2.1. Typical collinear antenna

the basic radios that you may consider. There is much more than this of course. The old adage of "if you can't hear them, you can't work them" makes sense.

If the long-distance station (DX) is inaudible at your station then you will never work him. What can be done to remedy this situation?

CHOOSING AN ANTENNA

No matter how much you spend on your shiny new or dusty second-hand transceiver it will always be improved by a better or more suitable antenna.

By now the newcomer should have a vague idea of where his or her main interest lies – if it is for local chatting on the FM simplex channels on VHF/UHF then even a modest outside antenna will give the transmitted (and received signal) quite a boost.

Many amateurs keep their antennas in the loft of the house, while others prefer to have them on the roof. Whichever you choose, the higher the better.

The standard quarter-wave antenna will radiate an omni-directional signal, that is a signal of the same strength in all horizontal directions. This is what we need for our hand-held. Convention has it that when using FM the antennas will be vertically polarised. This means that the radiating element will be in a up/down configuration. Don't assume that the antenna must always have the feeder at the bottom. There are circumstances, such as when the antenna is fitted under the eaves of the house, that it can be fitted with the feed point at the higher point and the antenna is then 'hanging upside down'. This will not make for any difficulties in transmissions – the antenna will still work very well. Fig 2.1 shows a typical collinear antenna.

Fig 2.2. Vertically and horizontally polarised antennas on the same mast. The upper one is a vertically polarised 70cm antenna, the lower one is a horizontally polarised 2m antenna

By looking at the roofs of houses around us we will see several antennas used for the reception of TV. Most of these types are called *Yagi beams*. These have directional properties in that they 'fire' the signal in one particular direction to the detriment of other directions. So, if that repeater you wish to access is too far away for the omni-directional antenna, put up a beam. Remember, for FM it should be mounted so that the elements are vertical and for SSB work it should be mounted horizontally. Do not do as one operator I know who mounted the Yagi pointing to the sky and wondered why his signals were not so strong! Fig 2.2 shows both vertically and horizontally polarised antennas.

You don't have to have two antennas if you swap between these two modes. You can buy antennas specially made for the job, where a single boom has two sets of elements running along it, one for vertical and the other for horizontal polarisation. You will need either two lengths of feeder to the shack and a switch box to select the polarisation required or you may decide to have a relay at the antenna and just a single line of feeder to the radio.

Of course the gain of any beam antenna works on receive as well as transmit. While we mention 'gain' in an antenna it must be remembered that if we supply an RF power level to an antenna of, say, 10W, there is no way that this antenna can increase this 10W level to a higher power level. What it can, and does, do is 'steal' a little of this power from one (unwanted) direction and push it in an other direction. We still have 10W being radiated from the antenna but not in every direction. Look at Fig 2.3. It can be seen that the loss of apparent power in one direction can give an apparent increase in another. In this case the 'loss' is to the rear of the beam and the 'apparent' gain to the front.

For those who prefer to sit and chat on the simplex FM

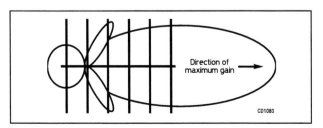

Fig 2.3. Yagi beam antenna showing direction of maximum gain

Fig 2.4. Typical VHF/UHF antenna system featuring two 2m, two 70cm and one 23cm beam

frequencies then some form of vertically polarised antenna will be required. This may be simply a vertically mounted dipole, a simple ground plane or a collinear array. For those who need to get a bit further in one particular direction then a beam may be required. The photograph (Fig 2.4) shows the antenna systems in use at my house.

The biggest and best antenna that can be put up is the one to go for. A careful look at antenna design will give guidance on which one will suit your particular location. But initially look for one that has a good forward gain and a good front-to-back ratio. This means that it radiates most of the signal towards the front and little from the rear. This front-to-back ratio is important as sometimes you may have a strong station behind you and by turning the beam a little you may be able to null them out. (Again, check the antenna chapter for more information.)

On VHF and UHF, although most will start out with just one beam, the wish to add another may come later, especially on UHF where many stations use two or more. A pair will increase the forward gain from the antennas by as much as 2.5dB. It has other advantages too. The receive capability will increase too as the gain of the antennas works both ways. If they are *stacked*, that is one mounted above the other, the radiation pattern will be narrowed in the vertical plane. This may help stop any potential EMC problems.

Having bought the antenna is not the end of it all – some means of turning it must be found. The local TV shop may well have a cheap rotator for sale in the window but these are usually intended for small TV beams only. They may last a year or more with a small VHF beam but it would be much better to get a proper rotator capable of handling the loading. The instructions that come with the antenna should tell you its wind loading. The rotator used should be capable of handling this.

How is it all going to be held up in the air, though? The dream of most amateurs is the 60 or 80ft tower with a cradle of antennas bunched at the top. Of course, some of us can get these up, but often neighbours and the local planning authorities don't see towers as much of a thing of beauty as we amateurs do. Many will use a chimney lashing kit to bolt a short stub mast to the chimney. The small rotator carrying the beam will be safe with this. But just for safety, how about using a double lashing kit and making sure, especially if a pair of antennas are intended?

If you do intend to erect a pair of beams, it is no good siting them a foot apart – they must be set the correct distance apart to get this 2.5dB gain. Check out Chapter 5 – 'Antennas and transmission lines' for more on this subject.

Antennas don't have to be out in the open of course. Many estates have restrictions on mounting antennas on houses above the eaves or the ridge line. All is not lost. Many operators use a small rotatable beam in the loft. If a rotatable one cannot be fitted, consider a pair of delta loops at 90° so you can select one or the other. The radiation pattern will be off the side of each. Not perfect but again a signal will be radiated.

Many amateurs use scaffold poles to mount the antennas. One easy way to do this is to beg, borrow, or buy two poles, one of about 2m and one of 7m in length. The shorter one is concreted into the ground and used as the support for the longer one. A hinged scaffold clamp is used and thus the whole can be lowered for work to be carried out on the antennas. If guy ropes are used even two poles maybe used. See Fig 2.5. Even unwanted windsurfer masts can be pressed into service but these should be used with care when brackets are bolted on.

FEEDER

There is no point in putting a good-quality vertical antenna up in the air and using a coaxial feeder such as RG58U. This feeder has a loss of 4.65dB per 100ft at 100MHz, so if your transmitter gave out 1W, and assuming no other losses, only about 200mW would be radiated from the antenna. By changing to a better feeder these losses can be reduced by a huge amount. The 'common or garden' RG213 has a loss of 1.9dB at 100MHz per 100ft, about a third of that of the RG58U. See Chapters 5 and 12 for more data on coaxial cables.

The benefit of choosing good-quality feeder is obvious. There are many types available on the market today, ranging from the very expensive Heliax type to the cheaper, but still very good, Pope H100 and Westflex. Remember that, although the transceiver gives you the results of the signal and the beam radiates it, it is the feeder that gets it to the rig and the connectors that join them together.

The station must be thought of as a whole, not as separate parts. If one part fails, the whole will fail.

OTHER EQUIPMENT

Several other items of other equipment will be found in most amateur shacks. Some of it will be essential, some may be

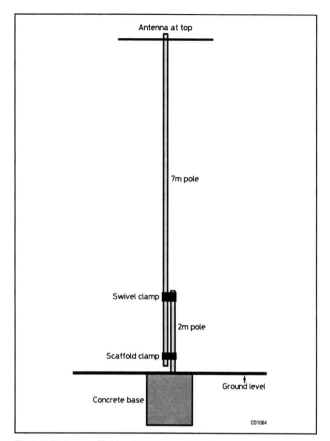

Fig 2.5. Using scaffold poles to mount antennas

just useful. Some may be borrowed from friends if they are only required from time to time.

One essential item when putting the antennas up is either a directional power meter or an VSWR (voltage standing wave ratio) bridge/meter. The intention of these is to measure the effectiveness of your antenna(s). Our requirement is that the minimum amount of power is returned to the transmitter. The directional power meter can be used to measure this actual amount of returned power. The VSWR (usually abbreviated to just 'SWR') bridge/meter will enable the user to measure the ratio of power levels in the system. Usually we try to tune for an SWR of unity or 1:1. This is often unobtainable, so anything under 2:1 will be acceptable.

The power supply to drive all this amount of equipment will be an essential item. The small 5A CB power supplies found cheaply are often not regulated to the extent we require. I have seen many trip into 'over-voltage supply', causing problems to the transceiver.

It may seem an extravagance but I would recommend buying the biggest power supply you can afford. It should be capable of delivering a very stable 13.8V under load. It is no point having a supply that 'sags' to 11V on load. A good one that will deliver 20A will suffice until a bigger one comes along.

Another essential is an accurate clock or watch. The type that relies on Rugby MSF time clock signals for accuracy is an excellent one. Some operators even have a pair in the shack, one with CET (Central European Time) and the other with local time.

The standard microphone supplied with the transmitter will

almost certainly provide good audio on the transmitted signal but a base (free-standing) microphone may prove beneficial and permit some hands-free use. The log book and notes can then be completed during the contact. Later on a complete headset (earphones and incorporated microphone) may be used with a foot switch to give totally hands-free operation.

Initially the only Morse key will be the hand key required for the Morse test. These can be used to provide good-quality Morse code for long stretches but this takes practice. A good electronic keyer with a twin paddle can provide easy sending without fatigue over long periods. The only thing that moves with the keyer is your two fingers. With the hand key the whole arm from elbow to fingers moves. Remember, when wiring your paddle and learning to send, that convention has it that the thumb sends the dots and the finger the dashes!

The transceivers we have discussed so far have been run 'barefoot', ie without the addition of any form of amplifier to boost the transmitted or received signal. There are three types of amateur when it comes to amplifiers:

1. Those with a 'big mouth and no ears' (big linear transmit amplifier and poor reception facilities)
2. Those with 'big ears and no mouth' (no big transmit amplifier but perhaps a masthead preamplifier). This is a much better configuration.
3. Finally, there are those who have both a 'big mouth and big ears'. These are the full contest-style stations who have possibly full legal output power available with multiple antennas and a masthead receive preamp.

Many commercial linear power amplifiers incorporate a preamplifier. While these will help a little with low signal levels they also tend to amplify the noise on the feeder too. The best place to fit the preamp is at the masthead where it amplifies the signal at the antenna and passes it to the receiver.

Most commercial linear power amplifiers are excellent but several will have been 'got at' by previous owners. Always check the signal quality of your new amplifier before going on the air and *never try to overdrive it*.

WHERE TO PUT IT ALL

So, the antenna(s) are up in the air and we have a pile of other bits in their boxes – where in the house is the best place to operate from? This will very much depend on the space you have available and the amount of equipment you have accumulated.

For the VHF and the UHF station feed length may be a little critical and the attic a good place to consider. Remember though that if it is in the attic sleeping children may hear your signals and during the summer it may get very hot.

Many operators use a spare room for the shack; others prefer a garden shed. Wherever you put your equipment make sure it is safe from burglars and away from small hands when not in use.

Remember, if you plan to operate for any length of time, that the operating position should be comfortable. There is no point in entering a contest when you have to sit awkwardly. Set up the desk so that each item is within reach without stretching. The most-used items such as the tuning control should be closest to hand.

OPERATING TECHNIQUES

For ease of use the whole of each amateur band is split into segments, and a list of these can be found in the *RSGB Yearbook* and other publications. On VHF and UHF in the UK we keep the bottom section for moonbounce (or *EME* as it is known from 'Earth-Moon-Earth') where amateurs try to bounce signals off the Moon back to Earth. The next section is for dedicated Morse code users. There are separate sections for those interested in meteor scatter (MS) operation using Morse code and another for those using MS SSB. The next section is for those using SSB in normal terrestrial modes. A small all-mode section is followed by the packet section, the beacon subsection and the FM simplex channels and finally the satellite section. There are also sections for amateur TV (ATV), QRP activity, and many more. Let's look a little more closely at a couple of these. (Check the current *Yearbook* for more details of the band plans.)

In the UK the main 'calling frequency' for FM work on 2m at present is known as 'S20' (simplex channel number 20). It is on 145.500MHz (on 70cm it is 433.500MHz and is currently known as 'SU20'). Operators should use the established calling frequencies to only make initial contact and agree another frequency to move to (QSY). Don't stay and chat on the calling frequency even if the band appears dead. Keep all conversation on calling frequencies to an absolute minimum.

The band is at the moment split into 25kHz sections so that 144.475MHz is known as 'S19', 145.525 is 'S21' and so on. However, a change to 12.5kHz spacing is currently taking place and the names for channels are being revised. For 145MHz the letter 'V' is used, and the number is the channel, counting in 12.5kHz steps, above 145.000MHz. So 145.500MHz ('S20') is now being called 'V40'. For 435MHz the letter 'U' is used, and the number is the channel, again counting in 12.5kHz steps, above 430MHz. Thus 433.500MHz (formerly 'SU20') is 'U280' in the new system.

In some areas such as London it may be difficult to find a clear channel but in the outer regions it will be easy.

On SSB, the calling frequency is 144.300MHz and this has often been the cause of contention. In the old days, it was the norm to call CQ and state that you were 'tuning high (or low) for a contact'. Modern rigs have very stable VFOs and this practice has now vanished.

Most UK and European mainland amateurs listen on 144.300MHz (50.150MHz, 432.200MHz) for an opening or the band to liven up. Again, if this frequency is used to establish a contact then a move of frequency to complete the contact should be made immediately away from 144.300/432.200.

We have covered part of the band plans and learnt to move away from the calling frequency, but what actually is a valid contact? If I hear a station calling CQ such as:

"CQ CQ CQ, HB9FAP, over"

and I answer with:

"HB9FAP, you're 59, roger? "

He then replies with:

"Roger roger, you're also 59 here, name Fabio, QSL?"

Is this a valid contact? No, of course not – let's look at this once again, only this time done properly . . .

"CQ CQ CQ, HB9FAP, over"

"HB9FAP, you're 59 from G0BPS, over"

" G0BPS from HB9FAP. Many thanks, you're also 59. My name is Fabio. G0BPS from HB9FAP, over"

In this case both callsigns have been given by both parties so there can be no confusion. In the first instance he may have been answering another station, not you. In the latter there is no mistake at all who he is talking to. A valid contact is where both callsigns have been exchanged and also signal reports in the usual RS(T) configuration. In some cases, especially on VHF and UHF, the designated worldwide locator should be given too. This comprises a set of two letters, two numbers and two letters. For example, my locator is JO01oc.

Contests are a great way to make some longer-distance contacts on all bands, but before jumping in listen for a while and find out just what information is being exchanged. On some contests the exchange of region may be required, in others your county or even your age. In most, though, it will be a signal report and a serial number. Your first contact in the contest will be 001 (zero zero one) and increase one by one from there. In most VHF/UHF contests the worldwide locator will also be required. You may well hear something like:

"DJ5VE from G0BPS, you're 59085 in JO01OC. QSL?"

and followed by "73 and good luck".

Above all, listen before jumping in – you'll be VERY unpopular if you ask the other station what information he requires if he has a pile-up going.

Never, never . . .

There may also be the occasion where you may hear a station calling CQ but in a specific direction. On the VHF/UHF bands you may hear a Dutch station perhaps (or even me) calling "CQ Oscar Kilo or Sugar Papa, CQ Oscar Kilo or Sugar Papa" (calling Czech Republic or Poland). It means that the station wants to speak to Czech and Polish stations *only*.

I have often heard newly licensed stations hearing this type of call and then calling the Dutch station. They do *not* want to hear from you – if they did they would be calling CQ G! The station calling a specific CQ as above *only* wants a call from that specific area. If he wanted just anyone he would call CQ (a general call for a contact), or CQ DX for further afield. On the VHF and UHF bands DX is relative – for those who have never worked further afield than the next county, the next country will be DX. However, for those who can regularly work 400–500km on a flat band, only a 500km+ contact will be considered by them to be DX.

The basic rule is *never* to call a station that is calling a specific CQ *unless you are in that country or area he is calling*. If you do answer them from a closer area, expect the proverbial 'flea in the ear'!

Often the station calling CQ OK or SP etc will be 'big', ie running full legal power to several rotatable antennas, masthead preamp, quality feeder etc. Your 10W to a five-element or so antenna does not make you DX, but if he slips up and just calls CQ you can justifiably call him.

Remember a band devoid of signals does not mean that the band is flat. It just means that there are no operators – often

there are people just listening for someone like you to call CQ. So, a short CQ call may well bring forth a station that may surprise you.

One of the most-misunderstood controls on many rigs is the 'clarifier'. This control is often referred to on HF as the 'RIT' (receiver incremental tuning). Its purpose is to enable the operator to move the receive frequency away from the transmit frequency.

Often we hear two newly licensed stations meeting and agreeing to move to, say, 144.330MHz. Both change frequency so that the dial on their rig shows this frequency and call each other. It is most unlikely that the true frequency of each rig exactly matches the other so the two stations are not *netted* (on the exact same frequency). In with the clarifier . . . and they can hear each other now. We now have in effect a duplex contact with both receiving on the other's transmit frequency which differs to their own.

The simple answer is to agree who will call who when you arrive at the agreed frequency. The other person should listen and use their ears to get to the frequency that makes the other station sound right. Ignore the tuning dial. It may well show '144.332' but if both stations avoid using the clarifier they will both be on the *same* frequency and be operating in a simplex mode or, as we say, 'netted' to each other. Best of all, ignore the clarifier except for very exceptional occasions.

Talking English

Having established a contact you will wish to exchange some information. Remember that if you bumped into a stranger at a party you would introduce yourself perhaps with: "Hello, my name is Dick and I live in Folkestone". How many times do we hear on the air "Personal here is Harry, QTH is Lyminge" or similar? You wouldn't talk at the party like that so why on the air? Use plain English and avoid the royal 'we', eg "We are running 100 watts . . ." when the operator is alone in the shack. The use of Morse abbreviations on the air should also be avoided – they were designed to speed up CW communications and should remain there. The exception to this rule, perhaps, is the use of 'QSL' when referring to the contact-confirmed card!

When passing the contact to the other operator do so clearly – listeners may want to know who is there, especially if you have hooked a rare one. "HB0QS from G0BPS back to you" or similar will suffice. If you are both a clear, strong signal with each other, ie 57 or so, then you may wish to avoid phonetics, but if conditions are difficult it may be beneficial to both to give full callsigns in phonetics. Stick to the proper ones too. The oddball ones may help in rare occasions but most operators' ears are tuned to the correct ones and can pick them out of the noise.

The pile-up

If you happen to hear a huge amount of noise on one frequency it will be almost certain that a rare station has appeared on the bands. This can provide you with two options. Sit on the frequency and shout your call in amongst all the others and hope, or . . . cheat!

Tune around the edges of the pile-up listening carefully as you go. Very often the loudest rare station will have another from the same area who is not so strong but is also audible. Those in the pile-up won't hear them, but those tuning the edges will snap up the rare one and grin as they pass the noise again.

If you do decide to go for the pile-up the first thing is to listen, listen and then listen. Unless you are running a 'big' station the only option is to get all the information you need such as callsign, locator and possibly their name first. When you have this information you can try for the contact.

Many times we hear an operator in the pile-up calling the DX station, getting answered and then asking for his callsign first. Oh dear . . . We say listen and listen again – is the DX station working simplex or on *split frequencies*? (That means calling CQ on one frequency and listening a little higher, or lower, in frequency.) If they are working 'split' *never, never* call him on his transmitting frequency – the wrath of all and sundry will fall upon you if you do. A transceiver with twin VFOs is essential if the other operator is working 'split'. Never try to work them by tuning between the two frequencies – it just won't work.

Having found his listening frequency, which may even be a small section of the band. you may then call him. If you are competing with some high-power stations then skill, not power, will be required. Listen for the style of his operating. Yes, I know this requires a lot of listening, but I get more hits than misses with my calls by listening carefully first. Having established his rhythm give your callsign quickly and just once without giving his. It will be assumed that all are calling the DX station. Try and find the gap between all the others. I know this will be difficult but that is the reason for listening so much first.

If the full call doesn't work try just giving the last two letters of your callsign – use phonetics and call twice in a gap. "Papa Sierra, Papa Sierra" is my way. Often the DX operator will call back "Papa Sierra again". You can then give his callsign and yours, his report and your locator and name. Do not give your station details etc unless they are asked for. You will get his information and then maybe just "73 . . . QRZ?" without waiting to see if you got the information. A good operator will do a check though and often give his callsign, locator and QSL manager where appropriate.

QSL cards are often exchanged to confirm contacts. It is not essential that you send a card for every contact made. Often you may see written that "a QSL is the final courtesy of a QSO". If you want a QSL card to confirm the contact, say so, asking politely, and you will probably get one. However, if you have worked that square many times you may not want it again, so say so. It is not essential to exchange cards for every contact – they should be treated for special use only, not as a matter of course for each contact.

Many stations that hold or use rare callsigns may prefer to use a QSL manager – this is usually a friend who is willing and able to handle the large amount of cards arriving for the DX operator and enable them to spend their time on the air rather than filling out cards. If a manager is given it is usual to use that route.

If a card is required by the direct route then it is usual to enclose one or two IRCs (International Reply Coupons) which are available from the Post Office. You may instead prefer to use a 'green stamp' – the name used by all amateurs throughout the world for a one US dollar bill. Needless to say, from one UK station to another a stamped, self-addressed envelope (SSAE) will usually suffice.

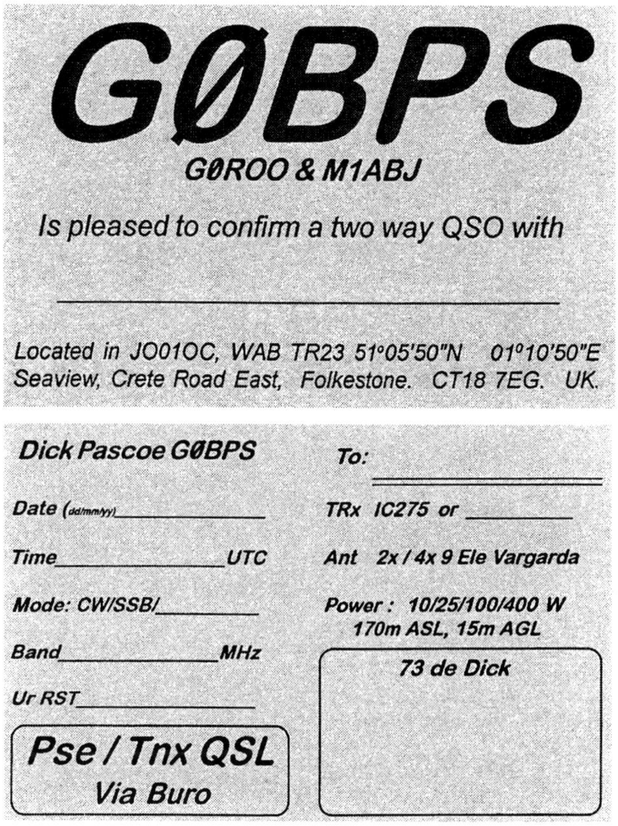

Fig 2.6. Front and rear of typical double-sided QSL card

QSL cards can be a pleasure – I have received many delightful ones in full colour but most are on thin card and quite plain. This is fine because I only need to have confirmation of the new square – it doesn't have to be a work of art. Talk to the members at your local club and ask them what they have on theirs.

Check out the adverts and send for samples. These will give you a fair idea of what you may wish to see on yours. As a minimum it should show your callsign, name, your locator, your power used, QSL PSE/TNX. You may also wish to add your address, your WAB information and your latitude/longitude. Simply add any information that you think the other operator may find interesting. See the copy of mine shown in Fig 2.6.

Single-sided cards are fine – double sided ones will cost much more. Check out your local printer too. They will often prove to be quite competitive when compared to those advertising in the magazines.

Finally, the best advice I ever heard for the newcomer to the bands is: "Listen, listen and then listen some more".

REPEATERS

A large number of repeaters are scattered across the UK and these are usually on the 2m and 70cm bands. Repeaters are just a way of getting your signal a little further. They are typically set on a high site with a range dependent on the others in the area. Each repeater is on a different frequency to those others nearby. They will require either a short 1750Hz tone burst of usually about 400 milliseconds. Most also have a CTCSS tone access. This is a sub-audible tone that 'opens' the nearby repeater for you to make a call. Each one will have

AMATEUR RADIO STATION LOG

DATE	TIME (UTC) start	finish	FREQUENCY (MHz)	MODE	POWER (dBW)	STATION called/worked	REPORT sent	received	QSL sent	rcvd	REMARKS
2 Nov '88	0800	0810	3	J3E	20	GM5ABC	59+10	59+5			Bert
"	0811	0820	145	F3E	16	G7XYZ	57	56			Terry first G7
"	0825	0830	14	J3E	20	CQ					No reply
"	1725	1735	145	F2D	16	GB7XYZ					Local packet mailbox
"	1740	Station closed down									
4 Nov '88	1030	/P	from 73 Antenna Lane, Squelch-on-Sea								
"	1031	1036	50	J3E	10	G1ØXYZ	55	56			Jim, Bridgetown
"	1036	1045	50	J3E	10	G7XYL	58	58			Anne, Nº Squelch-on-Sea. QRM
"	1205	1215	433	F3E	13	G2XYZ	46	47			
"	1220	Station closed down									
5 Nov '88	0945	/P	from 73 Antenna Lane, Squelch-on-Sea								
"	0950	1005	144	J3E	16	GB2GUY	56	56	✓		Catherine Fankesville
"	1010	1015	144	A1A	16	GD5ZZZ	542	541	✓		QSB! QSL via WF9XYZ
"	1526	1530	144	A1A	16	G7CW	579	589			Good keying!
"	1535	Station closed down and dismantled									
7 Nov '88	1810	1902	435	C3F	10	G7ZZZ	P3	P3			Ted, first ATV contact!
"	1930	1945	21	J2B	16	VK2ABC	559	569	✓		RTTY, Sid at Bandedge
"	1946	2005	21	J2B	16	ZL3222	569	559	✓		1st ZL on RTTY
"	2010	Test for TVI/Harmonic Radiation - Nothing noted.									
"	2020	Station closed down									
8 Nov '88	1735	1737	7	J3E	20	CQ					
	1738	1805	7	J3E	20	G1ØZZZ	58	58			Nobby - chatted about GSRV ant
	1930	1945	51	F3E	10	GØ5IX	55	55			Allen, wanted WIAB ref.
	1950	Station closed down.									

NOTES

Fig 2.7. Typical hand-written log page

a different CTCSS tone to stop operators opening those repeaters not required.

European repeaters in the 2m band use a 600kHz offset between the transmit and receive frequencies, and in the UK the user transmit frequency is the lower of the two. For example, the repeater outside Folkestone in Kent is GB3KS (Kent South) with an input frequency of 145.025MHz and a repeater transmit frequency of 145.625MHz. On 70cm the offset is 1.6MHz and on 23cm it is 6MHz except for ATV where it is variable (see the current *Yearbook* for details).

Repeaters were first set up to enable mobile stations to have contacts but of course base stations can use them, too. However, it is courteous to let any mobile station use take preference over base station use.

Often there will be gatherings of users in the mornings and evenings as amateurs travel to and from work.

There will be times during enhanced conditions when it may well be possible to chat through other repeaters. During one memorable opening a UK station was chatting to a Danish station through a UK repeater. Often stations in the Midlands will be able to access Southern ones. The use of CTCSS will help to stop this, though.

So far we have discussed terrestrial repeaters, but the amateur also has access to satellites that are solely for amateur use. These sometimes require two radios. Check the chapter on satellites for more information on these.

Finally, you may also hear the request for a QSL card for a repeater contact. You may of course exchange cards but they will not be accepted for any awards or contests. Why? Because you have been in contact with a repeater, not the other station direct.

MOBILE OPERATING

For those who do not have the facilities for an operating position in the house a parking spot with a good take-off can

provide hours of fun. Just because you are operating from a vehicle doesn't mean that you are restricted to FM only. Lots of fun can be had with the mobile whip on the gutter when using SSB. Yes, we know that the preferred polarisation for SSB is horizontal, but the difference between vertical and horizontal is only about 3dB.

What about your mobile whip? Will it lift out of the base and hang sideways, horizontally? Many do, and by rotating the whip around the base you can have a slightly directional antenna. Yes, it is cheating but it does work – try it!

Before I had an antenna on the roof of the house I would often take to the hills with a small beam antenna on a short pole attached to the side of the car and the roof rack. I would point the beam and call CQ either on FM or SSB from my old FT290R. Only 2.5W out but I could have hours of fun. I well remember taking to the hills at one of the better VHF/UHF spots in a country lane for one of the QRP contests, never dreaming that I would some years later buy a house only a few hundred yards away on that same lane.

LOGGING

Before the advent of computers, and their acceptance by most, all logging was done on paper. Many would keep a rough scrap of paper beside the operating position and make notes as time went past. They would then write up the log in a nice neat hand after the operating session was over.

A paper log must not be loose leaf, must be indelible, and must contain a certain amount of information. The minimum requirement is that you record: date, time, callsign of station worked or called, CQ calls made, frequency and the mode of transmission used.

Many, if not all, operators prefer to add to this essential list by including the reports exchanged, the power level used, the name of the other operator, and whether a QSL card has been sent and/or received. Fig 2.7 shows a typical written log page.

Since the advent of computers the rules have been relaxed and the log book may be kept on the computer. I use the hard disc drive for my main log and also every time I shut down the log program I save a copy to floppy disc. I even use two discs and alternate them. Fig 2.8 shows a computer printout log.

Apart from the essential information required by our licences we can add any information we want to our logs. Where possible, I always keep a note of names – it is so nice to hear a station, check the log for their name and call them with a "F6PBZ from G0BPS. Hello Mike, how are you?"

```
Amateur radio station GOBPS                                    Page 1

================================================================================
QSO    DATE      UTC  MHz   MODE   CALLSIGN   RSTs   RSTr   LOCATOR   REMARK       QSL
================================================================================
1091   25.07.96  2103 144   SSB    LC3LAT     59     59     JO59HJ    BJORN        S-
1092   25.07.96  2105 144   SSB    LA7TJA     57     57     JO59FG    JAN          S-
1093   25.07.96  2121 144   SSB    SM6VQW     59     59     JO67FA    OLA          --
1094   25.07.96  2126 144   SSB    SM6USS     59     59     JO67AT    DENNIS       --
1095   25.07.96  2200 144   SSB    SK6HD      59     59     JO68SD    FRED         S-
1096   25.07.96  2203 144   SSB    OZ1ABA/P   59     59     JO55LR    BOB          S-
1097   25.07.96  2208 144   SSB    DG2LBF     55     59     JO54BH    BERND        --
1098   30.07.96  2037 144   SSB    EA2AGZ     59     59     IN91      -----------  S-
1099   30.07.96  2044 144   SSB    EA1DDO     57     57     IN53UI    MAX          S-
1100   30.07.96  2047 144   SSB    EA1OS      55     53     IN53TI    AL           --
1101   30.07.96  2117 144   SSB    EA1DKV     59     59     IN53TJ    JOSE         S-
1102   30.07.96  2121 432   SSB    EA1DKV     55     55     IN53TJ    JOSE         S-
1103   30.07.96  2205 144   SSB    EA1BCB     57     58     IN63ID    SENEN        S-
1104   30.07.96  2254 144   SSB    EA1DDU     55     55     IN73FM    MICK         --
1105   30.07.96  2255 144   SSB    EB1EWE     00     00     ------    LOST         --
1106   30.07.96  2300 144   SSB    EB1HAL     53     59     IN63UN    -----------  S-
1107   30.07.96  2313 144   SSB    PAOGHB     59     59     ------    GERARD       --
1108   30.07.96  2333 144   SSB    PAOGHB     59     59     ------    GERARD       --
1109   30.07.96  2321 144   SSB    EA1OS      59     59     ------    TRYING 70CMS --
================================================================================

FASTLOG 3.2                                         Signature _____
```

Fig 2.8. Typical printout from a computer log

The particular opening shown was a great tropo opening covering most of Europe. In my listing will be seen the number of the contact, date, time in UTC, frequency, mode, callsign, report sent, report received, the worldwide locator of the other station, his or her name and the QSL status.

This program that I use is widely available for the PC on a share-and-enjoy basis from I0XGR and can be found from many software sources such as Venus Electronics. There are many other sources of logging software and each will be slightly different. There are also many programs specifically for contest logging and these may also be found at the various amateur software sources.

3 Propagation

INTRODUCTION

In the early 'twenties communication engineers decided that wavelengths of less than 200m were useless for serious message handling – so they generously gave them all to amateur operators. This was an action they were soon to regret, for by the end of 1923 two amateurs using a wavelength of about 100m had carried out two-way exchanges with another in France. The following year, transatlantic working was becoming quite commonplace down at 100m, using considerably less power than the 'big boys' were needing on their medium-wave circuits.

The authorities acted swiftly and predictably. They called a conference. At the end of it the amateurs found that they had lost all of their gift apart from a sequence of harmonically related bands – 80, 40, 20, 10 and 5m.

Amateurs began to progress their way through the list of assigned bands, tackling each in turn when it became practicable by the state of the art. Their professional counterparts were surprised to find that each time they seemed to work longer ranges with lower powers, all the way to the 10m band. Beyond that were 'ultra short waves', and there their luck appeared to run out. The 5m band really did seem to be a desert, with little prospect of any DX working at all.

Then came the war. Amateur activity ceased but many future amateurs were fortunate enough to acquire a solid grounding in radio communications while serving in the armed forces, where they had been able to use up-to-date (and expensive) commercial equipment rather than the customary pre-war home-brew.

A lot of that sort of equipment came on the market after the war at knock-down prices that people could afford. Many post-war amateurs began their activities using modified war-surplus gear and they were eager to find out just what it was capable of doing, given a free rein. At that time everyone started off with an interest in propagation, whether they admitted to it or not. A good proportion of those took it very seriously indeed.

In the UK, television swallowed up the old 5m (56MHz) band. So, in a way, everyone venturing on to VHF and UHF after the war was starting with a clean slate. In the years that followed they discovered that many of the features of propagation that they were taking for granted were things that rocked the foundations of previously held textbook theories. They were working far greater distances than their limited power should have allowed; they worked paths crossing mountain ranges that, at VHF and UHF, should have been blocked completely by the terrain; they were finding that the ionosphere could, on occasion, reflect signals of up to at least 200MHz – about four times higher in frequency than had been expected – and amateur experiments had revealed an unexpected mode

of propagation, trans-equatorial, that had stimulated a wide range of interest, particularly among broadcasters. They had projects covering a variety of other modes, including auroral, meteor-trail, moonbounce and propagation via field-aligned irregularities, all active on a truly international scale and all producing results which would have been unobtainable by other means.

As a result the Amateur Service enjoyed a rewarding relationship with professionals in the field of propagation research. But, although the two sides were working towards the same end, their reasons for doing so were poles apart. To an amateur a 'tropo opening' is like a heaven-sent reward for eating up all his spinach, whereas to a professional it signals a period of frustration, when co-channel interference creates interruptions in his data flow, patterning or breaking-up of his television signals and dents in his reputation for reliability. Despite that, both groups were interested in knowing such things as: "When?", "For how long?", "Where?", "To what extent?" and those were just the sort of questions that amateurs found themselves in an ideal position to answer.

Sadly, those golden periods of close co-operation are becoming less frequent nowadays. There are basically three reasons for that. One is that the professional research interest has moved beyond the VHF and UHF parts of the spectrum to much higher frequencies, well outside the province of this handbook, where point-to-point working involves extremely narrow pencil beams. Our large and dense networks of potential observers can contribute little to that sort of situation. Secondly, many of the former problems have been avoided by the routing of commercial traffic through satellite transponders. Thirdly, professional and commercial organisations are cutting back on expenditure to such an extent that research requirements are currently being shelved unless they can show an immediate financial return against the investment supporting them.

That last consideration affects our activities also. To analyse our own original signal records in terms of cause and effect we need an ongoing supply of solar and geophysical data from official sources. In the past we have been very fortunate in being able to get what we need either on an exchange basis or through various 'old boy' networks. But now, in many cases, such information has to be paid for and some of the rates are extremely high. As a result, amateurs are gradually being priced out of individual research. In that we are not alone; amateur meteorologists face a similar situation and frequently voice their frustration in that respect.

The bottom line of this is that when it comes to citing current sources of information this propagation chapter has had to be much less precise than we would have liked. It may well be that, during the time that this book is kept on sale, the situation will improve and new sources will become available. At the time of writing certain rumours abound, but nothing is certain. But do not let that stop you from undertaking research of your own. When the time comes to do something with it you can always contact the RSGB for some up-to-date advice on where to get the information you need.

But that, of course, is jumping rather far ahead. At this stage you will be wanting to see what VHF/UHF propagation is all about . . .

OUR FIELD OF INTEREST

The term 'radio wave propagation' really covers two objectives. The first is to determine the nature of the mechanism involved in getting signals from point A to point B, the second to explain the route in terms of physical quantities. To do this may require some knowledge of meteorology, the Earth's magnetic field and even of events taking place on the Sun. There will be one or two close encounters with mathematics, but surely nothing more complicated than is needed in order to gain a pass in the Radio Amateurs' Examination.

In the context of this handbook we are supposed to be concerned only with those amateur bands that fall between the lower limit of VHF (30MHz) and the upper limit of UHF (3GHz). But the various modes of propagation do not sit easily within those confines and, at some time, you should take a look at the wider picture that includes frequencies below (HF) and above (SHF etc) where similar principles apply but the end results may be very different. For example, there are several references to the ionosphere in this chapter but we shall not be concerned with the part it plays in everyday world-wide communications.

Long, long ago, the Ancients believed that the world had been formed on the top side of a disc, carried, it was said, on the back of a giant turtle. From the propagation point of view that would have simplified things considerably. Many of our problems stem from the fact that we live on the surface of a sphere. Electromagnetic radiation (which includes, among other things, visible light and radio waves) travels in straight lines so, if their rays are to be persuaded to follow the curvature of the Earth, they must get themselves bent by some means in order to achieve any significant distance and remain near to the ground. Fortunately for everyone concerned with radio communications, Nature has thoughtfully provided four alternative ways of getting beyond the horizon: reflection, refraction, diffraction and scatter. We shall see how they operate later on.

As you turn the pages you may be surprised to find references still to the 'old' form of QTH locator. That is not something left over from the last edition of the *VHF/UHF Manual* that ought to have been edited out. The so-called 'squares', 1° of latitude by 2° of longitude, which happen to be common to both the old and the current systems, represent a network of areas which are ideally sized for the needs of propagation research. Although the IARU Maidenhead locator (which is worldwide in coverage) has replaced the QTH locator in most logs by now, many research workers continue to use the two-letter designators when it comes to report storage and analysis. There are two good reasons for that, one being that only four characters serve to define a path instead of eight, the other that it is easier to familiarise oneself with a single grid of 26 × 26 lettered squares than it is to deal with

Table 3.1. Conversion between the old locator system and the IARU locator for main squares

Longitude (first QTH locator letter)

1st IARU letter	1st IARU figure									
	0	1	2	3	4	5	6	7	8	9
I	—	—	—	—	U	V	W	X	Y	Z
J	A	B	C	D	E	F	G	H	I	J
K	K	L	M	N	O	P	Q	R	S	T

Latitude (second QTH locator letter)

2nd IARU letter	Second IARU figure										
	0	1	2	3	4	5	6	7	8	9	
M	Q	R	S	T	U	V	W	X	Y	Z	South
N	A	B	C	D	E	F	G	H	I	J	
O	K	L	M	N	O	P	Q	R	S	T	
P	U	V	W	X	Y	Z					
P							A	B	C	D	North

Examples:
1. To find QTH locator equivalent to IARU locator JN18. Enter longitude table with first letter (J) and first figure (1) to find first letter (B). Enter latitude table with the second letter (N) and the second figure (8) to find the second letter (I). Required locator is BI.
2. To find IARU locator equivalent to QTH locator GP. Record indicated IARU first letter and the first figure (J-6-). Find second letter (P) within the boxed section of the latitude table. Record second letter and second figure (-O-5). Combine. The required IARU locator is JO65. Refer to the text for the use of the letters outside the boxed section.

six or seven grids of 10 × 10, even though the areas covered turn out to be much the same.

The propagation chapter in the RSGB *Radio Communication Handbook* contains tables showing how to convert between either the old locator or the new and latitude and longitude (or vice versa, of course), and nowadays there are computer programs which perform the same task. Here, what is most often required is a simple conversion between the two locator systems at the basic square level and that is provided by Table 3.1.

A word of caution, however. For locations at latitudes below 40°N (roughly the heel of Italy) and above 66°N (the north end of the Gulf of Bothnia) there is an ambiguity because the lettered squares repeat. But that is easily resolved by reference to the callsign of the station concerned. No trouble if you are doing it manually, but a point to watch if you entrust the job to a machine.

RECOGNISING VHF/UHF MODES OF PROPAGATION

At frequencies above 30MHz (following the definition of the terms 'VHF' and 'UHF') propagation by the regular layers of the ionosphere takes place but rarely and then generally only around times of maximum sunspot activity.

The usual mechanism governing the day-to-day performance between two Earth-based stations has its origin in the lower part of the atmosphere, at rarely more than 4–5km above the ground. *Tropospheric propagation* is descriptive of this mode and the fundamental properties of the air which have the most influence are the vertical distributions of temperature and water vapour, both of which tend to decrease with height and, in so doing, cause elevated radio rays, such as might otherwise escape into space, to bend back down towards the ground, and to reach it beyond the normal visible horizon. At times, when dry warm air overlays cool moist air, usually in the presence of an anticyclone, ranges extend dramatically and signals from distances up to about 2000km may be expected. At the same time the strength of nearer signals may be enhanced, effects which extend throughout the VHF and UHF parts of the radio spectrum. During a *tropo opening*, as it is often called, signals generally rise slowly, accompanied by a progressively slower rate of fading. At peak strength, fading may be absent altogether. A long period of enhancement generally ends when a cold front reaches one end of the transmission path.

Tropospheric scatter depends on the presence of small-scale refractive index irregularities and dust or cloud particles in a relatively small volume of the atmosphere towards which both the transmitting and the receiving antennas are directed. High power is required at the transmitter and good signal-to-noise performance at the receiver. Scattered signals are weak, spread in frequency by up to 1kHz either side of an unmodulated carrier, due to the differing motions of the scattering particles, and several rates of fading may co-exist, often giving the impression of a rough modulation. The rate at which intelligence may be sent is limited by *blurring*, introduced by the range of signal path transit times possible within the upper and lower limits of the scattering volume.

At the top end of the UHF band *atmospheric absorption* effects become noticeable, for beyond 3000MHz, in the SHF part of the radio spectrum but outside the scope of this book, *attenuations* due to oxygen, water vapour and precipitation (rain, snow etc) become increasingly important. These affect not only transmission paths that are wholly within the troposphere, but paths originating within and terminating without – ground to satellite, EME etc – although there the effects tend to diminish with increase of beam elevation as the length of that part of the path which contains the absorbers and attenuators decreases.

Although many textbooks still imply that the ionosphere has little effect at VHF and above, a number of very important events have their origin there. Nearly all of them are associated in some way with the level around 100km above the ground, which is generally occupied during the day by the regular E layer.

Of these the most important is *sporadic-E,* which radio amateurs have studied particularly at 144MHz for many years, despite the fact that its presence there, according to our professional colleagues, ought to be impossible. In 1980 the Amateur Service was invited to contribute to a symposium on sporadic-E held at the Appleton Laboratory, and it was clear that at that time the amateur activities concerning this mode of propagation came as a surprise to many of the distinguished authorities present. It is now acknowledged by them that such a mode does exist at frequencies that may exceed 200MHz for short intervals of time, although the feeling is that it may not be sporadic-E at all but an entirely different mechanism as yet unidentified. In this chapter, it will still be referred to as sporadic-E (or E_s) until such time as its true identity is discovered. VHF sporadic-E signals generally begin suddenly and unpredictably (hence their name), bring in stations from distances of 1000–2000km at excellent strength and clarity for periods of up to several hours, and then, with a rapid decline,

they cease. The duration of an opening decreases with increasing radio frequency, the higher frequencies starting later and finishing sooner than the lower ones. During the event the locations heard gradually progress from one area to another. Sporadic-E events at VHF within Europe are generally confined to the months of May to August.

Operators living in southern Europe make use of another VHF mode, which depends on the presence of *field-aligned irregularities* (FAI) in the distribution of free electrons in the ionosphere at E layer heights (around 110km). It has a similar seasonal variation to VHF sporadic-E but differs from it in that signals do not follow the direct path between stations but appear to originate from a scattering volume which is often situated near to the Swiss Alps or close to other mountainous areas at about the same latitude.

Another ionospheric mode is associated with the appearance in the northern sky of the aurora borealis (or 'Northern Lights'), which is caused by the interaction of streams of charged particles from the Sun with the Earth's magnetic field. Signals reflected from the very mobile *auroral-E* curtains, which usually accompany visual displays often seen in the Northern Isles and the north of Scotland but less frequently further south, are readily recognisable with their characteristic tone, variously described as "rasping", "ringing" or "watery", and the fact that beam headings for optimum signal strength are commonly well to the north of the great circle path joining the two stations in contact.

Short-lived trails of ionisation due to the entry into the Earth's atmosphere of small particles of solid matter (seen at night as shooting stars) can be responsible for *meteor scatter,* where two stations, usually widely spaced, can establish contact in intermittent bursts ranging in duration from several seconds down to periods which afford little more than occasional 'pings' of signal. Meteor-scatter signals should be looked for at times of meteor showers, which are listed later in this chapter. Duration of meteor reflections and their frequency of occurrence decline with increasing frequency. Meteor-scatter propagation has been used professionally at operating frequencies of between 30 to 40MHz for communication purposes.

Trans-equatorial propagation is usually confined to paths in which transmitter and receiver are situated approximately equal distances either side of the magnetic equator (eg the Mediterranean area and Zimbabwe). 144MHz openings seem to require high solar flux and low geomagnetic index; frequency spreading is apparent at 144 and 432MHz, with flutter fading, often giving the signals a quality similar to that of signals reflected from the aurora. On the Zimbabwe-Cyprus path openings were centred on 2000 local time at Cyprus. It is believed that extensions to TEP via E_s or tropo may be possible.

For many years any involvement of the F layers of the ionosphere with TEP was disputed but it now seems likely that some, if not all, of the extreme ranges that have been recorded may have come about as a result of double reflection at those heights, without intermediate contact with the ground.

Without question there is an involvement of the *regular F2 layer* at 50MHz around the peak period of the solar cycle. There should be no difficulty in recognising such signals because they ought to bear all the characteristics of normal DX working at HF. At the appropriate time the likelihood of

Table 3.2. Working frequency bands of various VHF and UHF propagation modes (megahertz, unless shown otherwise)

Aurora	50, 70, 144, 432
F2 layer	50
FAI	144
Meteor scatter	50, 70, 144, 432
Moonbounce	50, 144, 432, 1.3GHz, 2.3GHz
Sporadic-E	50, 70, 144
TEP	50, 144
Tropospheric	50, 70, 144, 432, 1.3GHz, 2.3GHz
Troposcatter	70, 144, 432, 1.3GHz, 2.3GHz

FAI = field-aligned irregularities in the E layer
TEP = trans-equatorial propagation

regular layer propagation at 50MHz and the paths concerned should be signalled in monthly ionospheric prediction tables.

Diffraction is a mechanism that is associated with signal paths that cross sharp mountain ridges (it is sometimes referred to as *knife-edge diffraction*). At the ridge a small degree of bending occurs, acting in the direction towards the ground. It is the likely reason for the ability of near-mountain stations to work out over seemingly impossible paths. However, it may be difficult to rule out assistance by tropospheric refraction, particularly for places where the mountain crest supports a blanket of snow which may be undergoing sublimation, that is, going directly from the solid state to vapour. As a rule, signals may be considered to have been diffracted when they have travelled along a path which has crossed a mountain ridge and similar contacts have been possible between the same two stations on a fairly regular basis.

Table 3.2 shows a summary of the bands in which the various VHF and UHF modes play a part in propagation.

TROPOSPHERIC PROPAGATION
The propagation of light
It may be found helpful to begin this study of tropospheric propagation by considering first some comparable aspects of the propagation of light. In most cases the analogy is a close one because radio and light are both forms of electromagnetic radiation, differing only in wavelength (or its inverse, frequency). However, light has the advantage of being readily detectable by its direct action on one of our senses and most of us have had many years of experience working with it. We do not usually think of a torch bulb as being a transmitter, nor our eyes as being receivers but they are nevertheless, and all the perturbing effects to which a radio wave is subjected within the troposphere have their visual counterparts with which we are very familiar already.

A beam of light normally travels in a straight line unless something is done to deflect it. This can be brought about by *reflection,* as in a mirror or from the surface of a still pond, *refraction,* when light passes from one medium to another causing a straight rod in water to appear to be bent, or by *scattering* as from the dust in a shaft of sunlight. Certain frequencies can be made to suffer *attenuation* by inserting one or more filters in the path of the beam, and a very important filter which occurs naturally is provided by a layer of ozone in the upper atmosphere which prevents harmful amounts of ultra-violet light from destroying life on Earth. Mist and fog are visible counterparts to attenuation and scatter.

It will be seen later that most tropospheric radio events of any importance are manifestations of refraction. In terms of light it is refraction which provides the lens with its well-known properties, whereby light leaving one medium, such as air, and entering another, such as glass, suffers a deflection. A Dutch scientist named Willebrord Snell discovered in 1621 that the sine of the angle made by the incident ray with respect to the normal, divided by the sine of the angle made by the refracted ray with respect to the normal, was a constant for a given pair of media. The property possessed by each of the materials involved is known as the *refractive index,* and Snell's constant (sin *i*/sin *r*) *is* equal to the inverse ratio of the refractive indices of the two media.

Changes in refractive index also occur in the atmosphere, due to variations in density, usually as a result of the juxtaposition of two unmixed layers differing greatly in temperature, or due to the presence of a steep gradient of temperature within a single layer. This is the origin of the optical *mirage.* When air near the ground is heated, as over hot sand in the desert or sometimes along a straight road, a line of sight directed downwards is refracted upwards, giving an unexpected (and usually unsuspected) view of the sky which appears as a shimmering pool some distance ahead. Conversely, where cool air underlies warm air a line of sight directed slightly upwards is bent down, so that objects which are in reality well beyond the normal horizon appear to be on it, or even above. There was a famous occasion in 1798 when the whole of the French coast from Calais to Dieppe became visible one afternoon from the cliffs near Hastings.

Effects such as these are even more pronounced at radio frequencies because the radio refractive index contains a term which is dependent upon the amount of water vapour present, and this is a parameter which is subject to considerable change in the lower atmosphere in both space and time.

The radio refractive index of air
There are two basic methods used to determine the refractive index of air; one is to measure it more or less directly using a device called a *refractometer,* the other is to derive it from other, more readily accessible, measurements of atmospheric functions.

Refractometers are beyond the scope of the radio amateur. They are usually airborne or tethered balloon-borne devices constructed and operated by large research organisations. They depend on the fact that the resonant frequency of an open microwave cavity is a function of the dielectric constant of the air within it, and that this is also a function of refractive index.

The more common method is to use upper-air soundings of pressure, temperature and humidity provided by meteorological services all over the world, generally on a twice-daily basis, at midnight and midday GMT. This information is obtained from cheap and simple balloon-borne telemetry devices called *radiosondes,* which have been in regular use since shortly before the Second World War.

The radio refractive index of the air, symbol *n*, is a quantity which is only very slightly higher than unity, but the difference between, say, 1.000345 and 1.000300 is all-important in propagation studies and may have a profound effect on the path of a radio wave. To bring out this importance, and to simplify subsequent calculations, it is usual to subtract 1 from

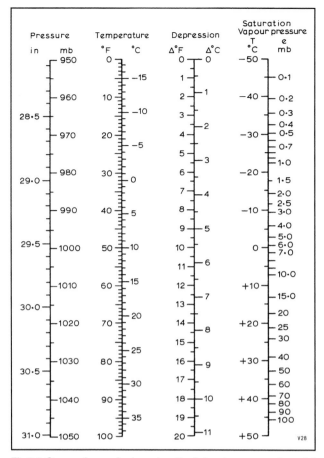

Pressure		Temperature		Depression		Saturation Vapour pressure	
in	mb	°F	°C	Δ°F	Δ°C	T °C	e mb

Fig 3.1. Conversion scales based on the following expressions: (a) Atmospheric pressure: inches and millibars. 29.53 inches Hg = 1000mb. (b) Temperature degrees Fahrenheit and Celsius. (°F) = 9/5 (°C) + 32. (c) Depression of wet bulb or depression of dew point. (Δ°F) = 9/5 (Δ°C). (d) Saturation vapour pressure, e, in millibars, given the ambient temperature in °C. See p3.6 for an expression for e

the refractive index value and then multiply the remainder by one million. This quantity is given the symbol N; in mathematical terms $N = 10^6(n - 1)$.

Before demonstrating how N values may be calculated from meteorological data it will be advisable to define the units involved, and, in some cases, to show how they can be obtained from measurements made at home.

METEOROLOGICAL UNITS
Pressure
According to international agreement the current unit of pressure is the hectopascal (hPa), which is equivalent to a force of 100 newtons per square metre. However, the United Kingdom Meteorological Office (who provide most of the weather observing and forecasting services in this country) have shown themselves to be strangely reluctant to adopt the name 'hectopascal' in their dealings with the public, preferring to stick with the millibar, which has exactly the same value. To avoid confusion that practice will be followed here but at some time in the future you may have to start getting used to the new name. Your home barometer probably still has a scale that is calibrated in inches, which is a relic of much earlier days when air pressure was measured by balancing against it a column of mercury and reporting its height. The units are

related such that 29.53 inches of mercury are equivalent to a pressure of 1000 millibars or 1000 hectopascals. For ground level values Fig 3.1(a) provides a rough conversion. Whole millibars are sufficiently precise for most propagation purposes.

Pressure decreases with height in an approximately logarithmic manner. Near the ground the rate of change is about 1mb in 10m, but this should not be presumed to extend over too great an interval because the relationship is actually a function of temperature also.

In meteorological studies it is customary to use pressure rather than height as a measure of vertical displacement and it will be found very convenient to carry over this practice into propagation work, because the physical processes of the atmosphere are a function of pressure, not of height, and any attempt to make them otherwise will complicate normally convenient relationships beyond belief. It requires some adjustment of ideas, not the least being that height is traditionally measured upwards from the ground, whereas pressure is measured from the top of the atmosphere downwards. But the radio wave, once launched on its way from the transmitting antenna, encounters nothing that can be identified directly with height. It 'sees' changes in air density and refractive index, which are themselves functions of pressure, temperature and water vapour content. Height, as such, is not one of the natural properties of the atmosphere, and that is why aircraft altimeters, which appear to measure it, have to be set to read zero at sea level before the pilot attempts to land, for they are really barometers carrying an approximate scale of feet or metres instead of an accurate one in millibars.

Very roughly indeed a pressure level of 900mb may be considered as being equivalent to a height of 1km and the 700mb level as being approximately 3km. Exact equivalents in respect of a given place and time form part of the basic meteorological data used in analysis work.

Temperature
In scientific work temperatures are generally expressed in degrees Celsius (°C, formerly known as Centigrade) or in kelvin (K). Strictly, kelvin are degrees Celsius plus 273.15 but for our purposes the constant may be rounded off to 273 in order to keep the working figures as whole numbers.

Relative humidity
This is a measure of the amount of moisture present in a sample of air, expressed as a percentage of the total amount which could be contained at the given temperature. It can be obtained from the readings of two identical thermometers, one of which has its bulb surrounded by a muslin wick moistened with distilled water.

They should be well-sited in the shade, and preferably enclosed in a properly ventilated screen. The difference between the two readings is the *depression of the wet bulb,* and the percentage relative humidity can be found from Fig 3.2. If the thermometers are calibrated in degrees Fahrenheit it is better to convert their difference using the scale of Fig 3.1(c) than to find the difference of two converted figures.

Dew point
If a sample of air containing a given amount of moisture is allowed to cool it will be found that the wet-bulb depression

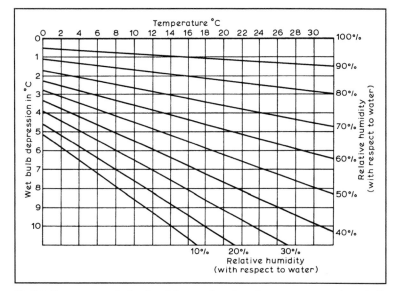

Fig 3.2. Percentage relative humidity as a function of temperature and wet-bulb depression

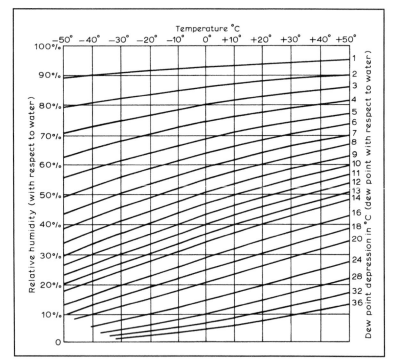

Fig 3.3. Percentage relative humidity as a function of temperature and dew-point depression (may be used to convert radiosonde data published in the 'wrong units')

decreases until eventually both wet and dry bulb thermometers read the same. The relative humidity will have become 100% and the air is said to be *saturated*. The temperature at which this occurs, the *dew point, is* therefore another way of expressing the amount of water vapour contained in a sample of air. Most upper-air reports nowadays show this as *dew-point depression*, the difference between the dry-bulb temperature and the temperature to which the air would have to be cooled in order to reach saturation, but some still refer to percentage relative humidity. The chart, Fig 3.3, can be used to make a conversion either way.

Vapour pressure

The water vapour present in a sample of air exerts a contribution of its own to the total atmospheric pressure. The scales of Fig 3.1(d) show saturation vapour pressures corresponding to a wide range of temperatures, but it has to be admitted that the scale is a difficult one to interpolate. The relationship between temperature and saturation vapour pressure is a complex one and in the past most calculations have involved the use of tables. Recently, however, a number of organisations have tried to find an acceptable approximation, making use of an expression which is within the capabilities of a 'scientific' pocket calculator. The following, which is due to Parish and Purtnam of NASA, has been used elsewhere in this chapter for the machine calculation of refractive index:

$$e_s = T^{-4.9283} \times 10^{(23.5518 - (2937.4/T))}$$

where e_s is saturated vapour pressure in millibars and T is the air temperature in kelvin.

When the air is not saturated the appropriate value of vapour pressure, e, can be found from the relationship:

$$e = e_s \times u$$

where u is the relative humidity expressed as a decimal (eg 72% = 0.72), or, more usually nowadays, from the dew point T_d or the dew-point depression, D (where $T_d = T - D$), using the expression:

$$e = T_d^{-4.9283} \times 10^{(23.5518 - (2937.4/T_d))}$$

where T_d is in kelvin (°C + 273) which will be found to be the most practical form for use with a calculator or computer. Of course, the same trick of using the dew point to find the actual vapour pressure as if it was a saturated vapour pressure may be performed on the scale of Fig 3.1(d) to provide the required value of e.

THE CALCULATION OF *N*

The basic equation is:

$$N = \frac{77.6}{T}\left(p + \frac{4810e}{T}\right)$$

where p is the atmospheric pressure in millibars, e is the water vapour pressure in millibars and T is the air temperature in kelvin. It is often more convenient to expand this into:

$$N = \frac{77.6p}{T} + \frac{3.733 \times 10^5 \times e}{T^2}$$

because it then separates conveniently into a 'dry' term, corresponding approximately to the optical value of refractive index, and a 'wet' term which contains all of the contribution due to the presence of water vapour. The values which result from these expressions are known as *refractivities*, but they are often referred to simply as *N-units*.

The degree of ray bending which results from refractive index changes can be assessed by calculating the decrease

Table 3.3. Minimum duct thickness for the VHF and UHF amateur bands

Band (MHz)	λ_c (m)	Minimum thickness (m)	Approximate millibar equivalent
50	6.00	317	31
70	4.29	263	26
144	2.08	176	17
432	0.69	96	9
1296	0.23	52	5
2300	0.13	38	4

Table 3.4. Computer or calculator program to obtain radio refractive index, N, from basic meteorological data

S = Store
R = Recall from store

Load stores with constants:
S1 = 273, S2 = 2937.4, S3 = −4.9283, S4 = 23.5518, S5 = 77.6, S6 = 4810

Input data for each level to be computed, pass to the indicated stores:

Enter p = pressure in millibars (or hectopascals). To S7 (p)

Enter t = temperature °C. Add R1 to convert to kelvin. To S8 (T)

Enter D = dew point depression °C. Subtract from R8. To S9 (T_d)

Program

1. Evaluate vapour pressure, e

   R9^{R3} * 10$^{(R4 - (R2/R9))}$ To S10 (e)

2. Evaluate radio refractive index, N

   R5 (R7 = R6 * R10 / R8) / R8

Round off the result to the nearest whole number.

Test

When p = 900, t = −3.0 and D = 8, then N = 272

Note: A step-by-step calculator program (based on the TI58/59 calculator but easily adapted to suit any similar programmable scientific calculator) may be found in the fourth edition of the *VHF/UHF Manual*, p 2.5. It works on the TI66 which may still be available.

over unit height change. The normal gradient from the ground may be regarded as being approximately −40N-units/km. Should it become −157N/km the curvature of the ray becomes the same as that of the Earth, while gradients greater (ie more negative) than −157N/km result in *ducting*, where the waves travel for great distances, confined within a relatively shallow range of heights, suffering alternate refractions at the steep-lapse layer and reflections from the ground.

Provided that well-marked contrasts in refractivity exist above and below a ducting layer it is not essential for the ground to be involved at all. Once signals have been trapped in an *elevated duct* they may travel considerable distances without being receivable by stations on the ground below the transmission path. The waves eventually leak out of the duct at some point where the necessary conditions are no longer being fulfilled.

For efficient duct propagation the wavelength concerned must be less than a critical value λ_c, such that:

$$\lambda_c = 1.9 \times 10^{-4} \times D^{1.8}$$

where D is the duct thickness in metres.

Table 3.3 shows the minimum duct thickness and the approximate equivalent pressure difference in millibars, centred on 850mb, the pressure at a typical ducting height. The figures cover all the VHF and UHF amateur bands.

The following example of a calculation directly from basic meteorological data may be found useful:

p = 900mb, T = −3°C (= 270K), dew point depression = 8°C.

From this the dew point must be −11°C (= 262K) and the corresponding vapour pressure from Fig 3.1(d) is 2.6mb. Hence:

$$N = \frac{77.6 \times 900}{270} + \frac{3.733 \times 10^5 \times 2.6}{270 \times 270}$$
$$= 259 + 13 = 272$$

Table 3.4 outlines a skeleton program to calculate radio refractive index N from basic meteorological data entered sequentially for each of the available levels. It should be readily adaptable for any type of scientific programmable calculator or a computer. Whole-number answers are adequate for propagation studies and there is nothing to be gained by trying to make the results seem more precise than the data can support. Before undertaking extensive calculations make sure that the test figures yield the result shown.

CAUSES OF TROPO DX

Having established a method of obtaining refractive index values from standard meteorological upper-air observations it is a natural progression to apply that knowledge to a study of the atmosphere during a well-marked tropospheric 'opening' – probably the main reason why radio amateurs take an active interest in this mode of radio propagation. For that purpose, consider the situation late in the evening of 20 January 1974, when continental Europe was 'wide-open' to the UK. This is a good example of a notable winter event and, as will be seen, it has been used to illustrate various aspects of a single occasion, as is shown in Figs 3.4, 3.5 and 3.6.

Fig 3.4 shows a cross-section of the atmosphere up to 700mb (about 3km in terms of height), from Camborne in SW England to Berlin. The *isopleths* join levels having equal values of refractivity, scaled in N-units. There is no mistaking the concentration formed in the lower part of the diagram. This indicates a steep fall of refractive index with height and is in the correct sense to cause the return to earth of rays which would otherwise have been lost in space above the horizon. Superrefraction of this sort produces bending towards the earth in the case of both ascending and descending rays. Because there is a normal tendency for refractive index to decrease with height, this effect is nearly always present in some degree and this accounts for the fact that radio communication at VHF and UHF is usually possible beyond the visible horizon. The presence in the lower atmosphere of a layer in which refractivity decreases very rapidly with height, as in the case being considered, is always accompanied by enhancement of signal strengths and an increase in working range. However, in the case where very-narrow-beamwidth antennas are used at both ends of the path, received signal strengths may fall, due to energy being deflected away from a path which has been optimised under conditions of normal refractivity.

From a cross-section, such as Fig 3.4, it would be quite possible to calculate the probable paths of rays leaving a transmitting antenna at various angles of take-off, using Snell's Law, as with optical ray-tracing, but this is an exercise which

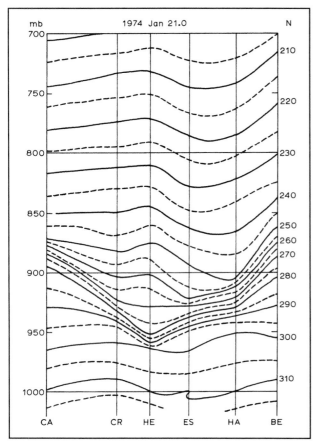

Fig 3.4. Cross-section from SW England to Central Europe at midnight (0000GMT) 21 January 1974, drawn in terms of conventional refractive index N. The vertical scale is in terms of pressure. 700mb = 3km approx. CA = Camborne, CR = Crawley, HE = Hemsby, ES = Essen, HA = Hannover, BE = Berlin

is probably outside the needs of most amateurs. It should be noted that the values of refractivity at ground level reveal little of the situation above. For that reason the only really effective study of tropospheric propagation phenomena involves the acquisition of upper-air meteorological data.

THE ATMOSPHERE IN MOTION

It does not require a great deal of experience on the VHF and UHF bands to realise that all the big 'openings' to the Continent occur during periods of high atmospheric pressure. Indeed, some amateurs look upon an aneroid barometer in the home as being their guide to the state of the bands. However, whereas good conditions are accompanied by high-pressure readings, high pressure is not always accompanied by good conditions. Why should that be? The answer lies in an appreciation of the role played by vertical motions in the atmosphere.

In general, rising air becomes cooler and moister, while descending air warms and becomes more dry. Air is sometimes forced into vertical motion by the topography in its path; it rises when it flows over hills and it descends into valleys. However, the present context mainly concerns vertical motion associated with the two main types of pressure system.

Consider first a low-pressure system or 'depression'. Air circulates round it in an anticlockwise direction (in the northern hemisphere), with a slight inclination towards the centre,

creating an inward spiral which leaves progressively less room for the volume of air in motion. There is only one escape route available, and that is upwards. So low-pressure systems are associated with rising air.

On the other hand, anticyclones (high-pressure systems) are characterised by light winds blowing clockwise round the centre but with a slight deflection outwards. As the air spirals outwards fresh quantities must be available to maintain the supply and the only source is from aloft, resulting this time in a downward flow. So high-pressure systems have descending air associated with them.

Adiabatic changes

Air in vertical motion changes in both volume and pressure (they are directly related) and in temperature also, although there need be no gain or loss of heat. This may appear at first to be a contradiction in terms, for heat and temperature might be thought to be alternative names for the same thing. In fact, heat is a quantity which can be distributed either over a small volume to provide a large increase in temperature, or spread over a large volume to appear as a small increase in temperature. Thus 1kg of air descending from a height of 3km may begin with a pressure of 700mb and a temperature of −5°C, to arrive at 1.5km with a pressure of 850mb and a temperature of 10°C with no change of heat being involved. Such a process is *adiabatic*, and it is an important principle in meteorology.

A homely demonstration of it at work may be found in the case of the bicycle pump, the barrel of which gets hot in use due to the air inside having been compressed.

When the air is anything other than dry another apparent paradox links the amount of water vapour and the corresponding humidity during the adiabatic process. Going back to the example, at 700mb 3.78g of water vapour would have been sufficient to produce saturation (100% relative humidity) in the 1kg sample of air, whereas at 850mb the same amount would give only 41.5% relative humidity because air at 10°C could hold 9.1g of water vapour. So, air descending adiabatically gets warmer and drier, although the actual amounts of heat and water vapour remain unchanged.

The action is reversible but only up to a point. Ascending air is accompanied by increasing relative humidity, which at some stage will reach 100%. Any further lifting will result in the appearance of liquid water, which will appear either as cloud or larger droplets, which are likely to fall out of suspension as rain. When condensation occurs, the rate of cooling is altered by the appearance of latent heat, and the precipitation will alter the amount of moisture in the sample of air.

No such considerations affect descending air once its relative humidity has fallen below 100%, although there will have been alterations to the rate of change of temperature if liquid droplets of water have been evaporating, again on account of latent heat.

If the sample of air is taken adiabatically to a standard pressure of 1000mb the temperature it assumes is known as the *potential temperature* of the sample. It follows from this that potential temperature is a quantity which remains constant during any adiabatic change: conversely, a change is an adiabatic one if it is associated with constant potential temperature.

Potential refractive index

Referring back to Fig 3.4 it will be seen that, quite apart from the region of interest referred to earlier, there is a general background of fairly regularly spaced isopleths which represent the normal fall-off of refractive index with height. A number of modifications to the standard procedure for calculating refractive index have been proposed from time to time, all with the intention of minimising this effect, leaving emphasis on the features that are of most interest to the propagation engineer.

Opinions have varied on the best way to do this. Most methods proposed have involved some form of model atmosphere and the calculation of departures from it, resulting in complex exercises for which a computer is advisable. Another disadvantage has been the difficulty of recovering the original values of refractive index from the final data (should they be required elsewhere, or at a later date). The method to be described was first proposed in 1959 by Dr K H Jehn of the University of Texas, who does not seem to have taken advantage of the full potential of his suggestion. Curiously, little has been done outside amateur circles to exploit its usefulness; it involves a unit known as *potential refractive index* (K).

It may be obtained from upper-air meteorological sounding data in just the same way as has been described for N-units, the only difference being that each sample of air, whatever its true level may be, is presumed to have been transported adiabatically to a pressure of 1000mb before the calculations are made.

The advantages of this form of normalisation are considerable. By adopting a procedure which imitates the natural process of the atmosphere, applying, for example, to the large mass of air which subsides from aloft within an anticyclone, each level of air is effectively labelled with a value of potential refractive index which remains with it during any adiabatic change.

The effect may be seen particularly well in time-sections, such as that of Fig 3.5(a), which shows how the potential refractive index pattern varied from day to day at a single station, Crawley, over a period which included that eventful evening of 20 January 1974.

There is no mistaking the extensive tongue of warm, dry, subsiding air associated with an anticyclone and the steep-lapse refractive index layer built up where it meets the opposing cool, moist air underneath.

Towards the right and left edges of the diagram may be seen evidence of rising air which is associated with two depressions, which preceded and followed the period of high pressure. These potential refractive index isopleths are very sensitive indicators of vertical motion in the atmosphere, and the patterns on cross-sections and time-sections take on an interesting three-dimensional aspect when viewed in conjunction with surface weather charts.

It is interesting to compare the potential refractive index

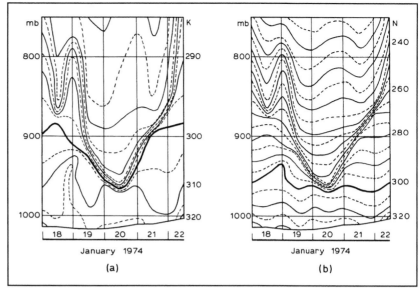

Fig 3.5. (a) Time-section showing isopleths of potential refractive index, *K*. Crawley, 18–22 January 1974. (b) Time-section showing isopleths of radio refractive index, *N*. Crawley, 18–22 January 1974

time-section of Fig 3.5(a) with the corresponding section drawn in terms of conventional radio refractive index, N, Fig 3.5(b). Note first that there are fewer lines on the potential refractive index diagram, indicating that the normal fall-off of refractive index with height has been considerably offset. At the steep-lapse layer, the concentration of isopleths has been greatly emphasised in Fig 3.5(a) but it is important to notice that this has not been at the expense of accuracy in indicating either the height at which the effect occurred or its vertical extent.

Because air undergoing adiabatic changes has been shown to carry its value of potential refractive index along with it, no matter what its level, it should not be surprising that the boundary layer across the whole of Fig 3.5(a) is formed of basically the same set of K-values irrespective of changes in pressure (or height). Fig 3.5(b) shows that the same is not true for conventional refractive index. This is not to suggest that the N-values are wrong, but rather to point out that they do not share this very useful attribute of coherence independent of height which appears in diagrams like these. That the same is true of cross-sections may be seen by comparing Fig 3.6 with Fig 3.4.

If values of atmospheric pressure are known (as they always are when radiosonde data have been used) a simple relationship exists between potential refractive index and N. This leads to the conversion chart shown in Fig 3.7, which may also be used as a plotting chart, having the property that an ascent plotted in terms of one of the units may be read off in terms of the other by using the appropriate axes. In this way the potential refractive index values may be converted to N-units for ray-tracing purposes, or compared with N-unit profiles produced elsewhere.

Alternatively, use may be made of the following expressions:

$$N = 0.00731 \times p^{0.712} \times K$$

and

$$K = 136.8 \times p^{-0.712} \times N$$

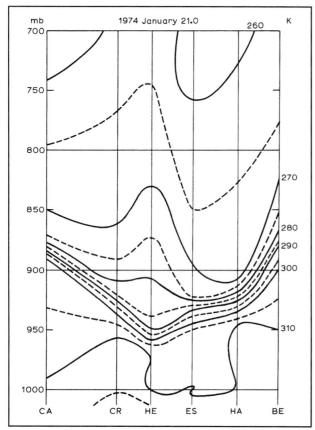

Fig 3.6. Cross-section from SW England to Central Europe, at midnight (0000GMT) 21 January 1974, drawn in terms of potential refractive index, *K*. Compare with Fig 3.4 and note here how the steep-lapse layer contains the same values along the length of the path

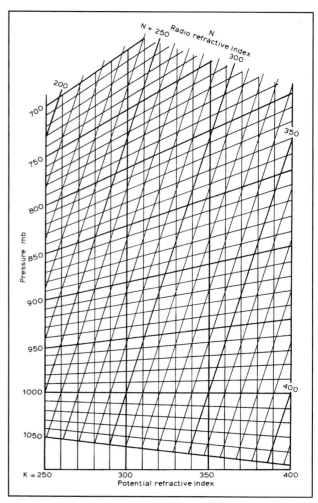

Fig 3.7. Refractive index plotting/conversion chart. Ordinate: pressure (mb). Abscissae: (vertical) potential refractive index, *K*; (slant) radio refractive index, *N*

which may be performed without difficulty on a scientific pocket calculator.

Although this conversion provides a way of obtaining potential refractive index it is usually better to calculate values directly from the radiosonde data. A method of doing that using a calculator or computer will be found later in the chapter, at Table 3.4.

ACQUIRING CURRENT UPPER-AIR METEOROLOGICAL DATA

A much-quoted Victorian lady, Felicia Hemans, began her poem 'Casabianca' with the words "The boy stood on the burning deck / Whence all but he had fled". Those two lines rather neatly sum up the situation as regards the present availability of upper-air meteorological data. Gone are the Morse, RTTY and facsimile broadcasts which used to keep us supplied with current information within an hour or so of the measurements being taken. Gone, too, are the printed daily records that appeared a few days later giving copies of the coded messages. And gone, never to return, are the microfiche summaries that would have served us well had they continued. All that remains for us on easy public access is a daily page of machine-plotted graphs on the back page of the *European Meteorological Bulletin*, published by Deutscher Wetterdienst who, as the name suggests, run the national weather service in Germany. It is to be hoped that the burning deck will continue to hold for some time to come, yet. It

is not that the basic messages to which we need access no longer exist.

The trouble is that the whole field of meteorological communications has been depersonalised. Nowadays a machine puts the message together and passes it on to a computer, which launches it on to the global network, by which means it reaches other computers located all over the world. Then, instead of appearing in print for human beings to decode and plot, each message serves its purpose as a set of instructions fed to an XY plotter which not only turns it into a set of graphs but draws the graph paper around them. The message itself never sees the light of day. From the meteorologist's point of view that is progress. For anyone wanting access to the basic information it is a disaster.

The sort of data we are considering used to be freely available as a public service. Not any more. Weather is big business nowadays and the organisations operating in that field jealously guard their products, demanding a high price to retrieve information from the memory banks of their computer. In a letter published in the October 1995 issue of the Royal Meteorological Society's journal *Weather* (page 359) a research worker from the University of Bristol revealed that he had been quoted £35 as the price of supplying just a single copy of a radiosonde ascent.

Fortunately for us, however, copies of the *European Meteorological Bulletin*, mentioned earlier, may still be consulted free of charge at the National Meteorological Library, London Road, Bracknell. Spare copies are also held for loan purposes. If you are unable to attend in person it might be worth the cost of a telephone call (01344 420242, ask for the library loans desk) to see if they would be prepared to meet your requirements by post.

The Bulletin is available daily on subscription from the publisher, Deutscher Wetterdienst, Frankfurterstrasse 135, 63067 Offenbach, Germany. In summer 1997 the price was DM456, plus postage, for a year's supply – rather high a price if you only need the back page. But you would also get seven other pages containing weather maps in colour, some for the whole of the Northern Hemisphere, others for just the Atlantic and Europe, for sea level and several upper levels. Each page is A3 size.

The aerological diagrams are displayed in eight panels, each panel containing two diagrams side by side, making 16 diagrams in all. Each diagram shows machine-plotted graphs of temperature and dew-point depression plotted against pressure for up to three stations, identified by the use of differing symbols. The size of each diagram is such that temperature runs from −40°C to +30°C in 61mm, dew-point depressions from 0°C to 30°C in 26mm and pressure from 225mb to 1000mb in 76mm.

You may find this hard to believe but, with care, it is possible to estimate the plotted values to a sufficient degree of accuracy to be able to provide meaningful cross-sections and time-sections for propagation studies.

Frequently you will find that temperature and dew-point depression turning points do not occur at the same pressure level. Remember that you need all three values to calculate refractive index so you will have to use the plotted curves to interpolate where necessary.

The published selection of up to 48 stations (occasionally one or two are missed) provides excellent coverage over Europe, as may be judged from Fig 3.8, which needs to be studied in conjunction with Table 3.5. All the diagrams show soundings made at 12UT.

Fig 3.8 may be used to select the upper-air stations most appropriate to a given signal path, which could be overlaid using the latitude and longitude scales. It will be found an advantage to extend your cross-section beyond the strict limits of the path, if possible, because two additional soundings help in drawing in the refractive index lines.

The *European Meteorological Bulletin* appears to be all that we have left for upper-air data at the present time, unless, that is, you happen to be, or decide to become, a practising professional meteorologist.

Perhaps there is a way to get current sounding data off the Internet or the World Wide Web. If there is, and you are fortunate enough to be able to tap into it, you will find details of how to use the information later on in the chapter.

Why not use historical upper-air data?

Every researcher feels instinctively that he or she has to work with the latest information available. That is fine if what you need for analysis is easily come by. But when it is in short supply or priced as if it were gold dust it makes sense to consider a more practical alternative.

The monthly VHF and UHF report columns of *Radio Communication* and (especially) the quarterly European report sections in the German magazine *DUBUS* regularly contain details of unusual or exceptional signal events, and have done for many years. Very few of those events have been properly analysed. So, why not look back 20 years or so to a time when the radiosonde network was much more extensive than it is today and the information was readily available? Twice a day, 00UT and 12UT, or, if you go back far enough, four times a day: 00UT, 06UT, 12UT and 18UT.

Why not consider going back to two periods of intense scientific interest the world over – the International Geophysical Year, 1957 and the International Quiet Sun Years of 1963 and 1964? Extremely well documented records covering a wide range of disciplines still exist in scientific libraries. The likes of the efforts that were put into those two periods will never be seen again. Why not put them to good use?

By changing your objectives Mother Hubbard's cupboard could be replaced by Aladdin's cave. To parody a notice which used to be common in general stores before the war – if you don't see what you want in the window, come inside and ask for something else.

Discontinued sources of meteorological data
Until 31 December 1980, the source of data from nine British and Irish upper-air stations was the *Daily Aerological Record*, published by the Meteorological Office.

There was a companion series, dealing with surface observations, the *Daily Weather Report*, which gave six-hourly observations for each of about 50 places located in all parts of the British Isles.

Those two publications had a very wide circulation in their time and copies may still be available in some specialised libraries in various parts of the country. They, and similar publications from other parts of Europe, are certainly available at either the National Meteorological Library in Bracknell or in the Meteorological Office Archives, about half a mile distant. The documents may be consulted without charge and you will find the staff in both places very helpful. Most of the information you want will be on open shelves but you will probably have to ask for some of the continental upper air reports because there is no longer space to keep them in the room open to the public.

EXTRACTING THE DATA
If you are fortunate enough to be able to access the messages circulating on the global network you will need to know that they are headed by an alphanumeric indicator which reveals the type of information concerned and the country or area concerned. Upper-air messages are split into two or more parts, not all of which are of interest in the present context. Printed copies may be similarly split, but the identifiers may have been edited out by then.

The first message, headed with a prefix beginning 'US' (eg USUK for British stations, USFR for French stations etc) and/or by the group 'TTAA', relates to observations at specific levels of pressure. The station number is generally the second of the numerical groups.

Next, look for a group beginning 99. This and the one following are in the form:

99ppp TTTDD

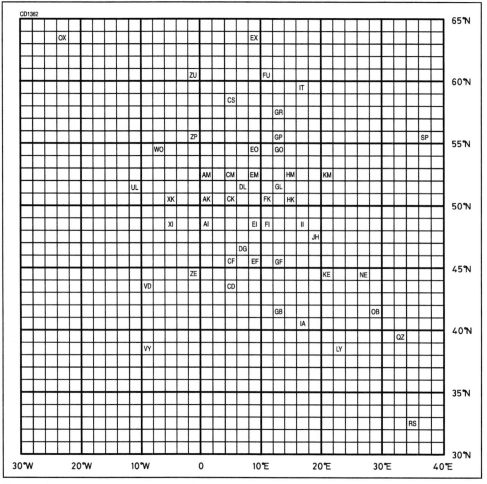

Fig 3.8. Chart showing the positions of meteorological upper-air stations relative to QTH locator squares. The stations may be identified by reference to Table 3.5

where '99' indicates that ground level data follows, 'ppp' is the pressure in whole millibars, with the initial 1 omitted for 1000mb and over.

'TTT' is the air temperature in degrees Celsius. If the tenths figure, the third one, is odd, the whole number is negative (ie 046 = 4.6°C, but 045 = –4.5°C).

'DD' is the dew-point depression in tenths of a degree up to 5°, then in whole degrees with 50 added (eg 46 = dew-point 4.6° below air temperature; 66 = 16° below).

Codes 51–55 are not used.

At regularly spaced intervals there will be further groups beginning 00, 85 and 70, indicators showing that the data which follows are for 1000, 850 and 700mb respectively. These groups and the ones which follow immediately have the form:

00hhh TTTDD . . . 85hhh
TTTDD . . . 70hhh
TTTDD

Table 3.5. Upper-air sounding stations currently (1997) featured in the European Meteorological Bulletin

QTH locator	IARU locator	Station number	Station name	Country	Height ASL (m)	QTH locator	IARU locator	Station number	Station name	Country	Height ASL (m)
OX	HP83	04018	Keflavik	Iceland	54	EX	JP43	01241	Ørland	Norway	7
UL	IO41	03953	Valentia	Ireland	14	FI	JN5B	10868	München	Germany	489
VY	IM58	08579	Lisboa	Portugal	105	FK	JO50	10548	Meiningen	Germany	453
VD	IN53	08001	La Coruna	Spain	67	FU	JP50	01384	Oslo	Norway	204
WO	IO64	03920	Long Kesh	N Ireland	38	GB	JN61	16245	Roma	Italy	21
XI	IN78	07710	Brest	France	103	GF	JN65	16044	Udine	Italy	53
XK	IO70	03808	Camborne	England	88	GL	JO61	10486	Dresden	Germany	232
ZE	IN94	07510	Bordeaux	France	61	GO	JO64	10184	Greifswald	Germany	6
ZP	IO95	03240	Boulmer	England		GP	JO65	06181	København	Denmark	42
ZU	IP90	03005	Lerwick	Shetland	84	GR	JO67	02527	Goteborg	Sweden	155
AI	JN08	07145	Trappes	France	161	HK	JO70	11520	Praha	Czech Rep	304
AK	JO00	03882	Herstmonceaux	England	52	HM	JO72	10393	Lindenberg	Germany	104
AM	JO02	03496	Hemsby	England	14	IA	JN80	16320	Brindisi	Italy	10
CD	JN23	07645	Nimes	France	62	IT	JN88	11035	Wien	Austria	209
CF	JN25	07481	Lyon	France	240	IT	JO89	02465	Stockholm	Sweden	14
CK	JO20	06447	Uccle	Belgium	104	JH	JN97	12843	Budapest	Hungary	139
CM	JO22	06260	de Bilt	Netherlands	15	KE	KN04	13275	Beograd	Serbia	203
CS	JO28	01415	Stavanger	Norway	9	KM	KO02	12374	Legionowo	Poland	96
DG	JN36	06610	Payerne	Switzerland	491	LY	KM18	16716	Athens	Greece	15
DL	JO31	10410	Essen	Germany	161	NE	KN34	15420	Bukarest	Romania	
EF	JN45	16080	Milano	Italy	103	OB	KN41	17062	Istanbul	Turkey	33
EI	JN48	10739	Stuttgart	Germany	311	QZ	KM69	17130	Ankara	Turkey	891
EM	JO42	10238	Bergen	Germany		RS	KM73	40179	Bet Dagan	Israel	35
EO	JO44	10035	Schleswig	Germany	48	SP	KO85	27612	Moskava	Russia	156

Note: In the QTH locator column an underlined letter signifies that care is needed to avoid ambiguity.

In more recent years 925mb has been used as an additional standard level.

'hhh' is the height above sea level of the pressure level in metres, omitting the thousands figure. For 1000mb this becomes a negative number when the pressure at sea level is below that value, and this is indicated by adding 500 to the code figure (ie 675 = −175m). The missing first figure is 1 for 850mb and either 2 or 3 for 700mb, whichever puts the value closer to 3000m. 'TTTDD' has the same significance as before.

The second message is headed with an indicator beginning 'UK' (eg UKUK, UKFR etc) and/or the group 'TTBB', signifying that it relates to turning points in the temperature and dew-point profiles. It is the more useful of the two because it contains everything necessary for propagation studies, apart from the relationship between pressure and height for the particular ascent. As before, the station number is generally second of the five-figure groups in the message. To decode the remainder, point off succeeding groups in pairs that begin with the figures 00, 11, 22, 33 etc. The pairs have the form:

NNppp TTTDD

where 'NN' enumerates the data points. '00' always signifies local ground-level. 'ppp' is the pressure, in millibars, at the level of the observation, with the initial 1 omitted if the value exceeds 1000. 'TTTDD' contain the temperature in degrees and tenths and the dew-point depression, coded as before.

For most tropospheric propagation studies there is little point in going beyond the level at which the pressure has fallen to 700mb, unless it is to interpolate a refractive index value for 700mb in order to provide a uniform 'top' to a cross-section.

In a radiometeorological study it is quite likely that all the work will be carried out in terms of pressure rather than height, not only for convenience because that is the form adopted in the radiosonde messages, but because the radio wave, once launched, does not 'see' changes in height but rather changes in air density, a quantity closely related to pressure. In the atmosphere, height, which seems so easy to understand on the ground, becomes a complex function of the integrated effects of temperature and humidity, and of the value of pressure at station height.

There are two ways of finding the heights corresponding to the various pressure levels reported in the Part 2 message. The more accurate, though time-consuming, way is to plot the ascent data on a standard tephigram (obtainable from HMSO, where it is known at Metform 2810B) and then to follow the instructions given on the form. Alternatively, and this may well be accurate enough for the present purpose, refer to Fig 3.9, which assumes an average vertical distribution of temperature and dew point, leaving the height a function only of surface pressure. The diagram is used as follows:

(a) Find the station height from Table 3.3 and draw a vertical line at the corresponding value on the horizontal scale. (Crawley, at 144m ASL, which appears in many of the examples used in this chapter, including this one, is no longer operational. Its place for observations over southeast England has been taken by Herstmonceaux.)
(b) Find the point where that vertical line intersects a horizontal line appropriate to the reported value of ground level pressure.

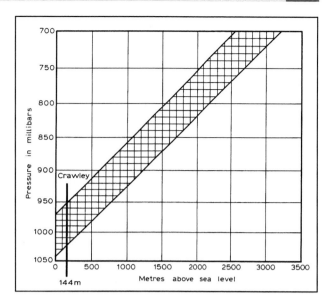

Fig 3.9. Relationship between pressure and height between the surface and 700mb, assuming an average contribution from temperature and humidity

(c) Through that point lay off a line which maintains a constant proportion of the space between the two sloping lines. (An overlay of tracing paper is useful here.)
(d) Approximate heights corresponding to given pressures may now be read from the horizontal scale.

This diagram may be used also to interpolate between the height values reported in the standard-level message.

Full details of all the codes used in meteorological broadcasts will be found in *Met O 920b: Handbook of Weather Messages, Part II, Codes and Specifications,* published by HMSO, London and also in the *Manual on Codes,* WMO No 306, in the section dealing with code FM35.

THE TEPHIGRAM

Meteorologists usually plot radiosonde ascent data on a rather complex thermodynamic chart known as a *tephigram,* (which may be used as a means of calculating potential refractive index) and a knowledge of its properties will help to achieve an understanding of the processes involved in the atmospheric movements we have been considering. Fig 3.10 shows an outline diagram, including a set of K-lines which will be explained in the next section. Reference should be made to the small inset diagram which identifies the various axes as they appear at the 1000mb, 0°C intersection:

P–P   are *isobars*, or lines of constant pressure.
T–T   are *isotherms*, or lines of constant temperature.
D–D   are lines of constant moisture content, which are followed by the dew point as the pressure alters during adiabatic changes.
A–A   are lines of constant potential temperature, followed by the air temperature during an adiabatic change.
W–W   is a saturated adiabatic, which marks the temperature changes followed by ascending saturated air (only one is shown here in order to simplify the diagram as much as possible).

Both temperature and dew point are plotted with reference to the T–T lines.

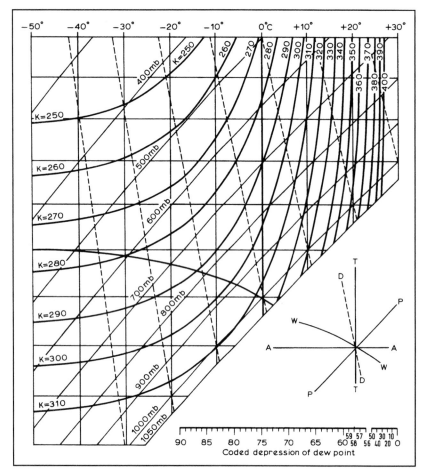

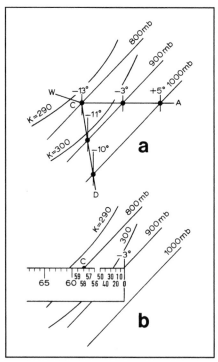

Fig 3.11. Alternative methods of determining values of potential refractive index from reported measurements of pressure, temperature and dew-point depression, using the tephigram modified as in Fig 3.10. (a) Intersection method. (b) Using scale of coded dew-point depression values

Fig 3.10. Skeleton tephigram (a meteorological temperature entropy diagram) showing the positions of additional curves, labelled K = 250 to 450, used for direct graphical calculation of potential refractive index values from published radiosonde measurements. For practical use it is recommended that the curves should be transferred to a standard full-sized tephigram, available from HMSO as Metform 2810B

An example of the use of the tephigram will help to emphasise the points which have been made earlier in the text. Consider Fig 3.11(a), which shows two points on the 900mb line, representing a temperature of −3°C and a dew point of −11°C. If that sample of air is taken to a pressure of 1000mb adiabatically, the temperature will follow the horizontal line CA, and the dew point will follow CD. At 1000mb the temperature becomes +5°C (by definition the potential temperature), and the dew point becomes −10°C. Lifting would cause the temperature and the dew point to come closer together, and they would become coincident at the point C, which is known as the *condensation level*, where condensed droplets of water begin to appear as cloud. Further lifting will cause the temperature to follow one of the saturated adiabatics such as CW, instead of an extension of AC, due to the liberation of latent heat.

OBTAINING POTENTIAL REFRACTIVE INDEX VALUES

Potential refractive index values may be obtained in one of four ways, the method to be used depending on the resources available.

1. From the expression:

$$K = \frac{77.6}{\theta}\left(1000 + \frac{4810000e}{p\theta}\right)$$

where p is the pressure in millibars at the level of observation and the potential temperature in kelvin:

$$\theta = (T_{°C} + 273)\times\left(\frac{1000}{p}\right)^{0.288}$$

e is the saturation vapour pressure at the dew-point temperature.

Example: p = 900mb, T = −3.0°C, dew-point depression = code 58 = 8°C below −3.0°C = −11.0°C, then:

$$\theta = 270\times\left(\frac{1000}{900}\right)^{0.288} = 278.3$$

and from Fig 3.1(d):

$$e = 2.6\text{mb (at }-11°C)$$

whence K = 292.8.

2. Using a programmable calculator or computer. Table 3.6 outlines a program which provides K values directly from pressure, temperature and either dew-point depression, dew point or percentage relative humidity.

3. Using a full-sized tephigram based on Fig 3.10 and a two-line construction. The curved potential refractive index lines labelled $K = 290$, $K = 300$ etc are so placed that the

Table 3.6. Computer or calculator program to obtain potential refractive index, K, from basic meteorological data

S = Store

R = Recall from store

Load stores with constants:

S1 = 273, S2 = 2937.4, S3 = -4.9283, S4 = 23.5518, S5 = 77.6, S6 = 4810, S7 = 0.288, S8 = 1000

Input data for each level to be oomputed, pass to the indicated stores

Enter p = pressure in millibars (or hectopascals). To S9 (p)

Enter t = temperature °C. Add R1 to convert to kelvin. To S10 (T)

Enter either:

D = dew point depression °C. Subtract from R10. To S11 (T_d)

or t_d = dew point temperature, °C. Add R1 to convert to Kelvin. To S11 (T_d)

or U = relative humidity, expressed as a decimal. To S12 (R_H)

Program

1. Evaluate vapour pressure, e
   Either (a) If dew point or dew point depression has been entered:

   $R11^{R3} * 10^{(R4 - (R2/R11))}$ To S13 (e)

   or (b) If percentage relative humidity has been entered:

   $R10^{R3} * 10^{R4 - (R2/R10)} * R12$ To S13 (e)

2. Evaluate potential temperature

   $R10 * (R8/R9)^{R7}$ To S14 (θ)

3. Evaluate potential refractive index, K

   $R5((R6 * R8 * R13)/(R9 * R14)) + R8/R14$

   Round off the result to the nearest whole number.

Test

When p = 900, t = -3.0, either D = 8 or t_d = -11.0, or U = 53/100 = 0.53 then K = 293.

Note: A step-by-step calculator program (based on the TI58/59 calculator but easily adapted to suit any similar programmable scientific calculator) may be found in the fourth edition of the *VHF/UHF Manual*, p2.14.

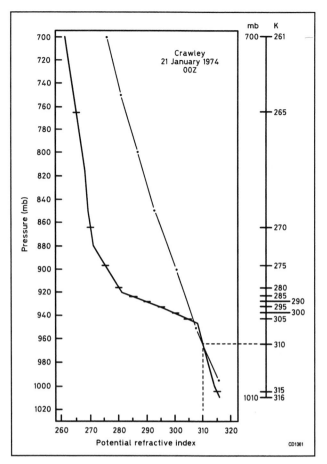

Fig 3.12. Potential refractive index profile from Crawley, 21 January 1974, at 0000GMT. The spaced values along the vertical line on the right have been used in the construction of both Fig 3.5 and Fig 3.6. The thin sloping line shows 'normal' K values for the second half of January (see Table 3.8, line B).

parallel), were it not for the fact that the dependence of K on dew point diminishes at low temperatures.

FROM PROFILE TO SECTION

Once the calculations have been made all the information necessary to draw a profile will be to hand.

A profile, such as the one shown in Fig 3.12, reveals immediately the presence of warm, dry, low-refractivity air overlying a ground-based layer of air which is cool, moist, and of high refractive index. The more abrupt the boundary between them, the more nearly horizontal will the transition appear on the diagram, and the more pronounced the bending experienced by the radio wave. Some of the occasions when conditions have been most favourable for DX have occurred during periods when there has been anticyclonic subsidence aloft with a contrasting depth of wet fog at the ground.

In some cases the refractive index profile is all that is required. It is much more rewarding, however, to combine it with others in order to make a section.

The first step is to project the pressures at which regular values of K occur across to a vertical line, as shown in the diagram. The spacings which result can then be transferred to form part of a time-section for the station in question (Fig 3.5), or a cross-section for a given path (Fig 3.6) – the one profile forms part of both diagrams.

required value of K may be read at the intersection of the dry adiabat through the temperature point and the moisture content line through the dew point, plotted on the appropriate isobar. These points are shown on Fig 3.11(a) at -3°C and -11°C (900mb), as in the previous example. The lines drawn as indicated intersect at the point C which, when referred to the K lines, gives the answer directly: K = 293.

4. Alternatively, the scale labelled 'coded depression of the dew point' may be transferred to the edge of a card and used horizontally on the diagram as shown in Fig 3.11(b), with the right-hand index against the point on the diagram defined by the temperature and pressure. The required K value is read against the coded dew-point depression (58, signifying 8° depression). The scale is the projection on to a horizontal of depressions along an isobar, using the slope of the moisture content lines. This method is strictly correct only on the righthand side of the diagram and the method would suffer a progressive loss of accuracy towards the left (because the moisture content lines are not

Table 3.7. Seasonal variation of radio refractive index *N* at Crawley. Six years combined data, 1972–7

Half-month period		Sfc N	Sfc P	950 N	900 N	850 N	850 H	800 N	750 N	700 N	700 H
JA	A	318	1001	297	278	260	1465	244	227	213	3001
	B	314	995	296	278	261	1407	244	228	213	2929
FE	C	313	991	296	278	261	1381	245	228	214	2909
	D	315	1002	294	276	259	1468	244	228	213	2995
MR	E	313	999	294	276	259	1444	243	227	213	2966
	F	313	1000	294	276	259	1455	243	228	213	2984
AP	G	312	997	294	277	262	1434	245	229	214	2958
	H	313	1002	294	278	261	1480	244	227	212	3014
MY	J	316	997	297	280	263	1443	246	229	214	2979
	K	319	1000	298	281	262	1483	244	228	213	3035
JE	L	321	1001	300	282	263	1497	245	228	213	3059
	M	326	1001	304	285	265	1510	247	230	213	3091
JL	N	330	1001	306	287	267	1513	247	230	213	3098
	P	331	1000	308	288	269	1503	249	231	214	3096
AU	Q	331	1001	307	288	268	1519	248	229	213	3102
	R	330	1001	306	287	266	1518	246	228	212	3098
SE	S	327	1000	305	285	265	1495	246	229	213	3067
	T	327	999	304	284	265	1479	246	228	213	3041
OC	U	323	997	302	282	262	1455	244	227	213	3014
	V	323	1000	300	280	260	1475	244	227	212	3030
NV	W	320	998	299	281	262	1448	245	228	213	2990
	X	315	998	295	277	260	1439	243	227	213	2968
DE	Y	316	998	296	278	261	1441	244	227	213	2973
	Z	318	1002	296	278	261	1469	243	227	212	3006
Overall six-year mean		320	999	299	281	263	1468	245	228	213	3015

The additional work involved in this type of exercise is amply justified by the sense of continuity which results. Thus the time-section shown in Fig 3.5 reveals in a single glance far more about the formation and eventual dissipation of a subsidence boundary layer than could be gained by a prolonged study of the 10 separate profiles which were combined in its construction.

'NORMAL' VALUES OF *N* AND *K*

It is in the nature of things that refractive index studies, requiring as they do a considerable amount of calculation and detailed graphical work, are carried out on an infrequent basis, as and when periods of interest come to light.

It means, inevitably, that a sense of continuity is lacking whenever an in-depth study is undertaken. It means also that researchers usually see only abnormal conditions and few of them can be bothered to do similar exercises when nothing out of the ordinary has been occurring.

The situation is further complicated by the fact that there is a marked seasonal variation in values of refractive index near to the ground, making it difficult to compare, say, a February event with one that occurred in July, unless one has access to information showing the sort of values that might be considered 'normal' in each of the two cases.

It might seem that monthly mean refractive index values could be obtained by putting mean monthly temperature and mean monthly dew-point data into the computer program in place of individual ascent figures. An inspection of the skeleton tephigram, Fig 3.10, will explain why that will not work. The temperature (T–T) and dew-point (D–D) scales are straight-line functions whereas the refractive index lines have a pronounced curvature which changes character across the chart. Mean figures of refractive index have to be obtained from daily refractive index values, not from means of the basic meteorological data.

That explains the origin of Tables 3.7 and 3.8, which were obtained from 4380 consecutive radiosonde ascents reduced to refractive index and potential refractive index spot values. They represent six years of real-time data gathering, 1972–1977 and are, so far as is known, the only statistics available for either index in terms of atmospheric pressure instead of height. They appeared first in *IERE Conference Proceedings No 40* (July 1978), to which reference should be made for further details and for other results of the study.

In this chapter refractive index and its distribution in the atmosphere are looked at from a meteorologist's viewpoint, having regard to the fact that the radio wave, once launched, is acted upon by atmospheric pressure, atmospheric temperature and the varying amount of moisture in the air through which it passes. Height, as such, does not come into the basic equations at all and only appears in expressions for refractive index gradients because radio engineers feel that they must have a fixed scale firmly anchored to the ground. Statistics based on specific pressure levels eliminate one of the variables

Table 3.8. Seasonal variation of potential refractive index _K_ at Crawley. Six years combined data, 1972–7

Half-month period		Sfc _K_	Sfc _P_	950 _K_	900 _K_	850 _K_	850 _H_	800 _K_	750 _K_	700 _K_	700 _H_
JA	A	318	1001	308	300	292	1465	286	279	275	3001
	B	315	995	307	300	293	1407	286	280	275	2929
FE	C	315	991	307	300	293	1381	287	280	276	2909
	D	315	1002	305	298	291	1468	286	280	275	2995
MF;	E	313	999	305	298	291	1444	285	279	275	2966
	F	313	1000	305	298	291	1455	285	280	275	2984
AP	G	313	997	305	299	294	1434	287	281	276	2958
	H	313	1002	305	300	293	1480	286	279	273	3014
MY	J	317	997	308	302	295	1443	288	281	276	2979
	K	319	1000	309	303	294	1483	286	280	274	3035
JE	L	321	1001	311	304	295	1497	287	280	274	3059
	M	326	1001	315	307	298	1510	290	282	275	3091
JL	N	330	1001	317	309	300	1513	290	282	275	3098
	P	331	1000	320	311	302	1503	292	283	276	3096
AU	Q	331	1001	318	310	301	1519	291	281	274	3102
	R	330	1001	317	309	299	1518	289	280	273	3098
SE	S	327	1000	316	307	298	1495	289	281	274	3067
	T	327	999	315	306	298	1479	288	280	274	3041
OC	U	324	997	313	304	294	1455	286	279	274	3014
	V	323	1000	311	302	292	1475	286	279	273	3030
NV	W	321	998	310	303	294	1448	287	280	274	2990
	X	316	998	306	299	292	1439	285	279	275	2968
DE	Y	317	998	307	300	293	1441	286	279	274	2973
	Z	318	1002	307	300	293	1469	285	279	273	3006
Overall six-year mean		321	999	310	303	295	1468	287	280	275	3017

and provide results that are in the right form for comparison with day-to-day radiosonde measurements.

For an example of the use of the annual statistics consider Fig 3.12, in which the thicker line shows potential refractive index values plotted against pressure for one of the profiles used in the examples of cross-sections and time-sections. The fine line shows the mean values for the time of year and it should be clear that the low values of potential refractive index encountered above 940mb have been the result of air subsiding from above. During an adiabatic change potential refractive index remains unchanged so a parcel of subsiding air brings its original value down with it but, remember, the same is not true of conventional refractive index, _N_.

Strictly, these statistics are valid only for south-east England, but they provide a useful indicator for adjacent areas, for which there are no comparable figures.

SIGNAL STRENGTHS AND RANGES ATTAINABLE
The effect of the boundary layer on signal strength

The time-section is an ideal way of comparing a series of upper-air soundings in terms of refractive index because, once you know the signs, you can see at a glance periods of rising or subsiding air and the formation and dissipation of steep-lapse layers of the sort that lead to periods of anomalous propagation, or 'openings' as amateur operators prefer to call them.

Fig 3.13 illustrates very clearly the way that VHF signal strengths rise during a week of anticyclonic subsidence. When this diagram was originally prepared there was a television station transmitting on 174MHz, located at Lille, in northern France. G3BGL, located at a site just to the west of Reading, used to monitor the strength of the sound carrier using a pen recorder, with the object of compiling statistics for a 300km VHF path (this was before the time that we had beacon transmissions on the amateur bands). The television station operated every afternoon and evening.

The potential refractive index pattern is typical of an anticyclonic opening. The bottom boundary of the isopleths shows that ground level atmospheric pressure reached a peak during 24 and 25 September. The 'inverted pudding basin' centred on the 22nd heralded the commencement of subsiding air, a feature which was to make its presence felt over the next six days. Note the way that the signal level rose as the subsidence boundary layer formed, then lowered and intensified. The highest signals appeared when the gradient was steepest, on the 25th. After that the gradient slackened and the received signal strength fell. On the evening of the 28th a cold front arrived and destroyed, by mixing, all traces of the boundary which had given the good conditions. A low-pressure system moving in is responsible for the rising isopleths of the 29th. The radiosonde station at Crawley was very close to the mid-point of the transmission path.

It is a point worth emphasising that this one time-section

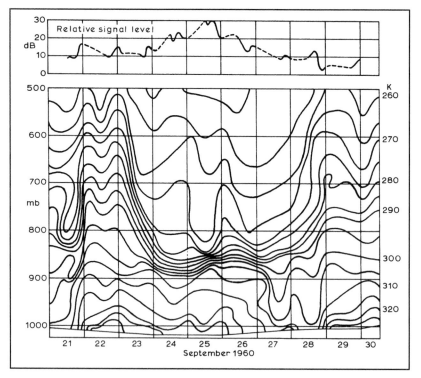

Fig 3.13. Potential refractive index time-section, Crawley, 21–30 September 1960, together with a record of signal strengths, obtained on a chart recorder located near Reading, from VHF TV transmissions originating at Lille in France. Note that the highest signals occur when the steep-lapse layer is most pronounced, and a sudden drop occurs as the anticyclone is replaced by a low-pressure system. With acknowledgements to *J Atmos Terr Phys*, Pergamon Press

shows, at a glance, all the significant information contained in 20 consecutive refractive index profiles.

The subsidence boundary layer may be thought of as being a battlefront. It comes about as a result of descending warm dry air coming up against cool moist air stirred up from the ground. If the two opposing forces are nicely balanced the layer stays where it is and intensifies. If the subsidence increases or the turbulence decreases the boundary falls and may even reach the ground. If that happens the good conditions immediately drop out.

If the low-level turbulence increases the boundary will rise and will eventually be lost through mixing. When conditions are at their best it is the contrast between the two opposing air components which is all-important. Given warm dry subsiding air from aloft in an anticyclone you cannot do better than find yourself surrounded by wet dripping fog.

At their best, tropospheric 'openings' are productive of ranges considerably in excess of conventional textbook expectations. Using an analysis of extreme-range signal reports it has been shown that if 1000km can be exceeded at 144MHz

there is a strong probability that 1500km will be reached, for there is a pronounced peak in the distribution at that range. Similarly, if 750km can be exceeded at 432MHz, there is a good probability that 1200km will be reached. Histograms showing these findings are included in a paper in *IEE Conference Publication 195*, Part 2, pp163–167 ('The use of a dense network of amateur radio stations to determine the limits of long-range tropospheric propagation within an anticyclone', by R G Flavell) to which reference should be made for further details.

Table 3.9 gives details of maximum confirmed tropospheric ranges for the six VHF and UHF amateur bands, as at the beginning of 1997.

EME (MOONBOUNCE)

Earth-Moon-Earth contacts are, as the name implies, contacts made using the Moon as a reflector. It goes without saying that high power and accurate aiming of a narrow beam are essential requirements.

The paths are line of sight to and from the Moon but tropospheric refraction effects could affect the performance at low elevation angles. Distance (around the Earth, transmitter to receiver) records are made and broken but they are a function of geometry rather than geophysical influences. All VHF and UHF bands apart from 70MHz have been used. Europe to New Zealand has been achieved on 144, 432MHz and 1.3GHz.

FREE-SPACE ATTENUATION

The concept of free-space attenuation between isotropic antennas, or basic transmission loss, L_b, provides a useful yardstick against which other modes of propagation may be compared. It is a function of frequency and distance, such that

$$L_b = 32.45 + 20 \log f + 20 \log d$$

where f and d are expressed in megahertz and kilometres respectively.

Table 3.10 provides a representative range of values against distance for various VHF/UHF amateur bands.

TROPOSPHERIC SCATTER PROPAGATION

Tropospheric scatter propagation depends for its effectiveness on the presence of dust particles, cloud droplets and small-scale irregularities in radio refractive index within a volume of the atmosphere which is common to both the transmitting and receiving antenna beam cones. The height of the bottom of this common volume is a function of distance between the stations concerned owing to the effect

Table 3.9. European VHF and UHF records (as at the beginning of 1997) – tropospheric			
50MHz	GJ4ICD (IN89WF) and OZ5W/P (JO64GX)	1 June 1996	1188km
70MHz	GM3WOJ (IO77WO) and G4KFR (IO90AS)	18 September 1988	774km
144MHz	GM0KAE (IO86CD) and EA8BML (IL27GX)	9 September 1988	3264km
432MHz	EA8XS (IL28GA) and GW8VHI (IO81CM)	5 July 1984	2786km
1.3GHz	EA8XS (IL28GA) and G6LEU (IO70ME)	29 June 1985	2617km
2.3 GHz	EA7BVD/P (IM78JD) and EA8XS/P (IL27GW)	8 July 1984	1481km

Source: John Morris, GM4ANB, for Region 1, IARU

of the curvature of the earth. Typical heights are 600m for a 100km path, 9000m for a 500km path. Path losses increase by about 10dB for every degree of horizon angle at each station so that a site with an unobstructed take-off is an important consideration.

Only a very small proportion of the signal energy passing through the common volume will be scattered, and only a small proportion of that will be directed towards the receiving station. Therefore the loss in the scattering process is extremely large and the angle through which the signal ray has to be deflected is an important characteristic of a troposcatter path; for best results it should be no more than a few degrees.

J N Gannaway, G3YGF, has made a critical study of the losses in tropospheric scatter propagation, which appeared in *Radio Communication* August 1981, pp710–714, 717. It should be consulted for a fuller discussion of the mode than can be given here.

Table 3.11 shows the path losses between two stations on a smooth earth, expressed as decibels below the free-space values, for VHF and UHF amateur bands. (Free-space losses have been given earlier in Table 3.10.) To these values must be added losses depending on characteristics of the sites – height, distance to the first obstruction, antenna coupling losses etc – and variables depending on seasonal and weather factors.

Table 3.12, which is taken directly from the work cited, shows the theoretical range that could be expected under flat conditions and from good sites, with the equipments shown against each of the amateur bands. The ranges are for a 0dB signal-to-noise ratio in a bandwidth of 100Hz, representing a weak CW signal; for SSB these ranges should be reduced by 130km on each band.

For distances approaching 1000km the equipment requirements are comparable to those needed for propagation by moonbounce.

Because signal-path transit times vary with height of scatter within the common volume a 'blurring' occurs which limits the maximum speed of transmission of intelligence; narrow beams have the faster capabilities.

IONOSPHERIC PROPAGATION AT VHF AND UHF
Regular layers
The regular layers of the ionosphere play only a small part in the properties of the VHF bands and, according to current thought at least, none at all at UHF and above. Around the

time of sunspot maximum and for perhaps a year or two after, there are occasions when maximum usable frequencies exceed 50MHz and cross-band working with North American amateurs becomes possible. The most favourable times for transatlantic contacts at 50MHz occur when the solar flux is high and the magnetic index is low, but the required conditions do not persist for long. On 8 February 1979 G3COJ and WB2RLK/VE made the first 28/50MHz transatlantic contact since 1958. On the other hand, when conditions are good, they are often very good. EI2W, the only 50MHz licensed amateur in northern Europe at the time, succeeded in working 40 states of the USA on 50MHz during 1979–80. Such contacts are made via the F2 layer. It is unlikely that transmissions above 30MHz would ever be propagated by the regular E layer. In the tropics some occasional periods of activity around noon in maximum sunspot years may be possible, using the F1 layer.

The current (1997) European record distance for 50MHz regular F2 layer propagation is 16,076km, set by OZ1LO (JO55VC) and UK3AMK (QF21NT) on 18 October 1991.

Any propagation at VHF which may take place via the regular layers of the ionosphere will have a very strong dependence on the solar cycle.

Non-regular ionisation
Contacts at VHF and UHF are occasionally possible via ionisation which may take the form of sheets, clouds, mobile curtains or long narrow cylinders. Most of these forms are active around E layer height, but they are not directly associated with the regular layers.

Some effects, those involving the equatorial ionosphere, for example, may take place at F layer levels. The varieties

Table 3.10. Free-space attenuation

Frequency (MHz)	Distance (km)								
	50	100	150	200	300	400	500	750	1000
50	100	106	110	112	116	118	120	124	126
70	103	109	113	115	119	121	123	127	129
144	110	116	119	122	125	128	130	133	136
432	119	125	129	131	135	137	139	143	145
1296	129	135	138	141	144	147	149	152	155
2300	134	140	143	146	149	152	154	157	160

Table 3.11. Troposcatter path losses on a smooth earth

Band (MHz)	Distance (km)								
	50	100	150	200	300	400	500	750	1000
70	47	49	53	55	61	69	75	91	109
144	50	52	55	58	64	72	78	94	112
432	55	56	60	62	69	76	82	99	116
1296	59	61	65	67	74	81	87	104	121
2300	60	63	67	70	76	83	90	106	

Table 3.12. Theoretical performance between good sites under flat conditions

Frequency (MHz)	Path loss (dB)	Range (km)	Transmitter power (W)	Noise figure (dB)	Antenna	Antenna gain (dBi)
144	240	870	100	3	2 × 16-el Yagi	18
432	247	790	100	3	2 × 25-el loop Yagi	22
1296	258	760	100	3	2 × 25-el loop Yagi	24
2304	262	720	50	3	6ft dish	31

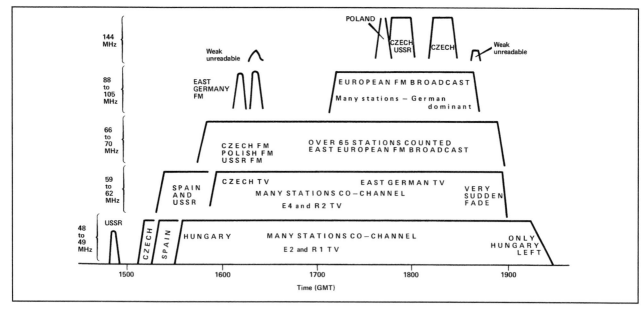

Fig 3.14. Frequency versus time for a major sporadic-E event recorded on 10 June 1980 at GM4IHJ, Saline, Fife

which will be dealt with here are sporadic-E, auroral-E, trans-equatorial propagation and meteor scatter.

VHF SPORADIC-E

As has been mentioned before, there is some question still regarding the nature of VHF sporadic-E. The reason is that sporadic-E at HF has been known about and recognised since the earliest days of ionospheric sounding in the 'thirties but what radio amateurs refer to as sporadic-E – typically extending to the 144MHz band and beyond – just does not show up on ionosondes. Even those times when HF sporadic-E does appear on the record it does not display characteristics which would be sufficient to support reflections well into the VHF band (over 200MHz has been reported).

For many years VHF sporadic-E was regarded with scepticism by professionals but its reality has now been accepted, largely due to the weight of evidence provided by amateur observers in a truly international project co-ordinated by the International Amateur Radio Union. For many successive years the co-ordinator, the late Serge Canivenc, F8SH, collected and collated reports from all over Europe to provide day-by-day summaries, which were submitted to CCIR, the International Radio Consultative Committee (now a section of the International Telecommunications Union).

The project is ongoing and the collection of reports showing which paths are open (and when) remains a task ideally suited to amateur observers.

In its conventional form sporadic-E consists of horizontal sheets about 1km thick and some 100km across, usually at a height of 100–130km. Clouds form in an apparently random manner, although there is an obvious preference for certain times and seasons. They do not behave consistently for, whereas some sheets may travel across continents for several hundreds of kilometres, others remain almost stationary. It has been claimed that there is a general tendency for them to drift towards the equator at about 80m/s. Both scattering and reflection modes are possible in the sporadic-E layers.

Above 30MHz, paths via E_s ionisation are rarely less than 500km. The maximum single-hop range is limited by the geometry of the system to about 2000km and double-hop from a single sheet is relatively rare because it would have to exceed 500km across in order to be able to accommodate the two points of reflection. Two-hop E_s propagation is more likely from two separate sheets, separated by less than 2000km, when the possible maximum range is extended to 4000km.

Sporadic-E at VHF is seasonal, nearly all of it (in Europe) occurring between May and August, although events outside that period are not unknown. The times of maximum activity are generally within the periods of 0700–1300GMT and 1500–2200GMT. The duration of events is an inverse function of frequency: that is, for a particular occasion the event will begin later and finish earlier at the higher of two given frequencies.

John Branegan, GM4IHJ, gave a very interesting analysis of the VHF sporadic-E event of 10 June 1980, as observed from Saline, Fife (Fig 3.14). This demonstrated very clearly how the longest opening – over 4½ hours – appeared on a 48–49MHz monitor, with progressively shorter periods on each of the other frequency bands checked. At 144MHz the event was confined, for the most part, to half an hour either side of 1800GMT. GM4IHJ had also produced a map showing the location of stations which have been positively identified during E_s openings (Fig 3.15). The symbols 'FM' and 'fm' indicate stations in the 70MHz and 100MHz FM broadcast bands respectively, while black dots are Band I TV stations around 50MHz. It may be seen that all the stations received were between 1000 and 2000km distant.

That being so – and, assuming a reflection height of 100–130km, the geometry of the path certainly lends support – how to account for the claimed record distances worked during E_s events (Table 3.13)? Clearly, in the case of 70MHz and 144MHz double hop is feasible, though probably not from a single cloud of ionisation. But, in the case of 50MHz, over 8000km in four hops seems to be stretching credibility a mite too far. Yet this report does not stand in isolation. In the

DUBUS magazine for the first quarter of 1997, the 50MHz E$_s$ Top List showed claimed distances in excess of 4000km (theoretical double-hop) in 36 entries out of a total of 81. If the reason for that is known it does not seem to have received very wide publicity.

Table 3.13. European VHF and UHF records (as at the beginning of 1997) – sporadic-E			
50MHz	G0DJA (IO93FP) and 7Q7RU (KH74MF)	24 August 1993	8446km
70MHz	GW4ASR/P (IQ82JG) and 5B4AZ (KM64MR)	7 June 1981	3465km
144MHz	OE1SBB (JN88FF) and RI8TA (MM37TE)	21 July 1989	4281km
Source: John Morris, GM4ANB, for Region I, IARU			

The maximum frequency at which sporadic-E has been observed in the European area was found to have been 203MHz, recorded by F8SH on 9 July 1974. It is not known if anyone else has continued his work in routinely seeking a maximum frequency, but it seems certain that 200MHz is reached but rarely and for periods of very short duration.

Several sporadic-E warning nets – some radio, some making use of telephone 'chains' – are in operation in various parts of Europe, including the UK. With their help a random network of several hundred amateur stations may be got on the air in a very short time, and a careful computer analysis of their collected reports, which need consist of no more than time, band, callsigns and QTH locators, is sufficient to provide details of the size, shape and movement of the areas of ionisation responsible.

AMATEUR AURORAL STUDIES

The radio aurora at VHF probably represents the field in which radio amateurs can do most to contribute to present knowledge of radio propagation and the behaviour of the high atmosphere

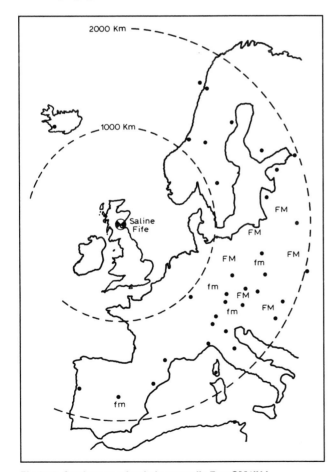

Fig 3.15. Stations received via sporadic-E at GM4IHJ

under the influence of solar emissions. A co-ordinated network of stations extending over a continent, each station equipped with nothing more complicated than a well-maintained receiver and operated by a person able to read and log callsigns, QTH locators and accurate times, can establish the existence and movement of areas of auroral ionisation on a scale that is impossible to achieve by any other means. The addition of steerable antennas and two-way communications increase the value of the observations still further, for these enable the location of the auroral reflection point to be established.

The geometry of the path is such that no two pairs of stations will reflect off exactly the same point on the radio auroral curtain so a number of near-simultaneous observations from a random network of stations can yield detail of an *area* of ionisation – its position relative to the Earth's surface and the direction of its main axis – and, if the process is continued throughout an auroral event, analysis of successive periods will reveal the motion of the ionisation in both space and time.

Unfortunately the aurora does not present itself as a perfect reflector placed perpendicularly to the surface of the Earth. Its vertical alignment tends to follow the curvature of the geomagnetic field so that a reflection from a relatively low altitude will appear to be above a point on the ground farther north than a reflection at a greater height. The reflection height is a function of the position of the two stations relative to the surface of ionisation, but the vertical and horizontal beamwidths of most VHF antennas are such that a large number of alternative paths are possible without change of beam heading, although not necessarily at maximum strength. There is much to be learned from a study of accurate times and bearings of maximum signal taken as near simultaneously as possible from the two ends of a transmission path. Those stations equipped with two-axis rotators, such as are used for satellite working, can contribute further by rotating in both azimuth and elevation for maximum signal.

From the foregoing it will be clear that, in general, the beam headings in the horizontal plane depart considerably from the great-circle directions between the stations. When amateur auroral studies began in earnest in the 'fifties it was commonly supposed that all stations had to beam their signals towards the north in order to make auroral contacts. During the International Quiet Sun Years (1963–4), when the GB3LER experimental beacon station was first set up beside the magnetic observatory at Lerwick, the beam direction for auroral studies was set at first towards 10° west of true north and nearly all reports of reception via the aurora came from Scottish stations.

A change was made to 25° east of true north, and this brought in reports from many parts of the Continent. That is not to say that 25° east of true north is an optimum direction, even for Lerwick. It is now known that beam headings can vary considerably during an aurora, and from one aurora to

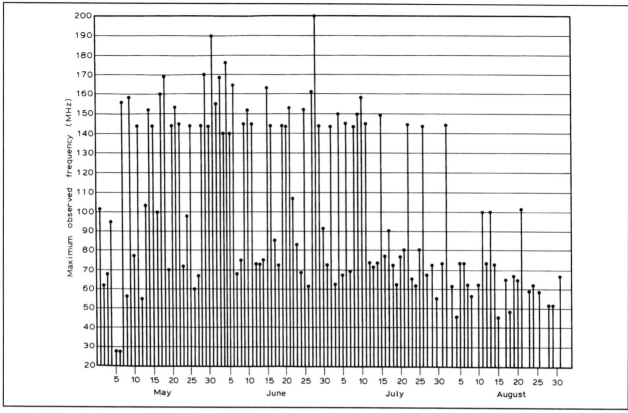

Fig 3.16 VHF sporadic-E activity in Europe during summer 1979

the next. No hard and fast advice can be given on this point, other than to suggest that an occasional complete 360° beam swing during an auroral event may produce results from an unexpected quarter, even when much of the activity appears to be concentrated in one fairly constant direction (Fig 3.17).

Charlie Newton, G2FKZ, who was for many years the IARU co-ordinator for amateur radio auroral studies, has established that, for any given station, there is a well-defined

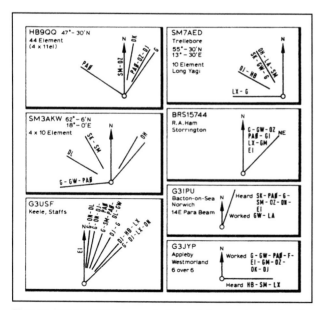

Fig 3.17. Beam headings recorded by certain operators during the aurora of 8 March 1970

area within which auroral contacts are possible, and he has shown that that area is a function of the magnetic field surrounding the Earth. He has called the perimeter of this area the *boundary fence* and has demonstrated that its shape and extent varies as different locations are considered as origin. As an example, Fig 3.18 shows the boundary fence calculated for SM4IVE (at HT68d); it is approximately elliptical, 2000km from east to west, 1000km from north to south. The large dots on the map indicate the centres of QTH locator lettered squares containing stations heard or worked by SM4IVE via the aurora – the lines are not signal paths; they serve only to indicate the line-of-sight directions and distances to some of the more-distant stations. At any particular time during an event only a small part of the area shown will be accessible to SM4IVE, but the audible 'patch' will move during the progress of an aurora and may differ considerably from one aurora to the next, although all the stations worked will lie within the boundary fence. For stations farther east the area of accessibility is larger; for stations to the west and south it is smaller. Stations in Great Britain suffer from the disadvantage that there are no stations within the western half of the boundary fence.

There is a fairly close correlation between the occurrence of radio aurora and the three-hourly indices of geomagnetic activity; the greater the magnetic field is disturbed, the further south the event extends. During the International Quiet Sun Years attempts were made to relate motions of the visual aurora at Lerwick to aurorally reflected signals from GB3LER as received on the Scottish mainland, but the results suggested that, on a short time-scale, the two phenomena behave almost independently, although they must stem from a common cause. At times the visual aurora appeared to the south of Lerwick and forward-scatter off the back of the beam was suspected on more than one occasion, although the point was never proved by turning the antenna because it was not accessible enough to be moved at short notice.

A study of pen recordings of signals from GB3LER, via the aurora, to Thurso on the Scottish mainland suggested that it was not the peaks of a geomagnetic disturbance that gave the strongest reflections, but rather the fastest rate of change in the components describing the instantaneous field, as recorded by the observatory magnetometers.

Every radio auroral event seems to be unique in some respect but there are characteristic patterns that regularly recur. The weaker or diffuse events, which are often only detected by northern stations, move little and slowly. They are often found to relate to minor irregularities on the magnetometer trace, known as *bays,* when the geomagnetic field deflects for a short while and then gradually resumes its normal diurnal pattern.

An intense auroral event typically opens suddenly with the appearance of signals having a characteristic 'flutter' tone from stations situated to the north or north-east. This often occurs in the early afternoon and contacts from European stations 1000km or more distant are likely. After perhaps two to three hours of activity it ceases and many operators unused to the mode may conclude that the event is over. The more knowledgeable stay on watch, and frequently their patience is rewarded by the appearance of a second phase, usually more

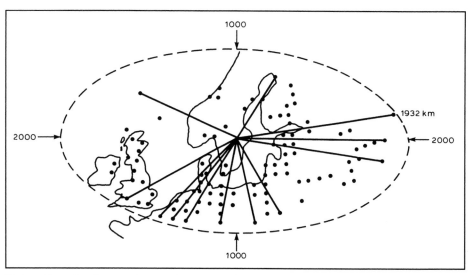

Fig 3.18. Boundary fence calculated for SM4IVE

Table 3.14. European VHF and UHF records (as at the beginning of 1997) – aurora			
50MHz	ES1CW (KO29HK) and G3NVO (IO91IK)	6 February 1994	1850km
70MHz	G3SHK (IO90DX) and GM3WOJ (IO89KB)	11 August 1982	904km
144MHz	GM4BYF (IO85JV) and RB5CCO (KN59XG)	1 December 1989	2465km
432MHz	PA0FRE (JO21FW) and RA3LE (KO64AR)	13 March 1989	1851km

Source: John Morris, GM4ANB, for Region I, IARU

rewarding than the first. The motion of the active region often follows the same general movement as the first phase, but reaching several hundred kilometres further south. Finally, when the event seems to have reached a peak, perhaps by late evening, all the activity suddenly ceases as though somebody, somewhere, has 'pulled the big switch' and gone off to bed (Fig 3.19).

Table 3.14 shows the maximum distances which have been worked by auroral reflection on three bands at VHF and one at UHF. It must be pointed out that these distances represent the great circle path between stations, not the path followed by the signals, which is considerably longer.

There is a tendency for a major radio auroral event to recur after an interval of slightly more than 27 days. That is because

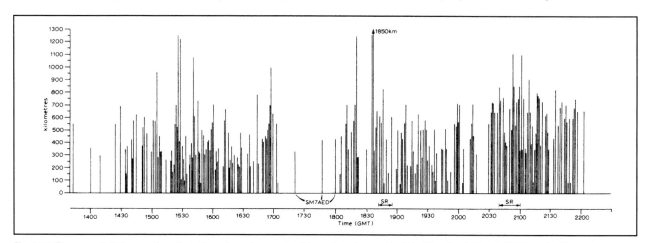

Fig 3.19. Times and distances for all stations heard or worked, based on logs submitted for the 8 March 1970 study. Note the pauses and the bunching of the longer-range contacts. The periods marked 'SR' indicate when a radar at Sheffield University recorded radio aurora to the north west

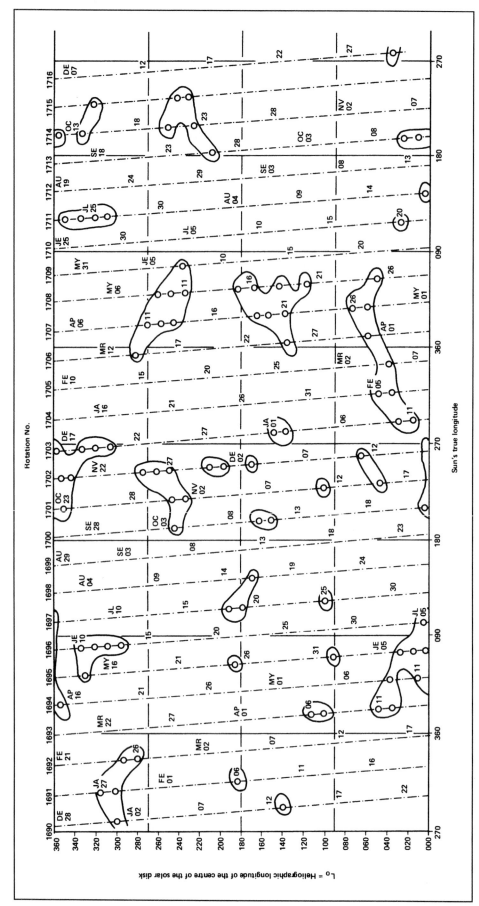

Fig 3.20. Days with reported radio aurora during 1981-2

the event has come about as a result of a disturbance on the Sun, and in that interval an active region has made a complete circuit of the Sun as seen from the Earth, and is in more-or-less the same position again. That position, at the time of the event, is generally about one day past central meridian passage (CMP), or, say, 13° west of the centre of the visible disc.

It is convenient to be able to record the dates of auroral propagation events in some way that links them to the rotations of the Sun. The chart shown in Fig 3.20 does just that. The vertical axis shows longitude on the Sun, L_0, following a sequence begun at Greenwich Observatory nearly 150 years ago. The horizontal axis is, in effect, a measure of where the Earth is around its orbit, passing through 000° at the time of the vernal equinox, 20 or 21 June. The sloping broken lines serve to connect a series of dots, each representing the date on which the indicated longitude, L_0, passed the centre of the disc of the Sun, as seen from the Earth, at 12UT. The sloping lines form a raster such that, if the diagram were to be rolled so as to make the top edge ($L_0 = 360°$) and the bottom edge ($L_0 = 000°$) coincident, they would form one continuous helix.

The chart may be used to record any event suspected of having a connection with events on the Sun. A horizontal trend corresponds to the rotation period of the Sun relative to the Earth; a trend of 45° (in the sense bottom left to top right) corresponds to the rotation period of the Sun relative to the stars. Known dates of radio auroral events are currently included in the propagation news section of the

GB2RS news bulletin service of the RSGB, and the patterns which emerge provide a useful guide to probable active and quiet periods up to about a month ahead. Fig 3.20, which shows the days when radio aurora was reported by UK stations during 1981–2 should be compared with Fig 3.21, which shows the days when the magnetometers at Lerwick recorded a disturbance of 5 or more on the conventional scale of geomagnetic *K*-units. It will be seen that there is a close relationship between the two patterns and this confirms the usefulness of the Lerwick data when dealing with the analysis of radio auroral events taking place in the region of north-west Europe.

Monitoring auroral propagation

In a contribution to the March 1977 issue of *Radio Communication,* Peter Blair, G3LTF, gave practical advice on monitoring distant VHF transmissions, which can be used as a guide to the onset of auroral propagation events on the amateur bands. Many of his remarks were directed towards observers living in the south of England, but his methods were applicable to other locations, provided that suitably placed transmitters can be found. What is required is a signal from a northerly direction in the low VHF region, for this will go auroral before the effects reach 144MHz. These requirements used to be met by one of the Band I BBC-TV sound transmitters. There are now 50MHz and 70MHz amateur beacon transmitters which may well serve the purpose. Two which operate at 100W and are

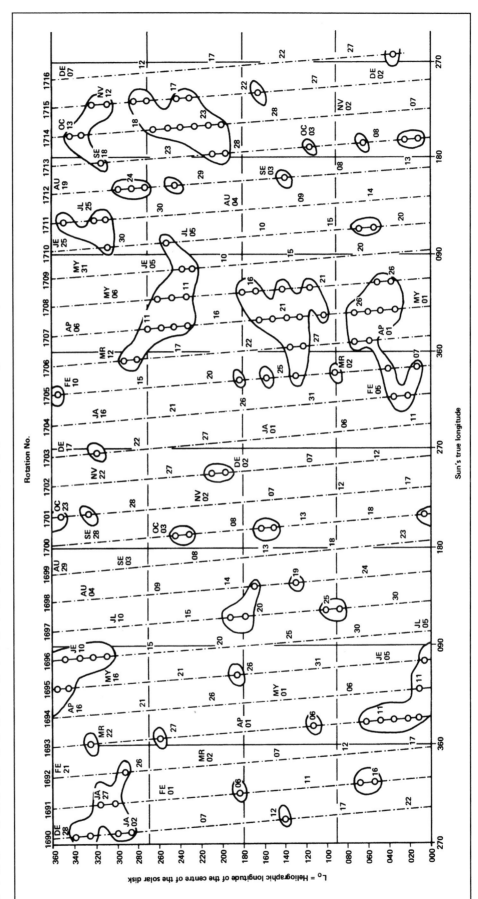

Fig 3.21. Days when Lerwick K-figure was five or greater during 1981–2

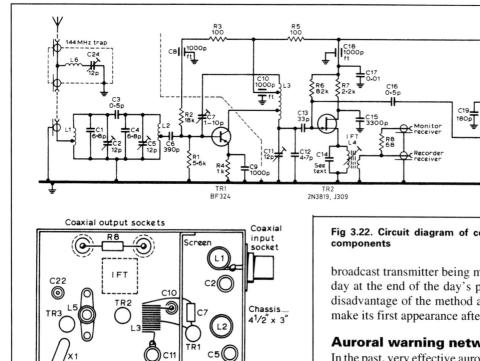

Fig 3.22. Circuit diagram of converter and layout of principal components

broadcast transmitter being monitored may close down each day at the end of the day's programmes, but this is no real disadvantage of the method as it is unusual for an aurora to make its first appearance after midnight.

Auroral warning networks

In the past, very effective auroral warning networks have been organised, both in this country and on the Continent, using the public telephone systems. The warnings are generally initiated by a northern monitoring station who either has firm evidence that an auroral opening has commenced, or who has good reason to believe that one is imminent. Each recipient of the warning passes it on to at least two other stations, working down from north to south, with built-in checks to hold the procedure if the event is a small one or fails to materialise.

At the time of writing it is not known if such a network still exists. It needs to be emphasised, however, that the

suitably placed are GB3LER (IP90JD) on 50.064MHz and GB3ANG (IO86MN) on 70.020MHz.

The suggested equipment for the aurora monitor is relatively simple. The antenna consists of two elements: radiator 95in by ³/₈in, reflector 105in by ³/₈in, spacing 30in, mounted 18 to 20ft off the ground, pointing north. This feeds a crystal-controlled converter, such as the one shown in Fig 3.22 and Table 3.15, which uses any convenient crystal which will produce an IF of around 7MHz. After alignment in the usual way the circuits should be peaked on the desired signal when the opportunity arises. The two outputs are at around 7MHz; one is intended for a simple fixed-frequency receiver, the AGC voltage of which drives a recording meter through a suitable DC amplifier. When correctly tuned, the 144MHz trap prevents the converter from being blocked in the presence of a local transmission.

Fig 3.23 shows the appearance of some typical auroral signal recordings. According to G3LTF a sudden (say within two minutes) onset of the auroral enhancement usually indicates that the effects will reach 144MHz within 10–15 minutes. A more gradual onset might herald a delay of up to about 30 minutes. It is rare for the effect not to reach 144MHz at all once it has been detected on the monitor. The equipment may also be used as an indicator for 70MHz but the respective time delays are considerably reduced.

The monitor should be left running during the day from about midday onwards. If the operator is unable to attend during the afternoon he or she may come home to find evidence of earlier activity. This should alert him to expect a second phase, and perhaps a third, later on. Where a more-or-less continuous watch is impracticable, the most fruitful times for checking the monitor are mid-afternoon, early evening and around 2200 local time. It should not be overlooked that a

Table 3.15. Components list for converter			
C1, C4	6p8 ceramic	R1	5k6
C2, C5, C11, C24	12p tubular trimmers	R2	18k
C3, C16	0p5 ceramic	R3, R5	100R
C6	390p ceramic	R4, R9	1k
C7	1–10p tubular trimmer	R6	82k
C8, C10, C18, C22	1000p feedthrough capacitors	R7	2k2
C9, C21	1000p ceramic	R8	68R
C12	4p7 ceramic	R10	4k7
C13	33p ceramic	R11	6k8
C14	22p (to suit IFT L4)	All ¼ or 1/10W carbon	
C15	3300p disc ceramic		
C17	0µ01 15V	TR1	BF324
C19	180p ceramic	TR2	2N3819, J309
C20	18p ceramic	TR3	2N3904
C23	0µ22 15V		
L1	10t ³/₈in ID 18 SWG enam close-wound tapped 2t up		
L2	As L1 but tapped 4t up		
L3	11t ³/₈in ID 18 SWG enam close-wound tapped at 1t and 5t from cold end		
L4	IF transformer appropriate to crystal chosen		
L5	6t 20 SWG on ¼in slug tuned form (for 65MHz crystal)		
L6	9t ¼in ID spaced wire diameter		

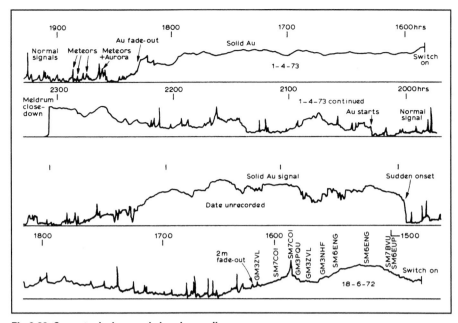

Fig 3.23. Some typical auroral signal recordings

Subsequent work has used 28, 50, 144 and 432MHz. During years of high sunspot activity the reliability of a TE path is considerable. On 50MHz the peak time during an opening was found to be 1845–1900. At 144MHz, using 100W RF into 16-element long Yagis, openings between Europe and southern Africa have lasted for up to two hours, centred on 2000 local time in Cyprus; high solar flux and low geomagnetic activity seem essential. Detrimental effects of geomagnetic storms are less evident at 50 and 28MHz than at 144MHz. Fig 3.25 shows the days on which TE signals were observed at 144MHz, plotted on a solar rotation base map, which reveals some tendency towards 27-day recurrences, particularly around the time of the equinoxes. On the American paths, peak occurrences at the equinoxes were noted.

On the Zimbabwe/Cyprus path there was a decline at that time, thought by ZE2JV and 5B4WR to be a peculiarity of the path connected in some way with the southern Africa magnetic anomaly which gives rise to high dip angles at the southern end.

In February 1979, ZS6DN, Pretoria, and SV1AB, Athens, held the world record for a 144MHz contact by the ionosphere, but at time of writing the current holders are ZS3B and I4EAT, who, on 31 March 1979, established transmission and reception in both directions over a distance just under 8000km.

Fading and chopping occur on the signals at rates which increase with transmission frequency. Slow chopping on 28 and 50MHz sometimes makes it almost impossible to read Morse code. At 144MHz the chopping rate is much faster, making the signal sound rough with an apparent raw AC note. Frequency spreading has been observed to 2kHz or more. The character of the signals may change considerably from day to day and from hour to hour in a random manner. Under the

capabilities of the system are such that a large-scale aurora can stimulate a level of activity amounting to several hundred transmitters being brought on the air during the early stages of the event. This cannot be matched anywhere outside the Amateur Service and offers a unique opportunity to put the service's talents to good use by doing no more than reporting its successes as soon as possible after the event.

TRANS-EQUATORIAL PROPAGATION

An aspect of research in which radio amateurs can justifiably claim to have played a major part is in the field of trans-equatorial propagation, TE or TEP for short. From its discovery just after the Second World War (between stations in Mexico and Argentina, reported in *QST* for October 1947) to the present day, amateurs have provided almost all the raw material for subsequent study. Some dedicated operators have spent 20 years or more setting up series of carefully controlled experiments designed to test theories proposed or to provide fresh material for consideration. For a particularly useful survey of progress to date of circuits between Europe and southern Africa, reference should be made to an article by ZE2JV and 5B4WR entitled 'Twenty-one years of TE', which appeared in *Radio Communication* June/July, August 1980, pp626–634 and 785–788. Some of the areas of the world which have contributed to the present knowledge of the mode are shown in Fig 3.24, where it will be seen that a prime requirement appears to be that the transmission path shall have the magnetic zero-dip equator (a) approximately at its mid-point and (b) nearly normal to it. The placing of the KP4/ZD8 path with respect to the change of direction of the zero-dip line over the Atlantic Ocean area is particularly interesting evidence in support of requirement (b).

The mode was first observed on 50MHz.

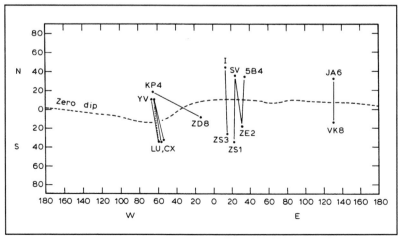

Fig 3.24. Areas of the world where trans-equatorial propagation has been observed

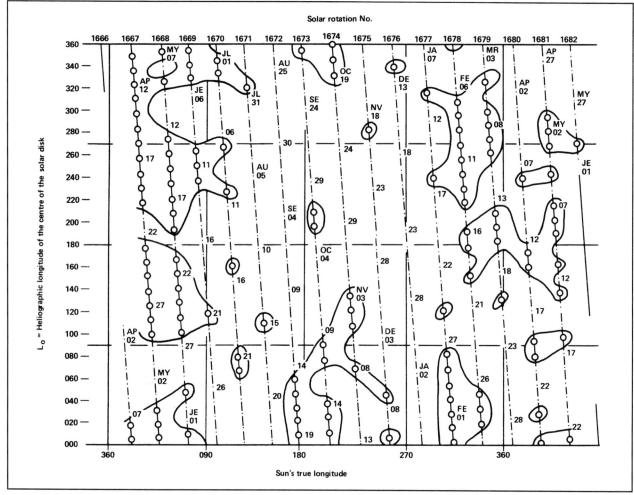

Fig 3.25. Trans-equatorial propagation. Reception of ZE2JV by 5B4WR (144.166MHz), 1630–1900GMT between 1 April 1978 and 31 May 1979

best of conditions 144MHz SSB is just intelligible. At other times the spread is so wide and the flutter is so rapid that no beat note can be obtained with the received signal, which then appears merely as a change in the background noise. At 432MHz the Zimbabwe beacon operated by ZE2JV was heard in Athens by SV1DH and SV1AB between 1816 and 1830GMT on 20 March 1979, and on 13 May 1979 by 5B4WR. Their comments were that the signals were rougher than on 144MHz and spreading more in frequency.

Time-delay measurements made in both directions along the Zimbabwe/Cyprus circuit showed afternoon intervals which at times corresponded with two-hop F2-layer propagation, but evening delays took about 10% longer, which may have been due to an extra ray-path distance of some 600km each way, or was in some way a function of the propagation mechanism. There appears to be no difference in delay time between 28MHz and 144MHz TE; although the character of the received signals differ on account of differences in fading rate.

Table 3.16 shows the European distance records for trans-equatorial propagation as they stood at the beginning of 1997. The mode does not normally extend into UHF.

METEOR TRAIL PROPAGATION

Propagation is also possible on an intermittent basis by means of scatter from short-lived trails of ionisation which appear as a result of small particles of solid matter entering the Earth's atmosphere and becoming heated to incandescence by friction. They are usually accompanied by streaks of light, popularly known as 'shooting stars'. These *meteors* (strictly the term applies only to the visible streak, although most writers use it as though it refers to the object itself) fall into two general classes, *shower meteors,* which follow definite and predictable orbits, and *sporadic meteors,* which follow individual paths and are present at all times.

Both the ionisation and the visual display occur simultaneously at heights of around 85 to 120km. Most of the objects responsible are no bigger than a grain of sand and they burn up completely in the upper atmosphere. Occasionally larger ones survive the descent and examples of some which have

Table 3.16. European VHF and UHF records (as at the beginning of 1997) – TEP			
50MHz	G4IGO (IO80NW) and CE8BHI (FD46)	2 November 1991	13,203km
144MHz	I4EAT (JN54VG) and ZS3B (JG73)	30 March 1979	7843km
Source: John Morris, GM4ANB, for Region I, IARU.			

reached the ground are to be seen in museums, where they are referred to as *meteorites.*

Numbers vary during the year from a maximum in July to a minimum in February, with a ratio of about 4:1. There is a marked diurnal variation, due to the combined motions of the Earth's rotation and its movement around the Sun, leading to a maximum at 0600 local time and a minimum at 1800.

Table 3.17. European VHF and UHF records (as at the beginning of 1997) – meteor scatter

50MHz	G4IGO (IO80NW) and SV1OE (KM17VX)	12 August 1990	2542km
70MHz	GJ3YHU (LN89XI) and GM3WOJ/P (IO89KB)	12 August 1982	1083km
144MHz	GW4CQT (IO81LP) and UW6NA (KN97VE)	12 August 1977	3101km
432MHz	SM2CEW (KP15CR) and PAODZL (JO21HM)	12 August 1989	1869km

Source: John Morris, GM4ANB, for Region I, IARU.

The initial trail of ionisation is in the form of a long, thin, pencil-like cylinder, perhaps 15 to 20km in length. As soon as it is formed it begins to expand radially and to move with the various motions of the air through which it passes. The length of time when the trail is capable of supporting communication is generally very short, often less than a second, although longer persistences of a minute or more occur from time to time. The durations (and the frequency of occurrence) decrease with increase in signal frequency.

Considerations of phase coherence lead to an aspect sensitivity which favours radiation meeting the trail axis at right-angles. Because of this only a small part of any trail acts as a reflector and the orientation of the trail relative to the antennas is of considerable importance because it determines the height and position of the main reflection point. Meeting the right-angle requirement from both ends of a transmission path demands that the trail must lie in such a way that it is tangential to an ellipsoid of revolution having transmitter and receiver antennas at the focal points, and if ionisation is to result this condition has to be met at a level which is within 80 and 120km above the ground. It follows that large numbers of meteors enter the Earth's atmosphere along paths which can never satisfy the tangent condition within the prescribed limits of height and in consequence do not contribute to propagation along a given path.

These requirements suggest that it is unwise to direct very narrow-beam transmitting and receiving antennas (to be used for meteor-scatter work) along the strict line-of-sight between the stations. The only trails which can be tangential to the ellipsoid of revolution in that direction are those lying parallel to the ground, and this is an unlikely attitude to be taken up by a solid body entering the Earth's atmosphere from interplanetary space. The most likely beam directions lie a few degrees to one side or the other of the direct transmission path (both antennas must be deflected towards the same side, of course), and the optimum headings may have to be determined by careful experiment. Where the antennas are less directional the great-circle path between stations may be found to give best results, however, because, although little is likely to be received along the direct path heading, the acceptance angles of the antennas may be wide enough to include the longer but more likely paths on both sides.

The short bursts of signal which result from MS (meteor scatter) can best be observed on stations situated 1000 to 2000km away. In southern England several hundred examples per hour used to be heard carrying signals from the 40kW FM broadcast transmitter at Gdansk, Poland on 70.31MHz.

Table 3.17 shows the European VHF and UHF distance records by meteor scatter, as of the beginning of 1997. It is

interesting to note that the record has been set on the same date (but in different years) for each of the four bands. August 12 is the date on which the Perseids shower reaches a peak.

A very detailed treatment of the subject was published in the February 1975 issue of *Radio Communication,* under the title 'VHF meteor scatter propagation'. In it J D V Ludlow, GW3ZTH, has given details of suitable equipments for receiving and recording signals propagated by this mode, and has provided a practical method of calculating beam headings and optimum times in respect of particular showers. For those wishing to follow up the relevant theory there is a very useful list of 25 references. Details of the current IARU Region 1 QSO procedure are given in the RSGB *Amateur Radio Operating Manual.*

Table 3.18 gives a summary of the main meteor showers likely to be of use to stations in the northern hemisphere. Full details, including times of transit and the directions from which the trails appear to radiate (an effect of perspective) appear each year in the current *Handbook of The British Astronomical Association* (see the Bibliography at the end of this chapter).

Commercial use is made of meteor-scatter propagation, particularly at high latitudes where it provides a hedge against the effects of polar cap absorption. The best-known system is the Janet Project of the Canadian Defence Research Board, which is described by G W L Davis and others in *Proceedings of the IRE* December 1957. Another, and later, application of the technique was seen in the 'Snonet' meteorological meteor burst system for collecting observations from remote sensors. Information recorded on magnetic tape at normal speed was played back (and transmitted) in the form of high-speed bursts when a monitor on a slightly different frequency showed that a path was open.

In more recent times the availability of satellite channels has weakened the attraction of meteor scatter for commercial data communications. On the amateur bands, however, interest continues to grow and very detailed logs from stations all over Europe appear in every quarterly issue of the German *DUBUS* magazine. For example, issue 3/96 contained 15 closely packed pages of reports, followed by two pages of operating procdures for meteor scatter QSOs, as adopted by IARU, Region 1. It is a very useful source of data for research purposes.

SATELLITE PROPAGATION EXPERIMENTS

A number of amateurs have suggested propagation experiments using satellites in ways that were not envisaged as part of the basic projects.

Pat Gowen, G3IOR, made use of Oscar 7 and Oscar 8 in its Mode A transponder configuration (145MHz up, 29MHz down) as a guide to conditions on 144MHz. Good tropospheric conditions were indicated by severe attenuation of one's own

Table 3.18. Calendar of the main meteor showers

Start	Dates of Maximum	End	Name	Comparative rate*	Transit Time	Elev
Jan 01	Jan 03	Jan 06	Quadrantids	6	09	90
Apr 19	Apr 21	Apr 24	April Lyrids	3	04	70
May 01	May 05	May 08	Eta Aquarids	3	08	40
Jun 10	Jun 16	Jun 21	June Lyrids	2	01	70
Jun 17	Jun 20	Jun 26	Ophiuchids	2	23	20
Jul 10	Jul 26	Aug 15	Capricornids	2	01	20
Jul 15	Jul 27	Aug 15	Delta Aquarids	4	02	30
Jul 15	Jul 31	Aug 20	Pisces Australids	2	02	10
Jul 15	Jul 30	Aug 25	Alpha Capricornids	2	00	30
Jul 15	Aug 06	Aug 25	Iota Aquarids	2	01	30
Jul 25	Aug 12	Aug 18	Perseids	5	06	80†
Aug 19	Aug 21	Aug 22	Chi Cygnids	1	21	90
Oct 16	Oct 21	Oct 26	Orionids	4	04	50
Oct 20	Nov 08	Nov 30	Taurids	3	01	60
Nov 07	Nov 09	Nov 11	Cepheids	2	20	80†
Nov 15	Nov 17	Nov 19	Leonids	2	06	60
Dec 07	Dec 14	Dec 15	Geminids	5	02	70
Dec 17	Dec 22	Dec 24	Ursids	1	08	60†

* Each step on the comparative rate scale represents a factor of 2.
† Above northern horizon.

returned signal, with deep and rapid fading when the satellite was just above the horizon. Brief and rapid 'pop-ups' of signal before and after predicted times of access were caused by scintillation of 144MHz uplink as it passed through tropospheric ducts. Sporadic-E effects were similar, but they may have taken place at quite high elevations. Fading suggested the presence of multiple diffraction paths in the ionosphere. Aurora caused marked degradation of tone on returned signals from some of the northern stations, often specific to small areas.

This topic has been brought back into prominence recently in connection with 136MHz aircraft-to-satellite-to-ground communications, 250MHz military satellite applications and global positioning systems working around 1.2 to 1.6MHz. (See, for example a paper by Dr J Aarons in *IEE Conference Publication* No 411.)

John Branegan, GM4IHJ, kept a regular check on where satellite scintillation occurred on polar paths and used it to define the instantaneous location of the auroral oval to provide an estimate of the total electron content along the satellite line of sight. In this way, very high electron densities were observed at heights above the normal 110km auroral reflection zone, considered capable of scattering frequencies of up to at least 250MHz. GM4IHJ, G3IOR and several Alaskan stations all heard double signals on 144MHz satellite transmissions, the second signal some 750Hz from the nominal frequency, sometimes with an auroral tone.

G4DGU and SM6CKU investigated the idea of using a large low-orbit satellite as a passive reflector. The relevant theory suggested that the total path length loss might be about 10dB better than moonbounce. There were problems – low-orbit satellite orbits soon decay and they could not be predicted with accuracy. There were very high Doppler shifts involved. At 432MHz signals are likely to appear first 12kHz high, shifting down at about 1kHz per second to become 12kHz low, six to eight seconds later, when signals disappear. Despite these difficulties, however, a four-second burst of SSB from G4DGU had been received by SM6CKU, 10dB over noise,

off a Cosmos third-stage launcher. The transmitter used was of 400W PEP into an array of eight 17-element Yagis. The receiver had been coupled to an 8m dish.

SOLAR/GEOPHYSICAL CONNECTIONS
Precursors

The relationship between events on the Sun and the associated effects in the Earth's ionosphere has been dealt with at length in the propagation chapter of the *Radio Communication Handbook*. Suffice it to record here that the main solar events of interest to VHF and UHF operators are solar flares, radio bursts and emissions of high-energy protons. Solar flare effects appear in three time scales. Within about eight minutes of a major flare suitably placed on the Sun, electromagnetic radiation brings about increased D-region ionisation, sudden cosmic noise absorption (SCNA), short-wave fadeout phenomena (SWF), sudden phase anomaly of ELF signals (SPA), sudden enhancement of atmospherics at LF (SEA), sudden frequency deviation at LF (SFD), and noise bursts (not all of these will be detected in one particular event). Within an hour of the appearance of the flare, high-energy corpuscular radiation is likely to cause polar cap absorption (PCA) of anything from 20 minutes to 20 hours duration, which may extend to VHF. Some 20–40 hours after the flare, low-energy corpuscular radiation brings about magnetic storms, ionospheric storms and auroras, which may persist for more than a day.

The probability that this chain of events will lead to a magnetic storm and an aurora is greatest when the solar activity occurs when the region concerned is near, but slightly beyond, the central meridian.

There is a tendency for solar events to recur after periods of approximately 27 days, as has been discussed in connection with auroral propagation. Table 3.19 shows the starting dates of all solar rotations between 1991 and 2002 calculated in continuation of Carrington's photo-heliographic series, using a method described by the Belgian amateur astronomer Jean Meeus in the journal *Ciel et Terre*.

Table 3.19. Solar rotation calendar, 1991–2002

1991		1992		1993		1994		1995		1996	
1838	JA16	1851	JA05	1865	JA21	1878	JA11	1892	JA28	1905	JA17
1839	FE12	1852	FE02	1866	FE17	1879	FE07	1893	FE24	1906	FE13
1840	MR11	1853	FE29	1867	MR17	1880	MR06	1894	MR23	1907	MR12
1841	AP08	1854	MR27	1868	AP13	1881	AP03	1895	AP19	1908	AP08
1842	MY05	1855	AP23	1869	MY10	1882	AP30	1896	MY17	1909	MY05
1843	JE01	1856	MY21	1870	JE06	1883	MY27	1897	JE13	1910	JE01
1844	JE28	1857	JE17	1871	JL04	1884	JE23	1898	JL10	1911	JE29
1845	JL25	1858	JL14	1872	JL31	1885	JL20	1899	AU06	1912	JL26
1846	AU22	1859	AU10	1873	AU27	1886	AU17	1900	SE03	1913	AU22
1847	SE18	1860	SE07	1874	SE23	1887	SE13	1901	SE30	1914	SE18
1848	OC15	1861	OC04	1875	OC21	1888	OC10	1902	OC27	1915	OC16
1849	NV12	1862	OC31	1876	NV17	1889	NV07	1903	NV23	1916	NV12
1850	DE09	1863	NV27	1877	DE14	1890	DE04	1904	DE21	1917	DE09
		1864	DE25			1891	DE31				

1997		1998		1999		2000		2001		2002	
1918	JA06	1932	JA23	1945	JA12	1958	JA02	1972	JA17	1985	JA07
1919	FE02	1933	FE19	1946	FE08	1959	JA29	1973	FE14	1986	FE03
1920	MR01	1934	MR18	1947	MR08	1960	FE25	1974	MR13	1987	MR03
1921	MR29	1935	AP14	1948	AP04	1961	MR24	1975	APO9	1988	MR30
1922	AP25	1936	MY12	1949	MY01	1962	AP20	1976	MY07	1989	AP26
1923	MY22	1937	JE08	1950	MY29	1963	MY17	1977	JE03	1990	MY24
1924	JE18	1938	JL05	1951	JB25	1964	JE13	1978	JE30	1991	JE20
1925	JL16	1939	AU01	1952	JL22	1965	JL11	1979	JL27	1992	JL17
1926	AU12	1940	AU29	1953	AU18	1966	AU07	1980	AU24	1993	AU13
1927	SE08	1941	SE25	1954	SE14	1967	SE03	1981	SE20	1994	SE09
1928	OC05	1942	OC22	1955	OC12	1968	SE30	1982	OC17	1995	OC07
1929	NV02	1943	NV18	1956	NV08	1969	OC28	1983	NV13	1996	NV03
1930	NV29	1944	DE16	1957	DE05	1970	NV24	1984	DE11	1997	NV30
1931	DE26					1971	DE21				

The rotation numbers follow Carrington's series. The quoted date shows the first day on which a new rotation value of L_o appears at 12UT.

A solar rotation diagram intended for use in connection with radio propagation studies appears each year in the *RSGB Yearbook*. It covers an 18-month period covering the year in which the *Yearbook* is current and the three-month periods immediately before and after.

Solar and geophysical data

There still remains much to be learned about the relationship between events on the Sun, their corresponding effect on the Earth's magnetic field and VHF/UHF radio propagation via the ionosphere as in sporadic-E, auroral-E and other similar 'openings' on the amateur bands. This is an interesting field for individual research but it requires access to basic solar and geophysical data. Four useful sources are suggested here.

The first, the easiest to obtain, is supplied by the brief summary of solar and magnetic trends over the previous week, together with a forecast covering the week to come, which is compiled from authoritative sources and included each week in the RSGB GB2RS news bulletin.

These are transmitted according to a schedule published regularly in *Radio Communication*. The summaries are compiled by Neil Clarke, G0CAS, who also edits a monthly 16-page booklet, which he calls *SunMag*, containing tables of relevant data, together with graphs and diagrams, as appropriate. For subscription details write to Neil at 39 Acacia Road, Cantley, Doncaster, DN4 6UR (Tel: 01302 531925). An explanation of the terms used may be obtained by post from RSGB Headquarters or through the RSGB Web Page at http://www.rsgb.org.

The second source of information is by far the most detailed, but it is subject to three to seven months' delay, which can seem a long time when waiting to analyse a particular period of observation. The material is to be found in the publication *Solar Geophysical Data*, produced in the USA by the Environmental Data Service of the National Oceanic and Atmospheric Administration (NOAA), of Ashville, NC. This appears in two parts each month – Part 1 (Prompt Reports) containing preliminary data covering the two months prior to the date of issue, and Part 2 (Comprehensive Reports) containing more-detailed data centred about six months prior to the date of issue. In this country the monthly parts arrive by post about the middle of the month following that shown on the cover.

For a trial inspection it is suggested that the most recent February issue (consisting of Part 1, Part 2 and a very detailed explanation booklet distributed annually at that time) should be requested through a library. In case of difficulty an approach should be made to a library specialising in science subjects.

Daily values of K_p, C_i, C_p, A_i, and other magnetic data, including an inferred interplanetary magnetic field indication derived from satellite observations, appear after a delay of about four months in the American publication *Journal of Geophysical Research (Space Physics)*.

Amateur radio-astronomical observations are co-ordinated by the British Astronomical Association and an edited summary appears as a regular feature in their *Journal*.

The third source ought to have been the data broadcaster GAM1, which was to have been operated by the Amateur Service to provide daily messages containing various solar and geophysical information obtained from 'official' sources, such as Meudon Observatory, Paris, and Boulder, Colorado. Table 3.20 shows the format of summary messages that used to be available 'over the air' (but no longer, unfortunately). It will serve here to indicate the type of information it was hoped to cover. After years of trying it now seems that we cannot get the authorities to allow the service to go ahead in the way we had hoped.

All is not lost, however. At the time of writing tests are being carried out by G4FKH which it is hoped will lead to an alternative approach. If the outcome is favourable no doubt full details will be printed in *Radio Communication*, but it is too soon to be able to give any reliable indications here.

The fourth source is the Internet/World Wide Web, but here again it may be unwise to attempt to be specific. However, it is clear that a great deal of information may be obtained from official sources if you know how to reach them. Neil Clarke, G0CAS, may be able to help you there. His e-mail address is

Table 3.20. Format of a typical GEOALERT message

GEOALERT CCCNN DDHHMMZ
9HHDD 1SSSG 2FFFB 3AAAE 4//// 5MMXX
QXXYY nnijk (QXXYY nnijk . . .)
(Plain-language details of major optical
flares and tenflares)
8hhdd 7777C QXXYY degree of activity . . .
(Plain-language forecast of activity)
SOLALERT JJ/KK MAGALERT JJ/KK

Note: There is no fixed length to a
GEOALERT message, groups being repeated as often as necessary.

Key

CCCNN	Originating centre (MEU = Meudon, WWA = Boulder); serial number of message
DDHHMMZ	Date and time of origin of message; Z = GMT.
9HHDD	Indicates that various daily indices follow, for 24 hours ending at HH hours on DD day of month.
1 SSSG	Indicates sunspot number, SSS, and number of new groups observed, G.
2FFFB	Indicates 2800MHz solar flux value FFF, and number of important bursts.
3AAAE	Indicates geomagnetic activity, AAA = A_k value; E = events (0 = no events, 1 = end of magnetic storm, 2 = storm in progress, 6 = gradual storm commencement, 7 = sudden storm commencement, 8 = very pronounced sudden storm commencement).
4////	Indicates cosmic ray data (not used on Meudon message).
5MMXX	Indicates flare counts: MM = daily total of M flares, XX = daily total of X flares.

Then follow groups identifying active regions on the Sun:

QXXYY	Q = Quadrant of the Sun (1 = NE, 2 = SE, 3 = SW, 4 = NW), XX = degrees of longitude, YY = degrees of latitude, relative to the centre of the Sun's visible disc.
nnijk	nn = total number of flares in active region indicated; i = number of flares greater than importance 1; j = number of M flares; k = number of X flares (in region QXXYY).
8hhdd	Indicates 24-hour forecast follows, starting at hh hours on dd day of month.
7777C	Indicator, C = types of observation used in forecast (1 = solar radio, 2 = partial solar optical, 3 = optical and radio, 4 = all, plus solar magnetic measurements).
QXXYY	Positions on the Sun, coded as before.
JJ/KK	Days of month between which the solar or magnetic alerts apply

Table 3.21. K-figures for Lerwick

0	0 to 10	5	140 to 240
1	0 to 20	6	240 to 400
2	20 to 40	7	400 to 640
3	40 to 80	8	640 to 1000
4	80 to 140	9	1000 or more

neil@g0cas.demon.co.uk ; his postal address and telephone number have been given earlier.

The June 1997 issue of *Radio Communication* carried a reference to Solar Warning and Real-time Monitor (SWARM) software which may be downloaded from http://solar.uleth.ca/solar/www/swarm.html and which is said to provide current real-time solar and geomagnetic data.

Geomagnetic data

Solar events and associated ionospheric disturbances are of less direct interest to the VHF/UHF operator than are geomagnetic variations, which correlate well with auroral events and, though to a lesser extent, with E_s and TE.

These are comparisons which fall within the scope and capabilities of interested radio amateurs, but many find it difficult to extract the necessary, elementary information from conventional manuals on the subject.

In the studies carried out on auroral propagation by the RSGB the region of interest is admirably represented by a knowledge of the performance of the magnetometers at Lerwick Observatory, Shetland, which location, at over 60° north latitude, often experiences spectacular displays of visual aurora. Valuable experience was gained there during the International Quiet Sun Years, 1963–4, when the GB3LER beacon transmitters were set up nearby and direct comparison of results against the magnetometer records became possible. The remainder of this section is intended to provide an introduction to the subject to those who take part in the Society's auroral observation work, which forms an important part of its Propagation Studies programme.

The terrestrial magnetic field at the Earth's surface is not constant, but is subject to both long-term and short-term variations in intensity ranging from periods of centuries or more to hours, minutes or even less. The transient variations are small in comparison to the total field; they are measured in gammas, which are equal to 10^{-5} gauss, the force being determined in terms of three components mutually at right-angles, either in the directions X (geographic north), Y (east) and Z (vertically downward), or H (horizontal intensity), D (declination) and Z.

The main variometers at Lerwick record H, D and Z photographically on a sheet of sensitised paper approximately 40cm by 30cm, on which all three traces appear side-by-side, together with timing marks every five minutes, and suitable baselines. The present sensitivities are such that H changes of 3.45 gamma, D changes of 0.94 minutes of arc (corresponding to 4 gamma at right-angles to the meridian) and Z changes of 4.35 gamma move their respective traces by 1mm. A system of prisms ensures that any trace which approaches the edge of its section of the chart appears again from the other side, thereby extending the effective width so as to be able to handle the widest excursions.

The traces exhibit two features, one a fairly regular diurnal 'background' change due to solar and lunar effects, the other a superimposed irregular, and often violent, variation, the extent of which depends on particle radiation from the Sun. It is necessary to examine initially a large number of traces obtained during magnetically quiet periods in order to be able to assess the appearance of the 'normal' diurnal curve, which has the form of a shallow letter 'S' on its side, and allowance has to be made for season, solar flare effects and certain decreases which follow a magnetic storm. The sum of the highest positive and negative departures from the 'normal' curve are converted into a quasi-logarithmic scale of K-figures, where the actual values for the lower limit of each number vary from one observatory to another depending on the magnetic latitude. For Lerwick the scale is given in Table 3.21.

At other observatories the ranges are proportional, and may be found from the value assigned for the lower limit of $K = 9$, which will be quoted as being either 300, 350, 500, 600, 750, 1000, 1200, 1500 or 2000 gamma.

Using this K-scale, the degree of activity is described for each directional component of the force during eight three-hourly periods of each day, and the highest of the three numbers for each period are grouped in two sets of four digits, separated by Greenwich noon, beginning with the period 0000 to 0300GMT.

A combination of K-figures from 12 widely spaced observatories (of which Lerwick is one) results in the planetary K-index, K_p, prepared monthly by the Committee on Characterisation of Magnetic Disturbances at the University of Göttingen, Germany, which is often preferred to single-station data in analytical work, particularly in connection with the ionosphere or when purely local effects are unwanted. The normal 0 to 9 scale is expanded into one of thirds by the addition of suffixes, eg $2-$, $2o$, $2+$, $3-$, $3o$, $3+$ . . .

A daily magnetic character figure, C, has been in use for over half a century, each observatory subscribing a figure descriptive of their assessment of the day's activity: 0 if it was judged quiet, 1 if it was moderately disturbed or 2 if it was very disturbed. The individual figures are rarely used, but an index C_i, the average to one decimal place of C-figures from a worldwide network of collaborating observatories, provides a convenient classification of daily activity. Another, apparently similar, character figure, C_p, is prepared directly from the K_p indices but, although its derivation is so different, it rarely differs from C_i by more than 0.2. To simplify machine tabulation the scales are sometimes expressed in terms of yet another, known as C_9, which uses whole numbers from 0 to 9 in place of the decimal range from 0.0 to 2.5.

The sum and arithmetic mean of the eight three-hourly K-figures provide further expressions of daily activity which are simple and convenient to obtain. They are not ideal, however, because the K-scale is a logarithmic one (as is the decibel scale), and the arithmetic average gives the logarithm of the geometric mean and not the logarithm of the arithmetic mean. To take an extreme example, consider the two series 1111 1111 and 0000 0008, both of which give a sum of 8 and a mean of 1; the first would be representative of a quiet day, whereas the second would be considered a highly disturbed day. For this reason it is preferable to turn each K-index back into an equivalent range, a_k, on a linear scale, by using the corresponding values:

K	0	1	2	3	4	5	6	7	8	9
a_k	0	3	7	15	27	48	80	140	240	400

which may be summed and meaned arithmetically to represent activity over a period. It should be noted that the same table used for all observatories, irrespective of their actual K-scales so that the resulting standardised figures are not the true gamma ranges, although those may be approximated from them, if required, by the use of a factor (which in the case of Lerwick is 4). The *daily amplitude* A_k is the average of the eight values of a_k for the day. In the case of the two examples cited above as leading to the same K-figure sum, the first, 1111 1111, gives an A_k of 3, whereas the second, 0000 0008, produces an A_k of 30, thereby reflecting the vastly differing states of activity.

A similar, but expanded, scale relates the planetary three-hour index K_p to the three-hourly *equivalent planetary amplitude*, a_p:

K_p	0o	0+	1−	1o	1+	2−	2o	2+	3−	3o	3+	4−	4o	4+	5−
a_p	0	2	3	4	5	6	7	9	12	15	18	22	27	32	39

K_p	5o	5+	6−	6o	6+	7−	7o	7+	8−	8o	8+	9−	9o
a_p	48	56	67	80	94	111	132	154	179	207	236	300	400

The *daily equivalent planetary amplitude, A_p, is* the average of the eight values of a_p for the day.

ACCURATE TIME RECORDING

When selected frequencies need to be monitored for propagation studies, some form of recording is essential so that the operator can attend to more productive things. It also results in a semi-permanent set of observations which can be transcribed and analysed as and when convenient.

Stereo cassette recorders provide a useful method of recording. The machines are relatively cheap because they are mass-produced and, as the tapes may be used again and again, running costs are low, particularly when compared with pen recorders using paper charts. The stereo facility provides the user with two synchronised (but entirely independent) channels, one of which may be used for signal data, the other for timing signals originating from one of the standard time and frequency radio transmissions.

For some purposes it is sufficient to record no more than the presence of the selected signal at a known time and for this the recorder may be connected to the output of the receiver in the conventional way. When an indication of the signal strength is required it is advisable to use some form of voltage-to-frequency or analogue-to-digital conversion before recording from either the AGC line or a special detector giving a suitable time-constant. This avoids the effects of differences between recording and playback, including the quality of the tape, from affecting the measurements.

Sometimes, to make more effective use of tape and to simplify the task of data reduction, discontinuous recording may be adopted. This can take the form of sampling, where, say, five minutes in every hour are transferred to tape and the transport mechanism is halted between-times, or by causing the tape to stop automatically in the absence of signals for more than a selected period. Both of these practices complicate the provision of radio time signals from the best-known sources, such as those which share 2.5, 5, 10 and 15MHz, because only minute and second intervals are available with no indication of absolute time.

MSF, Rugby, on 60kHz, carries time every minute in the form of a 0.5-second burst of pulse code modulation immediately before the minute indicator to which it refers. This could be recorded, together with successive one-second 'ticks' on one channel of a stereo recorder.

Nowadays very accurate time is a very cheap commodity. An analogue clock with a built-in decoder locked by radio to an atomic standard may be bought for under £25 from one of the big radio and electrical component chain stores.

For rapid access to a reliable time source try any teletext page from a terrestrial television station.

Finally, if you are using a computer as a real-time logging device, or to sample signal strengths through a suitable interface, then the internal clock is, or should be, a useful source

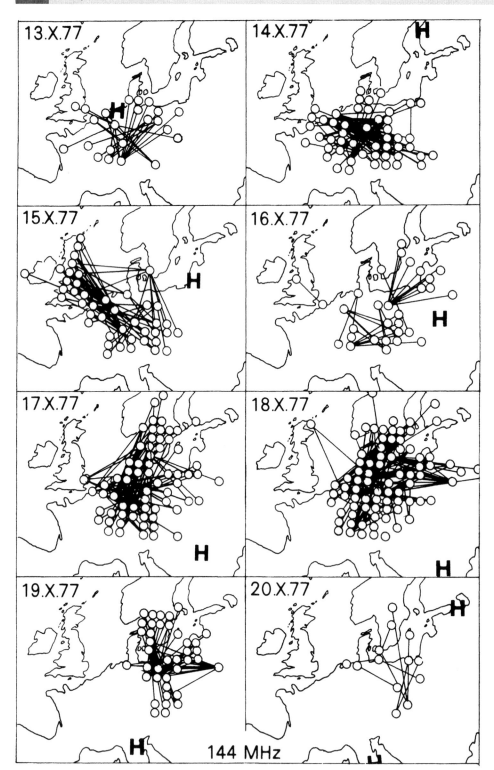

Fig 3.26(a). Analysis of 144MHz reports

organised groups of amateurs are particularly well placed to further our understanding of the physical processes involved in almost every mode other than direct line of sight.

There may never have been such an opportune time to put forward fresh evidence of the extent to which guidance given by such authorities as ITU and URSI to intending users of frequencies above 30MHz seriously underestimates the range and frequency coverage of the various modes in this part of the spectrum. The professionals acknowledge that such discrepancies exist and are looking to the Amateur Service for raw material that will help to bring present theory more into line with what is happening in the world outside.

There is a continuing need for long-term studies of over-the-horizon transmission paths, particularly those involving beacons. This type of work demands a degree of involvement that can be expected from only a very few individual amateurs, although it provides a very interesting project for a club, particularly one associated with an educational establishment, provided that continuity may be assured over long holiday periods and there is sufficient overall supervision to maintain the stability and calibration of the equipment.

Enough has been written already to show the value of studies which make use of a very high volume of simple reports from stations covering a large area. The mere fact that contact was made on a specified band, at a certain time, between two stations identified by callsign and QTH locator, is of little more than passing interest to either of the operators concerned. But when hundreds of such reports are collected and processed a powerful research tool emerges, and one, moreover, that is peculiar to the Amateur Service.

As an example of the capabilities of this technique, consider Figs 3.26(a) and (b), which were included in the IEE Conference paper referred to earlier in the section of signal strengths

that may be accessed along with the incoming data. But check it against a source known to be accurate before you rely on it.

AMATEUR NETWORKS AND FURTHER RESEARCH

It is hoped that the preceding pages of this chapter will have left the reader with the feeling that there is still much to be learned about radio propagation at VHF and UHF and that and ranges attainable using tropospheric propagation. The two sets of maps resulted from an analysis of many hundreds of individual reports, most of them collected in Germany by the DUBUS organisation. It is known that reporting amateurs were active in most parts of Europe during the whole of the period shown, and nearly all of them were within the boundaries of a very large anticyclone for a large proportion of the time, yet only a certain well-defined area was experiencing long-range anomalous propagation at any one time. That area is shown in the original paper to be where the steep-gradient boundary has formed between air of low refractive index, over air of high refractive index. Although subsidence is present elsewhere the sharp boundary is not present either because the turbulence in the lower atmosphere is too weak, allowing the low-refractive index air to reach ground level, or too strong, causing mixing at the interface and a consequent weakening of the gradient.

Observe how, in the course of the event, the centre of the anticyclone, marked with a letter 'H', moves from day to day, and how the axis of the really long-range paths rotates so as to maintain a broadside-on aspect relative to it. These paths form a chord across the curvature of the isobars (which had to be omitted from the diagrams in order to simplify them). In the last two maps the change in direction due to the approach of a fresh centre is of interest.

Another conclusion to be

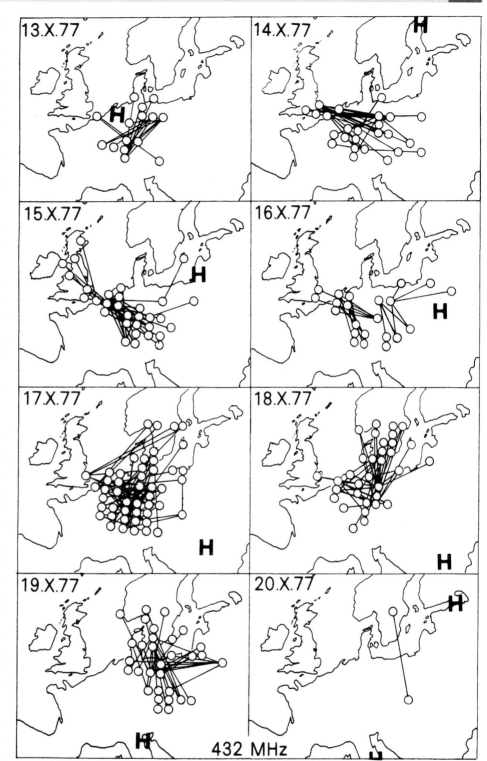

Fig 3.26(b). Analysis of 432MHz reports

drawn from the maps is that the area of enhancement is approximately the same at both frequencies, although the two sets of reports used are entirely independent of one another. Individual path lengths differed within the area, however, being roughly half as far again at 144MHz as compared to 432MHz.

It should be clear that these techniques, which require no more from operators than the reporting of contacts that may well have had nothing to do with propagation research in themselves, have enormous potential, not only in tropospheric propagation studies, but in VHF sporadic-E and auroral-E studies as well. It should be noted, however, that reports of bearings from both ends of the path are an important requisite of the latter.

It is only because of the truly international nature of amateur radio and the seemingly tireless enthusiasm of so many people, not the least those who collect the observations and make them available for studies such as the one described, that this technique can be employed to the full. Your reports may be the ones needed to complete the task.

BIBLIOGRAPHY

Radio Communication Handbook, Ed D Biddulph, G8DPS, 6th edn, RSGB, 1994, Chapter 11 – Propagation. ISBN 1 872309 24 0.

The Six and Ten Report (monthly). Subscription details from Dr Steve Read, G0AEV, Bridlands, Kington Langley, Chippenham, SN15 5NN.

DUBUS magazine: Communications for active VHF amateurs by active VHF amateurs (quarterly). Publisher: DUBUS Verlag GbR, D-22339 Hamburg, Germany. UK representative Roger Blackwell, G4PMK, 5 Tollgate Road, Culham, OX14 4NL.

'Effects of the troposphere on radiocommunication', M P M Hall, *IEE Electromagnetic Waves*, Series 8, London 1980.

Understanding the Earth: a Reader in the Earth Sciences, Ed I G Gass and others, Open University Press, 1972. SBN 85141 308 0.

Auroral Physics, C-I Meng and others. ISBN 0 521 38049 9.

Radio Auroras, C Newton, G2FKZ, RSGB, 1991. ISBN 1 872309 03 8.

Meteorology Today: An Introduction to Weather, Climate and Environment, C Donald Ahrem, 5th edn, 1994. ISBN 0 314 02779 3.

Meteorology – The Atmosphere in Action, Joe H Eagleman, 2nd edn, 1980. ISBN 1 877696 05 6.

Handbook of th e British Astronomical Association, published annually in October for the following year.

4 Receivers, transmitters and transceivers

THIS chapter is designed to give the reader a clear outline of the practical needs for receivers, transmitters etc in the VHF/UHF bands. As will be seen, these are different from those at HF and these differences will be identified. In receivers, the main difference is that, since external noise levels are much lower at VHF/UHF than at HF, the noise performance of the receiver must be that much better. The effect of stray capacitance and inductance on semiconductors is also important.

Note that devices such as ICs are mentioned only as illustrations and not as recommendations.

RECEIVER PARAMETERS [1, 2]

An ideal receiver would be stable, selective enough for the mode to be received and would convert an incoming VHF or UHF signal into an audio signal regardless of its strength or that of other signals whether or not they were close by in frequency. To do this it needs gain, stability, selectivity, a large dynamic range (see later) and detection. Needless to say, the ideal does not exist in practice but to approach it as closely as possible should be the goal of all amateurs, especially those wishing to read weak signals such as those from DX stations.

The factors causing deviation from the ideal are *noise, non-linearity, instability* and *gain compression*.

Noise

Noise is always present, and can come from within the receiver or from outside. The latter can be natural or man made and there is very little that can be done about it (but see below). Considering firstly the noise from within the receiver, a resistor R at any temperature above absolute zero (0K or −273°C) will generate a noise power w given by:

$$w = k.T.B$$

where w is in watts, k is Boltzmann's constant (a fundamental constant in physics/electronics) and B is the bandwidth in hertz. This is true for a resistor not carrying a current. Carrying a current will increase the noise and it will be worse for some types of resistor (eg carbon composition) than for others (eg metal film types).

Note that w is independent of the resistance of R. k is 1.38×10^{-23} watts per degree per hertz. Since k is very small, w is also small, eg at room temperature of 290K (17°C or 62.6°F) and a bandwidth of 2kHz, w is 8×10^{-18} watts or 8 attowatts. If the resistor has a value of 50Ω, the corresponding voltage is 0.02μV or 20nV.

Noise figure

This is often quoted along with the noise factor. Taking the latter first, it is defined as the signal-to-noise ratio at the input of a device divided by the signal-to-noise ratio at the output, ie:

$$\text{Noise factor (NF)} = \frac{S_{in} / N_{in}}{S_{out} / N_{out}}$$

and noise figure is simply the NF expressed as decibels, ie:

$$\text{Noise figure} = 10 \log \text{NF}$$

Noise is also generated by any device that dissipates energy. Pure capacitors and inductors do not generate noise but resistors, amplifying devices, semiconductors or valves do. If it is assumed that the noise due to the input resistance is doubled by the input amplifying device and added to further by noise from outside, a figure of about 0.1μV arises for 2kHz bandwidth. This sets a limit to the overall gain needed in the receiver. 0.1μV corresponds to 2×10^{-16}W. If an output of 1W is required the overall gain needs to be 5×10^{15} or 157dB. Less than this will be adequate since the full gain will produce 1W of noise. Narrow-band modes such as Morse code will allow less noise into the system and will therefore work with a smaller signal. However, they put a greater demand on frequency stability and selectivity.

Another way of looking at this is to consider a bandwidth of 1Hz at room temperature (290K) – the noise level will be −174dBm, ie −174dB relative to 1mW. This allows a very easy determination of signal-to-noise ratio under any circumstances when the various parameters are known. In a linear system such as for SSB, the signal-to-noise ratio is given by:

$$\text{S/N} = P_{in} + 174 - \text{NF} - 10 \log B \quad \text{dB}$$

where P_{in} is the input power in dBm, NF is the noise figure, and B is the bandwidth in hertz.

For example, a receiver with a 3dB noise figure with an input of 100nV (−127dBm assuming a 50Ω input impedance) will provide in an SSB bandwidth of 3kHz a S/N ratio of:

$$-127 + 174 - 3 - 35 = 9\text{dB}$$

This shows how important a narrow bandwidth is for ultimate sensitivity. However, since the effective noise bandwidth is only affected by the filtering to some 10 or 20dB down, the ultimate selectivity of high-performance crystal filters (ie the *stop-band* width, usually −60dB bandwidth) has little effect and simply from the requirements of detecting the smallest signal, stop-bands of 20dB are adequate.

Digital signal processing (DSP) at audio can provide an effective reduction of noise bandwidth greater than the actual bandwidth because DSP looks for correlation of the signal from sample to sample and so builds up the signal over time. This is because noise is essentially a random signal which tends to cancel over time while the wanted signal has some

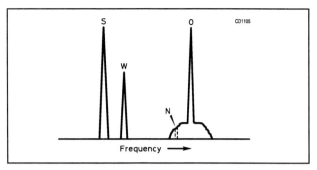

Fig 4.1. Phase noise. W is the wanted signal, S is a strong unwanted signal, O is the oscillator and N is part of the noise sideband of the oscillator. O – W = IF and N – S = IF noise

regularity. The details of DSP are rather complicated and will not be dealt with here.

In the case of FM, the output S/N ratio depends on the demodulator and the modulation index. As a guide, narrow-band FM (NBFM) analogue voice systems can provide an output S/N ratio of 12dB (usually considered the minimum acceptable) with an input carrier S/N ratio of as little as 3dB.

Sometimes the term *MDS* (minimum discernible signal) is used. This is the input level of a signal 3dB above the noise floor of the receiver.

As will be described later, optimising the receiver including minimising noise is achieved by using the best devices, proper matching and the correct distribution of gain within the receiver.

All receivers in current use are superhets and may have more than one frequency conversion. (Straight or TRF, direct-conversion and super-regenerative receivers are possible but are not used in practice at VHF/UHF and will not be considered further.) Frequency converters (also known as *mixers*) contribute more noise than amplifiers.

Phase noise is a special case and results from use of a noisy oscillator, usually in the first frequency conversion in the receiver. It is caused by the noise side-band on the oscillator mixing with a strong, unwanted signal or signals close to the desired one and producing a noise signal or signals within the pass-band of the receiver. See Fig 4.1.

External noise

This comes from a multitude of sources. Natural noise comes from the heat of the landscape and from the stars. In particular, the Sun is a potent generator of noise. Whether or not the noise gets into the receiver depends on the direction that the beam antenna is pointing (see Chapter 5) and on the narrowness of its beam (its *directivity*). Since directivity and beamwidth are directly related, a high-gain antenna, besides producing a stronger signal, will produce less noise than a lower-gain one.

The same applies to man-made noise unless the noise emanates from the same direction as the wanted signal.

Non-linearity and intermodulation

The hypothetical ideal receiver would have a linear relationship between the input of any stage and its output. The overall gain would be controlled but the linear relationship would still exist. In reality, amplifiers are non-linear. That is, if two signals are applied to the input, the output consists of the two, amplified, signals and products (not in the mathematical sense

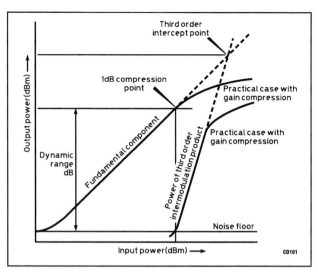

Fig 4.2. Noise floor, 1dB compression point, dynamic range and third-order intercept indicated on a mixer output versus input plot *(GEC-Plessey Professional Products Handbook)*

but harmonics, sums, differences and differences of products) of them. This is called *intermodulation* [1–3]. If the input frequencies are x and y hertz, then the output will contain:

$$x, y, 2x, 2y \text{ etc and } (x + y), (x - y), (2x - y), (2y - x) \text{ etc}$$

or, to generalise:

$$(mx \pm ny)$$

where m and n are integers (whole numbers), theoretically from one to infinity! Provided non-linearity is not too large, the higher-order products, where m and n are large, will be small. If x and y are close together, then $(2x - y)$ and $(2y - x)$ will be close to both of them. These are called *third-order intermodulation products* (3IPs).

These third-order intermodulation products are of most interest. It can be shown [1] that they grow at three times the rate of the wanted signal in an amplifier. If they are plotted on logarithmic paper (logarithmic in signal is also linear in decibels) the generalised result is shown in Fig 4.2. Third-order IPs in a receiver can produce unwanted signals in the pass-band of the receiver and need to be minimised.

Mixers are, by definition, non-linear since the required output is one intermodulation product, $y - x$, where x is the signal frequency and y is the local oscillator frequency. This assumes that the local oscillator frequency is higher than the signal frequency, a normal state of affairs. A simple mixer will have outputs of:

$$x, y, (x + y), (y - x), 2x, 2y, (2x \pm y) \text{ etc}$$

Only $(y - x)$, the intermediate frequency (IF), is wanted. All the others are eliminated by the selectivity of the IF amplifier. If the mixer is 'balanced' with respect to the input signal of the local oscillator (singly balanced) or to both (doubly balanced), a number of these output frequencies are balanced out.

For an unbalanced mixer Table 4.1 applies. In the case of a singly balanced mixer, there is half the number of mixer products (see Table 4.2). All the even 'y's are balanced out.

In the case of a doubly balanced mixer (Table 4.3), there is one quarter of the mixer products. All the even multiples of x

Table 4.1. Unbalanced mixer

	x	2x	3x	4x	5x
y	$x \pm y$	$2x \pm y$	$3x \pm y$	$4x \pm y$	$5x \pm y$
2y	$x \pm 2y$	$2x \pm 2y$	$3x \pm 2y$	$4x \pm 2y$	$5x \pm 2y$
3y	$x \pm 3y$	$2x \pm 3y$	$3x \pm 3y$	$4x \pm 3y$	$5x \pm 3y$
4y	$x \pm 4y$	$2x \pm 4y$	$3x \pm 4y$	$4x \pm 4y$	$5x \pm 4y$
5y	$x \pm 5y$	$2x \pm 5y$	$3x \pm 5y$	$4x \pm 5y$	$5x \pm 5y$

Table 4.2. Singly balanced mixer

	x	2x	3x	4x	5x
y	$x \pm y$	$2x \pm y$	$3x \pm y$	$4x \pm y$	$5x \pm y$
2y	*	*	*	*	*
3y	$x \pm 3y$	$2x \pm 3y$	$3x \pm 3y$	$4x \pm 3y$	$5x \pm 3y$
4y	*	*	*	*	*
5y	$x \pm 5y$	$2x \pm 5y$	$3x \pm 5y$	$4x \pm 5y$	$5x \pm 5y$

* This product is balanced out – see text.

Table 4.3. Doubly balanced mixer

	x	2x	3x	4x	5x
y	$x \pm y$	*	$3x \pm y$	*	$5x \pm y$
2y	*	*	*	*	*
3y	$x \pm 3y$	*	$3x \pm 3y$	*	$5x \pm 3y$
4y	*	*	*	*	*
5y	$x \pm 5y$	*	$3x \pm 5y$	*	$5x \pm 5y$

* This product is balanced out – see text.

and *y* are balanced out. This is relatively speaking – it is normal for the * terms to be 20 to 30dB below the other frequencies.

Note that harmonics up to five have been considered. Higher ones are possible but normally the fifth and higher ones are so small as to be negligible.

Other spurious responses in receivers

These can be classified into internal and external spurii. The former shows up with 'signals' appearing at various places in the tuning range(s) when there is no antenna attached to the receiver, ie no signal input. They arise from improper screening inside the receiver, allowing frequencies and their harmonics from intermediate stages to get to the input. For example, these could be harmonics of the beat frequency oscillator (BFO) or, in the case of double-superhet receivers, harmonics of the second oscillator. External spurii arise from *images* (the IF can be generated by subtracting the signal frequency from the local oscillator frequency, ie the frequency is as far above that of the local oscillator as the wanted one is below).

Gain compression

The output of, say, the RF amplifier (the 'front end' of a receiver) should be *x* times the input where *x* is the stage gain. This is always true up to a point but the stage can only give a certain output before it *saturates,* ie further increases of input cause no further change in the output. With most input devices, transistors or valves, this will be of the order of millivolts. Where inputs are made large, the graph of output versus input curves over (see Fig 4.2). Where there is 1dB difference between the actual line and the extrapolated (extended, dotted in the figure) line, this is called the *1dB compression point* and is often quoted in equipment reviews.

Blocking

One consequence of gain compression is *blocking* the receiver, ie reducing the output of the wanted signal to zero by the presence of a very strong signal close by in frequency. This will happen in all receivers to some extent. The better the receiver, the larger and closer can be the unwanted signal before it causes trouble.

Dynamic range

This depends on noise generated within the receiver which determines the *minimum discernible signal* (MDS). This is arbitrarily defined as 3dB above the noise level, ie twice as strong as the noise. The noise level referred to the input, ie that noise level at the input which would give the same noise output with a noiseless amplifier, is called the *noise floor*. The difference between this and the 1dB compression point is called the *dynamic range* and is often quoted in equipment reviews. It defines the maximum range of signal strengths that may be present at the input which do not cause unwanted responses.

There are, in fact, two dynamic ranges to consider:

1. that in which the limit is set by the onset of intermodulation;
2. that which is set by the effect of phase noise (see above).

The intermodulation-limited dynamic range, IMD, is also known as the *spurious-free dynamic range* (SFDR) and is given by:

$$SFDR = 2/3(I_3 - NF)$$

where I_3 is the *third-order intercept point* (see Fig 4.2) and NF is the noise floor in decibels referred to the input, ie that noise level which, at the input, would give the same output with a noiseless receiver.

RECEIVER BUILDING BLOCKS

This section describes the various sections of a receiver with a few details at the end on transceivers and transverters.

Before discussing actual circuits, it is worthwhile to look at basic components and their behaviour at these frequencies. All have associated with them a 'parasitic' component or components and these modify their behaviour from that at LF or HF. For example, the leads of a capacitor have inductance, and inductors have capacitance and resistance associated with them. A simple resistor will have inductance (due to the leads) and capacitance (due to the proximity of the ends). To quantify this, the inductance of a straight piece of round wire is given by:

$$L \text{ (nH)} = 0.461 \times b \times (\log_{10} 4b/a - 0.326)$$

where *b* is the length in millimetres and *a* is the diameter in millimetres. 'nH' is nanohenrys, ie 10^{-9} henrys. This implies that the larger the surface area, the smaller the inductance for a given length, hence the use of foil for UHF connections to reduce parasitic inductance.

Minimising the effects of these is done by designing the layout with the shortest possible leads and making those of foil rather than wire.

Individual components

The use of 'chip', ceramic dielectric, capacitors (with no leads) which either fit into a slot in the PC board or are soldered

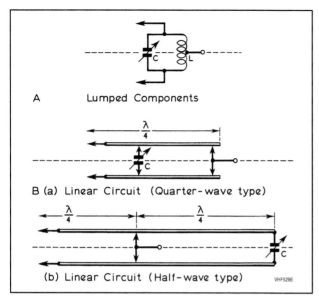

Fig 4.3. Three examples of tuned circuits

directly to its surface, gives the lowest possible inductance. Beware, however, of some multilayer surface-mounting capacitors which have internal inductance and sometimes a large loss. High-value components, eg above about 50pF, may have a large negative temperature coefficient.

Tuned circuits

As frequencies get higher, the conventional LC tuned circuit becomes smaller and smaller. It may be replaced, especially at the higher frequencies, by resonant lines or cavities as shown.

Fig 4.3 shows the conventional 'lumped' LC circuit (so called because the parts are 'lumps' of capacitance and inductance) and its equivalents in resonant quarter-wave and half-wave lines. Fig 4.4 shows the progression from a lumped circuit to a cavity resonator. The latter is normally used at 432MHz and above. The tuned line can be symmetrical, eg for a push-pull circuit, or an asymmetrical one such as a coaxial line. The latter is used in single-ended circuits both for

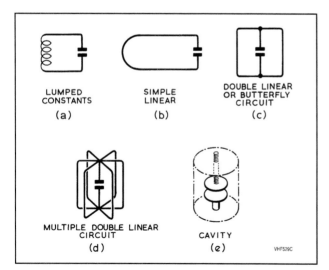

Fig 4.4. The development of the cavity from the original lumped-constant circuit

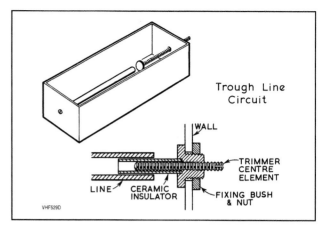

Fig 4.5. Trough-line circuits. The tuning capacitor may be either in line with the inner conductor (resonant line) or attached to the side wall of the trough. Another convenient method is to use a tube for the line and to fit into the end of it a ceramic trimmer centre element. In this case the outer element can be removed or connected to the line as required

transmitting and for receiving as a *trough-line* (Fig 4.5). Tuning for all types may be by conventional variable capacitors, by discs mounted on threaded rods (studding) or by *flappers* which are metal plates mounted with one end hinged by a flexible section and moved to or from the tuned line by means of an insulated cam or other insulated system. Occasionally, two plates may form a tuning capacitor and its capacitance is varied by moving a dielectric in or out of the gap between the plates.

If discs are used, the capacitance varies in a very non-linear manner with the distance between them. It is:

$$C\,(\text{pF}) = \frac{0.00885 \times \text{Area (sq mm)}}{\text{Spacing (mm)}}$$

DESIGNING RESONANT LINES

If this is for one frequency (eg for the output of a fixed-frequency oscillator), they can be cut to a quarter or half a wavelength and trimmed carefully to resonance. Otherwise, they should be cut shorter and have a tuning or loading capacitor which can be calculated from:

$$\frac{1}{2\pi fC} = \frac{Z_0 \tan 2\pi L}{\lambda}$$

where f is the frequency, C is the tuning capacitance, λ is the wavelength, L is the length and Z_0 is the characteristic impedance, calculated as follows. For a coaxial line:

$$Z_0 = 138 \log_{10}\!\left(\frac{D}{d}\right)$$

where D is the inside diameter of the outer tube and d is the outside diameter of the inner tube or wire. For parallel lines:

$$Z_0 = 276 \log_{10}\!\left(\frac{2D}{d}\right)$$

where D is the interline spacing and d is the line diameter. See Figs 4.6–4.9.

Fig 4.10 gives a series of graphs for coaxial and parallel lines where $f \times L$ (in megahertz and centimetres) is plotted against $f \times C$ (in megahertz and picofarads) for a number of different values of r or D/d.

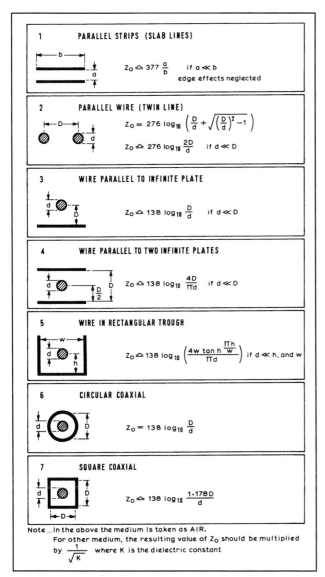

Fig 4.6. Various forms of transmission line

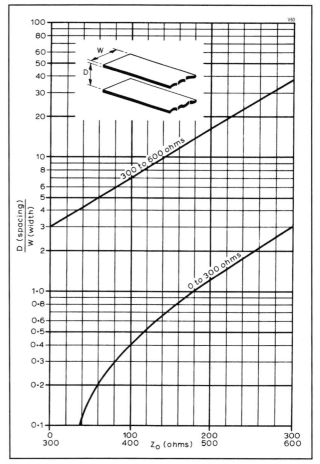

Fig 4.7. Characteristic impedance of balanced strip transmission line

Coupling to tuned circuits

Coupling is used to take energy out of a circuit or to put it in. The nature of the coupling depends on the impedance of the input or output.

With a lumped circuit, the coupling may be by means of another coil close to the tuned circuit or by means of a tapping on it. Fig 4.11A shows this. The lower the impedance of the coupling, the smaller is the coupling coil or the closer is the tapping to the 'earthy' end of the tuned circuit.

Fig 4.11B shows various ways of coupling to tuned lines and Fig 4.12 to trough lines, coaxial resonators or cavities.

Helical resonators

These form high-Q circuits and are roughly equivalent to quarter-wave coaxial lines compressed. Fig 4.13 shows the basic idea. They are used at VHF and UHF and can be tuned by a variable capacitor between the case and the upper end. They can also be cascaded by making slots in the side of the cases and bonding them together so that the resonators can 'see' one another.

The unloaded Q is $50Df^{1/2}$, where D is the internal diameter of the case and f is the frequency. If the case is of square section, this must be multiplied by a correction factor of 1.2.

Fig 4.14 shows a two-component filter using helical resonators. To design one, the following formulae are used:

$$\text{Pitch } (p \text{ in Fig 4.13}) = \frac{D^2 f}{90.6}$$

where p and D are in millimetres.

$$\text{Characteristic impedance} Z_0 = \frac{386}{fD}$$

These assume that $d/D = 0.55$ and $L/D = 1.5$.

Alternatively, the nomogram (Fig 4.16) will give an accurate enough answer for all practical purposes. Note that the dimensions are given in *inches*.

In order to maintain a high Q, it is desirable to plate the inside of the cavity and the outside of the wire with silver.

Microstrip circuits

At frequencies above 300MHz, microstrip circuits, which are formed directly on one side of double-sided printed circuit board, are useful. Figs 4.17 and 4.18 show quarter-wave and half-wave microstrip lines with the position of the tuning capacitor. It is essential that the other side or *ground plane* is bonded to the 'earthy' parts of the tuned circuit.

The dielectric should be as thin and of as low loss as

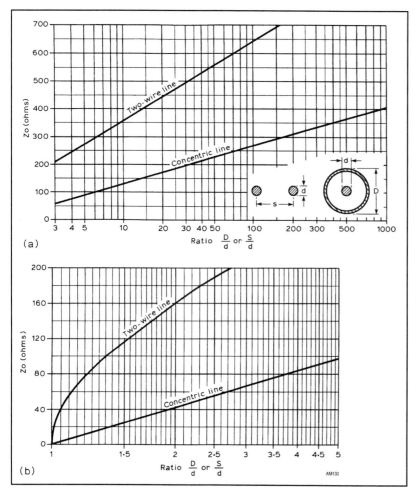

(a)

(b)

Fig 4.8. Chart giving characteristic impedances of concentric (coaxial) and two-wire lines in terms of their dimensional ratios, assuming air insulation. When the space around the wires is filled with insulation, the impedance given by the chart must be divided by the square root of its dielectric constant (permittivity). This ratio is called the *velocity factor* because the wave velocity is reduced in the same proportion

possible. PTFE (Teflon™ or Fluon™) is ideal but expensive. Glassfibre (epoxy resin reinforced with E-glass) is the next best material. The length is calculated in the same way as for a coaxial or trough line with modifications to take into account the different shape and the fact that the velocity of radio waves is lower where there is a dielectric other than air, just as the capacitance between two plates is greater when there is a solid dielectric present. The latter is greater by the dielectric constant which is about 2.1 for PTFE and about 5 for glassfibre-reinforced epoxy resin.

The exact value, which depends on precisely which epoxy is used, can be found by measuring the capacitance of a known area of double-sided material:

$$e = 113 \times C \times t/A$$

where e is the dielectric constant, t is the thickness in millimetres, A is the area in square millimetres and C is the capacitance in picofarads.

The width of the element depends on the design impedance Z and is given by:

$$\log_{10} W = 0.874 + \log_{10} t - 0.005 \times Z \times \sqrt{e} + 1.14$$

where t is the thickness in millimetres, e is the dielectric constant and W is the width in millimetres.

Having found this, the length is calculated from:

$$l = l_0 \times V_f$$

where l is the element length, l_0 is the length

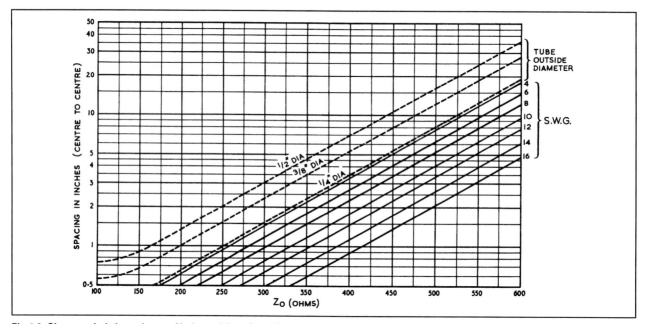

Fig 4.9. Characteristic impedance of balanced lines for different wire and tube sizes and spacings, for the range 200–600Ω. The curves for tubes are extended down to 100Ω to cover the design of Q-bar transformers. Air spacing is assumed

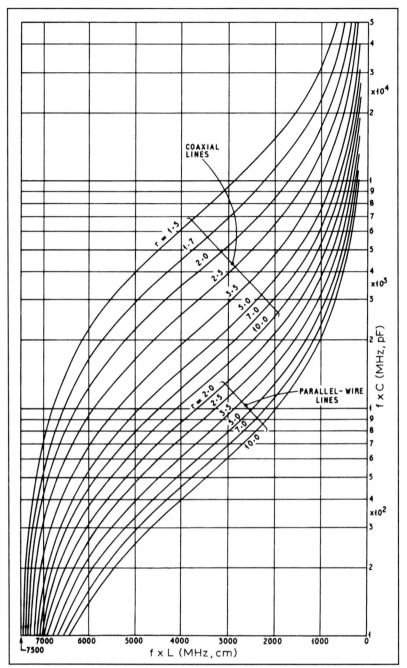

Fig 4.10. Resonance curves for capacitively loaded transmission-line resonators

(eg that of a half wavelength) in free space and V_f is the velocity factor which is related to the dielectric constant by:

$$V_f = \frac{1}{\sqrt{0.475 \times (e + 0.67)}}$$

Active components – handling precautions

Many active devices are sensitive to static discharge and precautions must be taken when handling them. FETs, both silicon MOSFETs and GaAsFETs, are especially sensitive and should be handled with extreme care. If particular, avoid wearing synthetic fibre clothing, walking on synthetic fibre carpets or wearing synthetic soled shoes. In winter, when the relative humidity is low, a static charge of up to 30kV (yes,

30,000V!) can build up on you just by walking across a room. 10–25V can destroy a MOSFET or a GaAsFET.

Other active devices are less sensitive but should still be treated with care. Device holders should not be used at VHF or UHF because they add to lead inductance and, at least, they can cause mismatching or, at worst, instability.

RECEIVER CIRCUITS

This section presents circuits for each section of the receiver. They may be combined to form a complete receiver or converter or, with the later section on transmitters, to form a complete transceiver or transverter. Designs for individual frequency bands follow the general introduction.

As mentioned above, these are always superhets and they may have more than one frequency conversion. Fig 4.19(a) shows a block diagram for a single-conversion superhet while Fig 4.19(b) shows the variation for a double-conversion superhet and Fig 4.19(c) for a double conversion superhet where the second local oscillator is the variable one, the so-called *tuneable IF* system. These are diagrams of multi-mode receivers. For dedicated single-mode receivers, FM or SSB/Morse, the switches S1 and S2 are omitted.

The distribution of gain between the RF, IF and audio stages is very important from the standpoint of strong-signal performance. Briefly, the gain between the antenna and the first sharp (IF) filter should be the minimum needed to overcome the noise created by the mixer(s).

In a single superhet (Fig 4.19(a)), this means an RF gain of about 20dB followed by a mixer loss of 6dB, giving an overall gain before the sharp filter of about 14dB. Methods for calculating exact values are given by G3SEK [1, 2]. Note, too, that a sharp crystal filter can behave in a non-linear manner if presented with a strong signal just out-of-band. In double superhets, there may be a need for gain between the two mixers before any sharp filter. In this case an amplifier with a very good strong-signal performance must be used.

There is a natural noise input from the antenna and all stages thereafter generate some noise. Mixers generate more noise than straight amplifiers so an RF amplifier must have sufficient gain to overcome the noise of the first mixer without contributing significant noise itself. It must also have a good large-signal handling capacity. This means good linearity.

Input circuits

A band-pass or low-pass filter is often placed between the antenna and the RF amplifier. In transceivers, this may be common to both receive and transmit circuits – in this case, a

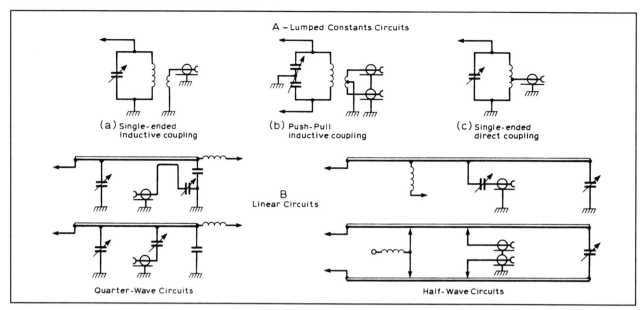

Fig 4.11. Methods of coupling to lumped constant and linear circuits

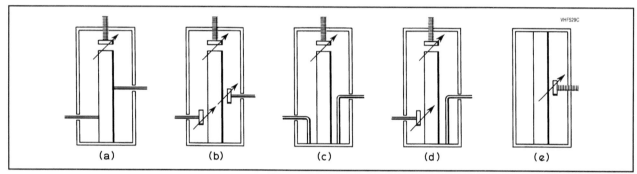

Fig 4.12. Methods of coupling to a trough cavity

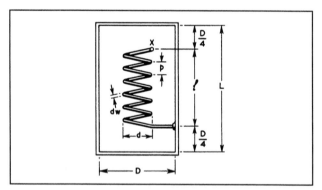

Fig 4.13. A helical resonator which can be used at VHF and UHF

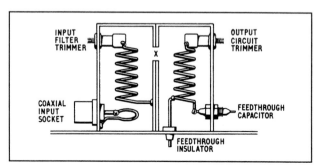

Fig 4.14. A typical arrangement of helical resonators

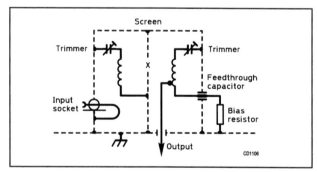

Fig 4.15. The equivalent circuit. This arrangement shows two tuned circuits as the input filter and input circuit to a grounded-gate amplifier. Coupling between the filter and input circuits is provided by an aperture in the screen (X). Alternatively, a normal coupling method can be used, such as a link, taps or probe. Note: when no bias is required, the feedthrough capacitor is omitted and the end of the helix is taken straight to earth

low-pass filter must be used. The alternative of a high-Q tuned circuit with a panel mounted 'antenna trimmer' (input circuit tuning control) is possible but not often used.

Fig 4.20 [8] shows a typical low-pass filter for 50MHz which has a cut-off (3dB down) frequency of 62MHz and an insertion loss of 0.2dB. Fig 4.21 [8] shows a typical band-pass filter, also for 50MHz, which has a pass-band of 3MHz centred on 51MHz.

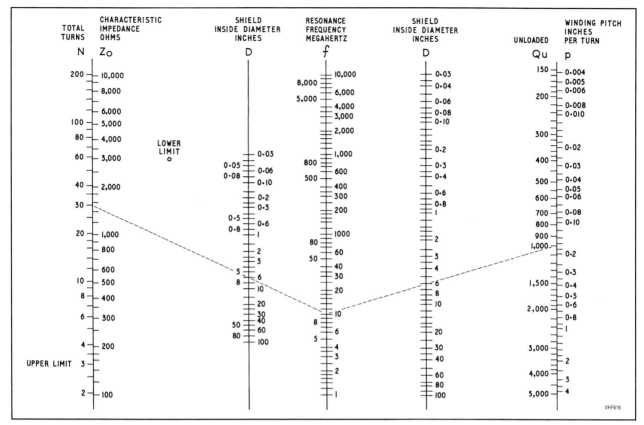

Fig 4.16. Design chart for λ/4 helical resonators. Lines indicate example

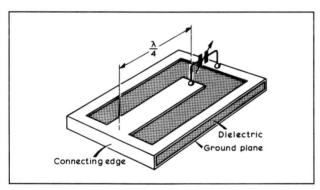

Fig 4.17. General arrangement of a λ/4 microstripline circuit

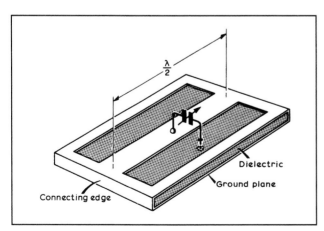

Fig 4.18. General arrangement of a λ/2 microstripline circuit

RF amplifiers

All modern RF stages are solid state. The best performance in terms of noise and linearity is from FETs, especially power devices such as the MGF1801 which can have a 3IP (third-order intercept point) of greater than +10dB. The snag is that they take a considerable drain current (about 60mA!) and are thus less suitable than ordinary MOSFETs for portable receivers. They are also expensive. A typical circuit of a slightly lower-grade design for a 50MHz RF amplifier using a BF981 is shown in Fig 4.22 [9]. C1, C2 and L1 form the input pi-circuit to match the antenna to gate 1 of the BF981 (C1 is the 45pF trimmer and the 33pF fixed capacitor in parallel). L2, L3 and C3 with their tuning capacitors form a band-pass output filter.

RF filters

These are placed between the RF amplifier and the mixer. Their purpose is to further reduce the level of out-of-band signals. They can have a higher insertion loss than the input filter since that can be compensated for by the gain of the RF stage.

At 50 and 70MHz, they are usually conventional coupled tuned circuits of the type shown in Fig 4.23. The coupling capacitor, C3, is chosen [6] to give a flat response over the band. It will be very small, of the order of 2pF. The position of the tappings on the coils will depend on the output and input impedances.

At 144, 430 and 1300MHz, helical filters (see above) come into their own. They generally have an insertion loss of 2–4dB and an input and output impedance of 50Ω.

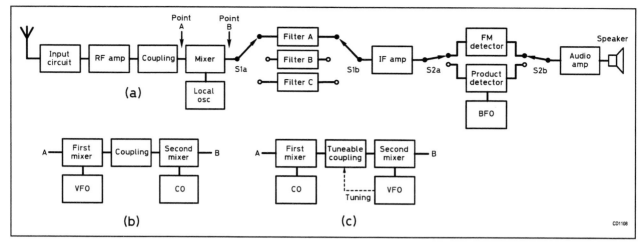

Fig 4.19. Block diagram of a multimode receiver

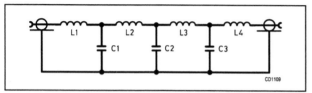

Fig 4.20. 50MHz low-pass filter with cut-off at 62MHz. L1, L4: 90nH, 5t 0.8mm wire close wound 4.8mm dia. L2, L3: 0.22μH, 10t 0.8mm wire close wound 4.8mm dia. C1, C3: 82pF silver mica. C2: 100pF silver mica *(QEX)*

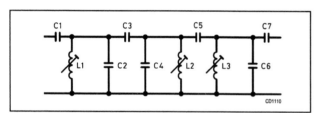

Fig 4.21. L1, L3: 293nH nominal; L2: 284nH nominal. All TOKO type MC130 (0.3μH adjustable). C1, C2, C6, C7: 15pF. C3, C5: 3pF. C4: 27pF. All capacitors silver mica

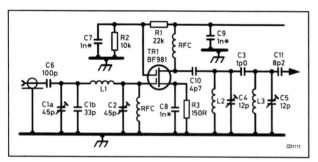

Fig 4.22. L1–L3: 0.87μH. RFC: 4.7μH. Asterisk (*) denotes ceramic chip capacitors *(VHF Communications)*

Mixers

Any non-linear device can in theory be used as a mixer. However, those commonly used are diodes, FETs and MOSFETs, ICs and occasionally bipolar transistors.

Diode ring mixers, which are doubly balanced (see above) are widely used because they contribute less noise than other types and have a better large-signal handling capacity.

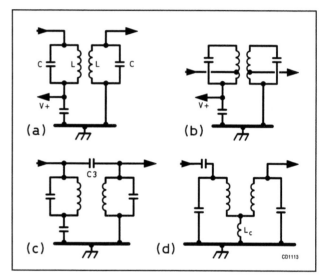

Fig 4.23. Coupled (band-pass) tuned circuits between stages

However, they do need a large oscillator injection and accurate matching at all ports. Also, the best ones are expensive. They have a conversion loss of between 6 and 10dB depending on type. They need a local oscillator input of 7 to 20dBm (decibels relative to 1mW, ie 0.5–2.5V into 50Ω). They can also be used in transceivers as mixers in the transmit chain.

A typical circuit for a 50 to 28MHz converter [9] using the Minicircuits TAK 11 is shown in Fig 4.24. The local oscillator level is +17.5dBm which corresponds to 1.7V into a 50Ω load. A similar circuit can be used at 144 and 430MHz.

Other forms of mixer are used. For example, in simple equipment, the dual-gate MOSFET is used with the signal into gate 1 and the local oscillator into gate 2. JFETs can also be used in a balanced circuit with excellent results.

There are ICs which work at these frequencies. One such is the NE600 which is the UHF version of the NE602, well known at HF. It has the advantage of being relatively cheap and of having a large dynamic range. It is noisy, having a noise figure of about 12dB at 1.3GHz, but this is overcome by a suitable RF amplifier. Also, it is only rated by its makers to 1.2GHz.

Finally, particularly at 1.3GHz, there are single diode

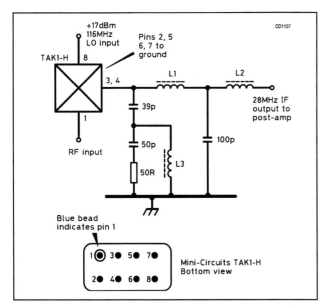

Fig 4.24. A 144MHz receive mixer and diplexer filter using a Mini-Circuits TAK-1H high-level mixer. The filter provides a 50Ω broadband resistive match for improved third-order distortion characteristics. L1: 0.35µH, 5t 24 AWG enam on T50-6 toroid. L2: 0.21µH, 4t 24 AWG enam on T50-6 toroid. L3: 0.18µH, 4t 24 AWG on T37-6 toroid

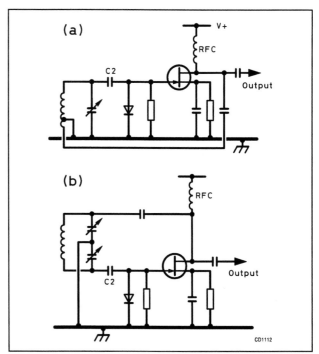

Fig 4.26. (a) Hartley and (b) Colpitts oscillators

mixers with either microstrip or solid 'interdigital' tuned circuits. One of the latter is shown in Fig 4.25 where the input is fed to the first resonator ('digit') followed by a tuned resonator and the diode mixer. The local oscillator is supplied at a quarter of the required frequency and harmonics generated by another diode. The correct harmonic is selected by a tuned resonator which is coupled to the mixer diode.

Local oscillators [4]

All oscillators except DDS [10] (see below) consist of a tuned circuit to set the frequency and a 'gain block' to make it oscillate. They start by small noise pulses being amplified and modified by the tuned circuit and increase until limiting in

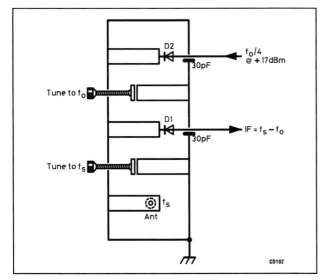

Fig 4.25. Single-diode mixer for 1296MHz. An interdigital filter provides isolation between ports. D1 (HP5082-2817) is the mixer and D2 (HP5082-2853) is the last multiplier in the LO chain *(QST)*

one form or another occurs. Some oscillators have a negative feedback system to limit the oscillations to sine waves [11]. This may not be a good thing as some mixers, especially diode rings, need hard switching by a square-wave drive, The gain is provided by a bipolar transistor, a JFET, a MOSFET or an IC. Best performance regarding noise is obtained from a JFET.

The two most important characteristics of a local oscillator are *stability* and *low noise*. In the case of single-conversion superhets, the oscillator must be tuneable over the width of the band for which reception is needed. This is 2MHz for 50 and 144MHz, only 0.5MHz for 70MHz, 10MHz for 430MHz and 85MHz for 1.3GHz. The latter bands would normally either be partially covered or would be covered in segments.

All oscillators drift in frequency and this is minimised by mechanical, electrical and temperature stability.

Frequency drift is of two kinds, short-term drift which, if very short term, is called *scintillation* or *jitter*, and is caused by mechanical instability, and long-term drift which is caused by thermal effects. This assumes that the power supply is stable. Thermal effects can be minimised by suitable choice of components in the tuned circuit and by operating the oscillator at the smallest power level possible.

Variable oscillators (VFOs)

There are four types of variable oscillator:

1. The *straight analogue oscillator* typified by the Colpitts, Hartley, Clapp, Vackar and Franklin (Figs 4.26–4.29) often followed by a frequency multiplier to get to the correct frequency. The various types differ only in the nature of the feedback circuits, eg the Hartley and Colpitts (Fig 4.26) use inductive and capacitive devices to provide the necessary phase shift. The source-follower Hartley and Colpitts (Fig 4.27) do not need the phase shift and a variant of the

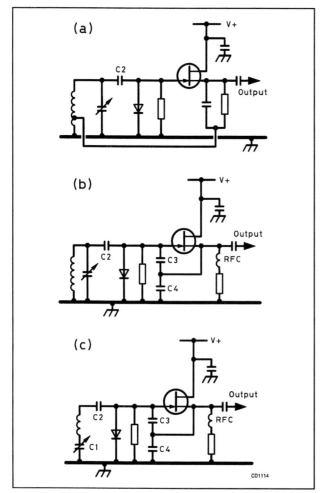

Fig 4.27. Source-coupled oscillators: (a) Hartley, (b) Colpitts and (c) Clapp

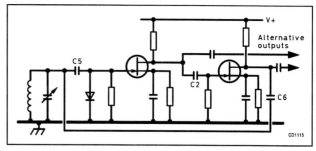

Fig 4.29. The Franklin oscillator

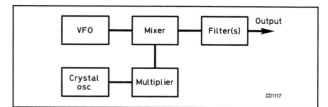

Fig 4.30. Block diagram of simple mixer-oscillator

latter, the Clapp, uses a 'series tuned' circuit but this is directly equivalent to a parallel-tuned oscillator with C1, C2, C3 and C4 in series. Since C3 and C4 can be large without affecting the oscillation, they effectively swamp the interelectrode capacitance of the active device. The

presence of the diode does not seem to be essential. A variant of the Colpitts is the Vackar (Fig 4.28) where the large drain-to-earth capacitance also swamps interelectrode capacitances.

Decoupled source resistors (for bias) are not always needed but if used should be 150–1000Ω – the larger, the better from a stability view so long as oscillations start easily and are of sufficient amplitude. Gate resistors should be 10kΩ–100kΩ, gate capacitors (C2) should be 47–100pF and the source follower capacitors (C3 and C4) should be 200–470pF with C4 being larger but still allowing easy starting and enough output.

There are some advantages to a two-stage oscillator such as the Franklin (Fig 4.29) because the two stages provide the necessary phase shift and the gain is so high that the coupling capacitors, C5 and C6, can be very small, so reducing the effect of the active device on the tuned circuit. Also, the output can be taken from the 'mid-point' of the amplifier. C5 and C6 should be of the order of 1–2pF and are determined by making them as small as possible while still getting easy starting. The Franklin has another advantage, that of needing only one switch wafer if band changing is necessary.

Every VFO should be followed by a low-gain buffer amplifier to avoid subsequent stages affecting the frequency (*pulling*).

2. The *mixer oscillator* where the variable oscillator is mixed with a fixed frequency (a crystal oscillator – see below) to give the desired frequency. Fig 4.30 shows a block diagram of a simple mixer-oscillator where the VFO and a crystal oscillator (CO) with or without a multiplier are fed to a mixer. At this level, a double-balanced IC mixer such

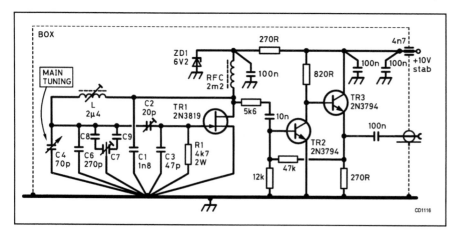

Fig 4.28. The high-stability FET Vackar oscillator developed by G3PDM to cover 5.88 to 6.93MHz for the Mk2 version of his *Radio Communication Handbook* (5th edn) receiver. C6 is silver mica. The replacements for the obsolete Tempatrimmer featured in the original design are: C7 (100pF + 100pF differential), C8 (100pF negative temperature coefficient) and C9 (100pF positive temperature coefficient)

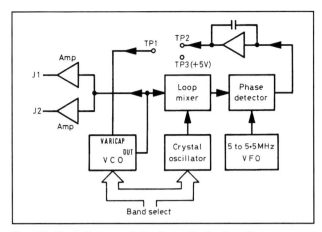

Fig 4.31. Block diagram of simple synthesised oscillator

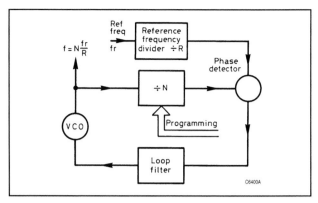

Fig 4.33. Basic PLL synthesiser

as the MC1496 is suitable. Its output must go through a suitable filter, normally a band-pass filter. This design is useful for transceivers because the CO can be changed to give the transmit frequency, leaving the VFO running continuously. This leads to low drift. In this case, a low-pass filter should be followed by a high-pass filter to include both frequencies.

3. The *synthesised oscillator* using digital systems and a phase-locked loop (PLL) comparing an adjustable fraction of the oscillator frequency with another frequency derived from a stable, crystal, oscillator. It uses a voltage corresponding to the difference in phase to keep the variable oscillator constant – a negative feedback system. Most designs for PLLs have most of the components within one IC. The IC manufacturers supply data on the operation of the IC and the realisation of the PLL circuit.

A simple synthesised oscillator has been described [12] for a HF receiver and can easily be adapted for VHF or UHF use by making it for one band only and either multiplying or by mixing with a suitable fixed frequency to get to the wanted frequency. Fig 4.31 shows a block diagram.

There is a halfway house between straight or free-running oscillators and the fully fledged synthesiser. This is called the *Huff and Puff* and was invented by PA0KSB. Its most recent development [13] is shown in the block diagram, Fig 4.32. The crystal oscillator has an overtone mode 50MHz crystal and the 5–5.5MHz VFO frequency is divided by M, say 50,000, to give an output of around 100Hz which is applied to the clock input of a high-speed D-type flip-flop (labelled 'digital mixer') so that the maximum frequency output is about 50Hz. If N is the ratio of the

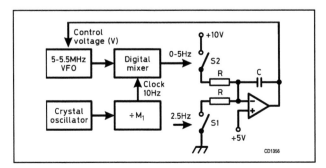

Fig 4.32. 'Huff and puff' oscillator block diagram (QEX)

crystal oscillator to the output (100Hz) of the divider, in this case $N = 500,000$, then the system will be stable and:

$$F_{VFO}/M = F_{xtal}/N$$

which rearranges to:

$$F_{VFO} = F_{xtal} \times M/N$$

With the above values of M and N and the crystal oscillator, the VFO frequency will be 5,000,000Hz (5MHz). The next stable point will be where N goes to $N + 1$ which results in a VFO frequency of 4.999990MHz, ie 10Hz lower, and so on. The steps are 10Hz only with these parameters and are perfectly suitable for reception of Morse or SSB.

On manual tuning the frequency 'creeps' to the nearest lock point and stays there. Bear in mind it is only as stable as the crystal oscillator which should be the best possible.

4. *Direct digital synthesis* (DDS) [10] where a digital signal several times higher in frequency than the desired frequency is applied to a digital device (a high-speed ROM – read only memory) which synthesises an approximate sine wave from which a pure sine wave is extracted using a low-pass filter.

All have their advantages and disadvantages:

1. Straight oscillators are generally unsatisfactory on stability grounds although, with great care, they could be used for a 50MHz receiver. They do have the lowest noise, ie the smallest noise side-bands.

2. Mixer oscillators also have a low noise and their stability is better than straight analogue oscillators because a small drift in frequency applies directly to the output while in the latter it is multiplied by whatever the original frequency was multiplied. Care must be taken with the two frequencies, the variable and the fixed, to ensure that harmonics and other mixer products don't fall within the receiver band and cause interference (*birdies*).

3. There are several forms of synthesiser. The basic PLL (Figs 4.33 and 4.34) uses a programmable divider for the voltage-controlled oscillator (VCO), the output of which is fed to a phase detector and compared with the fixed frequency divided down from a crystal oscillator. The output of the phase detector is a direct voltage proportional to the phase difference and is fed back to the VCO to counteract the drift. PLL synthesisers tend to have a higher phase noise than other types. The 'Huff and Puff' has a lower phase

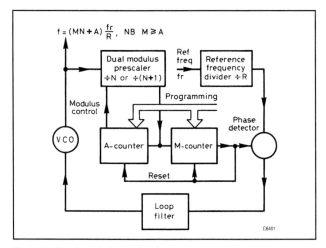

Fig 4.34. Dual modulus prescaler

noise than a regular PLL synthesiser but does not have a direct digital frequency readout and its frequency moves in steps.

4. DDS systems (Figs 4.35 and 4.36) need pulses generated at a very high frequency, at least three times the maximum frequency needed at the output, and consequently need very-high-frequency devices.

Both PLL and DDS methods depend on fast pulses which, in turn, generate many harmonics of the pulse repetition frequency (PRF). If not kept well screened, these can cause interference.

Fixed-frequency oscillators

These usually use quartz crystals as the frequency determining element, equivalent to the tuned circuit in the VFO. The crystal has a very large Q (values of 50,000–1,000,000 are possible) and produces a very stable frequency. Quartz is cut in different angles for this purpose and these cuts have slightly different properties, in particular, their temperature coefficient [14]. For frequencies between 5 and 20MHz, the usual cut is 'AT' with a temperature coefficient of ±50ppm (parts per million) between −10 and +60°C.

At higher frequencies, *overtone* crystals are used which vibrate at a mechanical multiple of the fundamental frequency (rather as a violin string can be made to vibrate at its third or fifth harmonic) which is not an exact multiple of its fundamental frequency although they are very close. For example, a 8.2013MHz crystal had a third overtone of 24.5773MHz while three times the fundamental is 24.6039MHz, a difference of 26.6kHz. All overtones are odd numbers and up to the seventh are available. Overtone crystals should be bought as such since they are finished in a different manner from fundamental crystals. See Fig 4.37 for a typical circuit.

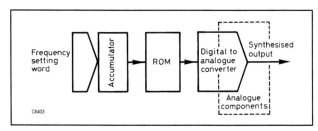

Fig 4.35. DDS concept

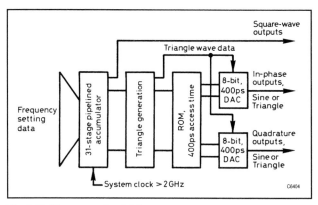

Fig 4.36. More complex DDS

Crystal oscillators may be varied in frequency a little by adding an inductor and a capacitor to the circuit (see Fig 4.38(a)). This is the so-called *VXO* (variable crystal oscillator). Only a small deviation from the basic frequency is possible. Fig 4.38(b) shows a varicap-controlled VXO which can be used to cover upper and lower sidebands in a SSB receiver with one crystal.

Frequency measurement

Since the frequency to which the receiver is tuned is related to the oscillator frequency ($f_{rec} = f_{osc} \pm$ IF for a single conversion superhet), measurement of the oscillator frequency with an offset of the IF gives the frequency to which the receiver is tuned. Digital frequency meters also depend on fast pulses and should be well screened from the rest of the receiver circuitry.

Intermediate frequency

Choice

IFs are chosen with three considerations in mind:

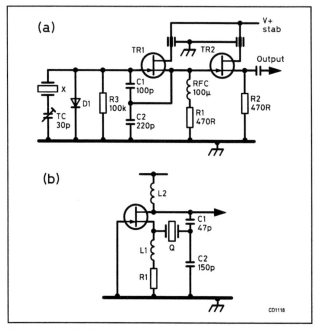

Fig 4.37. (a) Fundamental-mode crystal oscillator. The values shown are for a 10MHz crystal X. (b) Overtone-mode crystal oscillator. L1: 1.0µH. L2: 0.3µH. Q: 36MHz

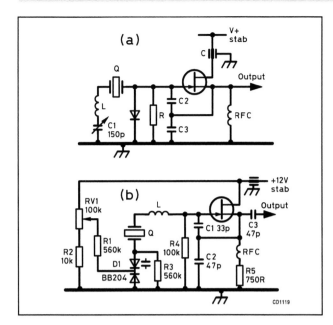

Fig 4.38. (a) L-C VXO. Values are for 10MHz crystal. (b) Varicap VXO with range 10.6990 to 10.7013MHz. L: 7µH. Q: 10.7MHz

1. Recognising the possibility of second-channel or image response. This means that the IF should be 7–10% of the operating frequency to make sure that the image is fully attenuated by the input circuits.
2. At the chosen IF there should be available relatively cheap crystal filters. This means that 10.7, 21.4 and 45MHz are preferred frequencies.
3. If dual conversion is used, the second local oscillator should not have harmonics within the band in use. For example, a 10.7MHz first IF and a 455kHz second IF needs a local oscillator at 11.155 or 10.245MHz. The former has a harmonic at 145.015MHz so the latter would be chosen for a 145MHz receiver.

If gain is needed between the first and second mixers in a double superhet, a highly linear amplifier with a large dynamic range must be used. A good example of this is a design by G3SBI [15] shown in Fig 4.39 with details of its performance in Table 4.4.

Table 4.4. Performance of 9MHz AGC-controlled amplifier		
Noise figure (dB)	0.6	0.6
Input impedance (Ω)	50	50
Output impedance (Ω)	50	50
Third-order intercept (dBm)		
Vs = +12V (max gain)	23	26
Vs = +20V (max gain)	28	30
Input for 1dB compression (dBm)		
Vs = +12V (max gain)	0	+3
(max AGC)	+7	+11
Vs = +20V (max gain)	+5	+8
(max AGC)	+11	+14

Amplifier input and output impedances are 50Ω regardless of AGC-controlled gain. Gain range is 45dB.

Selectivity

This is provided at the 'front end' of the IF strip by crystal filters. The bandwidth of these depends on the mode to be used. For Morse, a bandwidth of 500Hz is normal, while 2.5–3kHz is used for SSB. FM requires about 7.5kHz for the present system of 5kHz maximum deviation and 25kHz between channels. When this is changed to 12.5kHz between channels, a lower maximum deviation will be used and the bandwidth will be narrowed. It is of the utmost importance that the filters are correctly terminated. The manufacturer will give details of the proper resistance and capacitance for this. It should be noted that sharp filters are subject to overloading and this can cause non-linearity.

Further down the IF amplifier chain, so-called *roofing filters* are used to prevent noise generated by the early IF amplifiers and outside the pass-band from reaching the detector. These can be simple ceramic resonators or further crystal filters.

A wide-band IF chain with 100kHz (or so) bandwidth may be used to amplify sharp noise pulses which can then be used for noise blanking by cutting off the input to the main chain be means of a semiconductor switch.

Gain

Gain can be provided by any suitable devices – bipolar transistors, FETs or ICs. At present, ICs seem the most used and many combine 'gain blocks' with various types of detector to produce an audio output. The overall gain needed is about 100dB and this should be controllable by an automatic gain control for Morse and SSB reception. FM reception requires that the last IF amplifier saturates and limits the signal, so removing noise 'spikes'. This feature is built into ICs that are specific to FM – they also have a *squelch* facility which shuts off the audio amplifier in the absence of a signal to prevent noise getting through to the audio stages.

Demodulators or detectors

SSB/morse code

Here a product detector is the norm and it produces an output which is the

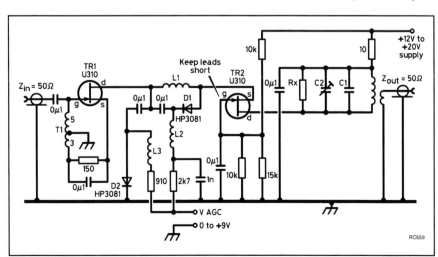

Fig 4.39. G3SBI's low-noise, AGC-controlled cascode IF amplifier

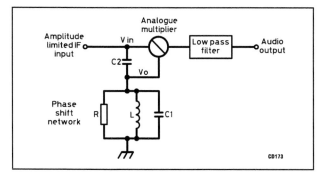

Fig 4.40(a). Block diagram of quadrature detector

product of the signal and local oscillator (or BFO, beat frequency oscillator) frequencies. This results in an audio signal, either speech from SSB or a tone from Morse code. A product detector is exactly the same as a mixer and all the mixer circuits can be used. Of course, at the lower frequency, other, simpler, product detector ICs are available such as the MC1496 which is a double-balanced mixer. At this signal level, exact balance is not important.

FM

ICs for FM demodulation are of three main types – the quadrature, the phase-locked-loop and the pulse counting. The *quadrature* or *co-incidence* detector (Fig 4.40(a)), as its name implies, splits the incoming signal into two parts, one of which

is at 90° different in phase (quadrature) from the other and feeds both into an analogue multiplier. This results in a number of output frequencies including the original audio which is recovered through a low-pass filter. In a practical circuit (Fig 4.40(b)), the MC3361 carries out a second conversion to, say, 455kHz and generates the audio from that. It also contains a limiting amplifier and a crystal oscillator.

The PLL detector is similar to a PLL frequency synthesiser except that the voltage needed to lock the oscillator to the incoming frequency is the audio signal.

In the pulse-counting demodulator, a second conversion to a low IF of 100kHz or less is made and converted into pulses. The pulse rate is measured and corresponds to the modulating frequency. An IC such as the SL6601 has a limiting amplifier, a pulse generator, a counting stage and a crystal oscillator for the frequency conversion all in one package.

A great deal of emphasis has been placed on the ability of a receiver's front end to cope with multiple strong signals. Less has been published on the IF/AGC system of the receiver, despite the fact it determines how every signal sounds. This design by Bill Carver, K6OLG [16] covers that important territory.

The IF/AGC subsystem shown in Fig 4.41 has a minimum discernible signal (MDS) level of 0.03µV in a 2.5kHz bandwidth, and its AGC can be set to have a few decibels rise in audio with a range of signal amplitudes of less than 0.1µV to over 0.2V. The input-intercept point is about 20dBm, so inband intermodulation distortion (IMD) is 40dB down even for S9 + 70dB signals. The constant-gain time interval of the 'hang' AGC circuit is smoothly and continuously varied from 100ms to 2s using a panel-mounted control. This IF/AGC system is intended for use with a front end having a net gain of +3dB and a 6dB noise figure (NF), and directly drives a +7dBm diode-mixer product detector.

AGC basics. An amplifier with feedback to control its gain can be resolved into two components: the amplifier itself and the detector and processing circuits that develop the gain-control feedback voltage.

The Analog Devices AD600 is a dual, low-noise, wide-band, variable-gain amplifier IC. The gains of the two internal 40dB amplifiers are controlled by the potential difference between the CxLO (that is, C1LO or C2LO) and CxHI (C1HI or C2HI) pins. This IC has about a 40dB gain control range with a constant-gain control scale factor of 32dB/V. CxLO voltage above or below the 0.625V difference leaves the gain at 0 or 40dB respectively. With a 2dB NF and 30MHz bandwidth, it's ideal for the gain portion of an IF system.

The logarithmic envelope detectors produce a 3V output change from an 8dB input signal change, a scale factor of 0.375V/dB. Coupled with the AD600, this produces a loop gain of 12, which means an input-signal

Fig 4.40(b). Practical circuit using the Motorola MC3361 (Motorola)

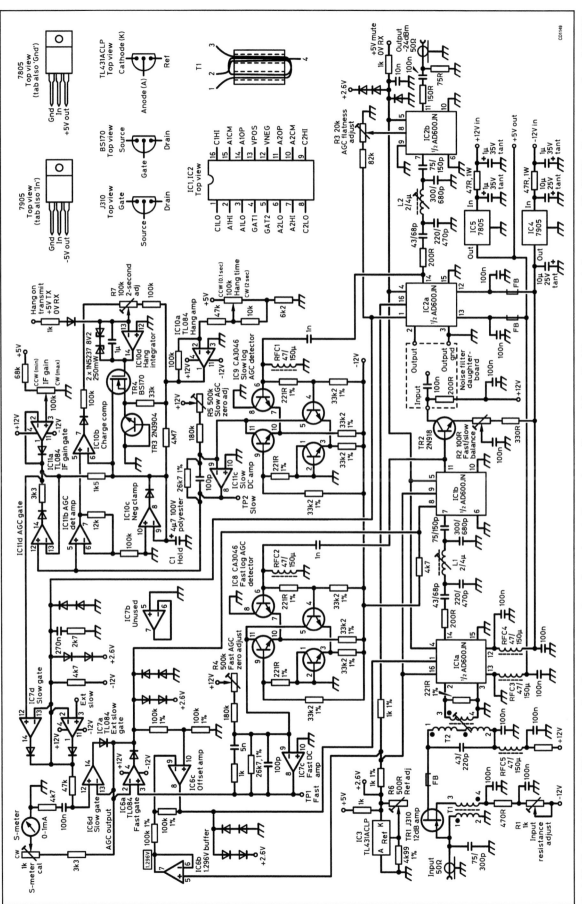

Fig 4.41. The IF/AGC circuit. Where two values for a component are shown (one before and one after an oblique line) the upper value is for use at an IF of 9MHz, the lower one for a 4.434MHz IF. IC8 and IC9 are shown uncharacteristically here so as to provide a better understanding of circuit operation. All diodes 1N4148 or equiv except as noted. FB = ferrite bead, -43 material (FB-43-101 ferrite beads can be used). L1, L2: (4.434MHz) 26t 30 AWG Amidon L45-7; (9MHz) 8t trifilar 30 AWG Amidon L43-6t. T1: (4.434 and 9MHz) constructed as shown on BN-61-202 ferrite form (do not substitute ferrite type). 1-2 = 4t 28 AWG, 3-4 = 3½t 28 AWG. T2: (4.434MHz) 15t trifilar 30 AWG on L45-7; (9MHz) 8t trifilar 30 AWG on L43-6 (QST)

change causes an output-signal change equal to the input signal change divided by 13. For example, a 65dB input signal change results in a 5dB output-signal change.

Two AGC detectors? Wide-band noise at the AGC detector would preclude using AGC for low signal levels; the amplifier's noise bandwidth must be limited. But the time delay of a filter placed between controlled stages and the AGC detector destabilises an AGC system, so AGC voltage to the gain-controlled stages ahead of the filter must be delayed. This permits brief clipping of large signals and envelope distortion at the leading edge of a signal.

This amplifier system uses two AGC detectors. The first one, called 'FAST', reduces the gain of the stages ahead of the noise filter, preventing them from clipping until the 'SLOW' detector – placed after the filter – can catch up. This prevents overloading IC1a and IC1b for signal levels above 10µV for a few milliseconds until the SLOW AGC responds. This 'minor' detail makes a big difference in how a receiver sounds even though most ears can't identify why.

Identical FAST and SLOW detectors operating at the same signal level – combined with the well-defined gain control characteristics of each AD600 – permit seamless combination of the detector outputs. TR2's gain is adjusted so both detectors have the same signal voltage when IC2a's gain is at minimum.

The JFET and first three AD600 amplifier stages. The AGC threshold occurs when a signal level of −32dBm appears at the output of IC2b. This results from an input-signal level of about −128dBm (0.09µV) when the signal-to-noise ratio is approaching 10dB. Maximum signal is reached with −20dBm at the output of IC2b, corresponding to an input-signal level of 0dBm (0.23V).

TR1 is a J310 FET with gate-source transformer feedback. Its theory of operation is covered in [17]; an almost identical implementation to this one was described by Colin Horrabin, G3SBI [15].

TR1's gain is 12dB and is set by the 2:1 transformer (T2), the load resistance of the following stage and the 221Ω metal-film resistor. The resistor value is optimised for the lowest AD600 noise figure. To produce a precise 50Ω input resistance, TR1's source current is adjustable and a capacitor across the input terminals cancels the leakage reactance of the feedback transformer T1. Minimum transformer loss is necessary to achieve a low noise figure, so the input transformer (T1) must be wound exactly as shown on a BN-61-202 balun core.

There are four amplifier stages in two AD600 packages. The first 40dB of gain reduction is done only by the third stage; the next 40dB in the second stage, and only the last 40dB reduction applied causes any gain reduction in the first stage. As AGC voltage passes halfway between the threshold of adjacent stages, gain control is being handed off from one IC to the next. This sequential gain reduction maximises signal-to-noise ratio.

To fully understand the AD600, you'll need a data sheet. Briefly, as the AD600's CxLO control voltage (either C1LO or C2LO) changes from −0.625 to +0.625V with respect to its CxHI, its gain changes linearly from +40dB to 0dB (unity gain). Because C1HI of IC2a is biased to 0.649V, its gain will change by 40dB as the AGC voltage at IC7 pins 2 and 13 changes from 0.024 to 1.274V. C2HI of IC1b is at 1.947V, so

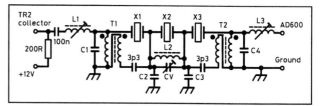

Fig 4.42. The ladder filter. CV: 1.5–7p. For X1–X3 = 4.434MHz, C1: 47p; C2, C3: 12p; C4: 53p (47p + 5p); L1: 11.7mH (27t 30 AWG on L-45-7 core in can); L2: 160mH (60t 34 AWG on FT-37-61); L3: 6.4mH (23t 30 AWG on L-45-7 core in can); T1, T2: 11.5t bifilar 30 AWG on BN-61-203 core

its gain will change by 40dB as the AGC voltage at IC6 pins 2 and 13 changes from 1.322 to 2.572V. The small gap between 1.274 and 1.322V provides a smooth transition of gain control from IC2a to IC1b, as explained in the AD600 data sheet.

The threshold of IC1a is also 1.947V, but 1.298V is subtracted from the AGC voltage by IC6c. Thus, the 40dB gain change of IC1a occurs as the AGC voltage changes from 2.620 to 3.870V. Taken together, as the AGC voltage at TP2 varies from 0 to 3.870V, the gain of the three cascaded stages changes by 120dB, with gain reduction starting at the last amplifier stage.

Noise filter. The home-brew crystal-ladder filter between the second and third AD600 stages is not intended for selectivity. This filter removes the broad-band noise generated by TR1 and IC1, permitting a lower AGC threshold. The filter is 2500Hz wide at the −3dB points, and 5500Hz wide at the −20dB points, removing much of the noise from the opposite side of zero beat, improving the IF NF and thus the overall receiver NF. Selectivity should be accomplished ahead of this IF strip.

After measuring the series resistance and motional inductance of your crystals, ladder-filter design becomes essentially a cookbook process using the X software bound with Wes Hayward's *Introduction to RF Design.* At 4.43MHz. the usual crystal-ladder filter cannot be made 3kHz wide. Hayward's article 'Refinements in Crystal Ladder Filter Design' in the June 1995 issue of *QEX* shows how the holder capacitance of each crystal can be parallel-tuned to permit construction of SSB-width filters.

Fig 4.42 shows the ladder filter. The middle crystal is parallel tuned as Hayward suggests. However K6OLG 'neutralised' the capacitance of the input and output crystals with a phase-inverting transformer, self-resonant at the IF. Winding information is given for 4.434MHz. Small trimmer capacitors could have been used to precisely adjust the neutralisation, but fixed-value 3.3pF capacitors work well and eliminate some adjustments.

At the 2500Hz bandwidth, the filter impedance is 2.9kHz. L-networks are used at each end to match the filter to the 100Ω input impedance of IC2a at one end, and the 200Ω collector resistor of TR2 at the other end. Every set of crystals will be different; exact values for the L-networks must be determined after the filter impedance has been computed by Hayward's X program. Once the filter is designed, breadboard it and verify proper operation before committing parts to a PCB.

At 9MHz, neither parallel tuning nor neutralising is necessary to get the SSB bandwidth and, if used only for receiving digital modes, you can even omit the neutralisation at

4.434MHz. Making a three-pole filter sounds more difficult than it is: with the X program and one of the many tutorial articles on ladder filters, it's a tedious process.

It is anticipated that many will choose to use a commercial filter instead of home-brewing a ladder filter. There's enough gain in TR2 to absorb a filter loss of up to 10dB. TR2's 200Ω collector resistor value can be increased to about 330Ω to match a commercial filter's impedance and eliminate one L-network. Using more filter poles and/or narrower filters may require increasing the value of C2 to delay the SLOW AGC more than the filter delay, although Harold Johnson, W4ZCB, didn't find this necessary with an eight-pole SSB-width filter he used.

Forward gain correction of the output. The fourth AD600 stage, IC2b, is outside the AGC loop. A signal 130dB above threshold causes the OFFSET SLOW AGC voltage at TP4 to increase from its zero-signal value of 0.625V to 3.125V, and with a loop gain of 13, the output of IC2a has increased by about 10dB. When about 10% of the OFFSET SLOW AGC voltage is applied to IC2b's C2LO pin, its gain decreases by 10dB, resulting in no signal change at its output.

R3 can be adjusted so the output is flat within a few decibels for signal levels of 0.23µV to 0.23V (−120dBm to 0dBm). Because of finite signal-to-noise ratio for small signals, it is not possible to compensate perfectly, but the resulting flatness is remarkable and addictive. Some may prefer the audio level to rise somewhat with increasing signal. R3 allows adjustment of IC2b's contribution to gain control to suit each builder's taste.

The output of IC2b is attenuated by a 150/75Ω resistor pair to produce a −26dBm signal level and 50Ω output resistance perfect for the +7dBm diode-mixer product detector. IC2b and the resistors produce low IMD and a high S/N ratio from the product detector while preventing BFO signal leakage to the SLOW detector.

Reference-voltage details. IC3 is a TL431 shunt regulator whose 2.6V output is divided by four identical 1% tolerance resistors to produce three close-tolerance voltages with only one adjustment: 1.947V for the C1HI threshold for IC1a and IC2b; 1.298V to offset the AGC voltage for IC1a and 0.649V for the threshold of IC2b. R6 is adjusted to produce 1.947V at TP3. The 1% tolerance resistors need only have the same value – between 1kΩ and 5kΩ. DigiKey and other suppliers offer suitable resistors at a modest price.

The AD600 CxLO and MUTE pins have 15 small-signal silicon diodes clamping the pins to ground or to the 2.6V potential at IC3. Normally, the diodes won't conduct. They're there to prevent damage to the expensive AD600s in case of misconnection, loss of a power supply or op-amp failure. Being a shunt regulator rather than a three-terminal regulator, IC3 is able to sink diode current should a fault occur.

The AGC detectors. The two AGC detectors, IC8/IC7c and IC9/IC11c, are not rectifiers but an interconnection of matched transistors that produce an average current equal to the logarithm of the applied IF signal over a range of signals. These detectors produce several DC volts from only 10mV of signal, and their logarithmic characteristic complements the AD600 scale factor almost perfectly.

Processing the AGC voltages. The large number of op-amps makes this circuit look complex. But the ideal performance of op-amps isolates each component's contribution to the circuit, making it easier to understand and troubleshoot than it may appear.

The SLOW detector output at TP2 and the IF GAIN potentiometer voltage at IC11a pin 3 are gated by IC11a and IC11d. Whichever one has the higher voltage charges the HOLD capacitor, C1, through its diode and a 4.7kΩ resistor. The output pin of the amplifier whose input is lower (not in control of the output) will swing to about −11V. This bizarre action is perfectly normal and logical, but takes some getting used to when troubleshooting. Similar action occurs at IC6a–IC6d and IC7a–IC7d.

The output from IC11a–IC11d is combined with an external AGC signal (if present) in IC7a–IC7d. Whichever signal is higher appears at IC7 pins 2 and 13, and controls the gain of IC2a. The output of IC7a–IC7d is combined with the FAST AGC detector output in IC6a and IC6d to control the gain of IC1b and drive the S-meter. Buffered by IC6b, 1.298V is subtracted from the combined detector outputs in IC6c to become the OFFSET AGC voltage with a total swing of −1.2 to 2.6V appearing at IC1a pin 1 to control its gain.

Hanging AGC. When the SLOW detector output is more than 90% of the voltage on C1, IC10b's output (pin 7) will be about 11V. Current through the 47kΩ resistor and diode to IC10D pin 13 charges the 1µF integration capacitor C1, its output moving toward the negative supply until the 1N5237 zener diode starts to conduct with about −8V at pin 14 of IC10d. TR4 is cut off by the negative base voltage and no drain current flows to discharge C1. The 4.7MΩ resistor slowly discharges C1, permitting the AGC to track modest amounts of fading with TR4 cut off. Clamp IC10c provides current as necessary to keep TR4 from developing a negative voltage on C1.

When the SLOW AGC detector voltage is not 90% of the voltage on C1, IC10b's output is negative and the integrator output swings in the positive direction at a rate determined by the setting of the HANG TIME potentiometer. It stops charging when C1 is discharged by TR4 down to 90% of signals-plus-background noise, or the other 1N5237 starts to conduct with 8V on pin 14 of IC10d. When the HANG TIME pot is fully clockwise, it not only takes a longer time for receiver gain to return, it returns at a slower rate.

S-meter. The linear-in-decibel nature of the AD600 AGC voltage means the 0 to 3.87V swing at TP2 corresponds to a 120dB gain change, plus the signal rise at the output of IC2a, a total of about 130dB. The AGC voltage is almost perfectly logarithmic or linear in S-units over this range.

Multiplier resistors develop a 1mA meter current for 3.75V at TP2. With appropriate changes to the resistors, more sensitive meter movements can be used. It's convenient to have a portion of the multiplier adjustable; K6OLG set his meter so the needle was vertical for an S9 signal. The linearity of the AD600 permits the S-meter reading to be corrected for the gain of a preamp or loss in a switched attenuator. For example, the voltage across the coil of a relay used to switch an attenuator can be fed to the S-meter through a variable resistor. Hence, the reduction in AGC voltage caused by the attenuator is perfectly compensated for by current developed from the coil voltage.

Adjustment. Seven potentiometers need adjustment. These adjustments do not interact and six of them are quick and easy to make.

1. Using a noise bridge (or other suitable impedance-measuring instrument), set the input resistance to 50Ω with R1. A ground connection is provided at the top side of T1 so that an additional half-turn can be added to the 1-2 winding of T1 if varying R1 does not produce the 50Ω input resistance. The input reactance should be very close to zero. At frequencies other than 4.434 or 9MHz, scale the input capacitor's value and verify zero reactance using a noise bridge.
2. Set R6 for 1.947V at TP3. The potential at IC6b pin 7 should be very close to 1.298V, (1.272min, 1.324 max). The voltage at IC2 pin 16 should be close to 0.649V (0.636min, 0.662 max).
3. Turn the IF GAIN pot fully counter-clockwise, to minimum gain. Adjust R5 for 0V at TP2, then adjust R4 to 0V at TP1.
4. Turn the IF GAIN control clockwise, and connect a signal generator to the input. Peak T2, L1 and L2 for maximum gain. These are broad-tuning, low-Q circuits. Adjust the noise filter L-networks and verify the expected filter bandwidth.
5. Apply sufficient signal to produce more than 1.6V at TP1. Adjust R2 so that the voltage at TP1 decreases slightly. This is the only tricky adjustment; don't be surprised if you have to repeat it several times before you get it right. Mid-scale S-meter linearity depends on proper balance of the two detectors. Large changes in the S-meter reading for small signal changes of around 10μV is a sure sign that R2 is not adjusted properly.
6. Connect a pulsed test signal to the input (receiving the signal from a keyed transmitter connected to a dummy load will do). Turn the HANG TIME potentiometer clockwise to its two-second position. Adjust R7 for a two-second delay between the end of the signal and the beginning of the voltage drop at AGC OUTPUT.
7. Adjust R3 (FLATNESS) to suit your taste. This can be done by ear – while listening to an on-the-air roundtable for example – or by using a signal generator and test instruments.

Additional points. This amplifier is insensitive to exact supply voltage, but the supply voltage needs to be stable so that the zero adjustments R4 and R5 will be stable. The +12 and −12V potentials are supplied by off-board 7812 and 7912 regulators respectively.

The 10kΩ resistor between the HANG TIME pot's wiper and the pot's low end simulates an audio-taper pot (these are hard to find!), providing the proper feel with a common linear-taper control. The IF GAIN control is also a linear-taper control. For computer control, both HANG and IF GAIN can be controlled by a 0 to 5V DC signal from a digital-to-analogue converter.

The 150μH RF chokes are parallel-resonant near the IF. RF choke values of 100 to 200μH will have virtually identical performance at 4.434MHz. At 9MHz, values between 27 and 47μH are suitable. There need be no fear of substitution.

Because of fading, on-the-air signals are not an ideal source of test signals. A keyed transmitter, known to have a good keying envelope, can be used with an oscilloscope to confirm

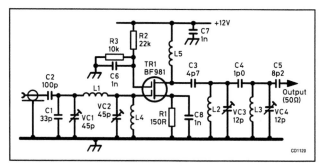

Fig 4.43. 50MHz RF receive amplifier. C6, C7: 1nF chip. L1: 0.13μH. L2, L3: 0.56μH. L4, L5: 4.7μH

proper circuit operation. Alternatively, you can use a diode mixer with a signal generator tied to the RF port, drive the DC-coupled IF port with a pulse generator and take the output from the LO port.

Transmit hang, diversity reception and external AGC. A 5V logic potential during transmit forces the hang integrator output to −10V and C1 discharges slowly through the 4.7MΩ resistor during transmit intervals. In fast-break situations (full QSK CW, AMTOR and sometimes even SSB) this causes the receiver gain to return to nearly its previous level rather than full gain. C1 discharges to 0V during longer transmissions.

With two IF strips and two mixers, connecting both SLOW to the EXT SLOW of the other gives gain control to the stronger signal, providing diversity reception to combat multipath reception on the digital modes. Some older, but very good Fredrick modems provide an AGC output that may benefit from the EXT SLOW connection.

Construction. K6OLG successfully used IC sockets on an 'ugly' groundplane breadboard, and with several iterations of PC board layout. On the other hand, an etched and drilled PC board saves a lot of time. Like the hand-wired board described earlier, the PC board is double-sided with a ground plane and the components on top, traces on the bottom. To minimise cost, the board doesn't have plated-through holes; component leads and grounded socket pins are soldered directly to the ground plane.

Although this amplifier is stable even as a breadboard, remember that it has a lot of gain. Its stability can become marginal with scope probes radiating signals at amplifier outputs. Given the opportunity, the amplifier can pick up the BFO signal. K6OLG eliminated this possibility by placing the BFO and product detector in a shielded box. In the final package, each circuit should be in its own shielded box and no BFO signal should be detectable in the IF output.

Designs for specific bands
RF amplifiers
With suitable switching, an RF amplifier can with advantage be placed at the feed point of the antenna – its gain will offset the loss of the feeder cable. Gains of 15 to 25dB will normally be sufficient to overcome that loss and the noise of the first mixer.

50MHz. Circuits based on the BF981 dual-gate MOSFET have been widely used. In one typical circuit (Fig 4.43), an input pi-network is used to match the antenna to the gate circuit of

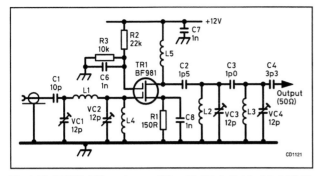

Fig 4.44. 145MHz RF receive amplifier. C6, C7: 1nF chip. L1: 0.08μH, L2, L3: 0.1μH

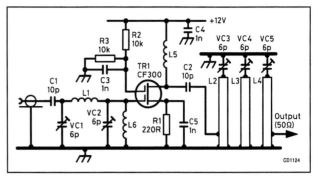

Fig 4.46. 432MHz receive amplifier. C3–C5: 1nF chip. L1: 25nH, L2–L4: stripline on 1.6mm thick epoxy glassfibre board, 70mm long, 2.8mm wide, spaced 2.0mm, L5: 0.1μH

the device and the output is taken to a band-pass filter and thence to the mixer. Tuning is fixed at the centre of the band so only the local oscillator needs to be tuned.

70MHz. There are few published circuits for 70MHz equipment because the band is of such limited appeal (it is only available to the UK, Gibraltar and to parts of Cyprus). Most circuits that work at 50MHz will also do so at 70MHz with suitable reduction (about 16%) in the values of the tuning components, L's and C's.

144MHz. Here again, circuits based on the BF981 are widely used and Fig 4.44 shows a typical one. Apart from the tuning components, it is very similar to Fig 4.43 above.

For more advanced work where absolute minimum noise, maximum immunity to nearby strong signals and unconditional stability is necessary, there is a modern circuit (by G4SWX) as in Fig 4.45. This has a fixed tuned input circuit in the form of a quarter-wave line and an aperiodic 50Ω output. It has a gain of 18dB, a noise figure of 0.4dB and its 3IP is +8dB. Its output is of the correct impedance to feed a multiple helical filter and then a double balanced mixer of the diode ring type (see above).

It could with care be used at lower and higher frequencies. At lower frequencies, it will probably be necessary to replace the input circuit by a 'lumped' circuit of a conventional coil and capacitor.

432MHz. FETs, especially dual-gate MOSFETs, are the preferred RF amplifiers at this frequency. While silicon devices will give good results, the lowest noise comes from using

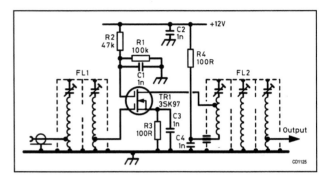

Fig 4.47. Wide-band 432MHz receive amplifier. FL1: 2-stage helical filter, FL2: 3-stage helical filter

GaAsFETs such as the 3SK97 or CF300. (*Note*: there are many others; these have been listed because they are most often mentioned.) The antenna input circuit can be 'lumped' but is usually resonant lines, either as wire/rod or as etched microcircuits (see above).

A typical RF amplifier is shown in Fig 4.46 and consists of a tuned line input and output and a CF300 amplifier. Note the essential screen between the input and the output sides of the circuit. Setting up is done simply by tuning the input and output for maximum signal at the desired frequency then retuning the input slightly for minimum noise factor. As it stands, the selectivity is high, being 6dB down at ±5MHz off tune and 20dB down at ±12MHz so it needs to be tuned to the part of the band of interest.

A wider-band device is shown in Fig 4.47. This uses a GaAsFET, the 3SK97.

1.3GHz. Power GaAsFETs provide the best gain with the least noise and a good large-signal handling capacity. Fig 4.48 shows a typical design (due to WA7CJO [18]) which uses a half-wave coaxial line for its input circuit, an MGF1402 power GaAsFET and an aperiodic (balun) output circuit. Its gain is 15dB, noise factor about 0.4dB and its output impedance is 50Ω.

The tuned circuit is the most difficult part to make but it is well within the capability of an amateur with only a modest workshop. The tuned line consists of 25mm diameter copper tube, 87.6mm long with the centre part 9.5mm dia. The plain ends are soldered in place. The input capacitor (C1, antenna coupling) is a 18mm dia copper disc soldered directly onto a SMA connector and screwed into the cavity. Because thin copper tube will not take a thread, a nut of the right size is

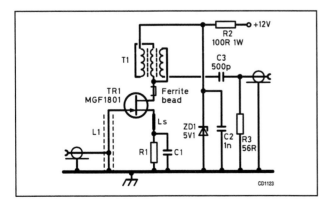

Fig 4.45. 144MHz MGF1801 preamp. R1: 2×47Ω chip. C1: 2×500pF chip. L1: 364mm long RG401, tap at 68mm from ground. Ls: 2 × 5mm. T1: 6t 30 SWG trifilar on T25-12 core connected as 1:2 transformer *(VHF/UHF DXer)*

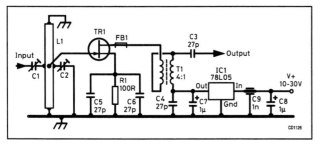

Fig 4.48. The WA7CJO preamplifier. See Table 4.5 for further details *(QST)*

Table 4.5. Components list for the WA7CJO preamplifier	
R1	100R nominal, adjust to get 8–15mA drain current
C1	0.7in dia, 20-mil thick copper disk attached to the SMA connector
C2	0.7in dia, 20 mil thick copper disc attached to a 10-32 brass flat-head screw
C3–C6	0.05 × 0.05in chip capacitors
FB1	Ferrite bead. Optional but may reduce the tendency of the circuit to oscillate
T1	4:1 balun, 3t 32 AWG enam wire, bifilar wound on a Siemens B62152-A008-X-060 double-aperture core
TR1	MGF1802, MGF1412, ATF10135 or similar GaAsFET

soldered onto the tube and the connector locked in the optimum position by a lock-nut. The tuning capacitor C2 is made in the same way but the disc is soldered onto a piece of studding. The connection to TR1 is made from 1.5mm dia wire. TR1 and the output circuit is mounted saddlewise in a box on top of the resonator.

Another method of overcoming the noise, stability and large-signal handling capabilities of GaAsFETs is to use multiple low-gain stages. The following design by Matjaz Vidmar, S53MV (formerly YT3MV), [19] shown in Fig 4.49 uses two stages of amplification to provide an overall gain of approximately 25dB, with very low noise figures attainable.

The L-band low-noise amplifier is housed in a small case made from 0.3mm thick brass plate, which is 50mm long, 20mm wide and 15mm high (Fig 4.50). It is thus small enough to permit no resonance below 7GHz, so that no absorber material is required for the damping of parasitic vibrations at these frequencies. The BNC sockets (UG 1094, without nuts or washers) must be soldered on, as shown in Fig 4.50.

Next, the six 470pF DC blocking capacitors are soldered into the tin case with sockets. They must be ceramic disc or

trapezoidal capacitors, not wire ended, and their value can be higher. When soldering them in, make sure that both the metal coating of the disc capacitor and the brass plate surface are well pre-tinned, so that the fragile capacitors are not destroyed by direct contact with the base plate bending in the heat.

Warning – in no case use multi-layer capacitors, as used in surface-mounted device technology! These capacitors display high levels of internal parasitic inductance and loss resistance, with natural resonances down to under 1GHz. In spite of their small dimensions, surface-mounted device capacitors and other multi-layer capacitors are completely unsuitable for microwave applications!

All the resistors used in the low-noise amplifier are wired miniature types rated at $^{1}/_{8}$W (0204). The source resistances marked with an asterisk in Fig 4.49 are not soldered in immediately, but are required only for calibration of the amplifier, and the final values are dependent on the ID tolerances of the GaAsFETs used.

The λ/4 chokes, L1 and L6, are each manufactured from a 6cm long piece of 0.15mm thick enamelled copper wire. The pieces of wire are first tinned over about 5mm at each end, and then the enamelled wire is wound around the shaft of a 1mm drill to form a coil. How many windings finally result from this is unimportant.

L2 is manufactured from a 0.6mm thick piece of silver-plated copper wire. For example, the internal conductor of an RG-214 unit can be used for this. For the frequency range from 1.5 to 1.7GHz, L2 has a single winding with an internal diameter of 3.5mm.

L3 and L4 simply represent the connection wires of the 1nF disc capacitor between the two transistors (Fig 4.50), each bent into a half-winding. Similarly, L5 is just a slightly longer connection wire of the output coupling capacitor. The inclination of the loop of L2 and the distance between L3 and L4 are adjusted last, on the basis of select-on-test methods.

The GaAsFETs are fitted last. After this operation, you should set your DC working points. In order to avoid any wild oscillations here, the input and output should be terminated with 50Ω.

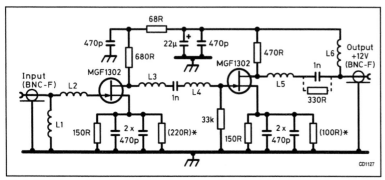

Fig 4.49. A two-stage GaAs FET antenna amplifier for L-band *(VHF Communications)*

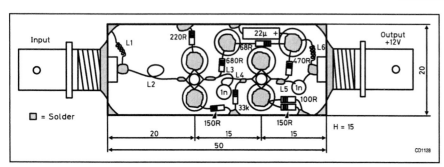

Fig 4.50. The low-loss structure with air as the dielectric makes an extremely low noise factor possible *(VHF Communications)*

The amplifier is now linked to an adjustable voltage source, which to start with should be set to about 7V. The DC voltage between drain and source is measured for both FETs. The thing to do now is to keep both drain-source voltages between 3 and 4V. To this end, you slowly increase the operating voltage and switch the initial source resistances of 150Ω in parallel again, until the final operating voltage of 12V is reached. Naturally, the parallel resistances should always be soldered on only when the operating voltage is switched off.

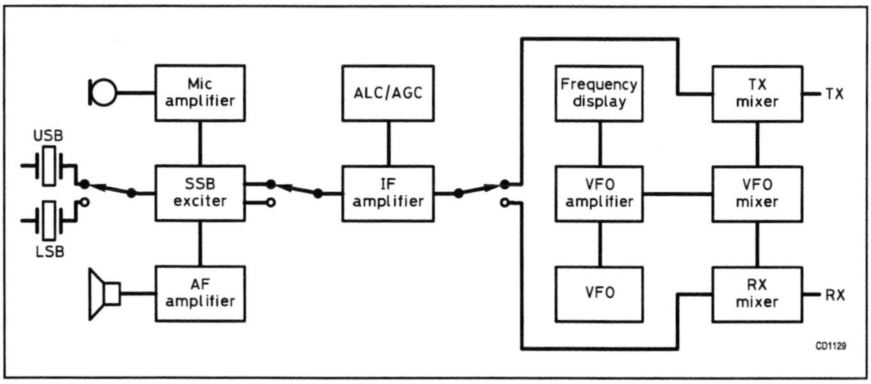

Fig 4.51. Block diagram of the 50MHz transceiver *(VHF Communications)*

The final voltage drop across the source resistances is typically 1 to 1.5V.

Now the amplifier must be put into a test rig to check amplification and noise factor. For this, you need a noise generator suitable for this frequency range (which does not need to be standard for calibration), a receive converter and an SSB receiver with a large S-meter (if necessary, display the AGC voltage externally), or with a low-frequency voltmeter connected to the audio frequency output and with the AGC switched off.

The noise factor is predominantly influenced by L2. L3 and L4 are to be set to maximum amplification, as is L5, even if its influence is much less than that of L3 and L4.

L3 and L4 are normally each up to 10mm long. The distance between the two can be precisely adjusted. L2 can also be precisely adjusted in the same way if you compress or expand the loop slightly.

If a FET with lower amplification is used in the second stage, such as the MWT11, or an older type from the CFY range, and/or more amplification is desired, then the output network can be modified. The aim is to increase the DC through the second FET. To this end, you remove the 470Ω resistor and in its place solder in a 330Ω resistor parallel to the output coupling capacitor. This is shown as a dotted line in Fig 4.49.

COMPLETE RECEIVER CIRCUITS

It would be a pointless exercise in reinventing the wheel to describe a complete receiver for any particular band – it is normally assumed that a short-wave receiver or, in the case of 23cm, a 2m receiver, is available. Thus what is required are receive down-converters for each band in question.

Whilst receive down-converters do exist, it is more general to find receive converters combined with transmit converters in single units, each sharing common circuits. These units are transmit/receive converters or, as they are normally called, *transverters*. This now means that we shall take our presumption a stage further, and assume that either a 28MHz or 144MHz transceiver is available.

Finally, because we shall now place the emphasis on transverter designs this section shall be dealing not only with receivers, but transmitters as well.

50MHz

The design featured below by Wolfgang Schneider, DJ8ES, [20] is the exception to the 'rule' set out above and is for a full transceiver for the 6m band. The concept of the design is that each sub-assembly is a stand-alone 50Ω module, thus allowing for simple interconnection, switching etc. A block diagram of the transceiver is shown in Fig 4.51.

The received signal arriving from the antenna at the RX input is amplified in the RX mixer, passed through a filter and then transposed to the IF level (9MHz). For that the module requires an oscillator signal tuneable between 41 and 42MHz. In this way the range 51 to 52MHz is covered. The oscillator signal needed is provided by the VFO unit. The tuneable oscillator works in the region from 5 to 6MHz. The amplifier following operates as a buffer and at the same time decouples the frequency counter and VFO mixer from one another. Mixed with a 36MHz crystal oscillator, it produces the desired output frequency of 41 to 42MHz.

The digital frequency display has eight digits, so the last digit shows hundred hertz units. This counter evaluates the VFO signal directly. To achieve an accurate frequency display the difference from the wanted frequency (ie 45.000MHz) must be programmed. The received signal now reaches the IF amplifier. Here the crystal filter limits the bandwidth to the 2.3kHz necessary for SSB. For the signal-strength display (S-meter) the received signal from the AGC/ALC module is processed. At the same time this is used to set the regulator voltage for controlling the IF amplifier. For demodulation the SSB exciter is employed. In this process, by activating the corresponding crystal oscillator, the desired sideband is selected. At the output of the ring demodulator the audio achieved in this way is passed to a low-pass filter and a two-stage amplifier. The power amplification needed for loudspeaker operation can be undertaken in a separate module.

During transmit, speech from the microphone is amplified and mixed in the SSB exciter with the desired sideband oscillator. At the output we get a double sideband (DSB) signal. The switchable IF amplifier is used in the transmit path. The crystal filter selects the desired sideband. By using an AGC/ALC circuit we can avoid over-driving the following stages.

The transmit mixer converts the SSB signal already produced up to 50MHz. Like the receive mixer, this contains filters and amplifier stages. At the output of the TX mixer we have around 100mW available on the desired frequency.

The tuneable oscillator (VFO) (Fig 4.52)

In this transceiver an oscillator from a Collins receiver is used. VFOs of this kind or similar ones can be found at radio rallies and boot sales.

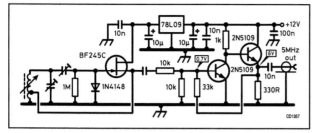

Fig 4.52. The tuneable oscillator (VFO)

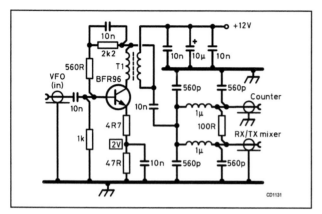

Fig 4.53. Broad-band amplifier

The VFO is designed around a Hartley circuit, which ensures good stability. The oscillator gets reverse feedback from a tap located about 10 to 25% away from the earthy end of the coil.

The higher the slope of the FET used, the less feedback is needed. This should only be enough to ensure foolproof operation of the oscillator – too much leads to instability.

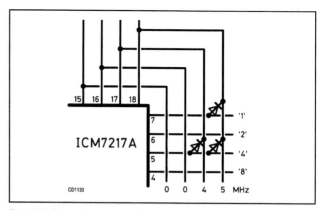

Fig 4.56. Sample programming arrangement

The oscillator is tuned using the core of the coil, giving a tuning range of around 5 to 6MHz. To decouple the VFO from the following stages a two-stage push-pull amplifier is used, and this ensures feedback-free operation of the VFO.

VFO broad-band amplifier and divider (Fig 4.53)
Following the VFO is a single-stage broad-band amplifier with an amplification of approximately 20dB. A Wilkinson divider is provided at the output to provide the two outputs, one for the frequency display and the other for the VFO mixer. A PCB design and component overlay are shown in Fig 4.54 in Appendix 1. The PCB measures 34 × 72mm.

Digital frequency display (Fig 4.55)
The digital frequency display is an eight-digit one and is constructed from two four-digit counters, type ICM7217A. These ICs are designed for seven-segment common-cathode LED displays and are programmable for display ranges. This feature is utilised here to programme a 45MHz offset in the display, required due to the fact that the counter is actually reading the 5 to 6MHz VFO. The method of pre-programming the display using diodes is shown in Fig 4.56.

The assembly is produced on two PCBs, one a standard display PCB for the LEDs, which can be remotely mounted from the driver board using ribbon cable. The driver PCB and component overlay is shown in Fig 4.57 (Appendix 1). Provision is made on the PCB to include the pre-programming diodes for the 45MHz display offset (these are not shown in the circuit diagram).

VFO mixer (Fig 4.58)
In this 50MHz SSB transceiver a VFO signal in the range of 41 to 42MHz is required, taking into consideration the 9MHz IF being used. This will enable coverage of the 6m band from 50 to 51MHz.

The required VFO signal is produced by mixing the 5 to 6MHz VFO with a 36MHz fixed-frequency oscillator, thus producing an output of 41 to 42MHz. The

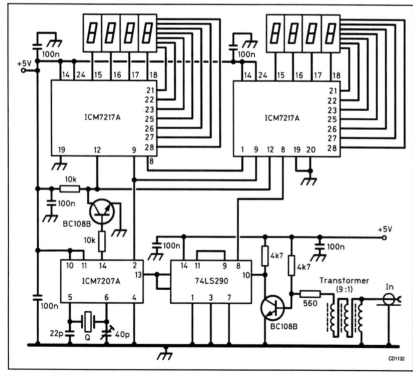

Fig 4.55. The programmable counter module

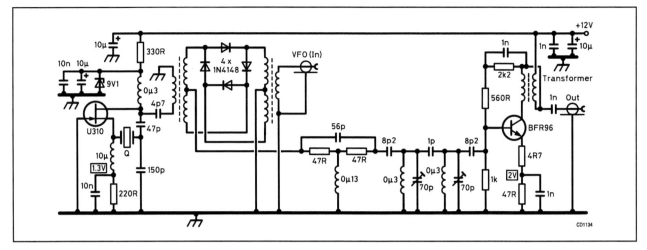

Fig 4.58. The VFO mixer

low-noise 36MHz oscillator is based around a U310 and produces of the order of 10mW into the ring mixer. The output from the ring mixer passes through a two-stage bandpass filter to a buffer amplifier, giving around 20mW tuneable in the range 41 to 42MHz.

In this and the previous broad-band amplifier, and elsewhere in this project, bifilar wound transformers are used. These are simply constructed as follows: take two equal lengths of 0.2mm diameter varnished copper wire and carefully twist around each other; six turns of this twisted wire are then wound onto a 5mm ferrite bead.

The transformer in the ring mixer is a trifilar one and is constructed exactly as the bifilar types but using three wires.

A PCB design and component overlay for the VFO mixer is shown in Fig 4.59 (Appendix 1). The PCB measures 53.5 × 72mm.

Receive mixer (Fig 4.60)

The receive mixer comprises a three-pole filter, first RF amplifier, ring mixer, second three-pole filter and a second RF amplifier. The PCB design is shown in Fig 4.61 (Appendix 1) and measures 72 × 72mm. The mixer is best aligned using a signal generator at the input set to 50.5MHz and a high-impedance detector at the output. The trimmer capacitors are then tuned for maximum output.

Transmit mixer (Fig 4.62)

The transmit mixer comprises a ring mixer, broad-band matching, three-pole filter and a broad-band two-stage amplifier.

With a drive level of 100μW (two-tone signal, each at −13dBm) there should be 55mW (+18dBm) per single tone at the output, corresponding to +21dBm PEP. Under these conditions the third-order intermodulation products (3IP) should be depressed by about 40dB and the 5IP products to 60dB. Although no harmonic filtering is included in this circuit, any harmonics produced should be below −40dBc.

A PCB design and component overlays for the transmit mixer are shown in Fig 4.63 (Appendix 1). The PCB measures 53.5 × 72mm.

IF amplifier with AGC/ALC (Fig 4.64)

The IF amplifier consists of a crystal filter, followed by an amplifier, a 20dB coupler for the AGC signal output, a pin-diode limiting stage and a final broad-band amplifier. A regulating signal from the AGC/ALC stage is fed into the pin-diode limiter.

The crystal filter used is an XF9B and is matched to 50Ω at its input and output by 9:1 transformers and 90pF trimmers. Special care should be taken when winding the transformers – any twist in the windings will have significant influence on the operation of the module. Matching of the

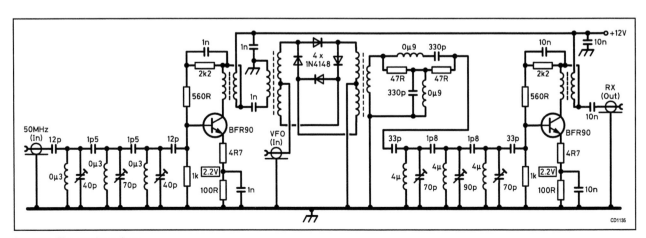

Fig 4.60. The receive mixer

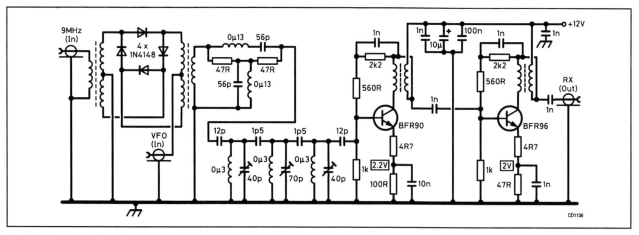

Fig 4.62. The transmit mixer

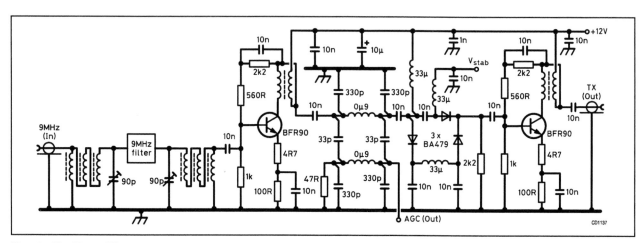

Fig 4.64. The IF amplifier

crystal filter is best achieved by feeding in a 9MHz DSB signal from the SSB exciter and tuning the trimmers for minimum residual carrier.

The PCB design and component overlay for the IF amplifier section is shown in Fig 4.65 (Appendix 1). The PCB measures 72×72mm.

The AGC/ALC module is shown in Fig 4.66 with the PCB design and overlay in Fig 4.67 (Appendix 1). The PCB measures 53.5×72mm. It is recommended that all the modules are built into tin-plate boxes. However, this is particularly important with this unit, as stray electrical fields may cause unwanted S-meter readings.

The circuit is based on the NE614 IC and the signal-strength output is utilised here. This output is buffered by an op-amp and then split into two paths. One path provides the S-meter signal and the other path the regulating signal for the IF amplifier pin-diode limiter.

Calibration of the S-meter is carried out when the entire receive chain is complete and operational. A signal of approximately −73dBm is fed into the RF input. This signal is adjusted until the AGC/ALC output level from the IF amplifier is −29dBm. This then equates to an S-meter reading of 8, and the series resistor $R_{S\text{-meter}}$ should be selected accordingly to give this meter reading

SSB exciter (Fig 4.68)

The SSB exciter consists of an SSB modulator, demodulator, USB/LSB oscillator,

Fig 4.66. Complete circuit for the AGC/ALC module

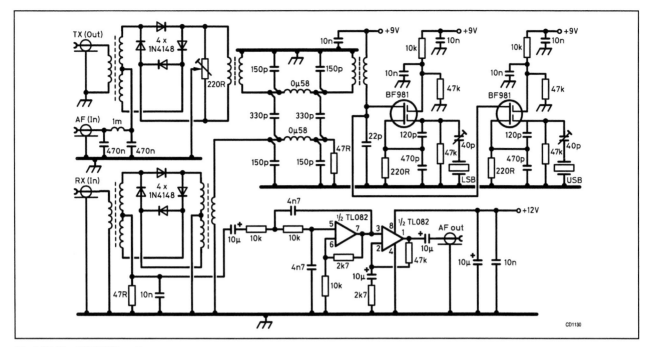

Fig 4.68. The SSB/CW exciter

microphone amplifier and a low-frequency amplifier. The sideband oscillator utilises the dual-gate MOSFET (BF981) in the oscillator stages. The two oscillators (LSB and USB) have common drain circuits and either is selected into operation by the application of the +9V supply for g2. The output from the oscillators is fed to a capacitively coupled hybrid, splitting the output to feed the TX modulator and the RX demodulator.

The amplified microphone signal is fed into the transmit modulator ring mixer via a low-pass filter. A 250Ω trimmer potentiometer is provided to allow for circuit balancing.

The audio output from the receive demodulator is fed to the low-frequency amplifier via a low-pass filter. The LF amplifier is configured using a TL082 operational amplifier.

The PCB layout and component overlay is shown in Fig 4.69 (Appendix 1). The PCB measures 72 × 72mm.

Microphone amplifier (Fig 4.70)
The microphone amplifier is constructed using the two halves of a TL082 op-amp. A standard 600Ω dynamic microphone is required and the output level required by the SSB

modulator (approx 1V) is adjusted by means of the 10kΩ potentiometer.

The PCB layout and component overlay is shown in Fig 4.71 (Appendix 1). The PCB measures 34 × 34mm.

AF amplifier (Fig 4.72)
The heart of the low-frequency amplifier is an MC34119 integrated circuit. This IC is available in SMD format in an SO-8 package. The audio output is 200mW into 8Ω.

The PCB layout and component overlay is shown in Fig 4.73 (Appendix 1). The PCB measures 34 × 34mm.

Interconnection of modules
Once all the modules have been assembled and pre-tuned they are ready for interconnection. Various supply voltages are required in the transceiver:

+15V AGC/ALC
+12V SSB exciter, microphone amplifier, LF amplifier, receive mixer, transmit mixer, oscillator, VFO amplifier, VFO mixer, S-meter
+9V SSB exciter
+5V Frequency display

Not only the various voltages, but also operational considerations play a part in the supplies. For example, the VFO,

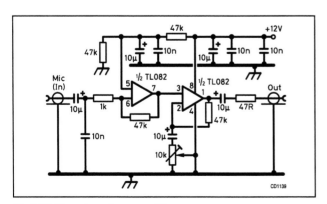

Fig 4.70. The microphone amplifier

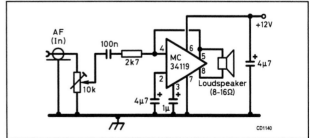

Fig 4.72. The AF amplifier

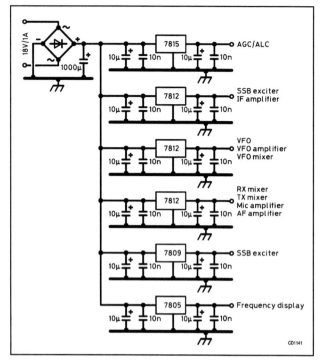

Fig 4.74. Separately stabilised voltages for the individual modules

audio amplifier and the mixer each require to have separate voltage stabilisers. This prevents interaction between the various units through a common supply. A suggested supply regulation circuit is shown in Fig 4.74.

The IF amplifier is used both in transmit mode and receive, thus switching must be provided to reverse the input and output connections. This is most simply achieved by using miniature relays operated by the PTT function. Similarly, the VFO and various supply voltages can be switched by relays. Suggested switching arrangements are shown in Fig 4.75.

Fig 4.76 shows the method for interconnecting the IF amplifier and the AGC/ALC unit.

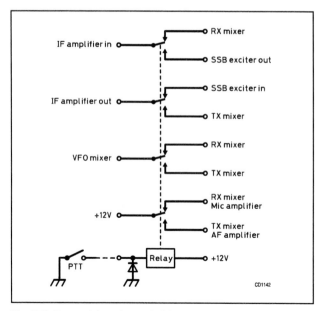

Fig 4.75. Transmit/receive switching

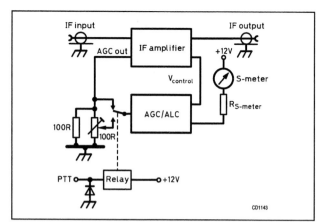

Fig 4.76. Interconnection of the IF amplifier and the AGC/ALC unit

70MHz

Again, due to the limited availability of the 4m band no specific designs are included here. It is conceivable that the 50MHz transceiver described above could be modified for use on 4m without much difficulty.

144MHz

The following 28MHz to 144MHz transverter was also designed by Wolfgang Schneider, DJ8ES [21]. This design incorporates features very important in equipment today, such as high signal strength handling, adjacent signal rejection and good spectral purity, which with increasingly occupied bands are perhaps more important than any other consideration.

The complete circuit of the transverter is shown in Fig 4.77. The design uses a fixed crystal oscillator running at 116MHz which is then amplified by a MMIC (microwave monolithic integrated circuit) device to give an level of 50mW to feed into the SRA1H mixer.

The input level from the 10m transmitter is fed into a pi-damping circuit comprised of R1, R2 and R3. Values for the three resistors (E12 or E24 range) for various input levels are given in Table 4.6.

In order to derive a clean transmit signal (intermodulation products < −50dBc) the mixer must be driven to full output with a maximum of 1mW at its input. The input pi-circuit also gives the mixer a good 50Ω match.

Parallel to the transmit input feed to the mixer is the take-off point for the received signal output. The received signal (144MHz now transformed to 28MHz) is amplified by TR3 (BF981) and fed to the RX output of the transverter.

In receive mode the +12V switched RX voltage, apart from supplying the receive chain, also biases D1 on, thus switching the received signal through to the mixer. The 144MHz

Table 4.6. Values for the three resistors (E12 or E24 range) for various input levels

P_{in} (mW)	P_{in} (dB)	R1(Ω)	R2 (Ω)	R3 (Ω)
1	0	–	0	51
2	3	300	18	300
5	7	120	47	120
10	10	100	68	100
20	13	82	100	82
50	17	68	180	68
100	20	62	240	62

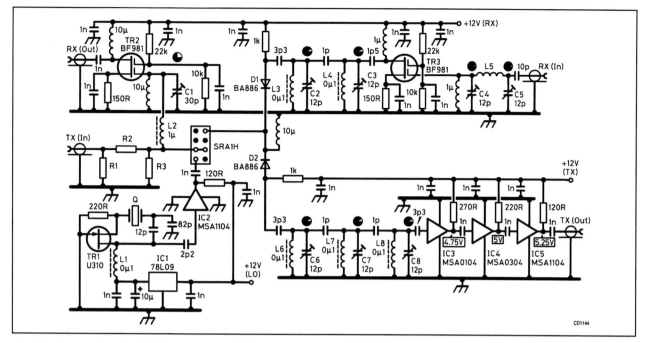

Fig 4.77. Circuit of the 28/144MHz transverter *(VHF Communications)*

signal from the antenna is filtered and then amplified by TR3 (BF981), and filtered again. The receive conversion gain of the unit is of the order of 20dB with a noise figure of the order of 2dB attainable.

In transmit mode the +12V TX supply line biases D2 on and feeds the transmit signal from the mixer to the MMIC amplifier chain via a three-pole filter network.

Note: although this may seem obvious it is not always appreciated – in a transverter such as this, the +12V RX and TX supplies should not be connected to the board simultaneously, but preferably relay switched by the action of the PTT from the controlling transceiver/transmitter.

The output level at the TX out should be of the order of 50mW with any harmonics present −55dBc or better.

Construction and setting up

The PCB layout and component overlays are shown in Fig 4.78 in Appendix 1. The PCB measures 54 × 108mm. Suitably sized holes should be drilled in the PCB in which to locate the MMIC amplifiers and the BF981 transistors, such that the connecting leads are flush with the circuit connections. Use a minimum of solder on all joints. The through connections required for the coils and the mixer are provided by 1.5mm copper rivets.

The unit is aligned as follows. First set all trimmers to the approximate positions as shown in Fig 4.77.

1. Tune the oscillator to 116.000MHz with L1.
2. Inject a 28MHz signal, after setting the values of the input pi-network according to Table 4.6. Adjust C6, C7 and C7 for maximum output (approx 50mW).
3. Using a strong 2m signal (eg a beacon) connected to the RX input adjust C2 and C3 for maximum signal strength on the 28MHz receiver.

4. Adjust C1 for maximum received signal on the 28MHz receiver.
5. Repeat steps 3 and 4 until no further increase can be obtained.
6. Adjust C4, C5 and L5 for best signal-to-noise ratio.

432MHz

Here is another transverter design by Wolfgang Schneider, DJ8ES [22], this time for 432MHz and again using 28MHz as the base frequency. The design of this transverter was based on the same premise and concepts as the 28/144MHz one, and in many ways the design is complementary.

The oscillator (Fig 4.79) is based around a well-known circuit using the U310 transistor. The 101MHz output from the oscillator is quadrupled by TR2 (BFR90a) and amplified by two MMIC stages to the required level of 50mW for the SRA1H ring mixer.

The circuit diagram of the transverter is shown in Fig 4.80. The input level from the 28MHz transmitter is again fed to

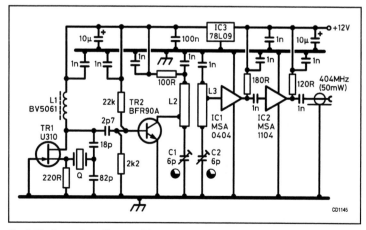

Fig 4.79. Crystal oscillator with quadrupler for 404MHz

the ring mixer via the same pi-damping circuit as used in the 28/144MHz transverter. Consequently, reference to Table 4.6 in the description of that unit will give the required values of the components in the input network, for various 28MHz transmit levels.

The 432MHz receive signal is routed to TR4, a dual-gate MOSFET preamplifier stage (CF300), via a pi-filter. The preamplifier is followed by a MMIC amplifier stage, which amplifies the signal sufficiently enough to overcome the losses in the following PCB etched three-pole filter (L5, L6 and L7). The receive signal from the

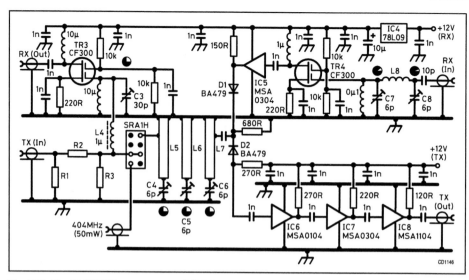

Fig 4.80. The 28/432MHz transverter (*VHF Communications*)

ring mixer is fed through a filter network to TR3 and the subsequent amplified signal taken to the 28MHz receiver from RX OUT. Transmit/ receive switching is accomplished using PIN diodes D1 and D2, which are switched by the appropriate TX or RX +12V.

In transmit mode, the output from the ring mixer passes through the three-pole filter and via PIN diode D2 to the transmit MMIC amplifier chain. The 432MHz output level at TX OUT is of the order of 50mW.

Construction and setting up

The transverter is split into two assemblies: the oscillator and the transmit/receive converter. The oscillator PCB and layout is shown in Fig 4.81 in Appendix 1 and measures 54 × 72mm. The transmit/receive converter PCB is shown in Fig 4.82 (Appendix 1) and measures 54 × 108mm. Construction is much the same as for the 28/144MHz unit, with the MMICs and transistors being mounted in holes drilled in the PCBs.

Alignment of the oscillator is as follows. First set all trimmers to the approximate positions as shown in Fig 4.79.

1. Set the oscillator to 101.000MHz using L1.
2. Adjust C1 and C2 for maximum output, which must be a minimum of 50mW.

Alignment of the transmit/receive converter is as follows. First et all trimmers to the approximate positions as shown in Fig 4.80.

1. Having correctly dimensioned the pi input filter, inject a 28MHz signal at TX IN. Adjust C4, C5 and C6 for maximum 70cm output at TX OUT. The level should be at least 50mW, with all spurious signals and harmonics better than −50dBc.
2. Using a strong 70cm receive signal (eg a beacon) adjust C3 for maximum received signal on the 28MHz receiver.

   Note: C4, C5 and C6 should not be adjusted in receive mode. If the received signal level is lower than expected, careful retuning of C4, C5 and C6 should be carried out in transmit mode only.
3. Adjust C7, C8 and L8 for best signal-to-noise performance.

1.3GHz

This 144Hz to 1.3GHz transverter designed by Michael Kuhne, DB6NT [23] is compact (55 × 74 × 30mm), has 1.5W power output, 1.4dB noise figure and 70dB spurious rejection. This is achieved by modern SMD techniques utilising the latest MMICs and power modules, an SMD double-balanced mixer and commercial pre-tuned helical filters. The performance renders it useful for small portable set-ups, as well as for home stations. The circuit diagram is shown in Fig 4.83, a PCB design in Fig 4.84 (Appendix 1) and a component overlay in Fig 4.85.

Design

A 96MHz crystal oscillator works with a J310 junction FET in a source feedback circuit. A quadrupler with a BFR92 feeds a helical filter on 384MHz. A subsequent tripler with a BFG93 and a helical filter on 1152MHz provides a clean 7dBm output on 1152MHz. A double-balanced Schottky mixer SMD-C3 is used for both transmit and receive. Its IF port is terminated in a diplexer and has switched attenuators for RX and TX. These allow for independent adjustment of transmit and receive gain.

In transmit mode the 144MHz IF is mixed with the 1152MHz LO to an output on 1296MHz. The mixer output is filtered by a helical filter and routed through a PIN-diode switch to the transmit chain.

This chain uses a MMIC INA10386, another helical filter and the output power module M67715, which can supply a linear output power of 1.5W. For higher output power a second, external power module with the M67762 can provide 15W at a drive power level of 0.2W.

A control voltage of 12V/2A for external use is provided by the transverter.

The RX chain is comprised of an RF stage with a MGF1302, a helical filter and a second RF stage with a MAR6 MMIC. The output is switched to the common mixer circuit by means of a PIN diode switch. The noise matching in the first stage is made by series-L matching. The two helical filters provide optimum RF selectivity for image and spurious rejection. The overall noise figure is less than 2dB and typically 1.4dB.

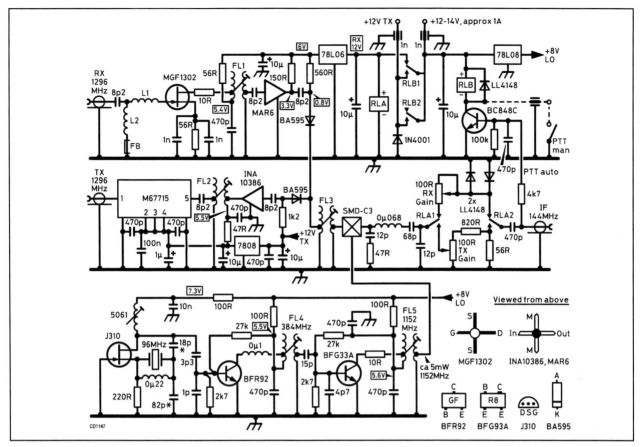

Fig 4.83. The 1296MHz transverter circuit diagram. Components marked with an asterisk (*) are temperature coefficient N750 violet (to suit quartz crystal). L1 and L2 are wound with 5t and 4t respectively of 0.22mm enam wire and have an inside diameter of 1mm. FL1–FL5 are helical filters. FL1–FL3: 367MN113F, FL4: 5HW36535A-385, FL5: 367MN110A. An MSA0685 can be substituted for the MAR6 MMIC (*DUBUS Technik IV*)

Construction

1. Cut PTFE board to dimension of the cabinet.
2. Drill PCB (0.8mm and 2 × 5.8mm for the two 1nF leadless disk caps).
3. Mount coaxial connectors.
4. Put PCB onto inner conductors of coaxial connectors and solder to the cabinet on both sides.
5. Solder feedthroughs.
6. Mount and solder all parts according to the pans layout except filters, MMICs, MGF1302 and SMD-C3.
7. The 1nF disk caps are soldered to the ground plane with small pieces of copper-foil.
8. Remove free leg from Neosid 5061 and also the ground lugs of the enclosure.
9. Mount all filters. Fully solder the enclosures to the ground plane.
10. Mount pots for TX GAIN (Cermet) and RX GAIN (SMD).
11. Solder 7808 to tin-plate enclosure.
12. Solder M67715 approximately 1mm above the PCB.
13. Mount the external cooler with heatsink and some thermal conductive compound.
14. L1 and L2 are made from 0.22mm copper enamelled wire wound closely on a 1mm form. Mount them with short legs.
15. Mount MGF1302 and solder L1 onto the free gate leg (bent through 90°).
16. Make contact troughs for the ground lugs of the MMICs.
17. Mount MMICs.
18. Mount BFR92 and BF093 'overhead'.
19. Solder 56Ω load resistor
20. Mixer C3 can be soldered after tuning of LO chain.

LO adjustment

Apply supply voltage and adjust core of oscillator coil 5061 until voltage at collector of quadrupler BFR92 drops to a minimum value. The 384MHz helical filter is tuned for minimum collector voltage at tripler transistor BFG93. Connect power meter via 50Ω coaxial cable to LO port (mixer SMD-C3 is not fitted yet) and adjust 1152MHz helical filter to maximum output (7dBm min). With the aid of a frequency counter the 96MHz crystal oscillator can be set to the exact LO frequency. Negative temperature coefficient (N750) components for the 10pF/82pF capacitors in the crystal oscillator circuit compensate for low-frequency drift, but may be changed in temperature coefficient in order to accommodate different types of crystals. An external TCXO or OCXO can be connected via a 47pF capacitor to the source of the J310. In this case the crystal and the 0.22μH choke must be omitted.

After finishing the tuning procedure mixer SMD-C3 should be fitted (see step 20).

RX adjustment

Adjust pot RX GAIN to minimum value. Connect antenna or 50Ω dummy load to RX input and a 144MHz RX to the IF

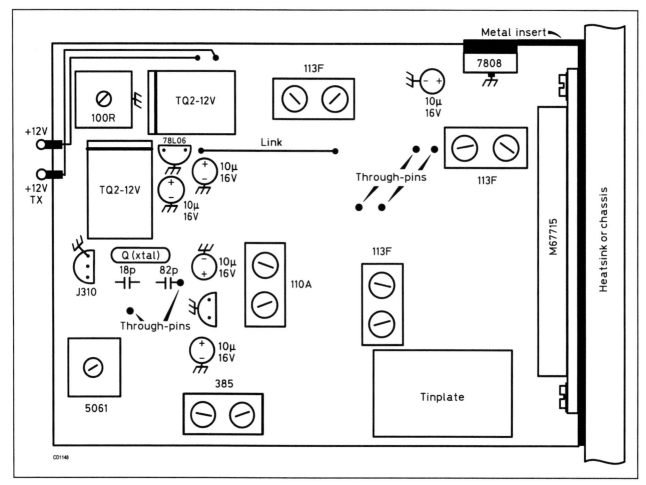

Fig 4.85. Component layout *(DUBUS Technik IV)*

output. Check operating voltages on the MGF1302 and the MAR6. Adjust helical filters in the RX chain to maximum noise level on 144MHz. Tweaking of the helical filters can be done with a signal generator or by listening to a beacon.

Normally tuning of L1 is not required because of its low Q characteristic, but if a noise figure meter is available, tuning can he done by squeezing coil L1 with a plastic tool.

Because maximum gain is quite large, an adjustment to the input characteristic of the 144MHz RX can be performed by adjusting the RX GAIN pot for an appropriate S-meter reading.

TX adjustment

Transmit/receive switching is initiated by a DC voltage on the IF line. Alternatively, an external facility could be fitted (see circuit diagram). Connect a power meter to TX output and switch to transmit. Check voltages on INA10386 and M67715. Key 144MHz TX and adjust TX GAIN pot for some readable output power. Adjust helical filters for maximum output power. Finally, the TX GAIN pot can be adjusted to a nominal output of 1.5W.

Measurement results

Power output = 1.5W
Spurious < −70dBc
Image rejection > 70dB
Harmonics <−40dB

RX gain = 16–18dB
Noise figure = 1.2–1.4dB

TRANSMITTERS

There are two main types of transmitter, one having a constant, if interrupted, output such as is used for Morse, data or FM, and the other for modes where the output must follow the input exactly such as for SSB. The latter are called *linear* circuits. A transmitter consists of several stages, some of which are common to receivers. For example, low-power amplifiers, mixers and some forms of modulator are common.

Fig 4.86 shows a block diagram of a transmitter suitable for 'on-off' modulation, ie for Morse code or data transmission. Fig 4.87 shows one for a FM transmitter and Fig 4.88 for a SSB system of the 'filter' type. Fig 4.89 shows a similar block diagram for a FM transceiver. A SSB transceiver is similar except that frequency translation is done by mixing rather than by multiplication.

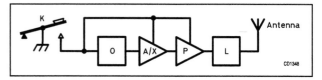

Fig 4.86. Morse code transmitter. *Key:* K – key; O – oscillator; A/X – amplifier/frequency multiplier; P – power amplifier; L – low-pass filter

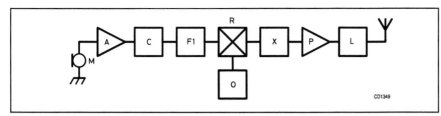

Fig 4.87. FM transmitter. *Key:* M – microphone; A – audio amplifier; C – clipper; F1 – low-pass AF filter; R – reactance modulator; O – oscillator; X – frequency multiplier; P – power amplifier; L – low-pass RF filter

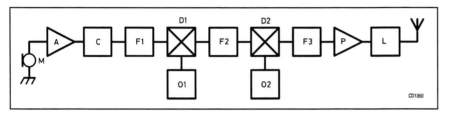

Fig 4.88. Filter-type SSB transmitter. *Key:* M – microphone; A – audio amplifier; C – clipper; F1 – low-pass audio filter; D1 – double-balanced modulator; F2 – sideband filter; O1 – fixed oscillator; D2 – double-balanced modulator; O2 – variable oscillator; F3 – filter; P – power amplifiier; L – low-pass filter

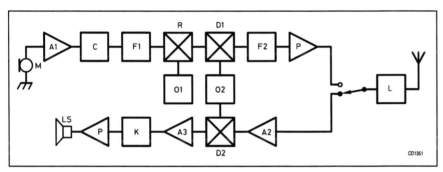

Fig 4.89. FM transceiver. FM is generated at O1 frequency which is equal to the IF. *Key:* M – microphone; A1 – audio amplifier; C – clipper or speech processor; F1 – low-pass audio filter; R – reactance or phase modulator; O1 – fixed frequency oscillator; D1 – double-balanced mixer; O2 – variable-frequency oscillator; F2 – RF filter; P – power amplifier; L – RF low-pass filter; A2 – receiver RF amplifier; D2 – double-balanced mixer; A3 – IF amplifier; K – FM demodulator; A4 – audio amplifier; LS – loudspeaker

The following paragraphs are a short introduction to the various blocks in the diagram. Note, however, that blocks which are common to receivers are dealt with in that section.

RF amplifiers

These follow exactly those in the receiver section – for further details see p4.21.

Frequency multipliers

These are RF amplifiers in which deliberate distortion of the waveform is carried out so that the output contains harmonics of the input. This is done by using very low bias in a bipolar transistor stage or high bias in a FET stage. In either case, the output is tuned to the desired harmonic. Single devices tend to produce better odd harmonic output while even harmonics can be better produced using a 'push-push' circuit in which the input is 'push-pull' and the output is parallel.

Fig 4.90 shows a circuit for an odd harmonic multiplier and Fig 4.91 one for even harmonics. Many devices will work in these circuits; those given are known to work but are not specifically recommended.

Interstage coupling

The coupling of signals between stages is important for one or two reasons:

1. It provides matching between the output of one stage to the input of the next and
2. It may provide selectivity, ie it may contain a tuned circuit. The second is not always the case since there are wide-band amplifiers which, for example, cover most of the HF part of the spectrum.

In general, in VHF and UHF transmitters, we are dealing with both reasons and, in the case of selectivity, this must be either low enough to cover the whole band, or tuneable with a front-panel control, or possibly cover only the section of the band of interest to the operator.

With tuned circuits, it is often possible to provide a low impedance output by means of a tapping or a link winding of relatively few turns. Fig 4.92 shows a typical interstage coupling between the collector of one transistor and the base of

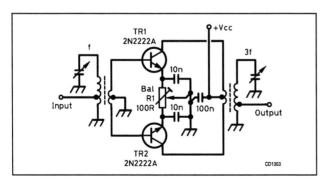

Fig 4.90. Odd-harmonic multiplier *(ARRL Handbook)*

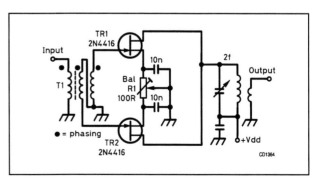

Fig 4.91. Even-harmonic multiplier *(ARRL Handbook)*

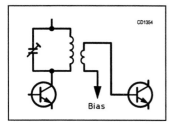

Fig 4.92. Tuned coupling between transistor amplifiers

the next. In general, FETs are easier to deal with because their input impedance is much higher than bipolar transistors. They do, however, have a large input capacitance which varies with bias and signal. Fig 4.93 shows a FET interstage coupling of the broad-band type.

Broad-band couplings are useable up to a point. At high levels, which may only mean 1W or so, by-product signals can be formed which can, in non-linear circuits, form unwanted signals, some of which may end up in the band. It is therefore necessary to put in some selectivity to attenuate all but the wanted signals.

Spurious outputs

In all cases the ideal transmitter will have frequency stability and a 'clean' output, ie with no other RF signals present than those wanted. This means no unwanted outputs such as harmonics or other spurious frequencies. It will also have means for controlling the power output so that minimum power necessary for communication can be used.

These ideals are not attainable in practice so it is generally recognised that, if the spurious outputs are lower than −60dBc (decibels with respect to the carrier power) or −30dBm (with respect to 1 milliwatt), whichever is the lower, then the output is clean enough. The VHF Contest Committee of the RSGB recommended a lower level of −90dBc but this has proved too difficult to achieve.

Power levels

The transmitter starts with low-power stages and only in the last stages does the power increase significantly. These high-power stages are dealt with later. Arbitrarily, a RF power of 1W is considered the boundary. Below this, many of the circuits are identical to those used in receivers although there are functions performed in a transmitter which do not occur in receivers.

Audio inputs

The average normal microphone produces a few millivolts (mV) and the modulator (see below) needs of the order of volts so a gain of about 1000 is needed. It is also necessary to 'tailor' the frequency response of the microphone to about 300–2500 Hz to avoid broadening the bandwidth requirement for SSB. Both operations can be carried out using low-noise op-amps. A quad op-amp can provide all the necessary functions. The first stage provides most of the gain, the second stage is a high-pass filter with a cut-off of 300 Hz and the third stage is a low-pass filter with a cut-off of 2.5kHz. The filters are of the Sallen and Key type (Fig 4.94) using selective feedback around

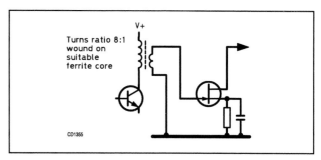

Fig 4.93. Wide-band coupling between transistor amplifiers

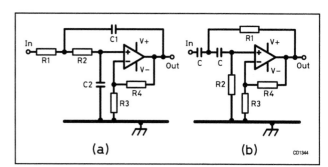

Fig 4.94. Low-pass (a) and high-pass (b) Sallen and Key type audio filters. V+ and V− are symmetrical about the earth line. Both filters have a Chebyshev response and a gain of 2

the op-amps and have a Chebyshev response. Fig 4.95 shows the practical circuit.

In order to control the maximum output, it may be useful to put a simple clipper between the amplifier (IC1a) and the filters. In this way some of the distortion products made by the clipper are removed.

Modulation

On-off modulation is used for Morse code and for data modes, and the only essential is that the on-off transitions are gentle. If they are sharp, a large number of sidebands will be produced and these appear as *key clicks*. The aim should be to have a waveform which is rounded (see Fig 4.96). This is done by arranging the rise and fall times to be 0.1 of the time of the bit. In the case of Morse, the bit is the single dot and in digimode, the bit is the 'mark' signal.

Frequency modulation (FM)

There are two methods of achieving this: the direct method and the indirect or phase modulation (PM) method. The former

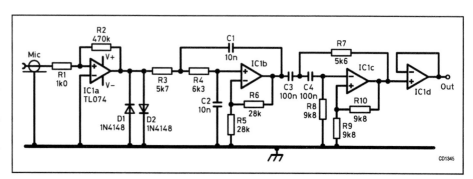

Fig 4.95. Practical filter circuit. 'Odd' values of resistors should be made up from series or parallel combinations. C1, C2 and C3, C4 should be matched if possible

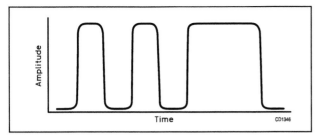

Fig 4.96. The letter 'U', showing gentle transitions from mark to space and vice versa

consists of a reactance modulation of an oscillator which, at its simplest, can be achieved by applying the audio signal to a suitable biased varicap diode (Fig 4.97) and the latter by attaching the same sort of varicap to one of the tuned circuits *after* the oscillator to alter the phase with the audio signal (Fig 4.98).

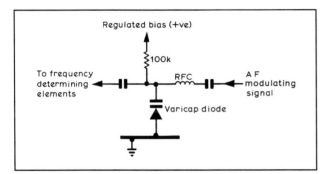

Fig 4.97. Basic varicap diode modulator

The two waveforms are shown in Fig 4.99 together with the audio signal (top). The FM is shown in the centre and the PM at the bottom.

It will be seen that there is little difference between the FM and the PM waveform. However, in PM the effective FM is proportional to the modulating frequency so to get true FM, in the PM system, the audio must be tailored to have an amplitude that falls with increasing frequency.

By whatever means FM is achieved, the signal is described mathematically by the Bessel function. It is not necessary to understand this, only to apply it. Table 4.7 and Fig 4.100 show the Bessel function as a function of modulation index (MI) which is defined as:

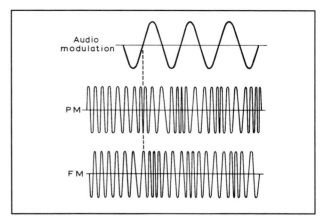

Fig 4.99. Angular modulation of an RF carrier

$$MI = \frac{\text{Deviation of the FM carrier}}{\text{Audio frequency producing that deviation}}$$

Fig 4.100 is easiest to understand as it shows the amplitude of the carrier and the various sidebands for various values of MI. It will be seen that the carrier *decreases* as MI increases and at a value of MI of about 2.4 (actually 2.405), the carrier disappears. When it reappears at higher MIs, it is negative which only means its has its phase shifted by 180°. Fig 4.101 shows the amplitude and distribution of sidebands at various MIs.

Maximum deviation needs to be set to suit the band and the system. At present, repeaters will not accept deviations greater than 5kHz and this is also used for simplex working at the present channel spacing of 25kHz. When the channel spacing is reduced to 12.5kHz, the maximum deviation must also be reduced to 2.5kHz.

The fact that the carrier disappears at a MI of 2.4 gives us a way of setting up an FM transmitter (or just an FM generator) to a specific deviation using an audio generator and a sharply tuned HF receiver. This assumes that the FM is generated on a carrier within the range of the HF receiver and multiplied up to the band in question. As an example, take a final frequency of 145MHz which is generated at 12MHz and multiplied by 12. If the final deviation is 5MHz, the deviation at 12MHz is 417Hz. If this is caused by an audio tone of 174Hz the carrier will disappear at a deviation of 417Hz (ie at a MI of 2.4). This disappearance is monitored on the HF receiver.

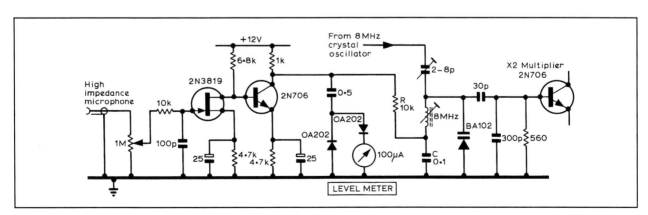

Fig 4.98. Practical circuit using a varicap diode

Table 4.7. Bessel function

Modulation index	Carrier value	1st set of sidebands	2nd set	3rd set	4th set	5th set	6th set	7th set	8th set	9th set	10th set	11th set	12th set	13th set	14th set
0.00	1.000	–	–	–	–	–	–	–	–	–	–	–	–	–	–
0.01	1.000	0.005	–	–	–	–	–	–	–	–	–	–	–	–	–
0.05	0.9994	0.025	–	–	–	–	–	–	–	–	–	–	–	–	–
0.02	0.9900	0.0995	–	–	–	–	–	–	–	–	–	–	–	–	–
1.00	0.7652	0.4401	0.1149	0.0020	–	–	–	–	–	–	–	–	–	–	–
2.00	0.2239	0.5767	0.3528	0.1289	0.0341	–	–	–	–	–	–	–	–	–	–
4.00	-0.3971	-0.0661	0.3641	0.4302	0.2811	0.1321	0.0491	0.0152	–	–	–	–	–	–	–
5.00	-0.1776	-0.3276	0.0466	0.3648	0.3912	0.2611	0.1310	0.0534	0.0184	–	–	–	–	–	–
7.00	0.3001	-0.0047	-0.3014	-0.1676	0.1578	0.3479	0.3392	0.2336	0.1280	0.0589	0.2035	–	–	–	–
10.00	-0.2459	0.0435	0.2546	0.0584	-0.2196	-0.2341	-0.0145	0.2167	0.3179	0.2919	0.2075	0.1231	0.0634	0.0290	0.0120

A negative sign indicates that the component is 180° out of phase with respect to the others. Blank spaces indicate that the values of the sidebands are insignificant

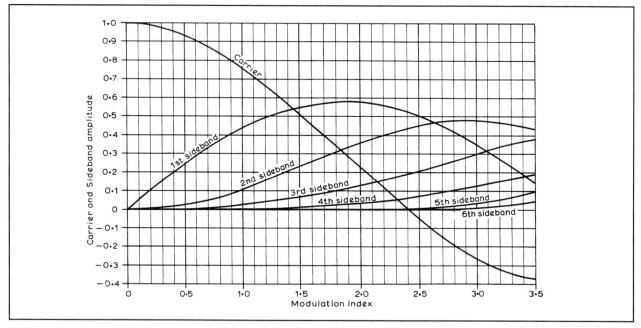

Fig 4.100. Bessel curves showing variation in carrier and sideband amplitude with modulation index

SSB

Fig 4.102 shows the relationship between the audio modulating frequency, the carrier frequency and the AM, DSBSC and SSB products. There are three methods for generating SSB.

The filter method

This is where a carrier is generated and fed to a balanced modulator (DBM, see above, the balanced mixer has exactly the same characteristics) which produces two sidebands with very little carrier (a perfect DBM produces zero carrier), ie a DBSC (double sideband suppressed carrier) signal. A sharp filter removes one of the sidebands and what is left of the carrier. This method is that used in the majority of commercial transceivers.

The mechanism can be expressed mathematically as follows. We assume that a simple tone is modulating a carrier:

$$\cos A \times \cos B = \tfrac{1}{2}\cos (A + B) + \tfrac{1}{2}\cos (A - B)$$

where A is the carrier frequency and B is that of the tone (cos or cosine functions are used because the mathematics are simpler than sine functions and the difference is only a 90° phase shift.) $A + B$ is the upper sideband and $A - B$ the lower. If B is biased so that A never goes negative, the carrier is not suppressed and the result is AM (amplitude modulation) – see Fig 4.102.

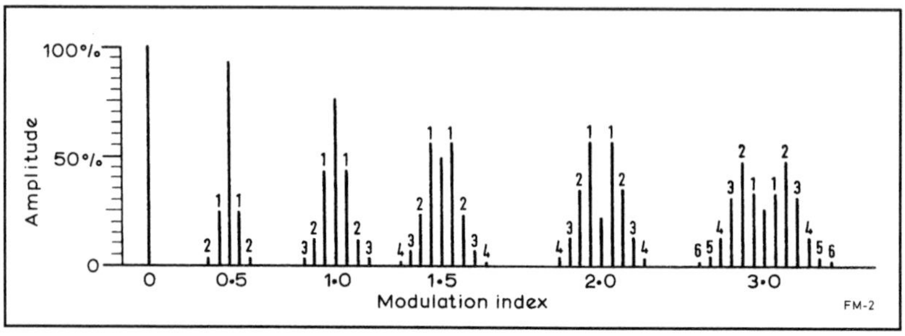

Fig 4.101. Relative carrier and sideband levels for various modulation indices

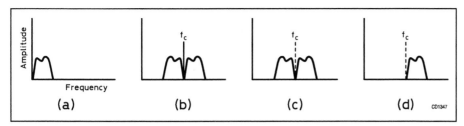

Fig 4.102. (a) The audio signal. (b) AM signal derived from it, f_c being the carrier frequency. (c) DSBSC signal, f_c being where the carrier would be. (d) SSB signal (upper sideband), f_c being where the carrier would be

The phasing method

In this method [24–26] the audio is used to generate two signals which are mutually at 90° phase difference to one another. These are used to modulate two carriers which are also at 90° phase difference and the resulting signals are combined. A SSB signal results and this can be shown mathematically.

If the two carrier signals are A and $A + 90$ and the two audio signals are B and $B + 90$, then:

$$\cos A \times \cos B = \tfrac{1}{2} \cos (A + B) + \tfrac{1}{2} \cos (A - B) \quad \text{(i)}$$

and

$$\cos (A + 90) \times \cos (B + 90) =$$
$$\tfrac{1}{2} \cos (A + B + 180) + \tfrac{1}{2} \cos (A - B) \quad \text{(ii)}$$

now

$$\cos (A + B + 180) = - \cos (A + B)$$

so by adding (i) and (ii) we get $\cos (A - B)$ and by subtracting (ii) from (i),we get $\cos (A + B)$ which are the lower and upper sidebands.

Analogue methods can be used to produce the phase shifts in the audio signal and these are quite complex if an accurate 90° phase shift necessary for good carrier and sideband suppression is to be obtained.

The Third Method

This is a different phasing method [27] which does not need two audio channels accurately at 90° phase to one another. The audio signal is passed to two DBMs which are fed in quadrature (90° phase difference) by a pilot tone at, say, 1.7kHz. Each produces a DSBSC signal from which the upper sideband is stripped by two low-pass audio filters. The resulting signals are passed to two further DBMs fed in quadrature by the HF oscillator. Finally, the four sets of sidebands are combined whern some reinforce and the others cancel, resulting in a SSB signal. The mathematics of the process are rather complex. The originator of the Third Method was D K Weaver [28] who was not a radio amateur.

All SSB signals are generated at HF and transformed to VHF or UHF by mixing with a suitable frequency and filtering out the unwanted sideband. Frequency multiplication cannot be used because this would multiply the audio frequencies.

It should also be noted that while all the information is transmitted on each sideband, it is not possible to regenerate the audio signal *exactly*. The normal technique is to adjust the added carrier until speech sounds 'normal', ie not like Donald Duck! For this reason, SSB cannot be used to transmit music unless there is some method for reintroducing the carrier exactly, eg by transmitting a very much reduced or

pilot carrier to which the receiver carrier can be synchronised.

SEMICONDUCTOR POWER AMPLIFIERS

Lower-power transistors are readily available from specialist suppliers and so can be used in designs intended for copying. Higher-power devices tend to be very expensive, the selection available to the amateur buyer is very variable, and it can prove difficult to duplicate some designs. Nevertheless, such designs are valuable in demonstrating the specialised design and construction techniques.

Cooling

Proper cooling is vital for high-power transistors as lot of heat has to be conducted through a small area with a low temperature rise. Philips' recommendation [29] for the heatsink is for a surface flatness of 0.02mm (0.001in) and a surface roughness of 0.5µm (almost mirror finish). These specifications are difficult to achieve without machining and probably unnecessary in most amateur applications, but most extruded heatsink shows a far from ideal surface. Sanding with fine wet/dry paper can make a worthwhile improvement in the flatness at the expense of roughness. It is worth asking local machine shops for a price for skimming a heatsink; some charge very reasonable prices. Figs 4.103 and 4.104 show enlarged views of the transistor/heatsink joint; if the surfaces are not flat there are few points of contact for heat flow. The heatsink is not the only source of imperfection; most transistor flanges are quite soft and can become distorted. If necessary, they can be sanded against fine wet/dry paper which is placed face upwards on a flat surface.

White heatsink compound should be used in preference to clear silicone grease and it is intended to fill the micro crevices in Fig 4.104, rather than the large gaps. Heatsink compound is a hundred times worse than metal at conducting heat (but slightly better than nothing at all), hence the emphasis on flatness and roughness to get maximum metal-to-metal contact at a microscopic level [30]. Before fitting the transistor, deburr the fixing holes well and clean all swarf, dust from sanding and solder/flux splashes from both heatsink and transistor using methylated spirits or similar; any debris whatsoever under the transistor will prevent the important metalmetal contact. Using a thin layer of thermal compound, just enough to obscure the metal, press the transistor into

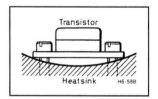

Fig 4.103. View of transistor on concave heatsink, showing gap

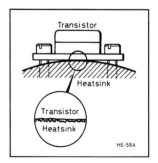

Fig 4.104. View of transistor on convex heatsink, showing gaps. Magnified view shows micro crevices in the transistor-heatsink interface

place as hard as possible with a finger, then remove it when any voids in contact will be obvious. It should be possible to achieve contact over the whole flange with this amount of thermal compound; if this is not possible, then either the transistor or heatsink is not flat enough. Be careful: thermal compound spreads a long way and does not wash out of clothes easily. Methylated spirits will remove and disperse it prior to washing.

Make sure that the fixing screws do not foul against the main body of the transistor or the BeO (beryllium oxide, or 'beryllia') between the flange and the leads might be damaged; particles of BeO are very toxic if inhaled. The top cap is made from alumina which is razor sharp if broken but non-toxic. Most transistors are designed to be used with American 4-40 UNC screws, but M2.5 or M3 can be used as an alternative. M2.5 is probably better as there is greater clearance for the head and less likelihood of overtightening (which actually reduces the thermal contact to the heatsink). Screws

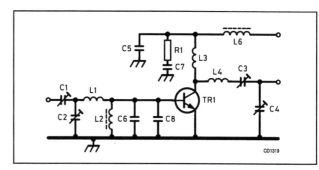

Fig 4.105(a). Typical VHF amplifier circuit

should be tightened to 0.7Nm, which is tight but well short of needing great effort. Always use a plain washer between the screw and the flange.

If the transistor is correctly fitted to the heatsink, a heatsink temperature of 70°C is a reasonable upper limit to apply. The

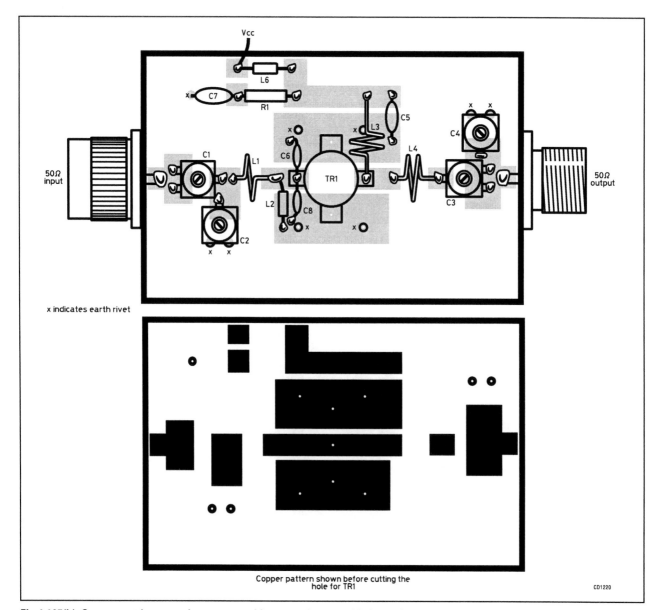

Fig 4.105(b). Component layout and component side copper (reverse side is continuous copper)

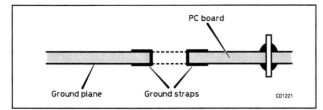

Fig 4.105(c). Earthing straps and wires

transistor will typically be operating with a junction temperature of around 120°C which will give very good reliability, and many of the other components in the circuit will have a temperature rating of 70 or 85°C. Remember that 70°C is hot enough to cause skin burns; using a fan or larger heatsink to reduce the heatsink temperature so that it is not uncomfortable to hold will provide extremely good reliability, provided that individual components are not over stressed.

It is also important to ensure correct mechanical alignment between the RF power transistor and the PCB. The transistor leads should ideally be level with the PCB; slight downwards tilt is acceptable, but avoid any upwards bend as this can result in the leads becoming detached or the top cap being dislodged. The PCB will normally need to be spaced away from the heatsink using, say, a stack of washers. For most flange and stud mounting transistors, a 4BA half nut (2.5mm thick) is about correct if the PCB is the most common 1.6mm thickness. The nut has a centre hole which gives clearance for a M3 screw.

Earthing and construction

An important aspect of all transistor amplifiers is earthing. The low impedances result in high RF currents and solid, low inductance earthing is key in ensuring circuits operate as expected. Normally, circuits will be built on double-sided PCB with the underside a continuous copper ground plane. Fig 4.105(a)–(c) and 4.106 show a typical amplifier circuit and a suitable way to construct it, including how the emitter leads should be connected to the ground plane with straps of copper or brass foil. Additionally, any areas of earth connection on the top surface should have pins or wires connecting the top and bottom together at regular intervals (20mm or less spacing).

Stability

VHF/UHF power transistors have increasing gain at lower frequencies which can easily bring about destructive oscillation. Many designs show no signs of instability until an 'equivalent' transistor, or even a different batch of the original, is tried. A precaution against this is to ensure that the transistor sees a resistive load at frequencies much below the operating frequency. In Fig 4.107 the RFC and RF decoupling are transparent at low frequencies and the transistor is loaded by the resistors through the LF decoupling to ground. The LF choke provides the DC path for the supply current. In the base circuit of a Class C amplifier, point X is grounded and C4/5 are omitted. Another technique which improves LF stability is resistive feedback, shown in Fig 4.108. The RF choke isolates the resistor at the operating frequency and the capacitor provides DC blocking.

Bipolar transistors in particular can also suffer from parametric instability. The collector base capacitance varies with

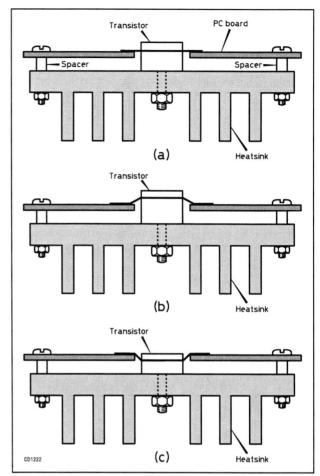

Fig 4.106. (a) Mounting arrangements for PCB, transistor and heatsink. (b) Acceptable lead forms (c) Incorrect lead form

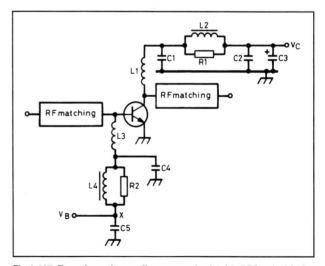

Fig 4.107. Transistor decoupling networks. L1, L3: RFC suitable for the operating frequency. L1 is usually an air-spaced inductor and L3 can be a moulded choke. L2, L4: ferrite-cored inductor, eg 2t on Siemens B62152 two-hole core, type A1X1 for L2, A4X1 for L4. C1, C4: decoupling at operating frequency; typically 1000pF. C2: 0.1μF ceramic. C3: 47μF. R1, R2: 10Ω 1W carbon or metal film

collector voltage throughout each RF cycle and thus provides a varying feedback path. Under some operating conditions spurious signals can be produced and, once present, the

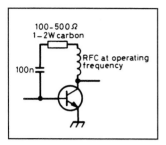

Fig 4.108. Transistor RLC feedback

non-linear feedback makes these self sustaining. The sustaining mechanism makes the effect prone to produce exact sub-harmonics ($f/2$, $f/3$ etc) of the input signal, although the signals will often interact with each other and produce a very wide band of spurii.

The effect is affected by the choice of matching circuits, supply voltage and operating power level. Avoiding heavy saturation is the single most effective preventative measure.

FETs are not totally immune to instability, but their internal feedback tends to be much lower than bipolar transistors and varies less with drain voltage, so the effects are not so severe.

Biasing

For linear operation transistors require some form of fixed bias. For FM only use, bipolars can be used without bias, although there is usually slight loss of gain. Power FETs always need fixed bias.

FETs are easy to bias as they only require a fixed voltage and, for normal amateur environments, temperature compensation is not needed. Biasing bipolars correctly is a little more complex. Bipolars are biased with current injected into the base. The bias source has to maintain a constant bias voltage as the base current varies over the RF and modulation cycles; the base current can be in the regions of 1A peak in high-power devices.

The base-emitter junction has the characteristics of a silicon diode, with a negative temperature coefficient of about 2mV/degree. As the transistor heats up, the base emitter voltage drops and, if the bias voltage is not reduced, more base current will flow, resulting in higher collector current, and more heating etc. The overall effect is termed *thermal runaway*. The solution is to use a diode, or another base-emitter junction, to sense the temperature of the power transistor (or the heatsink close by) and use this to adjust the bias voltage in line with the temperature.

Fig 4.109 shows a simple circuit using a power diode to set the bias voltage which is suitable for low-power amplifiers; the maximum base current of the transistor (I_{cmax}/H_{FE}) should not exceed about 10% of the current in the diode. For higher powers the bias circuit has to supply more current. Fig 4.110 shows the addition of an emitter follower to give higher current capacity; D1 is mounted by the RF transistor, D2

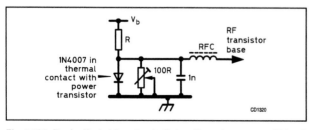

Fig 4.109. Basic diode bias circuit. Select R to give approx 250mA through the diode

should be mounted close to TR1 and compensates for variations in V_{BE} of TR1. Other bias circuits are used in the amplifier circuit examples and these can be applied to most circuits without difficulty.

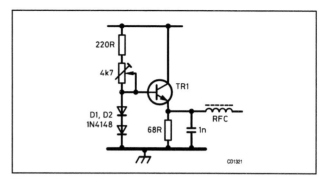

Fig 4.110. Emitter-follower bias circuit

Matching

The use of output impedance is inappropriate for RF power transistors; they are characterised in terms of load impedance. The external load impedance (often 50Ω) is modified by the matching circuits and presented to the transistor. The load impedance affects the balance between gain, linearity and efficiency at any given power level. Manufacturer's data will usually give figures for maximum output power and efficiency, and lower impedances might be needed for best linearity.

S parameters have very little value when applied to high-power amplifiers and transistors; by definition they are measured at signal levels where no non-linear effects occur and this is totally inappropriate for high-power situations. It is much more useful to define the load impedance required by the transistor for given operating conditions, and the input impedance of the transistor under those conditions.

The input matching circuitry converts the input impedance of the transistor to whatever impedance is needed to load the preceding stage. In the case of a stand-alone amplifier this will usually be 50Ω, but in an amplifier chain the conversion might be directly to the optimum load impedance of the previous transistor. This will simplify circuitry compared with matching each stage to 50Ω and then connecting them together, although it means that the output power of the driving transistor cannot be measured directly.

Modern simulation programs can use S parameters in conjunction with non-linear models of transistors to predict circuit behaviour but this is beyond the scope of this book.

$(V_{cc} - V_{cesat})^2/2P_o$ is widely used to establish a starting point for load impedance where this is not specified by the manufacturer. In practice, high-power transistors used near the upper limit of their frequency range will have an optimum load resistance which is one-half to one-third of the calculated value and which will also have a significant reactive component. The calculated value is still a reasonable starting point, but experimentation is likely to be needed to optimise performance in practice so there is benefit in using matching circuits which offer a wide tuning range.

At high powers, and especially at lower supply voltages (eg 12V), the load impedances can be very low with the resistive component being a fraction of an ohm. At 50W output, this corresponds to a RF current of 10A or more; components

Table 4.8. Capacitance of Philips 680 series miniature ceramic capacitors at 144MHz, lead length < 2mm	
Marked value (pF)	Measured value (pF)
2	2.2
4.7	4.7
10	10
15	15.5
22	23
47	53
100	132
220	480
330	2760

carrying this level of current must be of low loss and suitable for the purpose. Layout and construction become critical; inductors typically become wide printed tracks or thick copper straps to give large surface area. Do not use tinned copper wire, which is lossy as skin effect means that the RF current flows in the surface plating and not in the copper wire. Capacitors capable of carrying high current are normally either metal clad mica, or porcelain ceramic chips (ATC or equivalent) and very few other types are suitable in these situations. Often several capacitors are connected in parallel make up the total value and share the current. Using higher supply voltages brings several benefits: higher impedances which makes matching easier and less lossy, higher gain and lower price/watt.

To some extent at 144MHz, and certainly at higher frequencies, the parasitic inductance of capacitors must be taken into account. For both chip and metal mica types, this is about 0.5nH. At 432MHz this is a reactance of $+1.3\Omega$. A final reactance of, for example, -8Ω (46pF at 432MHz) actually requires a capacitor with a capacitive reactance of -9.3Ω. This is 40pF, 15% less than calculated. Table 4.8 shows another example, comparing the marked and measured values of leaded miniature ceramic capacitors at 144MHz. A leaded capacitor, even with minimum lead length, will have an unpredictable parasitic inductance of several nanohenrys. This makes it impossible to swap capacitors in matching networks with any certainty, so designs need to be reproduced accurately to have a good chance of success. Motorola application note EB46 [32] shows an excellent example; a VHF 80W amplifier is fixed-tuned in bands by component selection. The difference between 143–170MHz and 155–175MHz is that in the first, a 500pF capacitor is made from two 250pF components and in the second it is made from 200 and 300pF components.

The low impedances mean that there is a practical limit to the power level which can be obtained from a transistor. For example, trying to reach 150W by putting two 75W devices in parallel in one transistor package can reduce the impedance to a level which becomes unmanageable. One means of reaching the higher power level is to use two 75W devices in push-pull. Here the input and load impedances are in series, so the impedance is double that of a single transistor (see Fig 4.111), making matching much easier. Where the two transistors are mounted on a single package, further benefits arise. If the drive to the two halves of the device is truly antiphase, a RF ground point exists within the package and this means that there are no circulating ground currents in the external circuitry. If this circuit arrangement is used with two separate

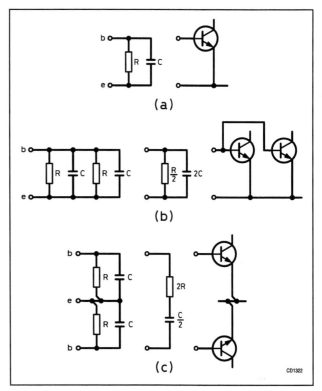

Fig 4.111. (a) Typical equivalent input circuit of high-power RF transistor. (b) Equivalent for two transistors in parallel. (c) Equivalent for two transistors in push-pull

transistors, the physical separation introduces current in the path between the transistors which then demands the same low-inductance ground connections as are needed in single-ended circuits.

At low frequencies the balanced drive signals are often generated with a conventional centre-tapped, wound transformer. Leakage inductance, stray capacitance and losses in ferrite make this unpredictable at VHF and transmission line transformers are widely used instead. The principle is shown in Fig 4.112. Basic laws of physics mean that if a current flows in the inner of a coaxial cable, exactly the opposite current flows in the outer. If the output end is not connected to ground, then the inner and outer are in antiphase or push-pull. Satisfactory operation depends on choosing the type and length of cable correctly. Lengths should not exceed 0.4λ and

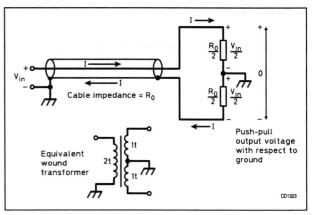

Fig 4.112. Operation of coaxial cable balun

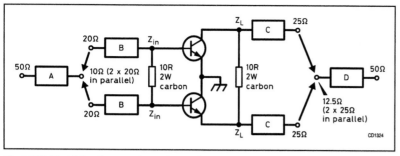

Fig 4.113. Matching for transistors in parallel (bias and power connections omitted). Impedance values shown are typical and need not be duplicated exactly

the minimum lengths needed depends on the cable size. As a rule of thumb, a length of λ/6 of UR43 type cable (5mm diameter) will have balanced outputs. If miniature cable is used (RG179 or smaller) then about half this length is adequate. As an alternative, a shorter length of cable can be loaded with low-loss ferrite material, sufficient to produce a few hundred ohms of reactance (calculated as if the cable was replaced by a single wire of the same diameter).

Another method for combining transistors in a circuit is to operate them in-phase [33]. Mechanically it is impractical to simply connect them in parallel, and Fig 4.113 shows how each transistor has some individual matching circuitry to a higher impedance and then the circuits are connected in parallel. There is a risk that the two-transistor circuit will form a push-pull oscillator, and resistors are often added to suppress this. If the two sides are in-phase and at equal amplitude, the resistors dissipate no power. In many instances where low-gain transistors are being used, these resistors can be omitted.

Matching circuits

At VHF, matching circuits are usually constructed from 'lumped', ie discrete, components and are usually designed to provide a useful amount of tuning range to allow for differences between devices, and as a result of variations in the construction of the circuit. The tuning range is also valuable where the impedances have been estimated and the actual values required can be significantly different to those calculated. At UHF and microwave frequencies, matching techniques tend to use printed striplines instead of wire inductors, and construction techniques become very important as even a millimetre of lead or track length represents a significant reactance. The formulae for estimating load impedance are highly inaccurate at these frequencies and designs need to be based on accurate data. Published designs need to be copied very accurately to ensure success.

Some circuit configurations widely used for narrow-band transistor amplifiers at VHF are shown in Fig 4.114 [34]. Power connections to the base and collector are not shown; these are assumed to be RF chokes so that they do not affect the operation of the matching circuit. The 'L' circuit of Fig 4.114(a) lacks flexibility in that the loaded Q is set by the impedance transformation ratio between R1 and R2, and there is limited tuning capability as the inductance is a fixed value; variable inductors are impractical in VHF power amplifiers.

The circuits of Figs 4.114(b) and 4.113(c) have greater flexibility through the use of two tuning capacitors. This allows the loaded Q to be chosen by the designer independently of

the values of R1 and R2 and provides a wider range of impedance matching. A convenient by-product of the circuit is the DC blocking action of the series capacitor. A loaded Q of about 5–10 is usually chosen. Higher values give higher harmonic rejection, but at the cost of higher RF current and voltage in the network which leads to increased losses. In practice, a harmonic filter should be used at the output of every amplifier, so there is no benefit in choosing a high loaded Q in the matching network.

Where the impedance ratio to be matched is high, component values become impractical if the matching is carried out in a single stage. In these cases, it is common to use two circuits in series, each carrying out about half of the total transformation. The intermediate impedance can be chosen by:

$$\sqrt{R_1 + R_2}$$

The definition of 'high' varies with frequency and impedance, but as a rough guide, a single three-component section will match an impedance ratio of up to 15:1 at 50/70MHz and 10:1 at 144MHz.

Quarter-wave coaxial transformers provide another convenient method of transforming impedances. As the transistor impedances are <50Ω, cable impedances of <50Ω are needed. Such cables are rare and expensive, but readily available 50Ω cable can be used by connecting lengths in parallel,

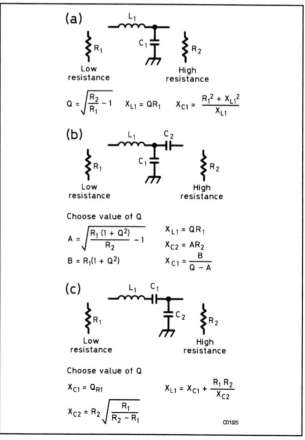

Fig 4.114. Transistor matching networks

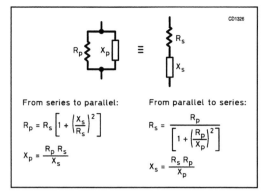

Fig 4.115. Conversion between parallel and series impedances

for example $2 \times 50\Omega$ behaves like 25Ω, and $3 \times 50\Omega$ like 16.7Ω.

All of the matching circuits discussed here are most easily designed when transforming between purely resistive values. In practice, transistor impedances normally include some reactive component. The design process involves cancelling ('tuning out') the reactive part of the impedance to leave a resistance and then designing the matching network to transform that resistance to the desired value. Impedances are normally given as series components; a resistance in series with a capacitive or inductive reactance. In designing matching circuits it is often useful to convert between series and parallel descriptions of the impedance; any given impedance can be defined in both ways, as shown in Fig 4.115.

General rules for designing matching networks

Input matching (Fig 4.116)

If the transistor impedance is inductive, convert it to the parallel form and add a parallel capacitor at the base lead to cancel the reactance of the inductive component, then match to the resistive value. If the transistor impedance is capacitive, add a series inductance to cancel the capacitive reactance.

Output matching (Fig 4.117)

If the manufacturer gives a load impedance for the desired operating conditions then proceed as follows. If the desired load impedance is inductive, transform the external load (50Ω) to give the correct resistive value and add a series inductor to give the required inductive reactance. Alternatively, the inductance can be provided as a parallel element, which doubles as the power supply connection. While this is often used it introduces high RF currents into the decoupling capacitors. For this reason, the technique is not recommended for those without experience or access to RF test equipment.

If the desired load is capacitive, convert it to the parallel form, make the resistive transformation from the external load to the required parallel

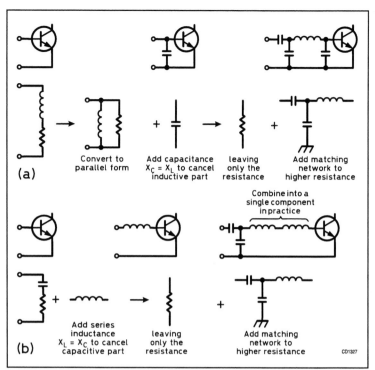

Fig 4.116. Transistor input matching. (a) Input impedance is inductive. (b) Input impedance is capacitive

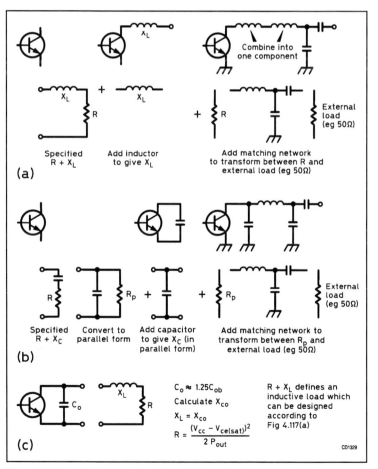

Fig 4.117. Transistor output matching. (a) Specified impedance is inductive. (b) Specified impedance is capacitive. (c) Estimated impedance

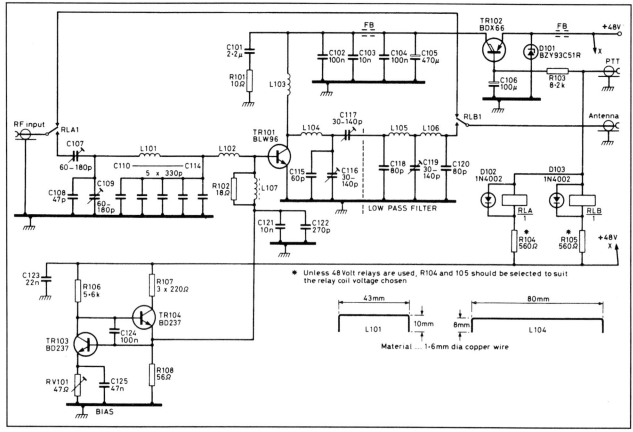

Fig 4.118. Circuit diagram of the amplifier

load resistance and add a parallel capacitor to give the required capacitive reactance.

Where the load impedance is being estimated, proceed as follows. The resistive part of the load is calculated from:

$$(V_{cc} - V_{cesat})^2/2P_0$$

V_{cesat} should be chosen according to the supply voltage and mode of operation; for 12V transistors this is 2V for FM only, and 4V for linear operation with SSB. For 28V transistors, the values are 4V and 6V respectively. The transistor output capacitance is difficult to define as it varies widely with collector voltage swing. If the transistor data shows a graph of C_{ob} versus voltage, use the value of C_{ob} at 60% of the supply voltage which will be used, otherwise use a value of about 1.25 times the C_{ob} figure given in the data sheet. In either case the desired load impedance is inductive, the inductive reactance being chosen to cancel the transistor's output capacitance.

Design example – 100W amplifier for 50MHz

G3WZT described a 100W linear amplifier for 50MHz [35] (Fig 4.118) which covered the process of designing input and output networks in some detail. Those portions of the article are repeated here as a comprehensive design example.

Input matching

The input matching consists of two T-networks which match the required drive impedance of 50Ω to the complex input impedance of the BLW96. T-networks are used in preference to the more simple L-arrangement, as there is no control of

the working Q when using the latter. As the Q of an L-network increases with the ratio of transformed impedances, high circuit Qs can exist. This makes adjustment very critical and temperature sensitive, and also causes unwanted narrow bandwidth and high circulating RF currents. Inspection of the manufacturer's data for the BLW96 shows an input impedance of $0.37 + j0.15\Omega$ (equivalent series components) at 50MHz. The reactive part of the input is very small (0.47nH) and in this instance may be ignored. However, other devices may have a much higher reactive component in the input impedance, and for this reason it will be taken into account as part of the input matching network in order to demonstrate the method.

To start the design, it is first necessary to decide the intermediate resistance between the two T-match sections (see Fig 4.119). Assuming both sections have the same Q, the intermediate resistance is the geometric mean value of source and load resistance R1 and R2'. Therefore, intermediate resistance:

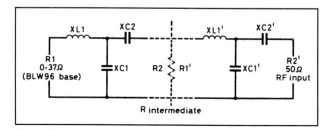

Fig 4.119. Input matching arrangement

$$R_I = \sqrt{0.37 \times 50} = 4.3\Omega$$

Working from the base, the first T-match section transforms from 0.37Ω to 4.3Ω, and the second section from 4.3Ω to the design source impedance of 50Ω.

The next requirement is to define the working Q of the sections. If too low a value is selected, component values become impractical; too high a value leads to the unwanted problems described earlier. The minimum working Q for given values of R1 and R2' is when:

$$R_1(Q^2 + 1)/R_2 > 1$$

If variables are selected which give a value of less than 1, the value of A cannot be solved. In order to satisfy this requirement and avoid high Q for the reasons given earlier, a Q of 4 in both sections is used for this design.

Referring to Fig 4.119, the following formulae are applied to obtain the values for X_L, X_{C1} and X_{C2}:

$$X_L = QR_1 \tag{1}$$
$$X_{C2} = AR_2 \tag{2}$$
$$X_{C1} = B/Q - A \tag{3}$$

where:

$$A = (B/R_2 - 1)^{0.5} \tag{4}$$
$$B = R_1(Q^2 + 1) \tag{5}$$

Inserting values into the formulae gives the following values:

From (5) $B = 0.37(4^2 + 1) = 6.29$
From (4) $A = (6.29/4.3 - 1)^{0.5} = 0.68$
From (3) $X_{C1} = 6.29/4 - 0.68 = 1.89\Omega$
From (2) $X_{C2} = 0.68 \times 4.3 = 2.92\Omega$
From (1) $X_{L1} = 4 \times 0.37 = 1.48\Omega$

To calculate the component values:

$$C = 1/2\pi f X_C \tag{6}$$
$$L = X_L/2\pi f \tag{7}$$

Therefore:

$$C_1 = 1/2\pi \times 50 \times 10^6 \times 1.89 = 1684\text{pF}$$
$$C_2 = 1/2\pi \times 50 \times 10^6 \times 2.92 = 1090\text{pF}$$
$$L_1 = 1.48/2\pi \times 50 \times 10^6 = 4.71\text{nH}$$

The final configuration and values for the first matching section are shown in Fig 4.120(a). Although in this case the inductive reactance of the transistor input is insignificant from a practical point of view, it will be subtracted from the value of L1 to keep the example correct. The value of L1 then becomes:

$$4.7 - 0.47 = 4.23\text{nH} \ (X_{L1} = 1.48 - 0.15\Omega)$$

The second matching section, transforming the intermediate value of 4.3Ω up to the required driving impedance of 50Ω, is obtained in the same way. A working Q of 4 is used again. Refer to Fig 4.119.

From (5) $B = 4.3(4^2 + 1) = 73.1$
From (4) $A = (73.1/50 - 1)^{0.5} = 0.68$
From (3) $X_{C1'} = 73.1/4 - 0.68 = 22\Omega$
From (2) $X_{C2'} = 0.68 \times 50 = 34\Omega$
From (1) $X_{L1'} = 4 \times 4.3 = 17.2\Omega$
From (6) $C_{1'} = 1/2\pi \times 50 \times 10^6 \times 22 = 145\text{pF}$
            $C_{2'} = 1/2\pi \times 50 \times 10^6 \times 34 = 94\text{pF}$

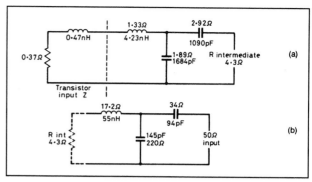

Fig 4.120. (a) First T-match section (input). (b) Second T-match section (input)

From (7) $L_{1'} = 17.2/2\pi \times 50 \times 10^6 = 55\text{nH}$

The circuit configuration, with values, is shown in Fig 4.120(b). In practice the series components C2 and L1' are combined into one component. The capacitive reactance (2.92Ω) is subtracted from the value of inductive reactance (17.2Ω). This leaves an effective inductive reactance of 14.28Ω, which represents a value of 45.4nH. The values shown in the circuit diagram represent this effective inductance. The calculated values tend to be rather impractical, of course, and far from standard-value components. Where possible, mica compression trimmers are used, based on the calculated component values.

Output matching circuit

Before work on the output matching is started, it will be necessary to determine the load impedance for the BLW96. This may be done in two ways. The first, by taking the values directly from the manufacturer's data sheets (only valid for a specific power level); or second, if these are not available, by means of a simple calculation.

Most data sheets include a simple graph of resistance and reactance plotted against frequency for a given output power. For the BLW96 at 50MHz the equivalent series load impedance is $4 + j3\Omega$. Unfortunately this value is quoted at the wrong power level for this design. It should be made clear that these values are the complex conjugate of the transistor load impedance and represent the *load* required to match the device correctly. In this particular case, the transistor is represented by a 4Ω resistor in series with a 1060pF capacitor. If a full data sheet is not available or, as in this example, values are quoted at the wrong power level, a close approximation may be made by using the following formula in conjunction with the output capacitance:

$$R_L = (V_{cc} - V_{sat})^2/2 \times P_{out}$$

Based on a saturation voltage of 2V and a power output of 100W PEP, the value of R_L is:

$$(48 - 2)^2/2 \times 100 = 10.58\Omega$$

The collector capacitance against voltage will normally be shown in the form of a graph or table. As large changes in capacitance occur over the range of collector voltages, a general rule-of-thumb is to take the value shown at 50% of the supply. In this case C_c amounts to 350pF ($X_c = 9\Omega$) at a V_{cb} of 25V. This value is in parallel with the load resistance of 10Ω previously calculated.

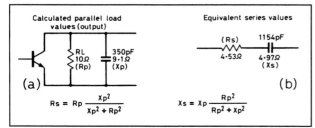

Fig 4.121. Output load conversions. (a) Calculated parallel load values. (b) Equivalent series values

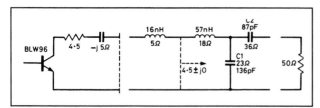

Fig 4.122. Output matching with values

For ease of matching, and to enable a comparison to be made with the published figures, the parallel circuit must be converted into an equivalent series circuit. The conversion formulae with the calculated values are shown in Fig 4.121. It will be seen that these figures differ slightly from the values in the data sheet as the calculation was carried out at a different power level. A good degree of accuracy is obtained if no other data is available at a specific power level.

Now that the required collector load impedance is defined, the output matching circuit can be designed to match from $4.5 - j5\Omega$ to the required output of 50Ω. Unlike the input matching, only one T-match section will be required as the impedance step-up ratio is lower.

Referring back to equations (1) – (5) and using a Q of 4:

$$B = 4.5(4^2 + 1) = 76.5$$

From (5) $A = (76.5/50 - 1)^{0.5} = 0.728$

From (1) $X_L = 4 \times 4.5 = 18\Omega$

From (2) $X_{C2} = 0.728 \times 50 = 36.4\Omega$

From (3) $X_{C1} = 76.5/4 - 0.728 = 23.3\Omega$

From (6) $C_1 = 1/2\pi \times 50 \times 10^6 \times 23.38 = 136\text{pF}$

Table 4.9. Components for G3WZT 50MHz amplifier	
R101	10R 0.5W carbon film
R102	18R 0.5W carbon film
R103	8k2 0.25W carbon film
R104, 105	Select to suit relays used
R106	5k6 0.5W carbon film
R107	3 × 220R 6W wire wound
R108	56R 0.5W carbon film
RV101	47R cermet trimpot
C101	2µ2 63V polycarbonate
C102, 104, 124	100n 100V monolithic ceramic
C103, 121	10n 100V monolithic ceramic
C105	470µ 63V tubular elec
C106	100µ 63V tubular elec
C107, 109	60–180p mica compression trimmer
C108	47p 50V ceramic chip
C110–114	330p 50V ceramic chip
C115	60p 250V Unelco mica or ATC
C116, 117, 119	30–140p mica compression trimmer
C118, 120	80p 250V Unelco mica or ATC
C122	270p 100V monolithic ceramic
C123	22n 100V monolithic ceramic
C125	47n 100V monolithic ceramic
D101	BZY93 C51R zener
D102, 103	1N4002
TR101	BLW96
TR102	BDX66 PNP Darlington
TR103, 104	BD237
FB	Suppression bead. Material, 3S2 (blue)
L101	See Fig 4.118
L102	15 × 7mm pad on PCB
L103	12t 1.2mm copper wire, 9mm ID, 28mm long
L104	See Fig 4.118
L105, 106	4½t 1.2mm copper wire, 10mm ID
L107	2½t 0.5mm enam copper wire wound through 6-hole ferrite bead
RLA, RLB	50R coaxial, type CX120P

From (7)
$$C_2 = 1/2\pi \times 50 \times 10^6 \times 36.4 = 87.4\text{pF}$$
$$L_1 = 18/2\pi \times 50 \times 10^6 = 57.3\text{nH}$$

The final matching circuit values are shown in Fig 4.122. An additional 5Ω must be included in the value of X_L, making a total of 23Ω. This additional reactance, being of opposite sign, cancels the capacitive reactance part of the transistor output impedance ($-j5\Omega$). Both the 16nH and 57nH inductors are combined into a single component.

Fig 4.123 shows the component layout for the amplifier. A component list is given in Table 4.9.

Combining for higher powers

A further method of reaching higher power levels is to combine a number of complete amplifiers. Normally these amplifiers will be identical, with very similar gains. In these

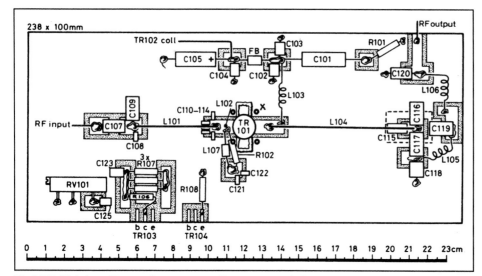

Fig 4.123. Main board layout. Connect top and bottom ground planes with pins at four points marked 'x'. Remove underside copper in dotted area

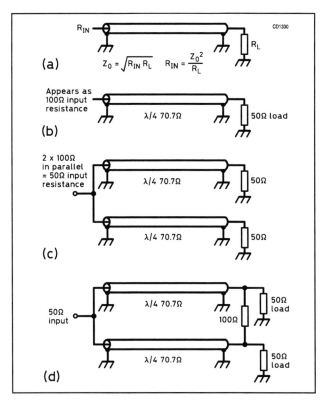

Fig 4.124. (a–c) Coaxial splitter/combiner and derivation. (d) Wilkinson splitter/combiner

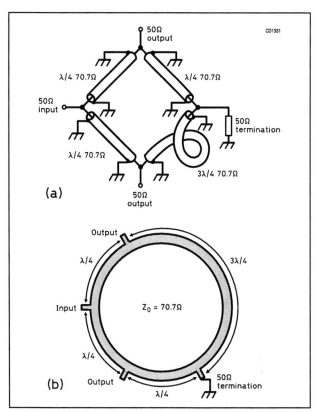

Fig 4.125. 'Rat-race' splitter/combiner. (a) Coaxial cable version. (b) Branch hybrid PCB form

examples, it is assumed that each amplifier is designed to work at 50Ω input and load impedances.

Splitters and combiners are basically the same; a splitter has one input and two or more outputs. Used in reverse the same circuit becomes a combiner with two or more inputs and one output. The combiner might use different components to cope with the higher power, but the circuit will be the same as the splitter. For convenience, the term 'combiner' is used here to cover both splitters and combiners.

In all of the examples discussed in this section, the lengths of cables and transmission lines relate to the electrical lengths, after taking account of the velocity factor.

The simple combiner in Fig 4.124(b) can be made using λ/4 coaxial cable transformers, as used to combine antennas. While simple, this suffers from the disadvantage of offering no isolation between the amplifiers. This can result in instability and, if the amplifier characteristics are not absolutely identical, loss of output power. The Wilkinson combiner is formed by adding a resistor between the divided points. This dissipates any imbalance and provides isolation between the two amplifiers; each one operates completely independently of the other. To get full isolation, it is important that the resistor is purely resistive and high-power flange mounted components are usually used. At UHF and microwaves, the capacitance of these resistors becomes too high for use in this configuration and it is better to use a configuration where the isolating resistor is a 50Ω load connected to ground. One such is the 'rat-race' (Fig 4.125), so called because of its form if made with printed transmission lines. This can be seen as an extension of the Wilkinson design. In these, the optimum impedance is 70.7Ω but in practice 75Ω coaxial cable works perfectly well.

Another family of combiners produce outputs which are have a 90° phase offset. For this reason they are often called quadrature couplers. These have the advantage that, when used as a splitter, the input impedance is always 50Ω as long as the impedances at the two outputs are the same (whatever the actual impedances are). This is of great value when making wide-band amplifiers but has limited importance in amateur applications.

The simplest, but most expensive, version is Sage Wireline™ (Fig 4.126). This can be viewed as a directional coupler

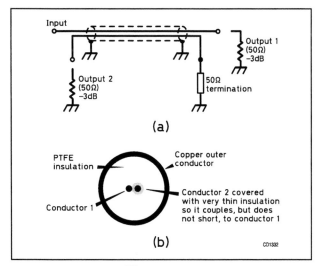

Fig 4.126. Sage Wireline™. (a) Shown schematically, as a directional coupler. (b) Shown mechanically as a cross-section through the cable

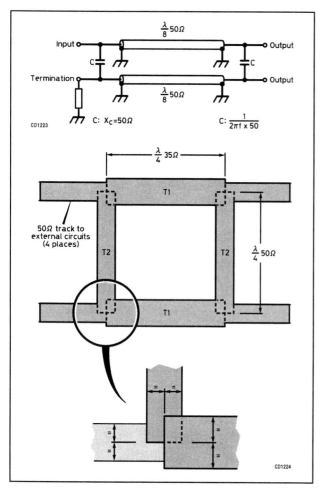

Fig 4.127. Eighth-wave splitter/combiner – coaxial cable and PCB versions

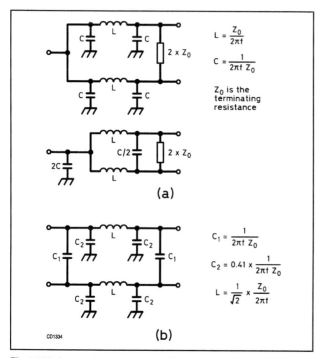

Fig 4.128. Lumped-component splitter/combiners. (a) Wilkinson. (b) Eighth-wave

where the coupling is 3dB when the electrical length is $\lambda/4$; at this frequency half of the input power transfers to the coupled line. Wireline also has the advantage of wide bandwidth; typically the coupling varies by ±0.5dB (±12%) over a 2:1 frequency range.

Two other forms of quadrature couplers shown in Fig 4.127 are the *eighth-wave* (or *capacitively coupled hybrid*) and *branch hybrid* designs. These have similar characteristics to Wireline, but operate over a narrower frequency range. The branch hybrid design is widely used at microwave frequencies as the whole combiner can be microstripline without discrete components to introduce unpredictable parasitic elements. Additionally, the split and combining connections are on the same side which is very convenient for circuit layout.

The Wilkinson and eighth-wave designs can be made using lumped components in place of the transmission lines (Fig 4.128). The bandwidth is reduced, but is still adequate for amateur band coverage. This is especially useful for the lower VHF bands where the coaxial cable lengths become unwieldy.

Fig 4.129 shows how amplifiers are connected using these combiners. The orientation of input and output on quadrature combiners is important; the wrong way round will result in all the output power going into the terminating resistor.

Hybrid modules

Modules are available for all VHF bands. They provide a simple and almost foolproof solution where low and medium output power amplifiers are required. A wide variety of output power and supply voltage ratings are available to suit a great many situations.

Philips, Motorola and Mitsubishi all produce ranges of modules for FM use in amateur or PMR transmitters and Mitsubishi, Icom and Toshiba also supply linear modules for all-mode use in the amateur bands. Major advantages of modules include small size, high gain within a single package, ease of use (no alignment) and guaranteed stability and ruggedness with normal loads. Prices are usually higher than for the equivalent amplifier in discrete components.

The use of the term 'hybrid' arises from the internal construction where a mixture of techniques is used. The RF power transistors and other semiconductors are often connected into the circuit with bond wires (about 0.001in/0.025mm diameter) directly from the silicon die to the circuit tracks, without the familiar package as an intermediate step. Capacitors are either conventional chip types, or silicon MOS capacitors which are manufactured on silicon wafers in a similar fashion to a transistor die. One connection is the surface which is bonded directly onto the track; the other connection is made by a wire bond between the other surface. The track resistors are usually thick-film types, formed directly on the surface of the substrate.

The substrate material is usually alumina (Al_2O_3) which has a dielectric constant of about 10, compared with 4.5 for normal epoxy glass PCB and 2.5 for PTFE-based materials. This is a key factor in miniaturising the circuitry as track widths and lengths in the matching circuitry both reduce significantly. Alumina has the disadvantage of being a brittle ceramic material and problems can arise if the module is subjected to shock or stress. For example, shock can arise if the module is dropped onto a hard surface, or marked with a centre punch.

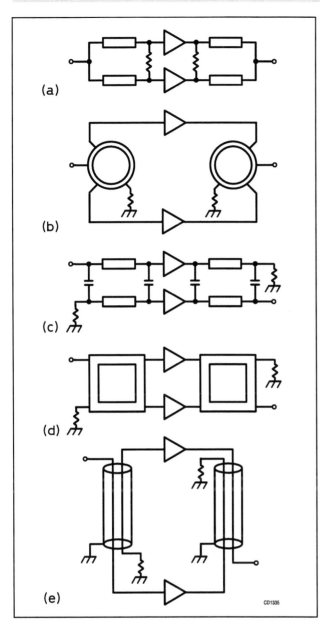

Fig 4.129. Combining amplifiers. The arrangement of input, output and termination connections is important in all cases. (a) Wilkinson. (b) Rat-race. (c) Eighth-wave. (d) Branch line. (e) Wireline™

Stress often arises when the module is fixed to a heatsink. If the heatsink surface is convex instead of flat, the situations shown in Fig 4.130 can arise; one fixing screw has been tightened, leaving the other end proud. If the other screw is then tightened, the flange of the hybrid will be bent, cracking the substrate. Motorola give detailed instructions explaining the need for the surface to be flat within 0.005in/0.12mm. Figs

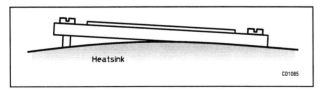

Fig 4.130. Hybrid module on convex heatsink with one fixing screw tightened

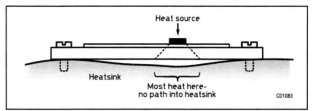

Fig 4.131. Here there is insufficient contact between a concave heatsink and the hot portion of the module

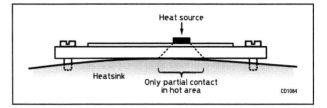

Fig 4.132. Here there is only partial contact with a convex heatsink

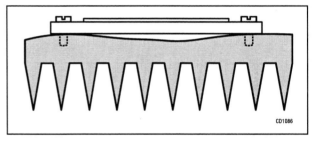

Fig 4.133. Exaggerated view of heatsink which is not flat across the fins

4.131 and 4.132 show problems of insufficient cooling which also occur when the mounting surface is not flat.

As discussed earlier, heatsinks are not normally flat across the fins, as shown in Fig 4.133. This can be seen, and corrected, by sanding very gently against abrasive paper placed face up on a flat surface. The aim is to end up with a flatter surface without making it heavily grooved; this is possible with gentle pressure and fine abrasives. Greater effort is needed than with discrete transistors because of the larger contact area. The module should be fitted to the heatsink using white thermal compound, just sufficient to give continuous contact between the module and the heatsink; the compound is intended to fill microscopic gaps between the surfaces and will not make up for surfaces which are not flat to start with.

Fig 4.134 shows typical circuits using modules. In all cases, LF decoupling should be added externally at each supply pin. In FM use, the output power can varied by adjusting the supply voltage to the driver stages (pin 3 of the BGY36 or V_{cc1} in Fig 4.134). For SSB, this is not usable because of the distortion which arises; the output power is controlled by adjusting the RF input power. Modules intended for SSB use have an additional supply input for the bias circuitry. This is usually a lower voltage than the main supplies so a stable bias source can be derived from a regulated voltage. In SSB use, the output power should not exceed 50% of the rated power of the module in order to ensure that IMD levels are acceptable. Fig 4.134 shows the bias supply for the linear module as 9V; for lower power modules designed for use with lower supply

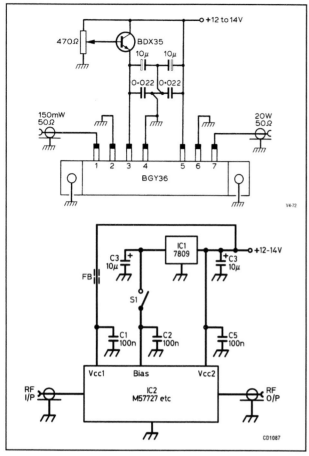

Fig 4.134. Typical hybrid module circuits

Table 4.11. Component notes for Fig 4.135

R_{E1}, R_{E2}	10R 0.1W chip (0805 size)
R_F	390R 0.5W carbon composition with 0.25in leads. It should be installed just above the transistor. 0.05in of lead length are in contact with the board, so the parasitic lead length is 0.20in on each side of the resistor
L_{E1}, L_{E2}	Parasitic inductances that affect the stability of the amplifier
RFC1, 2	RF chokes, roughly 300µH. 11t 26 AWG enam closewound, 0.166in ID. Use a No 19 drill bit as a mandrel
TRL1–6	50Ω microstriplines etched on 1/16in G-10 or FR-4 glass-epoxy circuit board
TR1	Motorola MRF581. This device is rated at a total device dissipation of 2.5W if the collector lead next to the package is kept at or below 50°C
J1, 2	SMA connectors were used in the prototype for convenience and ruggedness. Coaxial cable may be soldered directly to the board

voltages the bias supply is usually 5V, needing a 7805 regulator. Check the data before connecting power. A list of modules suitable for in amateur bands is shown in Table 4.10.

RF input requirements for modules with 1–25W output are typically in the region of 50–300mW. Figs 4.135–4.140 show some suitable linear driver circuits [36, 37] which can in turn be driven by MMICs typically used in modern transverter designs. Many crystal oscillator or synthesised sources will need only a single amplifier stage to reach the desired level for driving a module.

The M57762, giving 10W linear, 20W CW is particularly attractive for 1.3GHz use, where there are few alternative choices available. Some circuits have been published [38, 39] using specially produced transistors which NEC made some years ago, but these are long obsolete. Other transistors which have been used are usually intended for use at frequencies up to 800–900MHz and are unstable and/or of low gain at 1.3GHz. For higher power, modules can be combined. *VHF Communications* published articles [40, 41] which describe two and four modules combined; the two-module amplifier [40] uses combiners which provide no isolation between the modules, and the other [41] uses commercial four-way combiners which will typically cost at least as much as the modules themselves. Suitable combiner designs are discussed elsewhere in this chapter.

AMPLIFIER CIRCUITS
25W amplifier for 144MHz

Fig 4.141 shows this amplifier, based on reference [42], which is suitable for adding to low-power handheld transceivers; the amplifier includes RF driven T/R switching for automatic operation. The RF switching can be copied for use with other designs. The B25-12 transistor (CTC/Acrian) is no longer manufactured but similar types will work with little or no modification to L1 and L2. Construction can be in the form of Fig 4.105.

Table 4.10. A list of some hybrid modules suitable for use in amateur bands

Part no	Freq range (MHz)	Power (W)	Voltage (V)	Mode	Manufacturer
MHW710–1	400–440	13	12.5	FM	Motorola
MHW720–1	400–440	20	12.5	FM	
MHW720A1	400–440	20	12.5	FM	
BGY32	68–88	18	12.5	FM	Philips
BGY35	132–156	18	12.5	FM	
BGY135	132–156	18	12.5	FM	
BGY145A	68–88	28	12.5	FM	
BGY145B	146–174	28	12.5	FM	
BGY46A	400–440	1.4	9.6	FM	
BGY47A	400–440	3.2	9.6	FM	
BGY113A	400–440	7	7.5	FM	
M57735	50–54	10	12.5	SSB	Mitsubishi
M57796MA	144–148	5	7	FM	
M57713	144–148	10	12.5	SSB	
M57727	144–148	25	12.5	SSB	
M57726	144–148	35	12.5	FM	
M67727	144–148	45	12.5	SSB	
M57786M	430–470	5	7.2	FM	
M57716	430–450	10	12.5	SSB	
M57729	430–450	25	12.5	FM	
M57745	430–450	25	12.5	SSB	
M67715	1240–1300	1	8	SSB	
M57762	1240–1300	10	12.5	SSB	
SAV7	144–148	28	12.5	FM	Toshiba
SAU4	430–450	10	12.5	SSB	

FM modules have some stages biased in class C and are suitable for cw/FM only.
SSB modules are linear and can be used with all voice/data/cw modes.

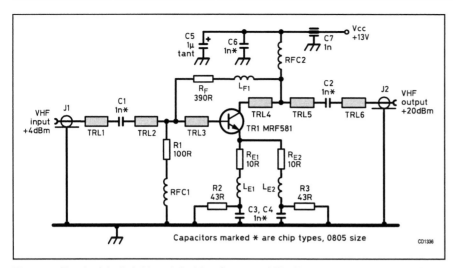

Fig 4.135. Circuit of the hybrid module driver for 50–144MHz. For component notes see Table 4.11. For the PCB layout and component layout see Figs 4.136 and 4.137 (Appendix 1) *(QEX)*

A small amount of the RF input signal is rectified by D1/2 and turns on TR1 and TR2, operating RL1–3. RL1/2 bypass the amplifier during receive and connect it into circuit during transmit. RL3 connects power to the bias circuit for TR3. D4 should be mounted in contact with TR3 to provide thermal compensation for the bias voltage. The current in D4 is adjusted with R4 to set the bias conditions for TR3.

Alignment

Disconnect R6 from L2 and apply 12V to the relay end of R5 but not to the rest of the circuit. Check the voltage across D4; varying R4 should allow the voltage to be adjusted smoothly over a range which includes 0.6–0.8V. This test is important as too high a voltage from a faulty bias circuit will destroy the RF transistor instantly. If the voltage is correct, reconnect R6 to L2. Set all variable capacitors to 50%, set R4 to minimum

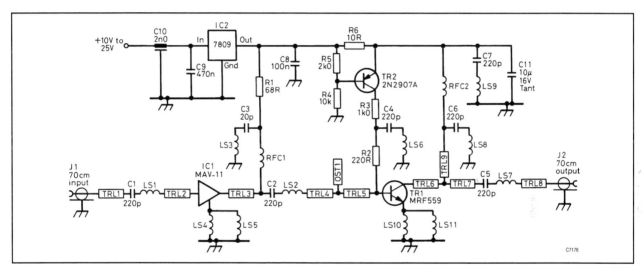

Fig 4.138. Circuit diagram shows the microstrip tuning elements used in the computer analysis. For component layout and PCB etching pattern see Figs 4.139 and 4.140 (Appendix 1) *(QEX)*

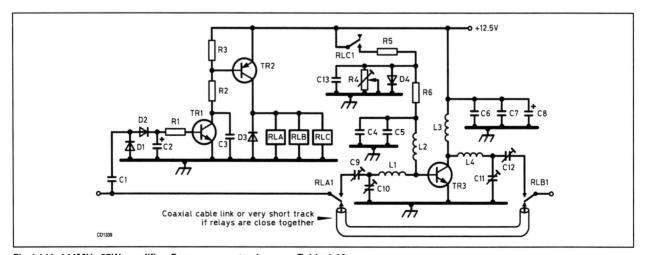

Fig 4.141. 144MHz 25W amplifier. For component values see Table 4.12.

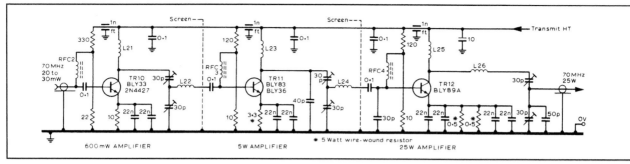

Fig 4.142. 20/30mW to 25W transmit amplifier

Table 4.12. Components list for Fig 4.141	
R1	22k
R2, R3	1k
R4	200R pot
R5	39R 5W
R6	1R
C1	3p3
C2	4μ7
C3, C4, C6	1n
C5, C7, C13	100n
C8	47μ
C9–12	Philips C808 60p (yellow)
D1–3	1N4148
D4	1N4007
TR1	BC109/BC547
TR2	BC182/BC557
TR3	B25-12, TP2320, MRF222 etc
RLA, RLB, RLC	Miniature 12V relay
L1	2t 1.6mm enamelled copper wire, 7mm ID
L2	As L1 but 3t
L3	0.5mm enam copper wire threaded through 6-hole ferrite bead
L4	6t 0.5mm enam copper wire, 4mm ID

resistance and connect 12V. The current should be low; a few milliamps maximum. Connect TR1 collector to earth so that the relays operate; the current should increase to about 300mA. Note this current and adjust R4 for an increase of about 100mA. Remove power and the earth at TR1 collector.

Restore 12V and apply about 0.5W RF drive; the relays should operate cleanly. Adjust the capacitors for maximum output power, about 4–8W, then increase the RF input to the full level of 2–3W. At this power level adjust the output capacitors for maximum output power and the input capacitors for minimum input VSWR. The output power and supply current should vary smoothly as the circuit is tuned; sudden jumps indicate instability.

This basic procedure can be applied to all amplifiers; check the bias, check DC conditions without RF, tune up at low power, and finally tune at high power.

C2 provides a delay before the amplifier reverts to receive so that the relays do not change over during every pause in speech when using SSB. For FM use this capacitor can be reduced to 0.01μF for rapid switching; for dual-mode use the larger capacitor can be switched in and out of circuit.

Amplifiers for 70MHz

These designs are taken from a transverter design by G3XBY and G3WOS [43]. The lower-power part (Fig 4.142) uses three cascaded stages to amplify from about 20mW to 25W. Bias in all the stages is set using emitter resistors which avoids the need for alignment and provides good thermal stability and improved linearity. The emitter decoupling capacitors should be mounted close to the transistor body with minimum lead length.

The 100W amplifier (Figs 4.143 and 4.144) uses two 2N6084 or BLY89 in parallel. The circuit uses an operational amplifier and emitter followers to give a very-low-impedance bias voltage supply. IC2 provides a negative supply voltage for the operational amplifier as the type used in the original (741) has input and output voltage ranges which cannot go close enough to ground without a negative supply voltage. Some later operational amplifiers can function in this application without the negative supply, but operation should be tested carefully before connecting to the RF transistors.

50MHz 25W amplifier

The 25W 70MHz amplifier was modified by GW3XYW for use on 50MHz [44]. The 2N6080 and

Fig 4.143. 100W transmit amplifier

Table 4.13. Components for 70MHz amplifiers	
L21	6t 18 SWG 3/8in ID, length 5/8in
L22	5½t 18 SWG, 3/8in ID, length ½in
L23	7t 18 SWG, 3/8in ID, length ¾in
L24	3t 18SWG, 3/8in ID, length 3/8in
L25	7t 16 SWG, 3/8in ID, close wound
L26	6t 16 SWG, 3/8in ID, close wound
L27, L28	2t 16 SWG, ½in ID, ¼in leads
L29, L30	1t 16 SWG, ½in ID, ¼in leads
L31, L32	5t 16 SWG, ½in ID, close wound
RFC2–5, 10	6t on Mullard FX1898 6-hole ferrite bead
RFC 6–8	10t 18 SWG on 5/8in diam toroid
RFC9	1.5mH choke

2N6082 transistors chosen by GW3XYW can also be used in the 70MHz design and might prove easier to obtain than the Philips types in the original. The 100W amplifier could likewise be modified for 50MHz use.

Figs 4.145 and 4.146 show the circuit and layout. Construction uses single-sided PCB with Veropins in tight-fitting holes to give anchorage points for the components. Where the connection has to be insulated from the ground plane, a small circle of copper is removed with a drill bit before the pin is fitted. Some components are fitted underneath the PCB so the power transistors have to be mounted to the heatsink on aluminium or copper spacers to provide clearance. These spacers are important in maintaining proper cooling for the power transistors and so should be as wide as possible with very flat contact surfaces. C126 and C127 are shown as 30pF air-spaced trimmers; 60pF rotary foil types should work perfectly well as an alternative.

144MHz 10W amplifier

A similar amplifier for 144MHz [45] is shown in Fig 4.147. The output power is about 10W for 10mW input and an attenuator at the input can be used to adjust the input level if greater drive is available. For drive levels of 100mW or more, the first amplifier stage can be omitted and the input connected to the alternative input point as shown.

144MHz 100W amplifier

This amplifier was designed as the driver stage of a 400W 144MHz amplifier [46]. In that application the circuit

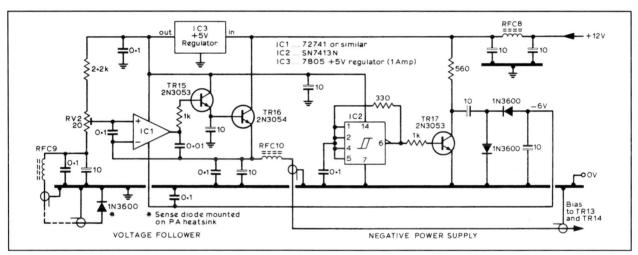

Fig 4.144. PA bias generator

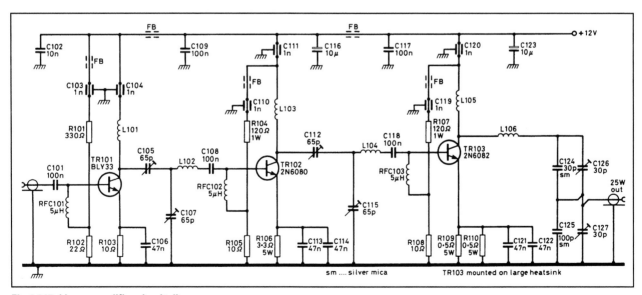

Fig 4.145. Linear amplifier circuit diagram

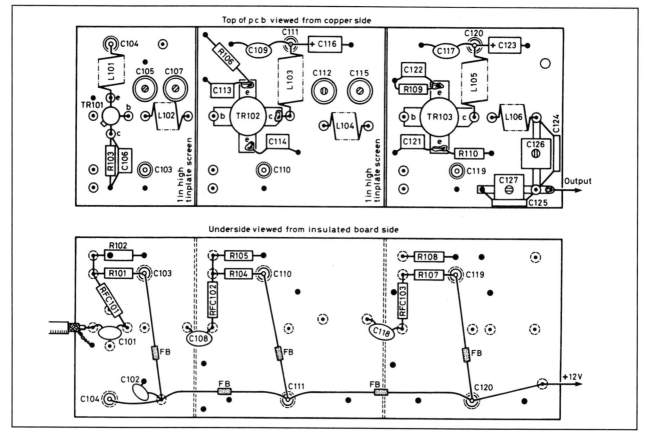

Fig 4.146. Linear amplifier component layout

operated at 75W output with very good linearity so that overall linearity was dominated by the output stages. Used alone, linearity will be acceptable at 100–120W output. The amplifier (Fig 4.148) uses a pair of BLW86 in push pull. The load resistance required is about 6.5Ω per device or 13Ω side to side. This is conveniently achieved by using a λ/4 transformer of 25Ω cable (2 × 50Ω in parallel) which converts from 50 to 12.5Ω. The cable also provides the balun function for push-pull operation. C8 optimises the load impedance for best linearity.

The 270pF capacitors cancel each transistor's input inductance to leave a resistance of 2Ω. A T-section network with a Q of 4 matches this to 6.25Ω and a λ/4 25Ω coaxial transformer matches this to 50Ω.

The bias circuit uses TR3 and TR4. TR3 base-emitter junction provides thermal compensation for the RF power transistors and TR4 supplies the output current. The two transistors also act as a voltage regulator, holding TR3 emitter voltage constant with varying bias current.

70MHz 200W FM amplifier

This amplifier (Fig 4.149) by G0MRF [47] uses a pair of transistors in parallel. These transistors are specified for use at 30MHz, 100W output but they still provide useful performance at higher frequencies and give excellent value for money. Unfortunately, not all transistors specified for HF use will work well at higher frequencies.

Clearly, this amplifier can be readily modified for 50MHz use, and bias added for linear operation (see Fig 4.106 for recommended decoupling arrangements if bias is added).

432MHz 4W FM amplifier

This simple amplifier (Figs 4.150 and also 4.151 in

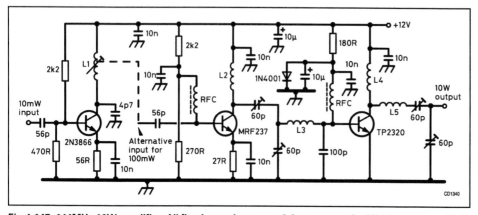

Fig 4.147. 144MHz 10W amplifier. All fixed capacitors are miniature ceramic. All trimmers are 60pF rotary, eg Philips C808 or similar. L1: Toko S18, 4½t, add tap at 2¼t. L2–L5 are 1.6mm enam Cu wire, 6.5mm ID. L2: 4t. L3: 2t. L4: 4t. L5: 3½t *(Radio and Electronics World)*

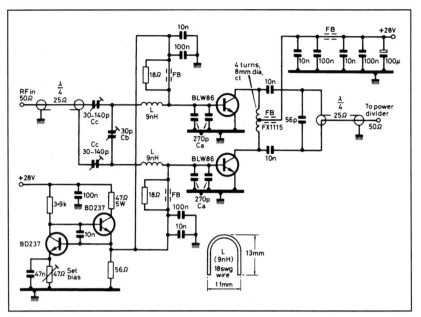

Fig 4.148. 75W drive amplifier circuit. Ca, Cb, Cc are mica compression types. Unmarked FB are 3S2 (blue). Coaxial transformers are two parallel 350mm lengths of UR110. 56p compensation capacitor is glass or ATC porcelain type. All other capacitors are chip ceramic. Quiescent current is set for 160mA total

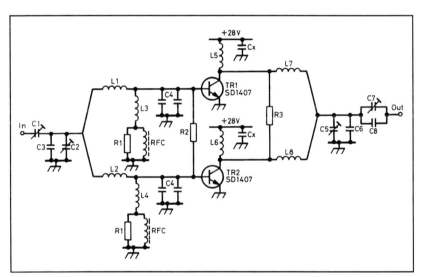

Fig 4.149. G0MRF's 200W FM/CW amplifier for 70MHz. Components are given in Table 4.14

Table 4.14. Components list for Fig 4.149	
R1	10R 0.5W
R2	47R 1W
R3	100R 2W (R1–3 carbon film)
C1	6–65p film trimmer
C2, 5, 7	10–100p high-voltage rotary type with PTFE film dielectric or mica compression
C3, 6, 8	47p silver mica, 350V
C4	4 ×100p (each base has 400pF to ground)
Cx	100µ + 0.01µ + 1n in parallel
L1, 2	2t 18SWG, 10mm ID
L3, 4	8t 22SWG, 2.5mm ID
L5, 6	6t 18SWG, 6.5mm ID
L7, 8	2t 16SWG, 10mm ID
RFC	2t 22SWG enam Cu through FX1115 ferrite bead
TR1, 2	SD1407

Appendix 1) [48] can be a useful addition to a low-power exciter or, with the addition of bias, an output stage to follow the circuit of Fig 4.138 in a transverter. The circuit diagram is similar to the other amplifiers, but the matching inductors have been replaced by printed tracks; hand-wound components tend to be too imprecise at higher frequencies. This amplifier is built on double sided 1.6mm glassfibre/epoxy PCB; for higher powers the loss can be excessive and glassfibre/PTFE is often used. At 0.4W input, output power is 3W at 12V and 4W at 14V supply. Collector efficiency is about 50%.

Broad-band 300W FET amplifier

With the addition of appropriate harmonic filters this amplifier covers all bands from 20m to 2m with up to 300W (about 200W linear) output, 15dB (30×) gain and without any tuning. Figs 4.152, 4.153 and Table 4.15 show the circuit and constructional detail. The design techniques are radically different to those used in the other amplifiers described here and are described in considerable detail in the original article in *Microwaves and RF* [49]. Reference to the full article is essential for anyone considering building this amplifier. The amplifier is available in kit form [50] and offers an interesting and maybe cost-effective alternative to a series of individual amplifiers for each band. Basically, a 9:1 impedance transformer is used to match the transistor input impedance to 50Ω and a 4:1 transformer gives a load impedance of about 12.5Ω side-side, or 6.25Ω for each transistor. Two identical transistors are mounted side by side on a single flange so that the push-pull circuit is readily constructed and fully balanced. The transformers use a novel construction to give broad-band VHF performance. The windings are made from pieces of semi-rigid coaxial cable which have a solid copper outer conductor. The outers are soldered together to make a single low-impedance turn and the inners are connected in series to give a turns ratio of 2:1 (input) or 3:1 (output). 'E' and 'I' cross-section ferrite cores fit around the cables to extend the low-frequency response (which is about 70MHz without the ferrite). R8 and R9 introduce feedback which stabilises impedances and controls the gain at lower frequencies. For prolonged use at higher frequencies the ferrite can get very hot and fan cooling of the upper surface of the circuit might be needed.

AMPLIFIERS USING VALVES

The 4CX250 family of tetrode valves has been the most popular choice by far for high power amplifiers for some time, at

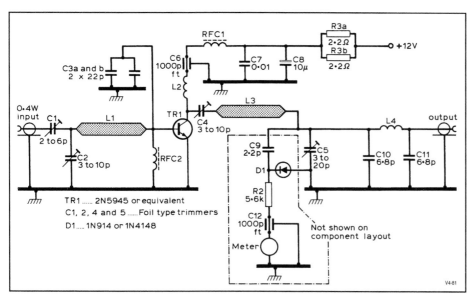

Fig 4.150. 432MHz power amplifier giving 3–4W output. L1: stripline. L2: 7t 6mm dia 22SWG wound. L3: stripline. L4 1t 7mm dia 18SWG. RFC1: 2t 22SWG ferrite bead. RFC2: 3t 20SWG large ferrite bead

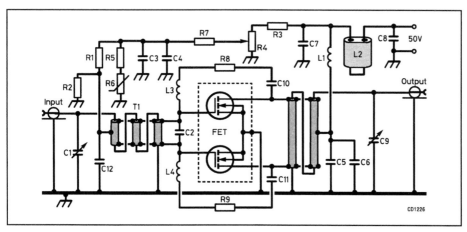

Fig 4.152. At the heart of the 300W amplifier is the Gemini push-pull transistor configuration. This broad-band amplifier operates in the 10 to 175MHz range *(Microwaves & RF)*

least partially because of ready availability of valves and bases on the surplus market. Recently alternative triodes have become more available at comparable prices.

Few amplifiers are built as exact replicas of published

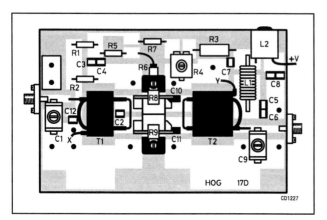

Fig 4.153. Component layout of the 300W amplifier *(Microwaves & RF)*

designs; there is usually some variation from the use of materials to hand. The examples chosen here are intended to demonstrate a variety of different techniques, as well as providing designs for duplication.

Cooling

Valves are like almost every other electronic component; if they overheat they die young.

Cooling power valves effectively has long been a neglected part of amateur amplifier building. Most fans are designed to move air against little or no obstruction and cannot force air to flow through the restriction of a valve base and anode. See Fig 4.155 which shows the suggested airflow arrangements, with cold air cooling the valve base, heater pins and grid spigot before going through the anode. To cool a 4CX250 at full power (250W dissipation), a minimum airflow of 6.4cfm (3l/s) is required [51] and this requires pressure in the grid compartment. This pressure, usually called the *back pressure*, is normally defined in terms of *water gauge*, that is the displacement seen in a water manometer connected to the pressurised area. The pressures required for the 4CX250 equate to 0.82in (21mm) WG. Allowing for screening mesh over the apertures, and airflow within the cabinet, the blower needs to

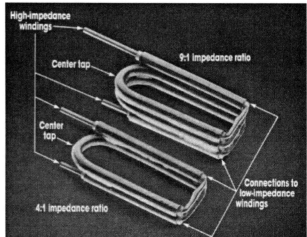

Fig 4.154. Construction of the wide-band transformer *(Microwaves & RF)*

Table 4.15. Components list for the broad-band amplifier

R1	1k, 0.5W
R2	1k5, 0.5W
R3	1k5, 2W
R4	1k trimpot
R5	6k8–8k2, 0.25W (depends on FET G_{fs}
R6	Thermistor, 10k @ 25°C, 2k5 @ 75°C
R7	2k, 0.5W
R8, R9	50R power resitor, EMC Technology Type 5310 or KDI Pyrofilm type PPR 515-20-3
C1, C9	8–60p, ARCO 404 or equiv
C2	130p ceramic chip
C3, C10, C11	100n cermic chip
C4, C5, C12	1000p ceramic chip
C6, C7	5000p ceramic chip
C8	470n ceramic chip, or lower values in paralle to match the value indicated
L1	10t 16 AWG enam, 5mm ID
L2	Ferrite beads, 1.5µH total
L3, L4	Lead lengths of R8 and R9, 20mm total
T1	9:1 RF transformer, 25Ω, 0.062in OD, semi-rigid coaxial cable
T2	1:4 RF transformer, 25Ω, 0.090in OD, semi-rigid coaxial cable
TR1	MRF151G

Notes: For T1, two type 75-26 E and I Micrometals powdered iron cores are required. For T2, three type 100-8 E and I Micrometals powdered iron cores are required.

All chip capacitors of 5000p or less are ATC type 100 or equiv.

be able to work at least 1in (25mm) WG. Some fans/blowers are shown in Fig 4.157. The 120mm axial fan cannot generate this pressure, regardless of airflow, and is completely

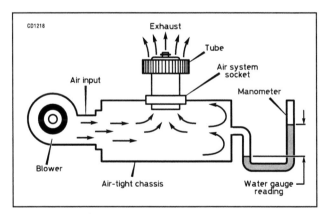

Fig 4.155. Grid blown cooling

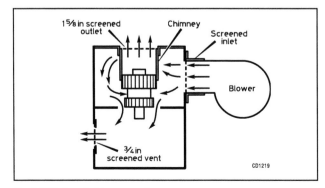

Fig 4.156. Anode blown cooling

Fig 4.157. Top: An 120mm axial fan. Middle: A small blower, the Papst RG90/18-50. Bottom: EBM G2E 1120 blower

unsuitable. The RG90/18-50 will produce slight airflow, sufficient for about 100W anode dissipation. The EBM G2E 1120 is well suited to the job, capable of 1.3in (33mm) WG and over 80cfm (170l/s) at 1in. Any blower capable of delivering adequate back pressure will almost invariably meet the volume requirement. See Table 4.16 for some suggested blowers.

Table 4.16. Blowers suitable for cooling external anode valves

Type	Pressure	Price	Supplier
Papst RG160-28/56S	30mm	£59	Farnell Electronic Components 0113 263 6311 order code 474400
Papst RG160-28/56S	30mm	£61	Electromail 01536 204555 order code 813569
Ziehl-EBM G2E 108-AA01-50 *	20mm	£92	Electromail 01536 204555 order code 223089
Ziehl-EBM G2E 120-AA12-50	33mm	£114	Electromail 01536 204555 order code 581262
ACI VBL5/3	28mm	£104	Air control Installations 01460 67171
ACI VBM5	30mm	£114	Air Control Installations 01460 67171
Etri 620CAZ016DC13	30mm	£180	Fan Technology 01403 275131

* Suitable for use as in Fig 4.156 only.

Cooling should be applied before the heaters are powered and ideally continued for some minutes after the heaters are switched off.

Circuit configurations

At VHF/UHF triodes are always used in grounded grid configuration with RF applied to the cathode (or heater if directly heated). For convenience, where 'cathode' is mentioned in the text, the alternative in brackets should be taken as read. If RF input is applied to the grid, the effect of the feedback capacitance from anode to grid has to be negated in order to prevent oscillation. This can be done by providing an antiphase signal (neutralisation) from anode to grid to cancel the feedback, or by reducing the resistance at the grid to a level where the circuit is stable. The latter results in low power gain and is frequency dependent. Neutralisation is used in small-signal triode amplifiers, but is impractical for the amateur in high-power circuits.

In the grounded-grid circuit, the grid forms a screen between the input at the cathode and the output at the anode, reducing the feedback to a small level which permits stable operation. The input impedance at the cathode is lower than when driving the grid in grounded cathode, so the circuit power gain is lower than offered by tetrodes such as 4CX250, but the power supply requirements are somewhat simpler. The circuits in grounded grid amplifiers can appear slightly confusing, and Fig 4.158 shows how the conventional grounded cathode circuit is developed to work with grounded grid connection, omitting the input and output matching circuits. Fig 4.158(a) shows a conventional circuit with RF input applied between the grid and cathode. M1 reads the grid current and M2 the anode current. M2' also reads the anode current, but in a much safer position where the voltage is close to ground.

In Fig 4.158(b) D1 holds the cathode positive with respect to the grid, equivalent to holding the grid negative with respect to a grounded cathode. C1 bypasses D1 for RF signals, so the RF input is applied between grid and cathode. Valves intended for grounded-grid operation are designed to need low bias voltage, typically in the range 0–12V, so D1 is a readily available power zener diode.

In Fig 4.158(c), (b) is rearranged so that the grid connection is grounded. The RFC moves so as to isolate the cathode from D1 and C1 in (b) is not needed. RF input is still between the grid and cathode. S1 is added to show transmit/receive switching. On receive, S1 is open-circuit, stopping all current flow. In practice, R1 is left in circuit to prevent the cathode floating.

In a tetrode, the problem of anode-to-grid feedback capacitance is overcome by placing an additional grid between them. This is grounded to RF signals and screens the anode from the grid, hence the name *screen grid*.

The low level of feedback allows the tetrode to be used in grounded-cathode configuration, with the RF input signal applied to the control grid. The higher impedance at the control grid means that a lower power is needed to provide the necessary grid-to-cathode voltage swing, so the power gain of the circuit is higher than for grounded grid.

Fig 4.159 shows the normal circuit arrangement. g1 bias is typically –40 to –60V for quiescent bias when transmitting and about –100V to shut the valve off when receiving. The screen grid bias is in the regions of 350V (TX) and 0V (RX). The 4CX250 family has screen grid characteristics which can result in both positive and negative screen grid current (the screen grid can source as well as draw current) under normal operating conditions as the output power varies. The screen grid supply must be able to maintain a constant voltage under all conditions, and so must be able to sink (absorb) as well as source (supply) current.

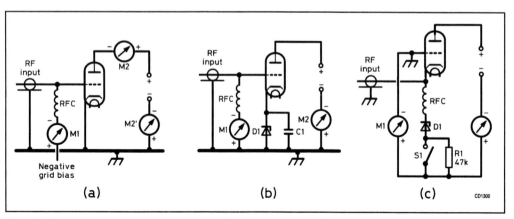

Fig 4.158. The evolution of a grounded-grid amplifier. (a) Conventional grounded-cathode circuit. (b) Cathode held positive with respect to the grid. (c) Rearrangement of (b) so the grid is grounded directly

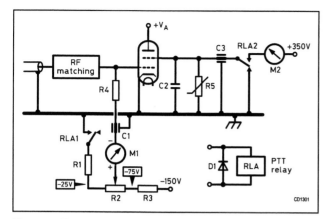

Fig 4.159. Typical tetrode amplifier circuit

Table 4.17. Components list for Fig 4.159	
R1	2k2 1W
R2	5k 2W
R3	6k8 2W
R4	See text
R5	MOV V275 LA40B or equiv (275V RMS, 140J rating)
C1, 2	1000–5000p 500V feedthrough
C2	Screen grid capacitor built into valveholder
D1	1N4001
RLA	DPCO coil voltage to suit available supplies
M1	5mA
M2	10-0-10mA centre-zero

Tetrode gain characteristics are dependent to a large degree on the screen grid voltage. Gain increases as the screen grid voltage is increased, but linearity is better with lower voltage. A value in the region of 325–350V gives an optimum balance for general use.

The control grid supply can be very simple, assuming that no grid current is allowed in normal operation. This will always be the case for linear use with SSB signals. If grid current is permitted, higher efficiency (at the expense of gain) can be achieved with increased RF input and different anode loading for CW and FM signals. This case will not be considered here as, under all normal circumstances, an amplifier set up for linear operation will give satisfactory operation with all types of signal.

On receive, S1 is open and the full negative voltage is applied to the grid via the various resistors. On transmit, R2 adjusts the voltage applied to the grid to allow the desired quiescent voltage to be set. In practice, if grid current is drawn, the change in grid voltage from the voltage drop in the resistors has little effect on operation. References [54] and [55] show more complex circuits which will hold the grid voltage constant when grid current is drawn.

R4 feeds the bias voltage to the control grid and also serves to load the grid circuit, effectively setting the gain. At high anode and screen grid voltages, a value of R4 higher than 2–3kΩ can give very high gain, leading to instability unless the amplifier is neutralised.

Output matching networks

An important factor in designing the matching network is the loaded Q (not to be confused with the Q of individual components). This is the ratio of reactance to resistance (see Fig 4.160(a)), and will vary from point to point in the matching network. The highest value at any point defines the value for the whole network.

Typically, a loaded Q of around 10–15 is used when designing the output matching network. This is usually chosen as giving a balance between loss and harmonic rejection, with both factors increasing with increasing loaded Q. Given that every transmitter should have effective low-pass harmonic filtering before the antenna, values of Q below 10 can be used to give lower losses, provided that the component values remain reasonable.

Depending on the anode voltage and output power, the load resistance required at the anode is usually in the range 2000–5000Ω.

At lower frequencies a pi-network, as in Fig 4.160(b), is commonly used. At VHF the operating (or loaded) Q of the circuit tends to become high, leading to difficulties in adjustment and higher circuit losses. The minimum loaded Q is determined by the minimum value of C1 which is in turn defined by the valve output capacitance and circuit strays. It can be seen that the problem gets worse with increasing frequency.

Fig 4.161(a) shows the calculations for a 4CX250 at 50MHz and 144MHz.

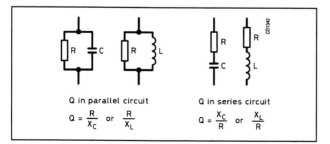

Fig 4.160(a). Q values in series and parallel circuits

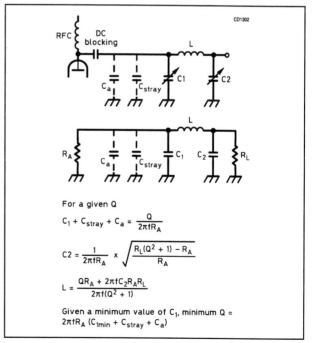

For a given Q

$$C_1 + C_{stray} + C_a = \frac{Q}{2\pi f R_A}$$

$$C2 = \frac{1}{2\pi f R_A} \times \sqrt{\frac{R_L(Q^2+1) - R_A}{R_A}}$$

$$L = \frac{QR_A + 2\pi f C_2 R_A R_L}{2\pi f(Q^2+1)}$$

Given a minimum value of C_1, minimum Q = $2\pi f R_A (C_{1min} + C_{stray} + C_a)$

Fig 4.160(b). Pi network

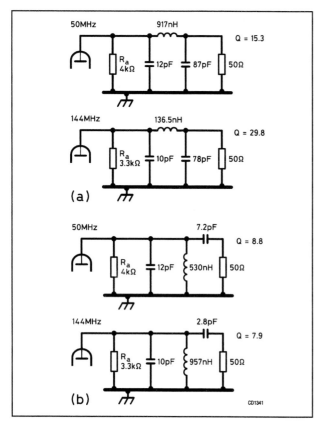

Fig 4.161. *Q* calculations

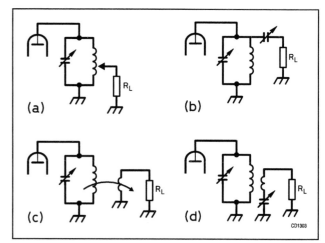

Fig 4.162. Various methods of tapping the load into the anode circuit

circuits can be replaced by lengths of transmission line tuned to resonance with the valve capacitance and a small amount of tuning capacitance. At 144MHz the resonant circuit is usually λ/4, grounded at one end, while at higher frequencies λ/2 is used as λ/4 is impractically short when chosen to resonate with the valve output capacitance, as shown in Fig 4.163. Any of the coupling methods shown in Fig 4.162 can be used in conjunction with a transmission line anode circuit.

Valve bases

With tetrodes reliant on the screen grid RF grounding for stability, and with a bias voltage applied at the same time, special valve bases are needed. Fig 4.164 shows a 4CX250 tetrode; the screen grid is connected to one pin and also to the lower annular ring. Fig 4.165 shows a cross section of the contact spring finger and the capacitor which provides the RF grounding. The contact fingers introduce some series inductance, reducing the effectiveness of the grounding as the frequency increases. This can lead to instability, especially where high gain and maximum output power are sought.

Bases for HF use often have no built-in screen grid contact and capacitor, relying on decoupling through the pin connection. This will not work at VHF/UHF. All bases with built-in capacitors and contact fingers are likely to work without problems for 50, 70 and 144MHz, but the only reliable choice for UHF is the Eimac SK630 [57–59] which was specially designed with low-inductance screen grid contacts and additional screening to minimise feedback.

Grounded-grid circuits likewise need low-inductance

The usual solution is to incorporate the valve and associated capacitances into a tuned circuit with the valve anode at the high-impedance point. The resistance at the anode (R_a) is set by tapping the load (in this case the antenna) into the circuit at the appropriate point, as shown in Fig 4.162(a). In practice, the 'tap' can be implemented in several other ways, some of which are shown in Fig 4.162(b)–(d). Circuits (a)–(c) give monotonic performance; the anode resistance is lowered (heavier loading) as the tapping point moves towards the anode in (a), or C2 is increased in (b) or the output coil is moved closer to the anode coil in (c). K2RIW shows [56] how the circuit in (d) can give misleading indications whereby C2 appears to have a definite tuning point, but the desired loading is not achieved. In this case, it is necessary to adjust the coupling between the anode circuit and the output coupling link until C2 can be adjusted to give the correct loading. This can be seen when older designs, optimised for maximum CW output, are used in linear service with SSB signals; the loading is often too light (anode resistance too high) for good linearity.

Using the previous example, the tuned circuit configuration allows a lower loaded *Q*; Fig 4.161(b) shows that a value of less than 10 is easily achieved.

At higher frequencies the lumped components in the tuned

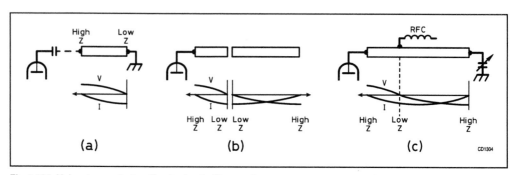

Fig 4.163. Using transmission line instead of lumped components

Fig 4.164. The 4CX250

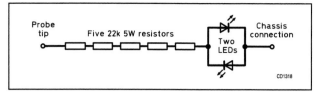

Fig 4.166. Discharge and indicator probe

apparently no chance of any voltage being present. The probe need be nothing more than a plastic rod with a bare wire hook at one end and a stout insulated wire which runs from the hook to the equipment chassis. The wire must be bolted or soldered in place at both ends; spring clips can drop off too easily. The hook allows the probe to hung onto circuits for extra security while working on them, but don't forget to unhook it before switching on again! Fig 4.166 shows an another design by G8DPS which both discharges and indicates the presence of voltage above about 200V.

Fig 4.167 and Table 4.18 show a typical anode voltage supply taken from reference [60] which includes a number of protection features which will help to avoid permanent damage in the event of problems occurring. Echoing the sentiments of GW4FRX in the article, the mains transformer will probably be the item which defines the mechanics of the PSU. Should it have to be replaced the chances of finding another

grounding of the grid for correct operation. This is more easily achieved as there is no voltage to apply and so a direct connection to the chassis can be made.

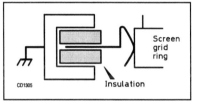

Fig 4.165. Cross-section through screen grid capacitor in valveholder

Power supplies

Never forget that high voltage WILL KILL YOU if you let it. Danger is not limited to anode supplies or mains; the grid bias supplies in a tetrode amplifier can be lethal too.

A good PSU will take at least as much effort as the amplifier it supplies. PSU problems are often behind disasters which are blamed on the RF section of the amplifier.

Anode supply

Depending on the valve(s) in use and the output power, the anode supply is likely to be in the region of 1–2.5kV at up to 0.5A. Anyone unfamiliar with working on such supplies should consider that this is equivalent to 12V at 100A, only MUCH more dangerous. A 12V 100A PSU is a major undertaking, and so is the high-voltage equivalent, albeit with different problems.

Large power supplies tend to be built around items which become available rather than from a list of catalogue items. This applies to transformers in particular, and other components in general.

The most important job before working on any power supply or amplifier is to make an insulated probe for earthing anything and everything to be worked on, even if there is

Table 4.18. Components list for Fig 4.171	
R1, 4	MOV 275V AC 140J
R2	2k2 2W
R3	470R 50W
R5–12	100k 2W
R13	68R 50W
R14	Select for M1 to read desired FSD
R15	1R0 25W for 0.5A FSD, 2R2 25W for 0.25A FSD
C1	10,000µ 25V
D1	1N5408
D2	Bridge rectifier, 20 ×1N5408 and 20 ×680k 2W
D3	50V, 60A diode or 35A bridge rectifier
RLA	24V, 300-400Ω coil, 16A min contacts
FS1	5A mains fuse
FS2, 3	1A high rupture current (HRC) fuses, 1¼in ceramic body

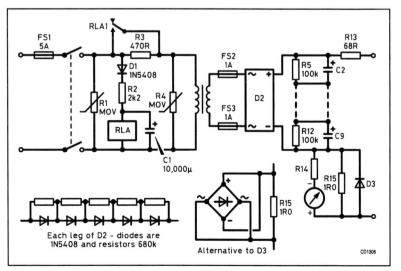

Each leg of D2 - diodes are 1N5408 and resistors 680k

Alternative to D3

Fig 4.167. Typical anode voltage supply *(VHF/UHF DX Book)*

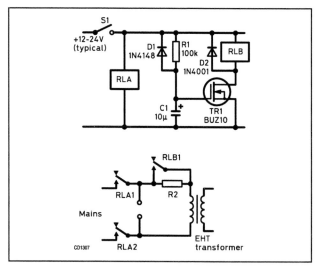

Fig 4.168. Alternative delay circuit. R1/C1 chosen to give delay of 1–5 seconds. S1: EHT on/off. RLA: DPNO 16A coil to suit DC supply. RLB: SPNO 16A coil to suit DC supply. TR1: N-channel power FET (eg BUZ10)

which is electrically and mechanically compatible is remote, unless it is a brand-new item, in which case it will have been very expensive. Either way, it is worth going to some lengths to ensure that the transformer is protected under all circumstances.

The input filter (not shown) and R1 remove noise and spikes on the mains supply, both of which can be significant when operating from generators. R1 is a metal oxide varistor (MOV) which behaves something like a zener diode; it has a high resistance up to threshold voltage, and then is able to conduct high current and absorb high transient energy, limiting the voltage peak. The surge limiting circuit around R3/RLA1 is much more gentle than most, limiting the primary current for about 10s rather than the few cycles allowed by most circuits. This allows the use of a lower value mains fuse than needed if surge currents have to be catered for.

An alternative delay circuit is shown in Fig 4.168. This uses a low-voltage supply which is usually present in most PSUs.

An important point here is that the circuits are simply delay timers. Some designs use feedback from, for example, the anode supply voltage monitor to switch the resistor out of circuit. This is fine until a fault occurs which loads the secondary side excessively so that the switch does not operate; then the limiting resistor has full mains voltage across it permanently and can overheat or burn out. With a timed switch, the mains fuse will blow if there is a problem.

Both secondary connections to the rectifier should be fused. This protects the transformer against shorts in the rectifier or capacitors and the voltage/current will be zero at some point each cycle which allows any arcing to extinguish. Use only ceramic HRC (high rupture current) fuses and do not use normal panel-mount fuseholders.

Modern diodes have improved reverse breakdown characteristics and the voltage equalising resistors shown in older designs are not essential, although unlikely to cause harm. Capacitors across each diode should not be used; transient protection should be provided in the primary circuit.

Smoothing capacitors should be chosen to give a voltage

rating of at least twice the output voltage; a total value of around 40µF will suit most applications. A string of resistors passing about 2mA provides a discharge path and equalises the voltage distribution between capacitors.

R13 limits the peak current in the event of a flashover, while dropping only 20–30V in normal operation. A fuse here will not provide adequate protection for either the PSU or the amplifier.

Current is measured in the return path so that metering is close to ground voltage. R15 must stay intact in the event of a flashover otherwise there is a risk of the chassis floating to +2kV. Choose a high-power resistor which will drop 0.5V at the desired meter FSD. A high-current diode across the resistor will carry the current in the event of a flashover, protecting the resistor and meter. A cheap and convenient solution is a high-current bridge wired as shown.

In addition to these measures, there must always be an independent heavy duty earthing strap between the amplifier and PSU chassis. Otherwise, if an invisible internal connection fails, you might only find out when you have an earthed connector in one hand and a chassis at +2kV in the other.

Heater supplies

For best life, heater voltages should be regulated to ±5% of rated value, measured at the valve pin as shown in Fig 4.169. The monitor point can be a small feedthrough capacitor or miniature socket on the grid compartment to allow the voltage to be measured without disturbing the airflow. The error introduced by the series resistor is minimal if a high resistance DVM is used for the measurement and no damage occurs if the

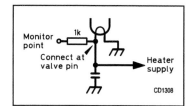

Fig 4.169. Monitoring the heater voltage

test point is accidentally shorted to ground. Eimac have also recommended [61] tighter control of +0/−5%, with further reductions to 5.5V at frequencies above 300MHz to allow for cathode heating from 'back bombardment'. For domestic use with reliable mains supplies, 'select on test' resistors are a typical solution.

For conditions where the mains supply is not stable enough, a small Variac supplying the heater transformer or more complex regulated supplies, such as given in reference [62], will be needed. An alternative circuit is shown in Fig 4.170 [63]. TR1 acts as a variable resistance in series with the transformer primaries, diodes D1–4 steering the current correctly regardless of mains polarity. TR2–4 control TR1 so as to maintain a constant voltage at the transformer primaries, and thus a constant voltage to the heaters. WARNING – the circuitry is at mains potential and TR1 will need adequate cooling.

Cold heaters have a low resistance so initial current surge can be quite high. It is beneficial to arrange some form of current limiting or gradual increase in voltage. K1FO [64] recommends choosing a transformer with about 20% too much voltage and using primary and secondary resistors to drop the output by about 10% each, as shown in Fig 4.171.

The minimum warm-up times of 30 seconds for 4CX250 and three minutes for all other types should be strictly

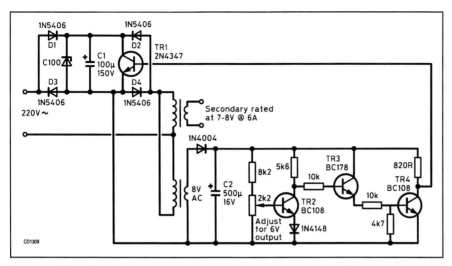

Fig 4.170. PA0LMD's AC regulator for stabilising the heater voltage applied to valves such as the 4CX250. Note that the electronics of the regulator are not isolated from the mains supply and suitable precautions should be taken

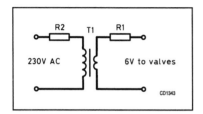

Fig 4.171. Use of primary and secondary resistors with the heater transformer as suggested by K1FO. R1: 0R47 10W for single 4CX250, 0R22 10W for pair of 4CX250s. R2: Select on test for final output voltage. T1: 9V secondary, 25VA min for single 4CX250, 50VA min for pair of 4CX250s

observed; if the cathode is not at a uniform temperature, emission is concentrated in the hot areas, and the current density can be high enough to strip the cathode with permanent loss of current capability.

Fig 4.172(a) shows a manual switching circuit which forces the correct turn-on sequence, but relies on the operator to allow the correct warm-up time for the heaters. Fig 4.172(b) [65] shows a simple circuit which can be used to automatically delay other supplies turning on until the heaters have warmed up.

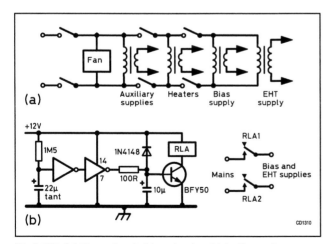

Fig 4.172. (a) Manual switching circuit which allows the correct sequence. (b) Simple circuit to delay switch-on automatically until the heaters have warmed up. The two invertors are CMOS types, eg CD4069) or inverting gates used as invertors. The 12V supply comes on when the heaters are switched on

Screen grid supplies

As discussed earlier, screen grid supplies for 4CX250s have to be able to source and sink current of about 10mA/valve while maintaining a constant voltage. This requirement lends itself to some form of shunt stabiliser. The simplest form in widespread use is a string of zener diodes in series, as in Fig 4.173. R2 provides a current of about 20mA through the diodes and this sets the maximum current which can be drawn by the valve before the voltage drops. The screen dissipation is thus limited to a maximum of 7W under normal operation and less than 12W (maximum rating) under worst-case fault conditions. This method of screen supply gives reasonable linearity but better results are achieved with active regulators which give much better regulation of the output voltage. Two such circuits are shown in Figs 4.174 and 4.175. The first is by G4XZL, used in the amplifier described in [66], the second is by G4IDE [67]. These and the zener diode circuit can suffer a problem if an anode-to-screen flashover occurs. A MOV is used to protect the capacitors in the valveholder. The type listed is specified not to conduct at voltages below 370V, but will start to conduct heavily at about 450V, with the capacity to carry thousands of amps for a few microseconds. For the duration of the flashover, the MOV acts to hold the screen grid voltage to about 650V (see Fig 4.176). The shunt regulator conducts heavily, trying to keep the voltage down to the set level, about 350V. This results in a brief high-current pulse. The regulator usually survives this, but meter shunt resistors and meters have been known to burn out. D1 can help to provide a measure of protection. In the case of the active regulators, the modification in Fig 4.177 introduces a current limit of about 70mA which protects the shunt regulator and meter from excess dissipation. References [68–70] contain alternative high-performance circuits.

Tuning up

Tuning procedures are different for tetrodes and triodes, although both start with 'heavy' loading, that is maximum coupling between the load and the tuned circuit so as to give a low anode resistance.

Correct loading for a tetrode is indicated by screen grid conditions. Apply a small amount of RF input, adjust the grid

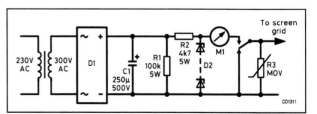

Fig 4.173. Simple screen grid supply for 4CX250. R3: 275V MOV. D1 1000V 1A bridge (4 × 1N4007). D2: 10 × 33V 5W zener diodes in series. M1: 10-0-10mA centre-zero. RLA: TX/RX switching relay

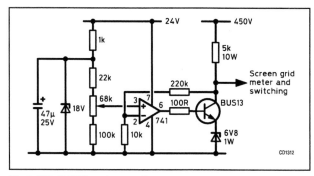

Fig 4.174. G4XZL active regulator

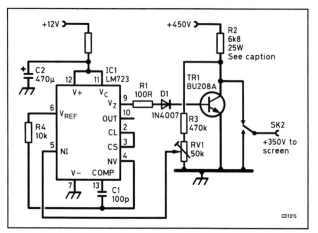

Fig 4.175. G4IDE active regulator. Set RV1 to give 250V for the screen at the collector of TR1. R2 should be chosen to give 25–30mA through the BU208A when the screen is not being supplied

and anode tuning for maximum output power and the grid input matching for lowest VSWR. Adjust the loading for most negative screen grid current possible, retuning the anode for

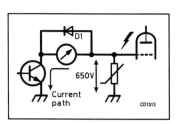

Fig 4.176. Use of MOV to give flashover protection

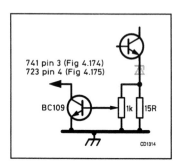

Fig 4.177. Modification to Figs 4.174 and 4.175 to give a current limit of about 70mA to protect the shunt regulator and meter from excess dissipation

maximum output power at each adjustment. Gradually increase RF input, continue retuning, adjusting the loading for most negative screen grid current until you reach approximately 50% of the intended peak anode current/input/output power. Do not alter the loading control again. Increase RF input until the screen grid current rises to about +5mA (per valve), and make final adjustments to anode and grid tuning for maximum output and minimum input VSWR. This is the maximum output at which the amplifier should be run. With low anode voltage, about 1500V or less, the screen grid current might not go negative and can be

Table 4.19. Typical operating conditions for a single 4CX250 at VHF				
Anode voltage	900	1250	1900	V
Anode current	245	200	310	mA
Quiescent current	100	100	70	mA
Screen voltage	300	315	350	V
Screen current	30	10	5	mA
RF input power	3.5	4	3	W
Output power	110	160	330	W

allowed to increase to 10mA peak. Below about 1000V, 20–30mA is acceptable. Table 4.19 shows typical values.

In grounded-grid amplifiers the loading is adjusted to give the required output power and efficiency, so a reasonably accurate RF power meter is essential. All tuning should be carried out iteratively as the input power is gradually increased, with final adjustments at full power because the input impedance varies with input power. The actual value of grid current is not significant provided it is within the limits specified for the valve. The output power from a triode amplifier does not saturate in the same way as a tetrode; it is possible to keep increasing the input power and get more output power up to the point where damage occurs.

Aiming for about 50% anode efficiency (45% at UHF) will give reliable, linear operation.

In grounded-grid amplifiers, the grid can be damaged if RF input is applied without anode voltage. An interlock circuit which detects anode voltage should always be used to protect the valve by preventing the amplifier switching into transmit mode if the anode voltage is absent. Fig 4.178 shows a simple circuit based on a design by G4IDE [71].

VALVE AMPLIFIER CIRCUITS

Simple amplifiers capable of 50–100W output from 1–2W drive can be built easily around QQV06-40/07-50 double tetrode valves [72], which can still be readily found in surplus equipment.

In recent years there has been a tendency to design amplifiers (especially those using 4CX250) with the intent of achieving the full output capability of the valve, about 275W clean PEP in the case of the 4CX250. This need not be difficult to achieve, but it does require a good valve, 2kV or more anode voltage and a number of protection measures to avoid

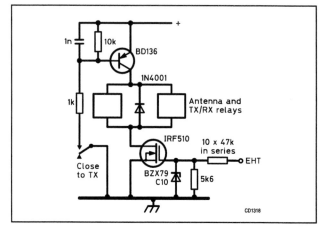

Fig 4.178. Simple grid protection circuit

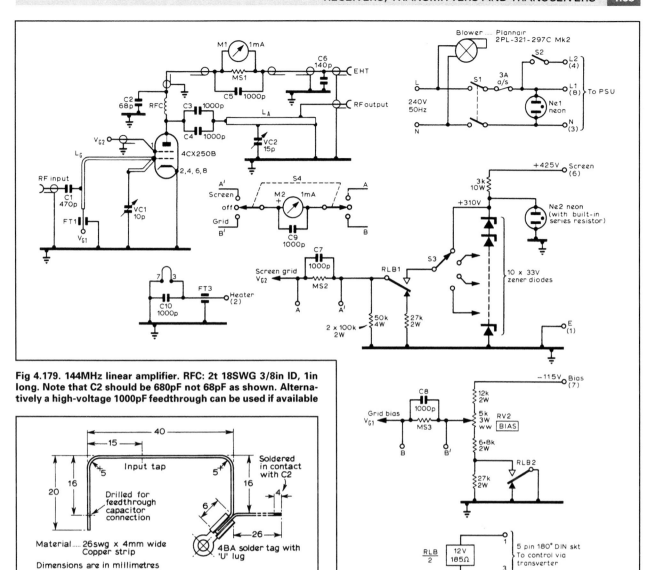

Fig 4.179. 144MHz linear amplifier. RFC: 2t 18SWG 3/8in ID, 1in long. Note that C2 should be 680pF not 68pF as shown. Alternatively a high-voltage 1000pF feedthrough can be used if available

Fig 4.180. Grid inductor. 'C2' refers to Fig 4.187 or VC1 in Fig 4.179

total destruction in the event of an anode voltage flashover. As an alternative, aiming for an output power of 150–200W (only one-third to half an S point less) can simplify things. For example, anode voltage can be reduced to 1–1.5kV; the lower secondary voltage makes a transformer easier to find, fewer capacitors are needed and the stored energy ($0.5\,CV^2$) is much lower. The STC data sheet for the 4CX250 specifies over 200W PEP output with acceptable linearity with an anode supply of 1500V. Very few old amplifier designs running at these voltages and powers had the range of protection circuits now considered essential. The reason: flashover and other problems were relatively rare. Amplifier gain was usually lower too, making the layout and choice of valve base less critical. For these reasons, the inexperienced builder is strongly recommended to aim at these lower targets initially. Nevertheless, the various protection measures outlined in the PSU section previously should be included for peace of mind at minimal cost.

Suitable designs have been featured in various editions of the *VHF/UHF Manual* and are repeated here. Despite their

age, more recent designs differ only in detail. Figs 4.179–4.186 and Table 4.20 show a 144MHz amplifier [73] whose origins can be traced to GW3ZTH. The anode circuit uses a shortened $\lambda/4$ transmission line tuned to resonance with the valve anode capacitance and VC2. Output loading is set by the position of the output connection on the transmission line. While this does not provide a fully variable adjustment, in most situations the loading does not need to be adjusted once the optimum setting has been found. Great care is needed and

Table 4.20. Operating conditions for 144MHz amplifier

	No signal	Single tone
Anode voltage (V)	1350	1200
current (mA)	100	200
Screen voltage (V)	315	315
current (mA)	—	10
Grid voltage	−32	−32*
current (µA)	—	<100
Power output (W)	—	150–170

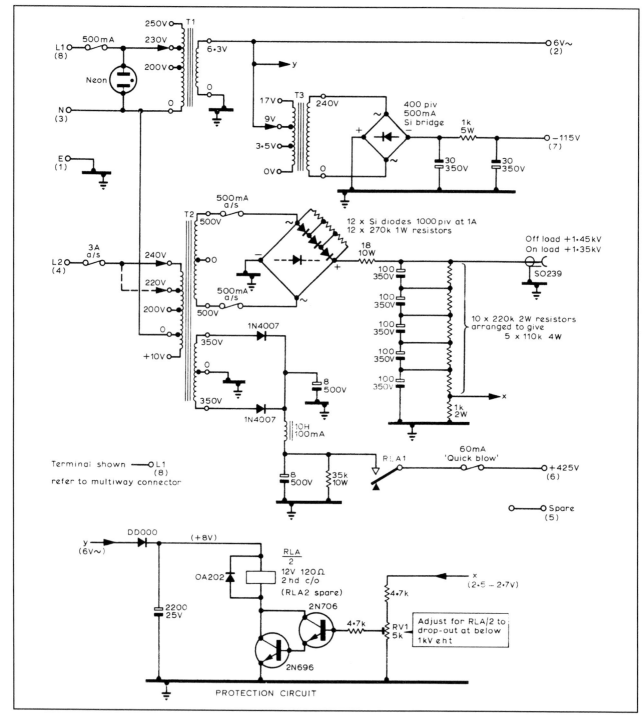

Fig 4.181. Remote power supply unit for 144MHz linear

the valve anode must be solidly earthed when working inside the anode compartment. Do not rely on disconnecting the anode supply; C3 and C4 can hold charge for a long time. The grid circuit uses a shaped strip as the inductor instead of a wound coil. The shape and dimensions fit nicely into a standard die-cast box, and should be followed closely to ensure correct tuning. A small variation in the length of the connection to VC1 should not affect operation. Input VSWR is optimised by adjusting the connection point of C1 onto L_G.

Figs 4.187–4.190 and Tables 4.20 and 4.21 show another design [74] which uses a lumped-component version of the

$\lambda/2$ circuit in Fig 4.163. Output coupling is adjusted by varying the position of the coupling coil with respect to the tuning coil. The low output power figures for this amplifier reflect the licence conditions of the time, which limited DC input to 150W maximum for FM or CW. Given the same operating conditions as the previous design, the same performance should be achieved.

An amplifier for 432MHz [75] is shown in Figs 4.191–4.193; this was also designed at a time when DC input power was more restricted. Die-cast boxes are used as cheap, convenient ready-made housings for the grid and anode circuits.

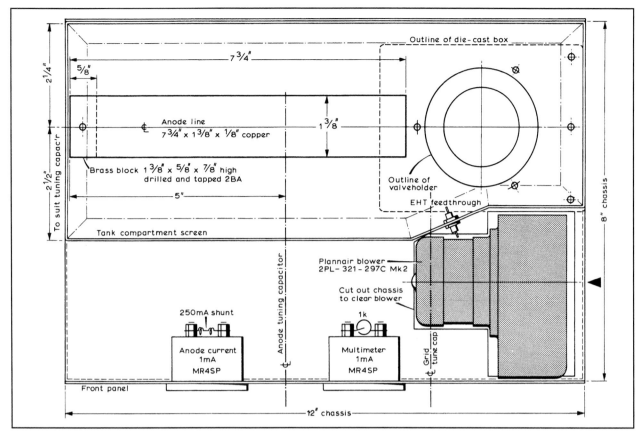

Fig 4.182. Above-chassis outline

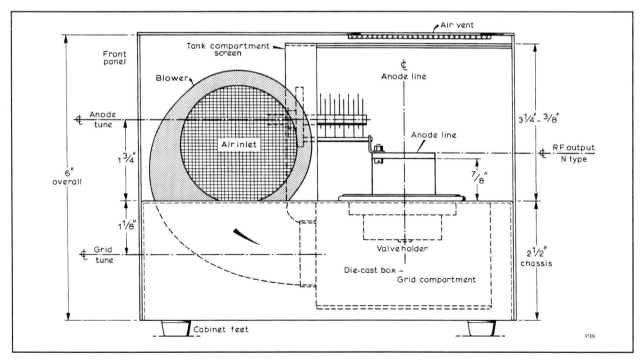

Fig 4.183. Side elevation

The design is capable of higher output power but the die-cast metal is not the best choice in high power RF fields and unpredictable effects might start to occur as the RF currents increase, although problems are unlikely to be seen at powers below about 175W. The output coupling might need some alteration to optimise the loading for linear operation, as described earlier. It would be beneficial to change the capacitor in the output coupling to an air-spaced piston type (eg

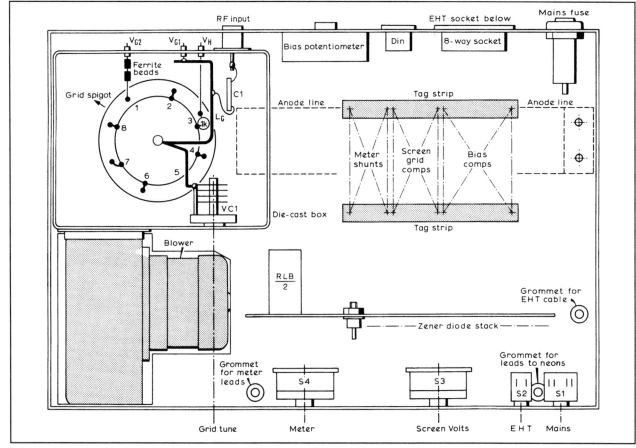

Fig 4.184. Below-chassis outline

Johansson) rather than the ceramic one used in the original. As an alternative, capacitive output coupling could be tried. Although widely used in other designs it must be stressed that this is untried in this amplifier. Estimated dimensions are a brass/bronze strip ½in wide over the anode line, 2.5in from the tuning capacitor end. The strip should extend to the mid-line of the anode line. See Fig 4.216 as an example.

A 'string' can be used as an alternative mechanism to adjust the anode tuning capacitor.

Higher-power amplifiers

In 1971 *QST* published an amplifier by W1QVF (later W1SL) and W1HDQ [76] using a pair of 4CX250s in push-pull, with λ/2 grid and λ/4 anode tuned circuits. This set a design standard which is regularly duplicated today. It achieved widespread popularity after being included in the *ARRL Handbook* for some years. An amplifier by G8LT using the same principles is shown in Figs 4.195–4.198 and Table 4.23.

A tuned circuit feeds RF voltage to the grids. The circuit is loaded only by the input impedance of the valves, which is

Fig 4.185. Interior showing fan, strip line and tuning capacitor

Fig 4.186. Underside view

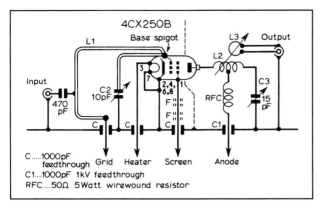

Fig 4.187. Circuit of compact 150W amplifier for 144MHz

Fig 4.188. Underside view of compact amplifier for 144MHz

Fig 4.189. Compact amplifier for 144MHz

Table 4.21. 150W amplifier components list

C	1000p feedthrough
C1	1000p feedthrough 1kV type
C2	10p C804 Jackson
C3	15p C804 Jackson
F	Ferrite bead
RFC	50R 5W wirewound
L1	Copper strip loop (see Fig 4.180)
L2	3½t ¾in ID 1/8in diam copper
L3	1t ¾in ID insulated
Valve socket	Eimac or AEI
Blower	Planair type 2PL 321-284C Mk3

Table 4.22. Performance of 150W amplifier

Anode voltage (V)	750	800
Anode current (mA)	200	200
Screen voltage (V)	250	250
Screen current (mA)	5	8
Grid voltage (V)	−100	−100
Grid current (mA)	6.6	8
Drive power (W)	2.6	3.0
Output power load (W)	90	100

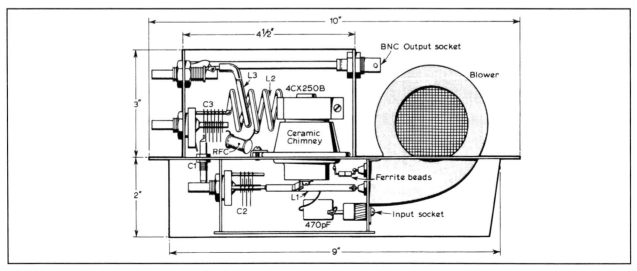

Fig 4.190. Side view of compact amplifier for 144MHz

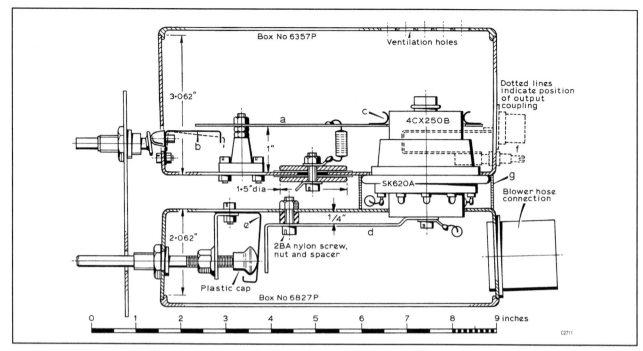

Fig 4.191. Section of complete assembly showing principal components for the 432MHz slab-line power amplifier

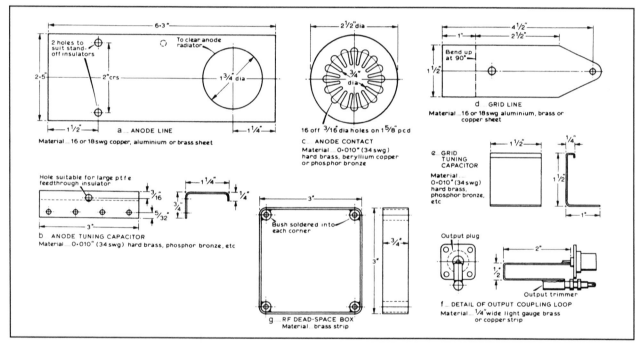

Fig 4.192. Details of components

Fig 4.193. The anode in its holder and the output loop

Fig 4.194. The grid line, input coupling loop and blower hose

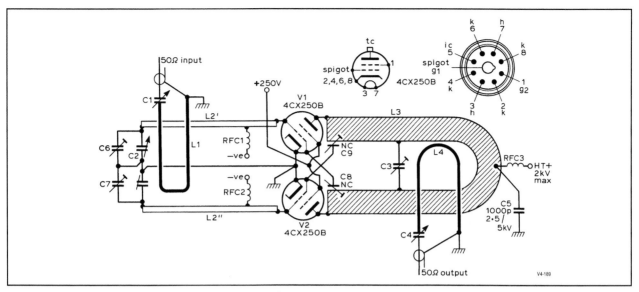

Fig 4.195. High-power 144MHz amplifier using a pair of 4CX250B valves

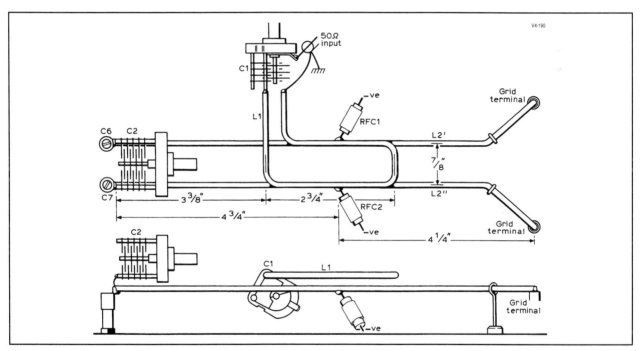

Fig 4.196. Grid circuit

Table 4.23. Components for G8LT amplifier	
C1, C4	50p (Polar C4.04)
C2	15 + 15p (Polar C8.52/1)
C3	Disc, 1½in diam
C5	1000p, 2.5–5kV bypass
C6, C7	10p piston trimmer
C8, C9	NC, plate attached to 16 SWG wire
L1	Input coupling loop (see Fig 4.196)
L2', L2"	1/8in diam copper 9in long (see Fig 4.196)
L3	1in × 1/6in copper strip (see Fig 4.198)

Left: **Fig 4.197. Close-up view of grid circuit with components labelled**

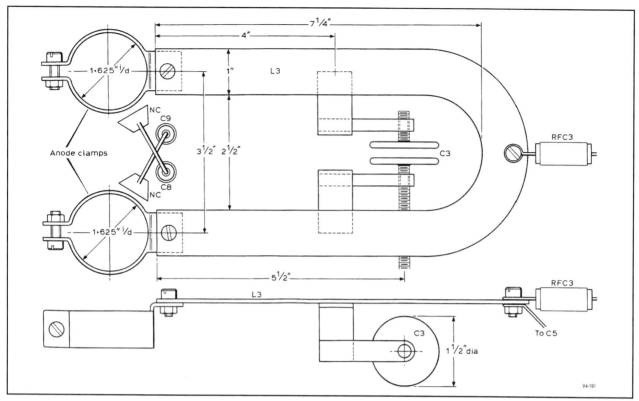

Fig 4.198. Anode circuit

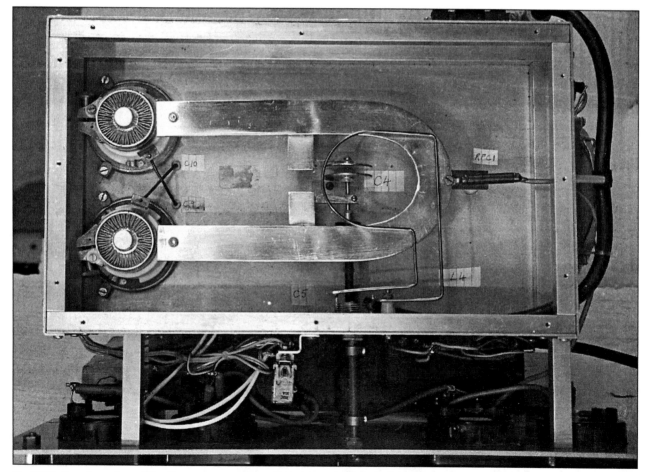

Fig 4.199. Top view of amplifier. Component numbers do not correspond to Fig 4.195

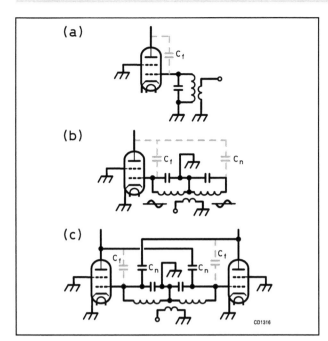

Fig 4.200. Evolution of neutralising circuit for a pair of valves. (a) Unwanted feedback. (b) Use of neutralising capacitor and additional circuitry for one valve. (c) Final circuit for two valves

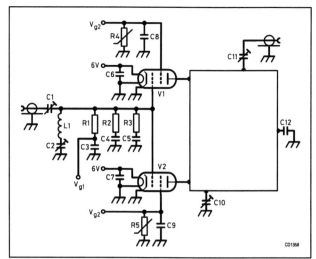

Fig 4.201. W2GN amplifier circuit. R1–3: 2 × 2k2, 3W in parallel. R4, 5: MOV, 275V AC, 140J. L1: 3t 1mm Cu wire, 16mm diam. C1, 2: 15p var. C3–7, 1000p 500V ceram. C8, 9: built into valve base. C10, 11: Mechanical flapper plates – see Fig 4.210. C12: formed from sandwich of metal plates and PTFE sheet – see Fig 4.212

fairly high, so there is a high RF voltage step-up ratio. This results in a high power gain for the amplifier; at least 20dB or 100× can be expected. The high gain means that the amplifier has to be neutralised. In Fig 4.200(a), the unwanted feedback signal path is represented by the anode-to-grid1 capacitor C_f. In Fig 4.200(b) an additional grid tuned circuit, coupled to the first one, is added and if the input signal is injected at the centre, the opposite ends will be in antiphase. By adding an external 'neutralising' capacitor C_n, an equal and opposite feedback signal is introduced which cancels that from C_f. The value of C_f and C_n is about 0.05pF, so C_n is not a physical component, but is made from a small brass tab held near the valve anode. The second valve can be drawn as a mirror image of Fig 4.200(b), and by sharing the same grid tuned circuit, the final circuit of Fig 4.200(c) is realised.

Neutralisation adjustments are straightforward, but can take a little time to get right [77]. Connect a load to the output, and leave the screen grid and anode supplies open-circuit. With the heaters on and control grid voltage set to about −35V (lower than the value normally needed to bias the valves), apply some RF input until slight grid current is seen. Peak the grid current with C2, reducing the RF input as necessary to get a few milliamps of grid current. Use C6 and C7 to balance the current between the valves. As C3 is adjusted to tune the anode circuit to the input frequency, some energy will be drawn into the anode circuit and the grid current will alter. The neutralising capacitors C8 and C9 are adjusted by changing their positions to minimise and eventually completely remove any effect of anode tuning on the grid current. The anode compartment cover must be in place when the neutralisation is checked. Depending on the valves and bases in use, the position and size of the tabs might be quite different from that shown in the diagrams. Initial changes should be made to keep C8 and C9 symmetrical but final adjustments might require small changes to one or other alone. It is important to

persevere until there is absolutely no effect on the grid current at any combination of anode tuning and loading controls. Once this is achieved, the amplifier can be tuned up as described previously. With an anode voltage of 1.5–2kV, and 100mA per valve quiescent current, a clean, linear output of 400–500W should be achieved for about 4W drive.

The axial fan used on this amplifier is rare and non-standard, capable of high-pressure operation. Readily available axial fans are incapable of cooling such an amplifier, and a proper high-pressure blower should be used, as discussed earlier.

W2GN described an alternative design [78] which uses two valves in parallel. The anode circuit is a λ/4 transmission line as in Fig 4.163(a), tuned to resonance with fixed and variable capacitive plates. Output coupling is through a 'flapper' capacitor adjusted with a screw through the box lid. Photographs and drawings of a version built by G8GSQ are shown in Figs 4.201–4.207. The resistors which load the grid circuit are split

Fig 4.202. Anode compartment

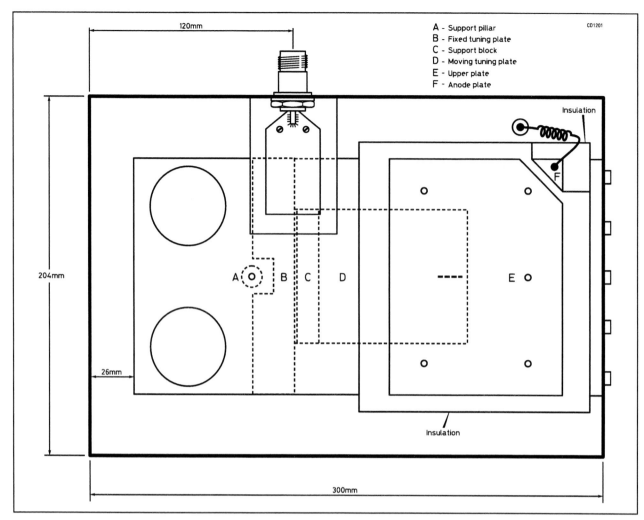

CD1201

A – Support pillar
B – Fixed tuning plate
C – Support block
D – Moving tuning plate
E – Upper plate
F – Anode plate

Fig 4.203. Overal view of anode compartment. A – support pillar, B – fixed tuning plate, C – support block, D – moving tuning probe

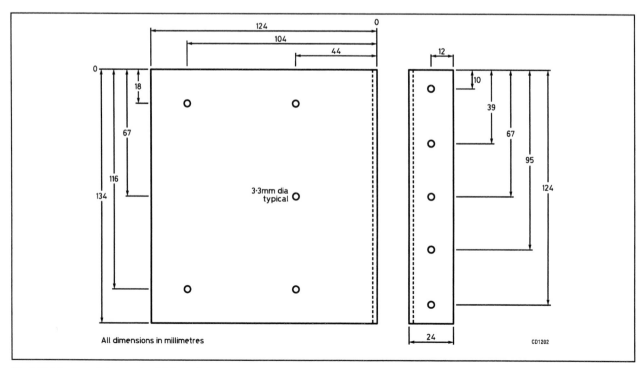

All dimensions in millimetres

CD1202

Fig 4.204. Lower plate, made of 1.2mm brass

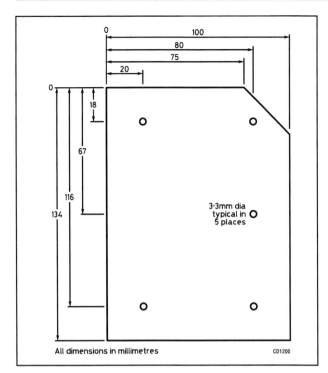

Fig 4.205. Upper plate, 1.2mm brass

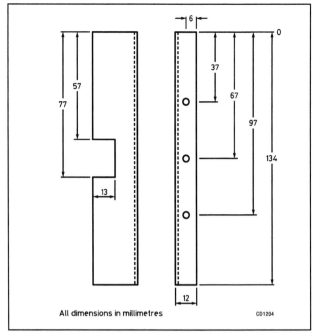

Fig 4.206. Fixed tuning plate, made of 0.5mm brass or copper

into three pairs to make use of available components. Because of the resistive grid loading the gain is reduced and neutralisation is not required. An alternative grid circuit shown in Fig 4.213 is a worthwhile modification so that the valves have individual bias control and so do not have to be selected as matched pairs.

The bases used in this version are ex-equipment types which have a PTFE chimney and a Y-shaped clip to hold the valve in place. The chimney and anode metal surround have been discarded. Following the example of the article, air is blown into the anode compartment; this was necessary as the original blower had marginal performance. A better blower has since been fitted and had this been available at the outset, the grid compartment would have been used as the air inlet. Originally the chimneys carrying the air from the anode to outside

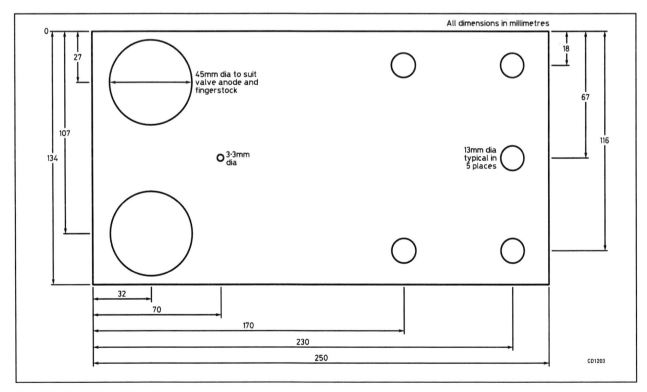

Fig 4.207. Anode line, 1.2mm brass

Fig 4.208. Close-up view of grid circuit

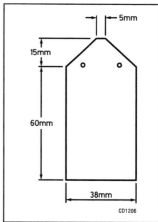

Fig 4.209. Output coupling, 0.4mm brass or beryllium copper

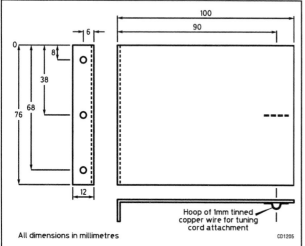

All dimensions in millimetres

Hoop of 1mm tinned copper wire for tuning cord attachment

Fig 4.210. Moving tuning plate, 0.4mm brass or beryllium copper

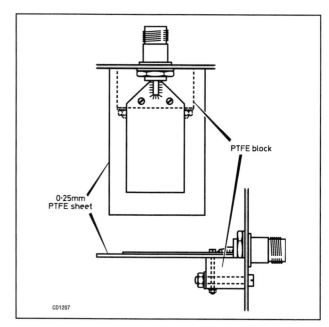

PTFE block

0·25mm PTFE sheet

Fig 4.211. Output coupling support block

were made from thin PTFE sheet rolled into tubes. Subsequently some suitably sized PTFE tube came to hand and this was cut to be a snug fit between the anode plate and the box

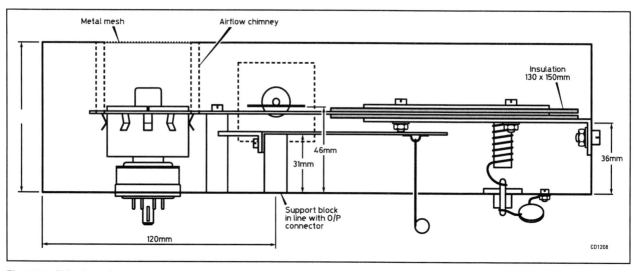

Metal mesh

Airflow chimney

Insulation 130 x 150mm

46mm

31mm

36mm

Support block in line with O/P connector

120mm

Fig 4.212. Side view of anode compartment

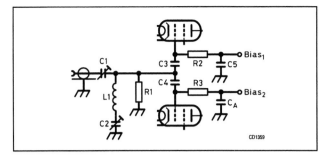

Fig 4.213. Alternative grid circuit

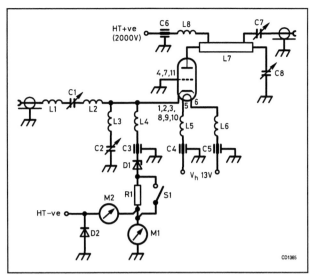

Fig 4.214. 3CX800 70cm amplifier circuit

lid. A peculiar effect was seen in continuous small variations (about 1%) in output power. This was eventually traced to the PTFE insulation on the output coupling capacitor flapping in the airflow.

The DC blocking capacitor in the anode line is made from 0.8mm PTFE/glass PCB with all the copper removed. The original design used 0.25mm PTFE sheet but this was replaced after a flashover caused by a microscopic piece of swarf which had punctured the soft PTFE. PTFE will give excellent long-term service provided extreme care is taken to remove all swarf and rough edges.

432MHz high-power amplifier

In 1972 K2RIW published an article [79] describing an amplifier using a pair of 4CX250s in parallel. A large number of these amplifiers have been built since, with varying degrees of success. The means of achieving satisfactory and reliable operation are now largely understood: a good-quality pair of valves, genuine Eimac SK630 bases and attention to detail in the mechanical components. If all of this comes together, linear output power of around 500W can be expected; investing in high-quality cable will achieve legal limit power at the antenna. The K2RIW design is not an amplifier to build using random bits and pieces without access to test equipment (and plenty of time) for debugging. The cost of a pair of good new 4CX250s is significant, and the correct bases are likely to cost somewhat more than the valves.

In 1979, K1FO published a 1kW input, 530W output amplifier [80] using the 8874 triode. This became very popular in the USA where the valves were more readily available. The grounded-grid circuit gives lower gain than the K2RIW design but the PSU is greatly simplified and there are no stability problems. In 1986 G4ODA adapted this design to use the 3CX800; coincidentally, K1FO published a similarly modified design in 1987 [81]. While the cost of a 3CX800 appears initially high, bases are readily and cheaply available. The increased output power capability allows cheaper, lossier cable to be used while maintaining the power delivered to the antenna. The overall difference in cost is lower than might be thought initially.

G4ODA's design is shown in Figs 4.214–4.224. The grid contact ring on the valve is the same size as the screen grid ring on the 4CX250. The grid contact used here was taken from a scrap 4CX250 base, and its choice appears to have been fortuitous. The design was duplicated using an Eimac grid connector which has 36 closely spaced contacts. This amplifier, while not unstable, can show signs of feedback at some tuning settings. K1FO describes how to modify the contact ring to raise the inductance and 'tune' the point of minimum feedback close to 432MHz by breaking off every other contact to leave 18, and then remove or insulate a further six to leave six pairs which closely resemble the pattern of the contact ring used by G4ODA.

The option of insulating the final six contacts is to allow for individual tuning, although K1FO observes that the characteristics appear to vary little between valves, and the contacts can safely be removed.

1.3GHz

The 2C39/3CX100 triode is the 'standard' valve for this band. Two designs which represent the best aspects of amplifier design are by G3SEK/G4PMK [82] and N6CA [83]. N6CA's

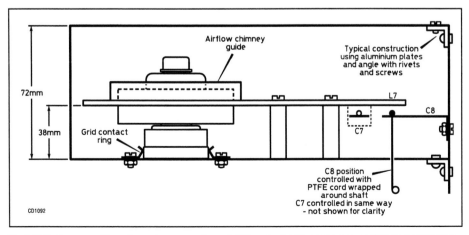

Fig 4.215. Cross-section of anode compartment. C7 controlled in same way as C8 but omitted for clarity. Also omitted for clarity are the EHT connections (L8/C6) and the airflow chimney

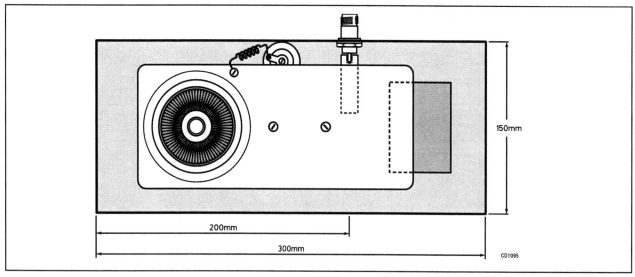

Fig 4.216. Overall view of anode compartment

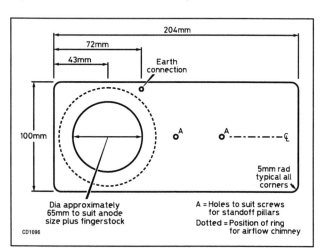

Fig 4.217. Anode transmission line L7

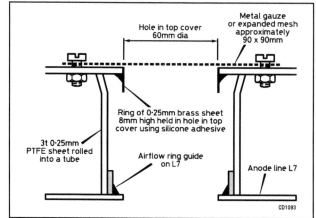

Fig 4.219. Airflow chimney

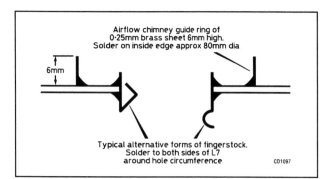

Fig 4.218. Cross-section through anode clearance hole

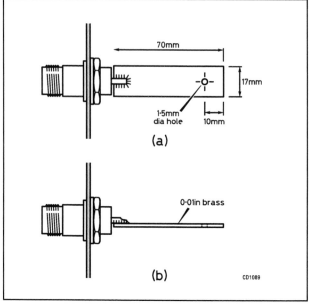

Fig 4.220. Output coupling flap C7

article is enormously detailed and emphasises achieving maximum output power.

The G3SEK/G4PMK design concentrates on maximising gain at modest output power, making it ideal to follow a transverter. In this design the depth of the cavity is fixed at 0.75in* and a coarse tuning screw is provided as described by

*All dimensions in this design are given in inches, because at the time brass strip and tubing were more readily available in inch than in metric sizes.

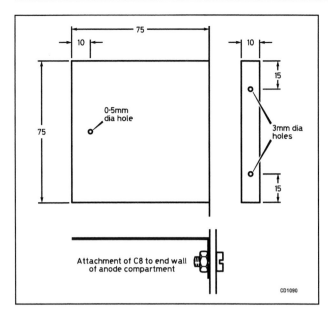

Fig 4.221. Tuning flap C8, 0.015 bronze or brass

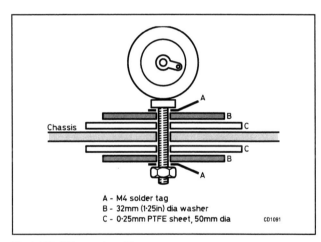

A - M4 solder tag
B - 32mm (1·25in) dia washer
C - 0·25mm PTFE sheet, 50mm dia

Fig 4.222. HT capacitor C6

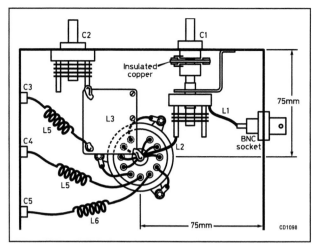

Fig 4.223. Grid circuit. C2 is two fixed, three moving vanes, air-spaced 0.8mm

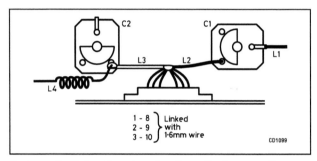

1 - 8 ⎤ Linked
2 - 9 ⎬ with
3 - 10 ⎦ 1·6mm wire

Fig 4.224. Partial section view showing cathode connections

Table 4.25. Typical operating conditions for 3CX800 amplifier	
Anode voltage on load	2100V
Anode current	550mA
RF output power	595W
Grid current	25mA (varies between valves)
Drive power	25W
Quiescent current	50mA (varies between valves)

Table 4.24. Components list for Fig 4.214	
C1	5p variable
C2	15p variable
C3–5	1000p feedthrough
C6	EHT feedthrough capacitor – see Fig 4.222
C7	0.25mm brass sheet 17 x 70mm – see Fig 4.220
C8	0.4mm (0.015in) brass or bronze sheet – see Fig 4.221
L1	2mm enamelled copper wire, 15mm long
L2	2mm enamelled copper wire, 30mm long
L3	0.25mm brass plate 40 x 34mm
L4–6	10t 2mm enam copper wire, 6.5mm ID
L7	1.6mm double-sided PCB 204 x 100mm – see Fig 4.217
L8	4t 1mm enam copper wire, 6.5mm ID
R1	10k 1W
D1	5.6V 10W zener diode
D2	50V 30A diode (flashover protection)
M1	100mA
M2	1A
S1	close to transmit

G3LTF and G3WDG [84]. The base plate is soldered to the walls, and the top plate, which regrettably has to be removable for access, is secured by no less than 20 screws. The result is a rigid, low-loss assembly.

There are several valves in the '2C39' family, which can differ mechanically as well as electrically. Not all variants have the grid sleeve: the other example in Fig 4.226(b) (a 7289/3CX100A5) has its grid contact ring only at the bottom (cathode) end. Inspection of the drawings for a professional amplifier shows that if the grid contact is made at the bottom of the grid sleeve and in the base plane of a 0.75in-deep cavity, then the bottom of the anode sleeve is flush with the top of the cavity.

This arrangement, shown schematically in Fig 4.226(b), was taken to be the 'correct' way to locate the valve in the cavity.

Grid and anode contacts

The greatest single problem in amateur designs using the 2C39 series of valves has always been the contact rings for the grid and anode. To insist on an extremely low-inductance grid contact, in the plane of the base plate, makes matters worse than ever!

Fig 4.225. The G4PMK/G3SEK 1.3GHz amplifier

'Straight' finger-stock (Fig 4.226(a)) is ruled out because it projects either into or out of the anode cavity. Folded-over finger-stock is used in commercial preformed grid rings, but it is not readily available; and N6CA's experiments [85] suggest that the inductance of the resulting contact is barely low enough.

The solution is to use a ring of spiral spring to contact the valve, the spring-ring itself being held in a collet (Figs 4.226(b), 4.227 and 4.228). In effect, the valve is contacted by several quarter-turns of the spring, all of which are electrically in parallel and combine to make a contact of extremely low inductance. The collet can be let into the base of the cavity, so that the contact is made in the correct plane.

The ideal spring-ring material is a loosely-wound, silver-plated spiral spring of about 0.25in diameter. A perfectly acceptable home-made substitute is a spiral wound from narrow (eg 0.1in wide) phosphor-bronze strip such as draught

excluder; this gives fewer contacts to the valve but each turn of the strip has lower individual inductance. Fig 4.227 shows the two alternative types of spring-ring in their collets.

Precise dimensions of the collet depend to a large extent on the available spring-ring material, and the prototypes were turned by 'cut-and-try' out of old brass vacuum fittings. The first step is to bore out the blank to just clear the grid sleeve of the valve. Then the internal groove is formed using a small boring tool (inset, Fig 4.228), repeatedly trying first the spring-ring alone for size, and in the later stages both the spring-ring and the valve. The fit of the valve can also be adjusted by pulling or squeezing the spring-ring. When all is well, the valve will be gripped gently but uniformly as it is twisted into place. Owing to the 'lay' of the turns of the spring-ring, the valve can only be twisted in one direction – the same for insertion and removal – so if spring-rings are used for both the grid and anode connectors they must be wound in the same sense.

The entire machining and fitting process is far easier than it looks, because no individual dimension is critical. The two

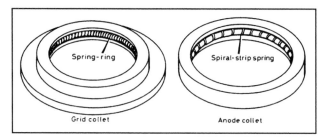

Fig 4.227. Grid and anode collets showing the two alternative types of spring material

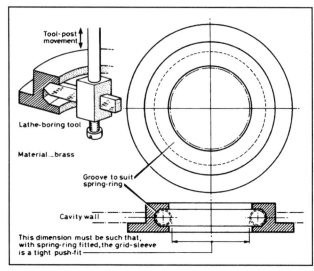

Fig 4.226. Old and new methods of mounting valves in a cavity (omitting details of anode DC supply)

Fig 4.228. Details of grid collet

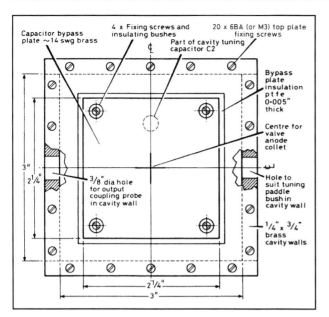

Fig 4.229. Top view of anode cavity assembly. The cavity top-plate has a 1.25in diameter hole in the centre to clear the valve anode sleeve

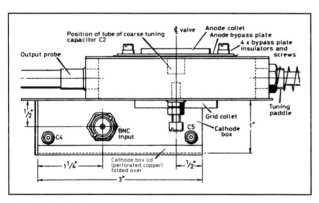

Fig 4.230. Side view

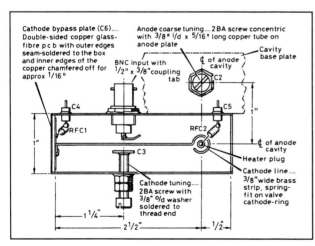

Fig 4.231. Details of cathode box and anode coarse tuning capacitor

prototype grid contact assemblies were produced in one lunch-time by a machinist with no delusions of competence!

The anode contact is much more forgiving of stray

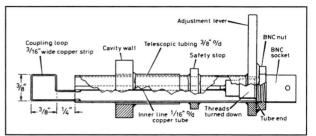

Fig 4.232. Output coupling probe

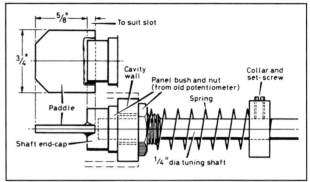

Fig 4.233. Tuning paddle

inductance than the grid contact, so a ring of ordinary finger-stock would probably suffice [84].

Correct axial location of the valve can be ensured if the flare at the top of the anode ring bears on the top of the collet, the latter being turned down to the correct thickness.

The cathode input circuitry closely follows an early design [84], the coarse-tuning screw has already been mentioned, and the fine-tuning paddle and coupling loop are also as before. Coupling with the magnetic field in the cavity is strongest when the loop is almost fully withdrawn to the cavity wall and at right-angles to the base plate. Coarse loading adjustment is by sliding the loop in and out, and fine adjustment by rotating it.

Dimensions and assembly

A general view of the amplifier is shown in the photograph, and leading dimensions are given in Figs 4.229–4.233. Non-critical dimensions are not given, being at the discretion of the constructor. Over-dimensioning the drawing would give a false impression that all dimensions must be slavishly followed: if that were true, we probably could not have built the prototypes! As noted earlier, the dimensions of the anode and grid connectors are only critical in that they must be adjusted to provide a good fit to the valve. However, the two collets must be coaxial in order to avoid shear forces on the valve, and detailed assembly instructions for the anode cavity are as follows:

1. Mark out the locations of the side walls and the centre of the cavity on the base plate. Drill a *pilot* hole in the centre of the base plate.
2. Solder the side walls into position. If the ends of the bars can be faced-off square (not impossible by hand or with a three-jaw lathe chuck) they may be pre-assembled into a square frame before soldering. After soldering, stone the top face of the side-walls flat.

3. Mark out and pilot drill the 20 fixing holes in the cavity top plate. Do *not* drill the centre hole yet. Tape the top plate accurately into position on the side walls, and on a drill press drill two holes in diagonally-opposite positions through the top plate and into the side walls. Tap these two holes and secure the top plate more firmly before drilling and tapping the rest of the fixing holes.

4. Again on a drill press, drill square through the pilot hole in the base plate, and through the top plate.

5. Use the pilot hole in the cavity top plate to locate the centre of the anode bypass plate, when marking and drilling through the latter for the four retaining screws.

6. Open out all pilot holes to full size. Be careful to retain concentricity.

7. Drill the four holes in the anode bypass plate slightly oversize for the shoulders of the available insulating bushes. Leave the retaining screws slack until the valve has been fitted squarely into place for the first time; then tighten them.

The cathode circuitry below the base plate (Figs 4.230 and 4.231) is assembled after the grid collet has been soldered into place.

Rather than fabricating the RF bypass capacitor for the 'cold' end of the cathode stripline [84] G4PMK and G3SEK chose to make the entire end wall act as a capacitor by making it from double-sided glass-fibre PC board (Fig 4.231), chamfering the copper from the inside edges to prevent a DC short-circuit.

The sliding loop coupling probe (Fig 4.232) is made using telescoping brass tubing available from good model shops. A safety stop must be provided to prevent the loop from touching the anode sleeve of the valve. The tuning paddle (Fig 4.233) needs to be well grounded to RF; this can be ensured by a strong compression spring over the shaft which maintains a firm contact between the paddle and shaft bushing. It is helpful if the external controls indicate the true orientations of the loop and paddle within the cavity.

As an optional extra, all the components can be silver-plated. The brass parts of the two prototypes were given an ultra-thin but tenacious coating of silver by the following method, which is a simple and effective way of applying a very thin but tenacious coating of silver to copper or brass, without resorting to electroplating and cyanide solutions. Although the coating is extremely thin, possibly less than the 'skin depth' for RF currents at 1.3GHz, tarnishing of silver affects its electrical properties far less than would tarnishing of untreated copper or brass, so the coating is worthwhile if only as a preservative.

Mix together two parts by weight of finely ground sodium chloride (common salt), two of potassium hydrogen tartrate (cream of tartar) and one of silver chloride. Store the mixture away from moisture or strong sunlight. To silver-plate an article, dampen a little of the powder with water and apply the resulting paste with a cloth using a vigorous rubbing action (wear rubber gloves). The abrasive nature of the paste will help remove any slight tarnish. When finished, wash the article thoroughly and dry it.

Cooling

The multiple fins of the anode cooler present a large surface area for efficient heat transfer, though only if the cooling air is forced between them. If air is merely blown in their general direction, it will take the easy way round the outside and will not cool the anode! A transverse-finned cooler is not as effective as a ducted axial-flow cooler (eg that of the 4CX250B) but a suitable air duct can be made from a variety of easily worked materials such as Perspex or Formica.

At the higher power levels, overheating of the grid can cause electron emission, leading to DC instability and shortened valve life. The problem can be avoided by efficient cooling of the anode (which otherwise tends to heat up the whole valve) and of the grid/cathode region. The spring-ring grid connector is a good conductor of heat as well as RF, and helps keep the grid cool. If the whole amplifier is mounted upside down, the cathode cavity is adequately ventilated by natural convection through the perforated cover. The anode cavities of the prototype amplifiers were not ventilated at all, a point which should be considered if this design were to be used at power levels of more than a few tens of watts.

All amplifiers of this general type can suffer from the problem that the different thermal loadings on transmit and receive lead to changes in the internal capacitances of the valve, and hence to drift in the output level as the amplifier warms up. The problem is obvious enough at high power levels, but it also occurs at very low drive levels because the valve is only lightly loading the high-Q cavity, making it more susceptible to drift. The difficulties can be largely overcome by cooling the valve adequately on transmit and reducing or removing the airflow on receive [86] so that its temperature remains more nearly constant. For example, it is possible to set the tuning paddle either so that the amplifier achieves maximum output within a few seconds and then drifts off tune after about one minute, or alternatively so that it takes about 20 seconds to reach full output and stays in tune for several minutes – for contests and ragchews respectively! A further improvement could be expected from the use of one of the modern temperature-compensated derivatives of the 2C39, eg the 7855.

Operating conditions

The circuit diagram of the amplifier is very simple (Fig 4.234). For maximum gain, a fairly high standing current of the order of 50mA is required, ie DC efficiency has to be sacrificed. At low drive levels the amplifier will operate at virtually constant anode current, so simple cathode-resistor biasing will suffice. During development of the amplifiers a 250Ω wirewound potentiometer proved perfectly satisfactory, and a $22k\Omega$ resistor connected from the cathode bypass to ground allows the valve to cut off safely during receive periods or if the bias resistor fails. At higher drive levels, constant-voltage biasing must be used in order to maintain linearity on SSB, and an arrangement in which a single transistor acts as both bias regulator and T/R switch is shown in Fig 4.234. The zener diode sets the cut-off bias on receive and limits the transistor's collector voltage to below V_{ceo}.

The usual precautions regarding heater voltage should be observed when using the amplifier; at no time must the heater voltage exceed 6V. It is important that the cathode of the valve be allowed to reach full operating temperature before the anode voltage is applied. A delay of 60–90 seconds is adequate.

The power gain achievable will depend on the type of valve, and on its operating history if it is second-hand. One of the

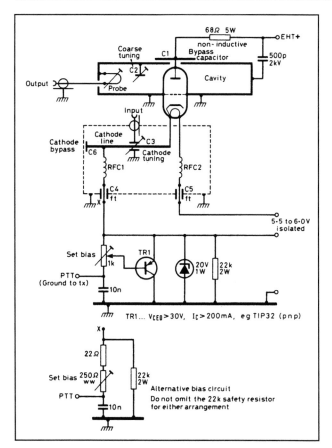

Fig 4.234. Circuit diagram of the amplifier

prototype amplifiers, using a 'good' but not remarkable 7289, gave the following measured performance with an EHT supply of 1kV, when the input and output matching were reoptimised to suit the available level of drive power.

Available drive power (W)	Output power (W)	Power gain (dB)
0.35	27	19
0.5	32	18
1.0	40	16

The lower power gains at higher drive levels do not imply that the amplifier is non-linear. If the adjustments had been optimised at the 1W drive level, then reduction of drive to 0.5W would linearly halve the output power to 20W. However, if no more than 0.5W drive were available, the amplifier could be reoptimised to give 32W of linear RF output. The prototypes were developed using EHT supplies of 1–1.1kV. Some reduction in gain was found at 800V, and in a brief test using 1.5kV one of the prototypes gave 60W RF output for 1W of drive.

An alternative anode circuit [87] using a $\lambda/2$ stripline is shown in Figs 4.235–4.238. This offers reduced gain, output power and efficiency compared with the cavity design, but it also demands less effort and metalwork in construction.

The anode circuitry fits inside a standard die-cast box (Eddystone 26908PSL) and the amplifier is assembled onto a 1.6mm copper plate which replaces the box lid (the plate fits over, not inside, the box). The plate and lid need to be in good contact for best performance and this is aided by making a gasket from thin copper foil folded into four layers. Grid

Fig 4.235. The tripler

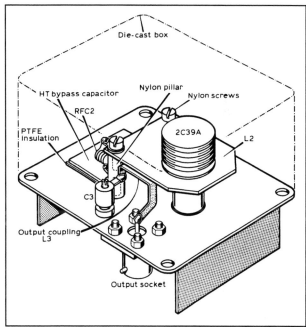

Fig 4.236. General arrangement of anode circuit

and cathode circuitry can be as the previous example. The support pillars for the anode line are 21mm high, and are preferably PTFE or ceramic rather than the nylon shown in Fig 4.236. With the alternative output probe G4DGU [88] reported 75W output at 8dB gain from 900V anode supply. At these power levels, forced cooling is essential and screened holes will have to be provided in the box sides to allow a blower to supply cooling air.

REFERENCES

[1] *VHF/UHF DX Book,* ed Ian White, G3SEK, RSGB, 1995, Chapter 5.
[2] Ian White, G3SEK, *Radio Communication* 1985, pp264, 367, 445 and 537.
[3] Peter Chadwick, G3RZP, *Radio Communication* March 1994, p223.
[4] Peter Saul, G8EUX, in *Radio Communication Handbook*, 6th edn, ed Dick Biddulph, G8DPS, RSGB, 1994, Chapter 5.

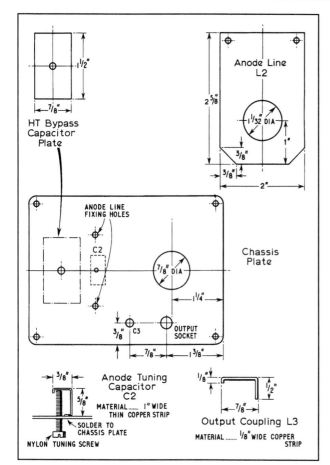

Fig 4.237. Construction details of anode circuit

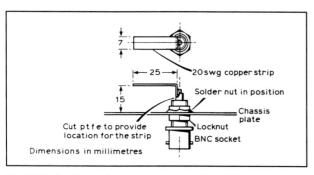

Fig 4.238. An alternative output probe and position

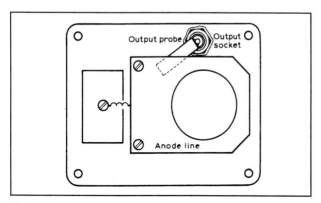

Fig 4.239. Approximate position of the output probe for 80Ω output impedance

[6] *Radio Data Reference Book*, 5th edn, R Hewes, G3TDR, G Jessop, G6JP, RSGB, 1985, Chapter 5.

[7] *Motorola RF Device Data*, Motorola, Inc.

[8] Z Lau, KH6CP/1, *QEX* September 1995, pp25–27.

[9] W Schneider, DJ8ES, *VHF Communications* 4/1993, p221.

[10] Peter Saul, G8EUX, *Radio Communication* December 1990, p44.

[11] J Hardcastle, G3JIR, *Radio Communication* October 1995, p 45.

[12] Ian Keyser, G3ROO, *Radio Communication* December 1993, p33.

[13] K Spaargaren, PA0KSB, *QEX* February 1996, pp19–23.

[14] *Shortwave Wireless Communication*, Ladner and Stoner, 4th edn, Chapman and Hall, 1946, Chapter 11.

[15] C Horrabin, G3SBI, *Radio Communication* May 1995, p61.

[16] B Carver, K6OLG, *QST* May 1966, p39.

[17] *Introduction to RF Design*, W Hayward, W7ZOI, ARRL.

[18] J Vogler, WA7CJO, *QEX* January 1995, p27.

[19] M Vidmar, S53MV, *VHF Communications* 2/1992, p90.

[20] W Schneider, DJ8ES, *VHF Communications* 4/1992, p241; 1/1993, p48; 2/1993, p101.

[21] W Schneider, DJ8ES, *VHF Communications* 4/1993, p221.

[22] W Schneider, DJ8ES, *VHF Communications* 2/1995, p98.

[23] M Kuhne, DB6NT, *Dubus Technik* IV, p253.

[24] M J Gingell, *Electrical Communications* Vol 48, 1973, pp21–25.

[25] J P Hawker, G3VA, *Radio Communication* 1973, p699.

[26] J R Hey, G3TDZ, *Radio Communication* 1976, p656.

[27] P Rhodes, G3XJP, *Radio Communication* June 1996, p28; July 1996, p59; August 1996, p60; September 1996, p61, October 1996, p61.

[28] D K Weaver, *Proc IERE* Vol 44 (12), 1956, pp1703–1705.

[29] *Philips Components Data Handbook* SC08b, 'RF power MOS transistors', 1991, p29.

[30] 'Modeling RF transistors when the heat's on', J Scholten, *Microwaves and RF* February 1984, pp97–105.

[31] 'A 15 watt AM aircraft transmitter power amplifier using low cost plastic transistors', D Hollander, Application Note AN793, *Motorola RF Device Data*, Vol II, 5th edn, 1988.

[32] 'A single device, 80 watt, 50Ω VHF amplifier', T Bishop, Engineering Bulletin EB46, *Motorola RF Device Data Book* B055, 1984.

[33] 'Design considerations for parallel combined rf power amplifiers', R Magill, Applications Note 2.0.8.1F, CTC, 1978.

[34] *VHF/UHF Manual,* 4th edn, Ed G R Jessop, RSGB, 1983, pp5.14.

[35] 'A single stage linear amplifier for 50MHz', J Matthews, *Radio Communication* June 1986, pp404–409.

[36] 'A VHF driver for hybrid power modules', Z Lau, *QEX* March 1994, pp29–30.

[37] 'A no-tune driver for 432MHz', Z Lau, *Radio Communication* July 1993, pp38–39.

[38] *ARRL Handbook,* 17th edn, Ed Schetgen, ARRL, 1992, pp32-19–32-21.

[39] 'A 20W linear amplifier for the 23cm band', K Hupfer, *VHF Communications* 1/86, pp38–40.

[40] '24/23cm band linear power amplifier module M57762', J Berns, *VHF Communications* 4/89, pp211–215.

[41] 'A solid state broadband amplifier for 24cm', A Vilaseca and S Riviere, *VHF Communications* 2/94, pp85–92.

[42] 'Single stage 15W linear amplifier for the 2m band', M Ulbrect, *VHF Communications* 4/79, pp216–221.

[43] '70MHz transverter', D Harvey and C Gare, *Radio Communication* February 1977.

[44] 'A 50MHz receive/transmit converter', D Jones, *Radio Communication* April 1986, pp260–263.

[45] '2m transverter', H Roberts, *Radio and Electronics World.*

[46] 'Guidelines for the design of semiconductor VHF power amplifiers', J Matthews, *Radio Communication* September and December 1986.

[47] Technical Topics, *Radio Communication* May 1993, pp56.

[48] *VHF/UHF Manual,* 4th edn, Ed G R Jessop, RSGB, 1983, pp5.102–5.103.

[49] 'Building push-pull, multioctave, VHF power amplifiers', H Granberg, *Microwaves & RF* November 1987, pp77–86 (Available as Motorola Application Report AR305).

[50] Kits available from: (a) Communication Concepts International, 508 Millstone Drive, Xenia, OH 45385, USA. Tel: 513 426 8600, fax: 513 429 3811. (b) Mainline Electronics, PO Box 235, Leicester, UK. Tel: 0116 277 7648.

[51] Eimac division of Varian, technical data for 4CX250B.

[52] Eimac division of Varian, technical data for 8873, 8874, 8875.

[53] 'A stripline kilowatt amplifier for 432MHz', R Knadle, *QST* April 1972, pp49–55 and May 1972, pp59–62.

[54] 'Power supply and control circuits for a 4CX250B amplifier', A Wade, *Radio Communication* October 1977, pp762–768.

[55] 'A power supply and control system for tetrode amplifiers', J Nelson and M Noakes, *Radio Communication* December 1987, pp902–907 and January 1988.

[56] Knadle, see reference [53].

[57] 'VHF/UHF power amplifier mods and designs' – notes to accompany high-power amplifier kits sold by G Brown, GJ4ICD.

[58] 'Technical Correspondence', *QST* July 1975, p47.

[59] 'Transmitters, power amplifiers and EMC', J Nelson, in *The VHF/UHF DX Book,* Ed I White, DIR Publishing Ltd, England, 1992, pp6-19–6-21.

[60] J Nelson in *The VHF/UHF DX Book,* Ed I White, DIR Publishing Ltd, England, 1992, pp11-2–11-8.

[61] 'External anode tetrodes', W Orr, *Ham Radio* June 1969 pp23–27.

[62] 'Recipe for a longer life – keep the heaters under proper control', J Nelson and M Noakes, *Radio Communication* July 1988, pp529–532.

[63] 'Technical Topics', *Radio Communication* October 1990, p29.

[64] 'A 3CX800A7 amp for 432MHz', S Powlishen, in *The ARRL UHF/Microwave Projects Manual,* ARRL, USA, 1994, pp8–21.

[65] 'Technical Topics', *Radio Communication* April 1986, p266.

[66] *Radio Communication Handbook,* 6th edn, Ed D Biddulph, RSGB, 1994, pp8.50–8.52.

[67] 'Technical Topics', *Radio Communication* July 1989, p37.

[68] Wade, see reference [54].

[69] Nelson and Noakes, see reference [55].

[70] 'Active screen regulator', M Noakes, in *The VHF/UHF DX Book,* Ed I White, DIR Publishing Ltd, England, 1992, pp11-9–11-11.

[71] 'Technical Topics', *Radio Communication* July 1989, p37.

[72] *Radio Communication Handbook,* 6th edn, Ed D Biddulph, RSGB, 1994, pp5.29–5.31.

[73] *VHF/UHF Manual,* 4th edn, Ed G R Jessop, RSGB, 1983, pp5.84–5.87.

[74] *VHF/UHF Manual,* 4th edn, Ed G R Jessop, RSGB, 1983, pp5.82–5.83.

[75] 'A plate line pa for 432MHz', L Williams, *Radio Communication* October 1976, pp752–755.

[76] 'New ideas for the 2 meter kilowatt', T McMullen Jnr and E Tilton, *QST* February 1971.

[77] J Nelson in *The VHF/UHF DX Book,* Ed I White, DIR Publishing Ltd, England, 1992, pp6.29–6.31.

[78] 'Stripline kilowatt for two meters', F Merry, *Ham Radio* October 1977, pp10–24.

[80] 'A gounded grid kilowatt amplifier for 432MHz', S Powlishen, *QST* October 1979, pp11–14.

[81] Powlishen, see reference [64].

[82] 'More gain from 1.3GHz power amplifiers', R Blackwell and I White, *Radio Communication* June 1983, pp500–503.

[83] 'A quarter kilowatt 23cm amplifier', E R 'Chip' Angle, *QST* March 1985, pp14–37.

[84] *Radio Communication* January 1976, p24.

[85] *QST* June 1981.

[86] *Radio Communication* August 1981, p732.

[87] *VHF/UHF Manual,* 4th edn, Ed G R Jessop, RSGB, 1983, p9.13–9.15.

[88] 'Microwaves', *Radio Communication* April 1979, p342.

5 Antennas and transmission lines

THE antenna and its associated feeder or transmission line are arguably the most important elements of any VHF or UHF station, but are frequently considered least in its assembly. Without a good antenna system, and equally good feeder arrangements, much of the RF power generated by the transmitter will be dissipated as heat before it reaches the antenna. If the antenna is badly sited, or unsuitable for the location, the power reaching it may be radiated in the wrong direction, or scattered from other nearby antennas and structures, again wasting the RF generated by the transmitter. The problems of line loss increase with increasing frequency, and greater care is required to make the most of the power available – and it is generally more difficult (or expensive) to generate more power as the frequency increases.

Similar arguments apply to reception – why throw away a large percentage of the signal captured by the antenna before it reaches the receiver? Solutions using mast-head preamplifiers are discussed in other parts of this book, but they entail some complexity and expense if the antenna is to be used for both transmission and reception.

Of course, it is not always possible to find and erect an ideal antenna in an ideal location, particularly in an urban environment. This chapter describes the principles of antenna and transmission lines for the VHF and UHF amateur bands, such that the reader can make informed choices about installations that are both practical and effective for their environment. The designs for home construction are practical, and can be built with confidence that they will work *if the details are followed closely*. However, at VHF/UHF small deviations from detail can affect the performance of the antenna quite markedly, and if suitable measuring apparatus is not available, much frustration can ensue in trying to make the antenna work. This chapter includes some more complex antennas that require some measuring facilities to optimise performance after construction; these are for the enthusiastic antenna experimenter.

However, before tackling the selection and installation of antennas, it is useful to understand some of the underlying theory of their operation and use.

ANTENNA FUNDAMENTALS

All antennas have certain basic properties which can be well defined. These are:

- Radiation pattern
- Polarisation
- Gain
- Input impedance
- Impedance and radiation pattern bandwidths

Of these, the radiation pattern is generally the most basic

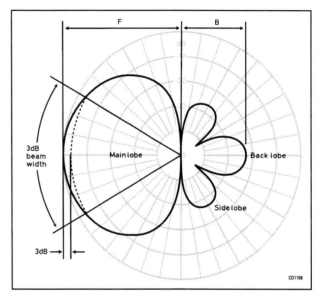

Fig 5.1. Typical polar diagram of a VHF Yagi antenna

parameter used for selecting an antenna for a particular purpose. Many amateurs use highly directional antennas which require rotation to point in the desired direction of communication. However, antennas providing all-round (omnidirectional) coverage are usually required for repeater stations, and are of course essential for vehicle installations.

Radiation pattern

The *radiation pattern* describes the spatial distribution of the power radiated by the antenna, that is, the directions in which the signal is transmitted or from which it is received. The key characteristics of directional antennas are usually expressed as the beamwidth in two principal planes at right-angles to each other, known as the *E plane* and the *H plane*, and described in the next section. The beamwidth in these principal planes is usually defined as the angle including the main beam at which the radiated energy falls to one-half the maximum level. This is called the *half-power beamwidth*, and the points on the radiation pattern are often called the *3dB* or *half-power points* of the radiation pattern, being 3dB below the main beam. See Fig 5.1.

Fig 5.1 shows the spatial distribution of power in one principal plane for a typical directional VHF antenna. This representation is called a *polar diagram*, where the power in a given direction is indicated by the distance of the curve from the centre of the diagram (in this case, where the *lobes* touch), and can be thought of as a plan view of the variation in radiated power. The radiation pattern can be presented on a variety of polar diagram charts, the principal difference being the

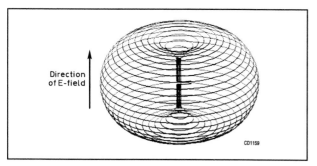

Fig 5.2. Radiation from, and polarisation of, a dipole antenna

arrangement of the radial scale. The most usual forms are *linear*, where the radius of the pattern is directly proportional to the radiated power in a given direction, and *logarithmic*, where the radius represents the relative power in decibels.

Key features of the radiation patterns of the antenna shown in Fig 5.1 are the main lobe or main beam, and the presence of several minor lobes including one pointing in the opposite direction to the main lobe. The *front-to-back (F/B) ratio* is the ratio of the energy radiated by the peak of the main lobe to that in the opposite direction, and is often used as an estimate of the 'goodness' of a beam antenna. This ratio is usually expressed in decibels. As more power is radiated in minor lobes, less power is available in the main lobe, and the *gain* of the antenna is reduced (see below). Omnidirectional antennas ideally have a circular radiation pattern in one plane, but will still have a shaped radiation pattern in the other principal plane, at right-angles to the first.

The linearly scaled graph is useful for measuring the beamwidth of the main lobe accurately, whereas the logarithmically scaled chart more clearly shows the levels of the sidelobes, which may be barely visible on the linear chart. The ARRL has promoted the use of a hybrid chart which combines features of both types of graph, by using a quasi-logarithmic radial scale marked in decibels [2].

Polarisation

Radio waves comprise both electric and magnetic fields mutually coupled at right-angles to each other and at right-angles to the direction of propagation. From this derive the two *principal planes* used in describing radiation patterns; the *E-plane* lies parallel to the electric vector or E-field in the main lobe, and the *H-plane* lies parallel to the magnetic vector or H-field in the main lobe. Accordingly, these two principal planes will be at right-angles to each other.

The polarisation of an antenna is defined in terms of the orientation of the electric field vector in the direction of maximum radiation. The maximum radiation from a dipole occurs in a plane bisecting its centre and at right-angles to the dipole arms. The electric field vector in this plane lies parallel to the arms of the dipole, see Fig 5.2.

Thus a dipole mounted horizontally above the ground is said to radiate *horizontally polarised* signals, and the same dipole mounted vertically would radiate *vertically polarised* signals.

Whilst many amateurs use vertical or horizontal *linear* polarisation for terrestrial communications, satellite users often use *circular* polarisation to reduce the effects of propagation, ground reflections or the spinning of the satellites on

the signals. The effect of circular polarisation can be visualised as a signal emanating from a dipole rotating about its centre at the frequency of radiation. The tip of the electric vector traces out a corkscrew as it propagates away from the antenna, and like a corkscrew, the polarisation is described as *right-* or *left-handed circular*, dependent on the direction of rotation of the electric vector as seen from the transmitter.

A fixed linear dipole will receive an equal signal from a circularly polarised wave whether it is mounted vertically, horizontally or in an intermediate position. The signal strength will be 3dB less than if a circularly polarised antenna of the same sense is used; however, a circularly polarised antenna of the opposite sense will receive no signals. Both these effects are due to *polarisation mismatch* between the wave and the receive antenna.

In practice, an antenna may radiate unwanted polarisations in a variety of directions, including the main lobe. This is called *cross-polarised radiation*, and for linearly polarised antennas it will be perpendicular to the wanted radiation. In circularly polarised antennas, the cross-polarised element is that part of the signal that is radiated as circular polarisation of the opposite sense to that intended. The relationship between wanted and unwanted signals is often expressed as an *axial ratio* or *ellipticity*, the definitions of which can be found in reference [1]. The smaller this figure, the better.

It is worth noting that with linearly polarised antennas, particularly beams with complex polar diagrams, radiation from the sidelobes can be of the opposite polarisation to the main beam, and will often be complex or elliptical, especially outside the principal planes. Hence the reception of signals from a cross-polarised station may often be stronger with the beam pointing away from, or at an angle to, the transmitting station.

Gain and directivity

The gain of an antenna is a basic property which is frequently used as a figure of merit. It is defined as the maximum signal radiated in a given direction relative to that of an *isotropic radiator* fed with the same power. An isotropic radiator is a hypothetical, lossless antenna which radiates equally in all directions. In practice, a half-wave dipole is often used as the reference radiator; if the dipole is lossless, it has a maximum gain of 1.64 (or $10 \times \log_{10} 1.64 = 2.15$ decibels) relative to the isotropic antenna.

The *directivity* of an antenna is defined purely in terms of its radiation pattern, as the radiation intensity in a given direction to the radiation intensity averaged over all directions. A practical antenna may have good *directivity*, but poor *gain* if the antenna is lossy through poor design, use of lossy components or poor mechanical construction. If the antenna is lossless, the gain and directivity will be the same.

High directivity is achieved by compressing or focusing the radiated power into a small *solid angle*, the product of the half-power beamwidths in the two principal planes. An isotropic radiator radiates equally in all directions, which can be imagined as equal illumination over the surface of a sphere. A good, directive VHF antenna will confine most of its radiation to a few tens of degrees around the main beam, corresponding to the beam of a pencil torch illuminating the inside of the sphere.

If antenna losses are small, and the side and backlobes are

also much smaller than the main lobe (which we would expect for a well-designed beam antenna), there is an approximate formula which relates the 3dB beamwidth of the antenna in the two principal planes (E and H) to the gain of the antenna:

$$\text{Gain relative to a }\lambda/2\text{ dipole} = \frac{27{,}000}{\theta_E\theta_H}$$

where θ_E is the angular width, in degrees, between the half-power points in the E-plane, and θ_H is the angular width, in degrees, between the half-power points in the H-plane. The gain can be expressed in decibels relative to a half-wave dipole (dBD) by taking the logarithm of the expression:

$$G_{dBD} = 10\log_{10}\left[\frac{27{,}000}{\theta_E\theta_H}\right]$$

This formula is reasonably accurate (within 2dB) for well-designed, efficient antennas with gains greater than 10dBi (8dBD), and can be useful for estimating the beamwidth where a radiation pattern is only available for one plane and the gain of the antenna is also known. The gain in decibels relative to an *isotropic* radiator is found by adding 2.15 to G_{dBD}.

Input impedance

The impedance presented at the feedpoint by an antenna is a complex function of the size and shape of the antenna, the frequency of operation, and its environment. The impedance is affected by the proximity of other conducting objects, where the induction of RF currents alters the impedance through *mutual coupling* between the antenna and object. The elements of a Yagi antenna are mutually coupled together, and the driven element would present a very different impedance if measured in isolation from the rest of the structure.

Input impedance is usually complex. The resistive part is composed of the radiation resistance, which can be thought of as dissipating power by radiating it as electromagnetic energy (desirable), and loss resistance, which dissipates power as heat (not desirable). The reactive part arises from the behaviour of antenna elements as resonators, or tuned circuits, and it can change rapidly with variations of frequency.

Impedance bandwidth

The impedance bandwidth of an antenna is defined as the frequency range over which the antenna impedance results in a voltage standing wave ratio (VSWR) less than some arbitrary limit. This may be typically 1.5:1 for amateur operation with solid-state transmitters or higher values for other applications. Ideally, an antenna should be impedance matched to the feedline and thence to the transmitter or receiver. Although *tuned feed* arrangements are sometimes used at HF, where a high standing wave ratio may be acceptable on the feedline, the losses in VHF feeders and tuning components usually preclude this approach at VHF and UHF. Feeders and matching arrangements are discussed later in this chapter.

Radiation pattern bandwidth

Antenna radiation patterns are also dependent upon the operating frequency. Using the analogy of the Yagi antenna's elements as tuned circuits, the loss of resonance away from the design frequency results in small currents in the elements and a consequently severe loss of performance. In the case of the Yagi antenna this results in a sharp decrease of gain, and destruction of the desired radiation pattern. For beam antennas, such as the Yagi, the radiation pattern bandwidth is often defined as the frequency range over which the main lobe gain decreases to 1dB less than its maximum.

It should be noted that the impedance bandwidth and radiation pattern bandwidth are independent of each other. It is quite possible for the impedance bandwidth to be greater than the radiation pattern bandwidth, especially with high-gain antennas, and to be able to feed power into an antenna that then wastes it by radiating it in other than the desired direction!

ANTENNA ARRAYS
Purpose

The gain achievable with any antenna structure is ultimately limited by the fundamentals of its operation. However, higher gains can be achieved by using several antenna elements in an *array*. The array can comprise antennas *stacked* vertically above each other, or arranged side by side in *bays*, or a combination of both. These are *broadside* arrays, where most of the radiated power is projected at right-angles to the plane in which the elements lie. An array can also be formed where the main beam is projected along the array of elements; these are *endfire* arrays, of which the HB9CV and Yagi antennas are examples.

An array of elements has a narrower beamwidth, and hence a higher gain, than the individual antennas. The maximum achievable gain could be N times greater than one element fed with the same power ($10\log_{10} N$ decibels) if there are N elements in the array. However, more complex feed arrangements can reduce the VSWR bandwidth and introduce losses, reducing the array gain. Arrays need care in construction and attention to detail, especially at UHF and above, but the results reward the effort expended.

Broadside arrays

If a pair of identical isotropic radiators or *point sources* are fed in phase with equal power, an interference pattern will be set up. The field will be a maximum at right-angles to the array. However, cancellation will occur at other angles where the wave from one antenna has travelled an odd number of half-wavelengths further than from the other antenna – see Fig 5.3.

The same principle can be applied to more than two point sources, which if they are equally spaced, produce a radiation pattern of the form:

$$E_\vartheta = \left[\frac{\sin\left(\dfrac{N}{2}\psi\right)}{\sin\left(\dfrac{1}{2}\psi\right)}\right]$$

$$\psi = 2\pi d\sin\theta + \beta$$

where θ is the angle measured normal to the line of the array, d is the separation of the point sources in wavelengths, β is the phase difference between the elements (usually zero) and N is the number of elements.

The electric field at any angle to the array is calculated by adding together the fields from each point source, taking into

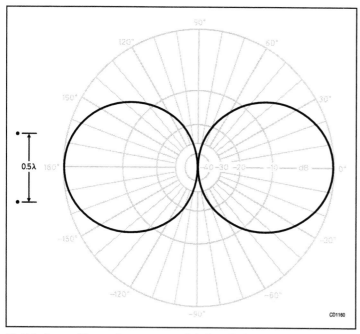

Fig 5.3. Array of two point sources and their radiation pattern

Table 5.1. Calculations for the radiation pattern of a four-element collinear dipole array			
Angle relative to normal (°)	Array factor factor	Dipole pattern (voltage)	Radiation pattern
0	4.00	1.00	4.00
5	3.74	0.99	3.71
10	3.00	0.98	2.94
15	1.98	0.95	1.88
20	0.89	0.91	0.81
25	−0.06	0.87	−0.05
30	−0.73	0.82	−0.59
35	−1.05	0.76	0.80
40	−1.06	0.69	−0.74

account the phase delay of the field from each source, ie *vector addition* of the fields. The resulting pattern for arrays of point sources is often known as an *array factor*.

In a practical array, each point source will be replaced by a real antenna, a half-wave dipole or perhaps a Yagi antenna. Provided that all the antennas are pointing in the same direction, the pattern produced by such an array can be found by multiplying together, at each angle of interest, the array factor just calculated and the *pattern factor* or radiation pattern of the antennas used in the array.

This means that any nulls in the element pattern will be reproduced in the array pattern, which is why arrays of complex elements often result in many sidelobes.

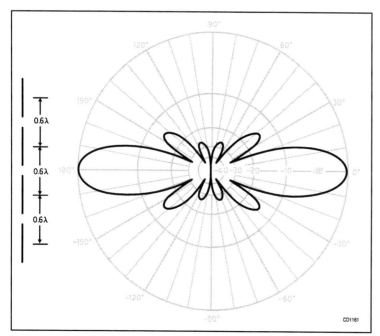

Fig 5.4. Plotted radiation pattern for a four-element collinear dipole array

The radiation pattern of such an array can be calculated by programming a computer, in a spreadsheet, or by hand by setting out a table as shown in Table 5.1.

Note that if working from antenna patterns or data expressed in decibels, the directivity at each angle *must* be converted to a fraction before multiplying by the array factor. For example, if the directivity at a given angle is −2.8dB relative to the peak of the main beam, the directivity in linear terms is:

$$10^{-2.8/20} = 0.7244$$

or antilog$_{10}$(−2.8/20) for those with log tables. It is easiest to scale the directivity to the peak of the main lobe prior to carrying out the calculation.

Endfire arrays

If a pair of point source antennas are separated by one quarter-wavelength, and are fed with a phase difference of 90° between them, the radiated field from one antenna will reinforce that of the second in one direction, and will completely cancel the field from the second in the opposite direction – see Fig 5.5.

The equation for the radiation pattern is the same as shown for the broadside array above, except that the phase angle β is now 90°. Other spacings may be used, provided that the phase difference is adjusted to ensure that the radiation is cancelled in the desired direction. Antennas such as the HB9CV (shown later in this chapter) use this technique to provide directivity and a good front-to-back ratio from mechanically compact structures. Both elements are fed by the transmitter. The Yagi antenna generates its radiation pattern using similar phasing principles, but only one element is fed as described later in this chapter.

Antenna array theory can be found in almost any book devoted to antennas. However, a good treatment with many radiation pattern examples can be found in references [3] and [4].

Practical considerations and limitations of arrays

Stacking separation

High gain cannot be achieved by simply stacking many elements close together. If we consider a

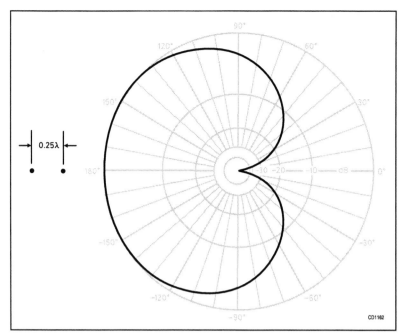

Fig 5.5. Radiation pattern of two point sources separated by one quarter-wavelength and fed in quadrature

dipole collecting power from an incident field for delivery to a load (receiver), it can be thought of as having a collecting area or *effective aperture* that is somewhat larger than the dipole itself. The higher the directivity of the antenna, the larger the effective aperture, as given by the relationship:

$$A_{\text{eff}} = \frac{\lambda^2}{4\pi} D$$

where D is the directivity of the antenna and λ is the working wavelength.

If the effective apertures of adjacent antennas overlap, the incoming RF energy is shared between them, and the maximum possible directivity (or gain) of the elements cannot be attained.

The optimum stacking distance is a function of the half-power beamwidth of the elements in the array, and is given by:

$$S_{\text{opt}} = \frac{\lambda}{\left[2\sin\left(\dfrac{\phi}{2}\right)\right]}$$

where ϕ is the half-power beamwidth. Note that this is usually different for the E and H planes, so that the spacing of the elements is also usually different in each plane.

Also, when antennas are placed close together, *mutual coupling* between elements occurs. This leads to changes in the current distribution on the elements, changing both the radiation pattern and the feed-point impedance of each element. The changes to the feed impedance often result in unequal powers being fed to the elements of the array, with consequential loss of gain. Optimum stacking rules are based on the assumption of minimum mutual influence which can be difficult to predict for composite antennas such as Yagis. However, antennas with low sidelobe levels are less susceptible than those with high sidelobes, as might be expected intuitively.

The coupling and effective aperture overlap problems cannot simply be solved by arbitrarily increasing the separation of the elements. As the element spacing increases, *grating sidelobes* appear, which reduce the forward gain. The grating lobes are due solely to the array dimensions, and can be seen by plotting the array factor for the chosen configuration.

Power divider and transmission line losses

The usual arrangements for feeding an array of antennas require each antenna to be fed an equal amount of power in the same phase as all the other elements in the array. There are several ways that this can be achieved, as shown in the section on antennas for construction later in this chapter. The power can be divided N ways at one point, from which equal length transmission lines feed each element, or groups of elements may be fed by several power dividers which are in turn fed by another power divider. Each system has its merits but losses incurred in the power dividers and cables erode the gain provided by the array.

Each time a cable connection is required, whether to a power divider or an antenna, the connection usually creates a small impedance mismatch. Power will be reflected from this mismatch and others in the system, reducing the gain of the array. The cumulative degradation of the power distribution to each antenna element can be startling, and of course the same degradation occurs when the antenna is receiving. In general, the simplest feed arrangements incur lowest losses and best performance.

Phasing errors

The small mismatches described above can result in errors in the phase of the current injected into the array elements, again leading to loss of gain and filling of nulls in the radiation pattern. Incorrect line lengths can result in the same effect. In constructing feeds for UHF and above, care must be taken in cutting and connecting cables.

A knowledge of the *velocity factor* of the actual cable used is essential if good results are to be achieved. The velocity factor is the rate at which the RF propagates along the cable relative to the speed of light (or RF) in a vacuum, and is modified by the dielectric constant of the cable insulator. A cutting error of 2mm in a solid polythene dielectric cable (such as URM67) will result in a phase error of 5° at 1296MHz. Measurement of the cable characteristics as described in references [5] and [6] can help eliminate many of the uncertainties of cable harness fabrication.

Alternatively, the velocity factor can be found with a dip meter coupled to a very small loop at the end of an open-circuit length of cable. At VHF, this loop should be no greater than 3mm radius. At higher frequencies, it is sufficient to trim the dielectric of the cable flush with the braid, fold the inner over the dielectric and solder to the braid, especially for larger-diameter cables. The dip will appear when the cable is an odd number of quarter-wavelengths long; if the frequency is checked with a counter or calibrated receiver, the velocity factor can be accurately calculated from:

$$v = \frac{4Lf}{300n}$$

where L is the length of the stub in metres, f is the resonant frequency in megahertz, and n is 1, 3, 5, the length of the stub in quarter-wavelengths. The lowest resonant frequency corresponds to $n = 1$.

Velocity factors are typically 0.66 for solid polyethylene, 0.72 for solid PTFE, and around 0.85 to 0.95 for foamed dielectrics or semi-airspaced cables. Very-low-loss Heliax-style cables which support the inner on small dielectric stand-offs can have velocity factors of 0.98.

Size, weight and wind loading

The size and weight of an array grows rapidly as the number of elements increases. The thoretical increase in gain over a single element follows the power law:

$$G_{max} = 10 \log_{10} N \quad \text{decibels}$$

where N is the number of elements.

Two elements provide 3dB gain, four elements 6dB gain, eight elements 9dB, 16 elements 20dB gain and so on, under ideal conditions. However, given the spacing constraints, the weight and wind loading of the array can quickly become unmanageable, especially if low-gain elements such as dipoles are used. It is for this reason that most high-gain antenna arrays constructed today use Yagi antennas for the array elements, as relatively few driven elements are required. This also simplifies the feed arrangements, which in turn reduces the losses and the cumulative phase and mismatch errors that tend to occur as the feed arrangements become more complex.

TRANSMISSION LINES

Antenna feeders or, more correctly, transmission lines, can make or break the performance of a station. At UHF and higher, the losses in the transmission lines feeding the antenna can be significant, dissipating RF power as heat, and requiring much larger antennas to achieve the desired radiated power. At these frequencies, there are essentially two useful types of transmission line for antennas: open wire and coaxial cable.

Open-wire line

The open-wire transmission line, comprising two parallel conductors held apart at intervals by spacers or spreaders, is still often used for feeding HF antennas. It provides a low-loss, easily constructed feeder capable of handling high powers, and the characteristic impedance can be adjusted by changing the wire diameter or spacing. The characteristic impedance is given by:

$$Z_0 = 276 \log_{10}\left(\frac{2D}{d}\right)$$

where D is the spacing between the wire centres, both wires having diameter d.

At VHF and higher frequencies, dielectric losses can become significant, but are minimised in the parallel-wire line. Apart from the spacers, the dielectric between the lines is air, and only a vacuum provides a better dielectric. The velocity

factor is very close to unity. However, the spacing between wires must be much less than the wavelength if power is not to be lost through radiation. At VHF and above, this forces the selection of thinner wires or lower characteristic impedances if the feeder is to remain reasonably robust, and to some extent limits the uses of this type of transmission line to providing low-loss feeds to antennas in arrays, where the ability to adjust the impedance by varying the spacing is useful. Open-wire line is not really practicable for frequencies above 432MHz. This, and the difficulties of rigging long runs of closely spaced lines and of bringing them through the wall of a building (or round the antenna rotator) have probably discouraged their more general use.

Where open-wire line is required, use enamelled soft-drawn copper wire and solid PTFE rod for spacers if possible. The wire should be stretched to straighten and work-harden it immediately prior to assembly. Great care should be taken to ensure both wires are of equal length and made up/mounted symmetrically with respect both to dielectrics and conducting objects adjacent to the line.

Coaxial lines

Coaxial transmission lines, as their name implies, comprise an inner conductor mounted centrally within an outer conductor. The characteristic impedance for concentric circular conductors is given by:

$$Z_0 = \left(\frac{138}{\sqrt{\varepsilon}}\right) \log_{10}\left(\frac{D}{d}\right)$$

where D is the inside diameter of the outer conductor, d is the diameter of the inner conductor and ε is the dielectric constant of the insulator (1 for air).

A square-section outer can be used to simplify connector mountings for home-constructed power dividers and transformer sections. The characteristic impedance is approximated by:

$$Z_0 = \left(\frac{138}{\sqrt{\varepsilon}}\right) \log_{10}\left(1.08 \frac{D}{d}\right)$$

where D is now the inside dimension of the square outer conductor.

The principal advantage of coaxial transmission lines is that the surfaces carrying the RF current and the dielectric are inside, allowing robust, weather-resistant design and simple mounting on metal surfaces or masts. The disadvantages are dielectric losses (which increase rapidly with frequency), cost and weight.

Flexible cable designs use a braided outer conductor which, if it does not thoroughly cover the dielectric, will allow the RF to leak out through gaps in the braid. Cheap, so-called 'RG58' cable sold for Citizens' Band use should be avoided at all costs, as the braid coverage can be less than 50% – at VHF and above little power will reach the antenna. There are also cheap cables using a single wire and metallised plastic wrapping as 'braid' which are useless for VHF purposes.

Good-quality flexible coaxial cables have thick, close woven single or double outer braids. Genuine RG58 or URM67 cables provide flexibility with acceptable losses, especially for short lengths. Where longer cable runs are necessary, cables with semi-air spacing and copper-foil outer conductors provide better performance, although some care is needed in sealing the ends of these types to prevent ingress of moisture which will rapidly degrade the cable irretrievably. The ultimate in coaxial feeders are the Flexwell or Heliax types of cable, with a continuous corrugated copper outer, and air-spaced or PTFE foam dielectrics, together with special connectors to ensure good sealing and minimal mismatch. The performance of some typical 50Ω coaxial cables under impedance-matched conditions is shown in Table 5.2. Note that losses will be higher if appreciable standing waves exist on the cable. There is further information in Chapter 12 – 'General Data'.

Table 5.2. Attenuation of coaxial cables

Cable type	Diameter (mm)	Velocity factor	Attenuation (dB/100m) at				
			50MHz	70MHz	144MHz	432MHz	1296MHz
URM76, RG58CU	5.0	0.66	12	14	19	32	N/A
URM43	5.0	0.66	8.1	10.2	16.1	28.5	N/A
URM67, RG213U	10.3	0.66	4.6	5.6	8.3	15.5	27.0
Westflex 103	10.3	0.85	2.0	2.5	4.5	7.5	13.0
$3/8$in Flexwell	12.3	0.89	2.0	2.4	3.0	6.4	10.8
$5/8$in Flexwell	23.0	0.92	1.25	1.5	2.5	3.8	6.8
$7/8$in Flexwell	29.0	0.92	0.83	1.0	1.45	2.5	4.4

Table 5.3. Miniature and special-impedance cables for stubs and transformers

Cable type	Impedance (Ω)	Diameter (mm)	Dielectric	Velocity factor	Attenuation (dB/100m) at		
					100MHz	300MHz	1000MHz
URM95	50	2.3	Polythene	0.66	27	46	85
RG174U	50	2.3	Polythene	0.66	—	—	—
URM70	75	6	Polythene	0.67	15	27	52
URM111	75	2.3	PTFE	0.72	25	44	81
RG62AU	95	6	Air-spaced polythene	0.83	—	—	—

An optimised installation would use rigid, low-loss cable for the fixed runs, with a short section of flexible cable to bridge the antenna rotator.

Matching stubs and transformer sections (discussed below) often require cables with characteristic impedances other than 50Ω. Also, miniature cables are sometimes desirable for constructing matching networks and filters. The higher loss is usually acceptable, as the length of cable used is small. Characteristics of a few readily available special cable types are shown in Table 5.3.

Impedance matching circuits

At VHF and above it is usual to use transmission lines, rather than lumped components, to obtain an impedance match between systems of different characteristic impedances. They can also be used to match arbitrary impedances (such as an antenna) to its feeder, of which a few techniques are shown below. Other methods addressing the design and calculation of matching circuits and components in detail are shown in references [7] and [8]. An excellent article on the behaviour of transmission lines and their use as circuit elements, together with some computer programs, can be found in reference [9].

Single stub matching

A short-circuited section of lossless transmission line behaves as a pure reactance at its input terminals. This impedance is given by the formula:

$$X_{in} = Z_0 \tan \beta l$$

where βl is the electrical length of the line (taking into account the velocity factor) and Z_0 is its characteristic impedance

The input reactance is inductive until the line length is a quarter-wavelength. The input impedance is then infinite, ie an open-circuit. As the line length is increased further, the reactance becomes negative, and the line behaves as a

capacitor at the input terminals, although the remote end is a short-circuit. When the line is exactly one half-wavelength long, the input terminals appear to be short-circuited with no residual reactance. This cycle is repeated as the line is extended further.

An open-circuited stub behaves in a complementary manner to the short-circuited line. The input impedance is given by:

$$X_{in} = \frac{Z_0}{\tan \beta l}$$

Now the short length of line appears as a capacitor at its terminals, becoming a short-circuit at one quarter-wavelength, appearing inductive as it lengthens further, and becoming an open-circuit at one half-wavelength.

The term *matching* is used to describe the process of suitably modifying the effective load impedance to make it behave as a resistance and to ensure that this resistance has a value equal to the characteristic impedance of the feeder used. To make a complex load (ie a load possessing both resistance and reactance) behave as a resistance, it is necessary to introduce across it a reactance of equal value and opposite sign so that its reactance is effectively cancelled. The stubs described above provide the means to supply this reactance. Although there is no need to make the characteristic impedance of a stub equal to that of the transmission line, it may be desirable to do so for practical reasons.

In addition to tuning out the reactance, a match still has to be made to the transmission line characteristic impedance. The impedance at any point along the length of a $\lambda/4$ resonant stub varies from zero at the short-circuit to a very high impedance at the open end. If a load is connected to the open end and the power is fed into the stub at some point along its length, the stub may be used as an impedance transformer to give various values of impedance according the position of the feed point.

This is shown in Fig 5.6. The distance L is adjusted to tune the antenna to resonance and will be $\lambda/4$ long if the antenna is already resonant. The distance l is adjusted to obtain a match to the line. However, it can be convenient to have a stub with

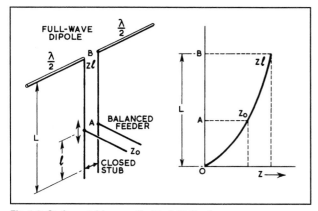

Fig 5.6. Stub matching applied to λ/2 dipole

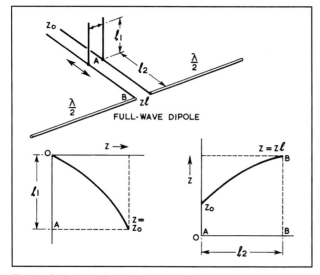

Fig 5.7. Stub matching with a moveable short-circuited stub

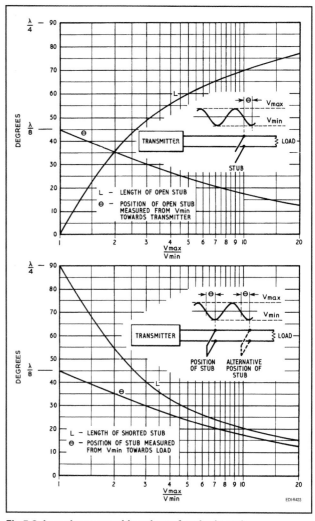

Fig 5.8. Impedance matching charts for single stub

an adjustable short-circuit which can slide along the transmission line (see Fig 5.7).

In practice, matching can be achieved entirely by the 'cut-and-try' method of adjusting the stub length and position until no standing waves can be detected. The feeder line is then said to be *flat*. However, the frequency range over which any single-stub matching device is effective is quite small, and where wide-band matching is required some other matching system may be needed. Fortunately, for most amateur purposes the bandwidth required is relatively narrow and the single-stub technique is usually sufficient. Fig 5.8 shows the positioning of open- and short-circuited stubs when the VSWR and the position of the VSWR minimum are known.

Two-stub matching
It is in making stub adjustments by 'cut-and-try' that the open-wire transmission line comes into its own because of the relative ease of repositioning the stub and the short-circuit. With coaxial line it is impracticable to construct a stub with an adjustable position. However, two fixed stubs spaced by a fraction of a wavelength can be used for matching purposes (see Fig 5.9).

The spacing usually employed is λ/8 or a multiple thereof. With this spacing, independent adjustment of the short-circuit stub lengths gives a matching range over 0.5 times the

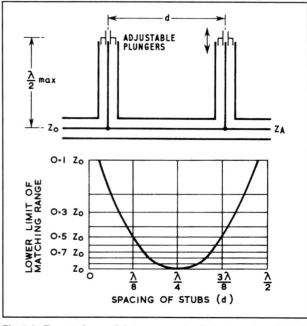

Fig 5.9. Two-stub coaxial tuner graph. Z_0 is the characteristic impedance of the feeder

characteristic impedance (Z_0) of the transmission line upwards. As the spacing between the stubs is increased towards $\lambda/2$ or decreased towards zero, the matching range increases, but the adjustments become extremely critical and the bandwidth narrow. The theoretical matching range limits cannot be realised in practice because of finite losses in the stubs, so attention should be paid to providing reliable short-circuiting plungers in any home-built adjustable two-stub tuning units.

Adjustable stub tuners suitable for use at 144MHz have largely disappeared from the professional inventory, and are therefore extremely scarce in amateur circles. However, if the impedance of the device to be matched can be measured, the position of the stub can be calculated from Fig 5.9, or by the methods described in detail in references [7] and [8]. Co-axial feeders and stubs carefully cut to length and checked (see 'Practical considerations and limitations of arrays' above) will usually achieve a reasonable match, which can then be adjusted by trimming the stub for best results. If trimming worsens the match, replace the stub with a slightly longer one, and start trimming again.

Transmission line transformers

Quarter-wave transformer

A length of transmission line of a different characteristic impedance than the feeder can be used to transform impedance, providing an alternative technique which may be used to match a load to a transmission line. A special condition occurs when the length of the section of line is an odd number of quarter wavelengths long when the following formula applies:

$$Z_t = \sqrt{Z_0 Z_1}$$

where Z_t is the characteristic impedance of the section of the line and Z_0 and Z_1 are the feeder and load impedance respectively. For example, if Z_0 is 80Ω and Z_1 is 600Ω then:

$$Z_t = \sqrt{80 \times 600} = 219\Omega$$

This matching section is useful for transforming impedance and is called a *quarter-wave transformer* – see Fig 5.10. Note that the dimensions are in wavelengths and that allowance must be made for the velocity factor of the wave if dielectrics other than air are used to separate the conductors (see 'Practical considerations and limitations of arrays' above for typical velocity factors).

'Cot' transformer

The preceding methods require the use of special-impedance cable sections which, although they may be readily constructed in open-wire form, are difficult to realise in coaxial cable. There is another technique which can be used to transform between two cable systems of different impedance using short, equal length sections of the two types of cable in the sequence System 1-Z_2-Z_1-System 2 as shown in Fig 5.12.

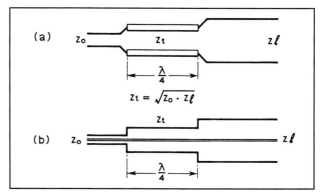

Fig 5.10. Quarter-wave transformer construction in (a) open wire and (b) coaxial forms

The formula for the electrical length of the matching sections has been simplified by G3KYH to:

$$\cot^2 \theta = \frac{Z_1}{Z_2} + \frac{Z_2}{Z_1} + 1$$

where $\cot^2\theta = 1/\tan^2\theta$ and θ is the electrical length of each section in degrees.

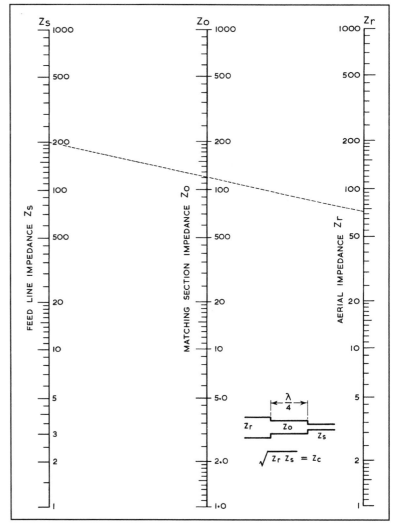

Fig 5.11. Chart showing impedance of quarter-wave transformer required to match between Z_s and Z_r

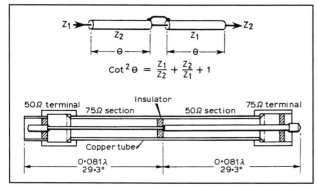

$$\cot^2\theta = \frac{Z_1}{Z_2} + \frac{Z_2}{Z_1} + 1$$

Fig 5.12. Transmission line transformer for matching 50Ω to 75Ω systems

To transform between 50Ω and 75Ω or vice versa, θ = 29.3°. The physical length must take into account the velocity factor of the sections imposed by their construction. One way of realising the transformer is shown in Fig 5.12.

Tapered line transformer
A section of tapered line can also be used to effect an impedance transformation. Again, a λ/4 section is only a special case, and to achieve a match in a particular installation the line length and the angle of taper should be varied until a perfect match is achieved. This form of matching device is called a *delta match* and is only really practical with open-wire feeders.

Power dividers

The quarter-wave transformers described above can be used to build power dividers to feed antenna arrays where interconnection cable lengths or available cable types will not permit transformation through the cables. This is especially valid for UHF systems, where it may be convenient to split the power at one place and feed the elements of the array with cables that have been cut to be of identical electrical length.

Two methods for achieving a two-way power divider are shown in Fig 5.13 below. Two outputs, connected together, can be fed by a suitable single λ/4 transformer section. This works well if the two loads are well matched both in

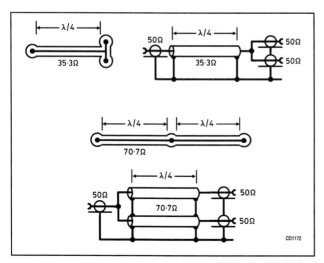

Fig 5.13. Two types of quarter-wave power dividers

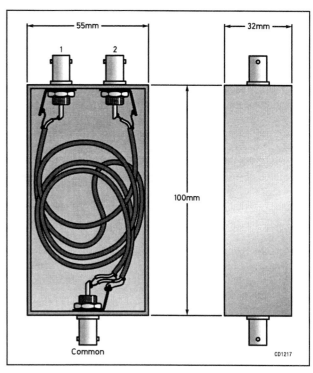

Fig 5.14. Compact two-way power divider for 145MHz

magnitude and phase. The second method uses separate quarter-wave transformer sections to feed each output, which can provide better overall performance if the two loads are well matched but not absolutely identical, as may be the case with the outer elements in an array. The separate transformer sections ensure that identical in-phase currents will be provided at the outputs despite minor differences in load impedance.

Construction of power dividers depends largely on the division ratio, the frequency of operation and the materials available. Square section tubing can provide faces for up to four output connectors if suitable inner conductors can be found to provide the correct transformation ratio. However, such dividers for 50 and 144MHz are large, and more compact but equally efficient dividers can be constructed from suitable coaxial cable, coiled up to fit within a box – see Fig 5.14. The example shown uses miniature 75Ω PTFE cable (URM111) for two-way power division at 145MHz for powers no greater than 50W. For higher powers, larger diameter, lower-loss cable should be used in a larger box.

Baluns

In many cases, antennas require a balanced feed with respect to ground, with equal and opposite currents in each leg of the feed. Coaxial cables are not symmetrical and, if they are connected directly to a balanced antenna, current will usually result on the *outside* of the braid – see Fig 5.15. The effects of this current is usually unwanted radiation, manifested as distorted radiation patterns, or interference with other electronics (EMC problems) where the feeder outer carries the unwanted RF to the susceptible equipment. In extreme cases, it can result in 'hot shack' effects – RF burns or changes to the impedance seen by the transmitter as other pieces of equipment are connected to the transmitter. These effects can be eliminated by suppressing the unwanted currents on the outer

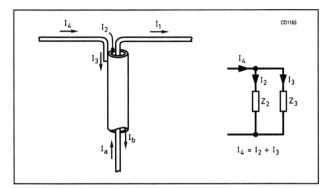

Fig 5.15. Currents inside and at the end of a coaxial cable

of the feed cable through the use of a balance-to-unbalance transformer (*balun*).

Under normal operation, the RF current flows on the *inside* of the outer conductor and the *outside* of the inner conductor of the coaxial cable. Under these circumstances, I_a and I_b are equal and opposite. However, at the end of the cable braid, the current I_4 may divide into two parts: I_2 flowing on the inner of the braid (and hence not capable of radiation or interference) and I_3 which flows on the *outside* of the braid and can be a potential source of trouble. The fraction of current on the outside of the braid is directly related to the impedance presented by the path on the outside of the braid (Z_3) to the characteristic impedance of the cable (Z_2), as shown in the figure. Balun designs increase the value of Z_3 and may also provide impedance transformations which are not part of the true balun action.

A coaxial sleeve balun is shown in Fig 5.16 below. The short-circuited quarter-wave stub surrounding the end of the coaxial cable presents an impedance of several thousand ohms to any currents that would flow on the cable outer. Most of the current then flows on the *inside* of the cable outer as required. Similar results are achieved with the Pawsey stub, Fig 5.17, which operates in exactly the same manner as the sleeve balun.

Good results can also be obtained with thin cables by coiling the cable close to the feed point to form an inductive choke with the outer of the cable, but care is necessary to ensure that the capacitance between turns (increased by the cable jacket) does not tune the choke below resonance which will prevent it from being effective. Ferrite beads or sleeves

Fig 5.16. Coaxial sleeve balun

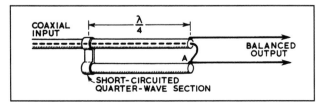

Fig 5.17. Quarter-wave open balun or Pawsey stub

may be used on very small cables but this is more appropriate for low-power circuits than for antennas, where care is required in selecting the right materials; many ferrites are lossy at VHF and may melt the cable or shatter under even modest RF power.

An example of a much-used transformer balun is shown in Fig 5.18. This uses a half-wavelength of cable to invert the signal for the second leg of the balanced feed, and in the process also provides a 4:1 impedance

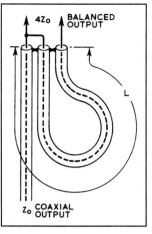

Fig 5.18. A coaxial balun giving a 4:1 impedance step-up

increase. There is no connection between the balanced circuits and the outer of the feeder, hence no current flows on the outer of the feed. The length of the phasing cable should take into account the velocity factor of the cable, and all outer braids may be connected together close to the balanced output as shown.

Transmission line filters
The characteristics of transmission line stubs and transformer sections can be used to create effective filters and diplexers. An excellent series of articles by G4SWX [15, 16] covers the design and adjustment of a range of harmonic and TVI filters, together with diplexers for several VHF/UHF bands. The diplexers can be useful where several transmitters and receivers are connected to a single broad-band antenna, or where concurrent transmission and reception on different bands are needed, as in certain types of satellite communications.

SELECTING AND INSTALLING ANTENNAS
This section deals with the essentials of choosing an antenna and its optimum location. Choice may be limited by the location of the station, planning considerations and the funds available, but is ultimately determined by the purpose of the station and the operator's interests.

Many of the decisions and trade-offs are between antenna beamwidth and gain. If interests lie with mobile stations or packet radio, steerable antennas can be a nuisance. Simple omnidirectional antennas, such as a monopole on a ground plane, will provide good local coverage, but higher-gain omnidirectional antennas, such as collinear arrays, may be desirable for hearing stations further afield. Most mobile and packet stations use vertical polarisation, placing another constraint on the choice of fixed antennas.

An antenna with very high gain will have a narrow beamwidth and few sidelobes. This is fine if you know where to point the array, but many stations will not be heard because they are outside the beam. Gain can be achieved with a relatively wide beamwidth in the horizontal plane by stacking elements vertically; the horizontal beamwidth is then determined by that of a single antenna element in the array, and the vertical beamwidth is narrowed by the array of elements in that plane. Slot-fed Yagi antennas are an efficient example of this type of antenna.

The converse may apply if using a steerable array for satellite communications; the azimuth angle is usually known, or can be found by steering the antenna, but the elevation varies as the satellite crosses the sky. A relatively narrow horizontal beamwidth and a broad vertical beamwidth with an antenna that is tilted upwards a few degrees will permit good communications without requiring the complexity and expense of elevation rotators and control equipment. Such an array can also be used for terrestrial communications with little loss of performance.

As the user's interests develop, the type of antenna or antennas required for optimum operation will become clearer. However, for beginners, relatively low-gain antennas offer a low-cost start with the greatest chances for success – the more complex the installation, the greater the chance it will not work first time, and the more difficult it is to find a fault which is often manifested as poor performance rather than total failure!

Polarisation

As stated above, most mobile and packet stations use vertical polarisation. However, at VHF and above, horizontal polarisation offers some advantages for long-distance propagation. This is due, to some extent, to the way that waves are scattered and diffracted by the ground, whether a plain, buildings or a hill edge, and also by atmospheric refraction effects. However, the use of horizontal polarisation for directional arrays is largely driven by the difficulties encountered in mounting vertically polarised Yagi arrays on metallic support masts without the mast interfering with the radiation pattern or compromising the mechanical integrity of the array. Whilst a horizontally polarised Yagi may be mounted mid-boom to a conductive vertical mast without ill effect, the radiation pattern of a vertical Yagi thus mounted would be completely destroyed. Dielectric masts of adequate strength also affect the radiation patterns at 144MHz and above, and so the antennas should ideally be supported from behind the reflector element. This presents considerable mechanical difficulties, especially with long Yagis, unless counterbalancing weights are fitted. The whole structure becomes much larger and heavier than necessary for horizontal polarisation, and is generally not used by amateurs.

Man-made interference, especially impulsive noise from motor vehicles and electric appliances, tends towards vertical polarisation, so the use of horizontal polarisation may also be beneficial in these circumstances.

Satellite communications do not require, but can be enhanced by, the use of circularly polarised antennas. Many satellites generate circularly polarised signals, and others may be spinning or tumbling whilst producing linear or mixed polarisations. A circularly polarised antenna will often reduce the short-term fading caused by satellite rotation, and by interfering rays scattered from the ground. There is a downside – if the available wave is largely of the opposite polarisation to the receive antenna, very little signal will be received (see 'Polarisation mismatch'), perhaps less than would be received by a linearly polarised antenna. Whilst the direction of polarisation can be reversed by suitable switching, this adds to the cost and complexity of the antenna. Circular polarisation can also be beneficial under conditions where the path is marginal and changing due to refraction or reflections, as in the case of communicating with mobile stations. However, the gain of a circularly polarised system against a linearly polarised source is 3dB less than would be obtained by correct linear polarisation at both ends under the same conditions.

What is of over-riding importance in choosing antenna systems is that the polarisations of the source and receiving antennas are the same, ie matched. Cross-polarisation between systems can result in losses of 15 to 20dB, which could completely negate the gain of the antenna system.

Height gain

When an antenna or array is mounted over ground, some radiation will strike the ground and be scattered or reflected by it. A remote receiving station may, in the simplest case, receive some power directly from the transmitting antenna, and some from the point of reflection – see Fig 5.19.

Similar effects occur when large reflecting objects such as electricity pylons or buildings are partially illuminated by the main lobe or side lobes of the transmitting antenna. The effect of the interfering ray will depend on its strength relative to the direct ray, the differential distance travelled, the nature of the reflecting object and other factors. However, if the reflection is relatively strong, the received signal will generally be improved as the height of the antenna is increased.

Several considerations apply when deciding the height of the antenna above ground. For optimum performance the antenna should be above any local screening from buildings and other obstacles. In addition, the rule-of-thumb figure of approximately 12m (40ft) is worth considering as it often raises the antenna above the layer of electrical interference and also the signal variations caused (at higher frequencies) by the heat layer above buildings. Such a height may also reduce the problems that arise when RF is coupled into house wiring, or directly into consumer electronic equipment, causing TVI and EMC problems.

If there is no screening by buildings, and assuming the antenna is over ground that is reasonably flat for several miles, the main lobe radiation from it will tend to be raised in the vertical plane. As the antenna height increases, the direction of the main lobe will level off in the required horizontal plane. Performance may be degraded by secondary lobes from the antenna. In general, however, as height increases, the pattern

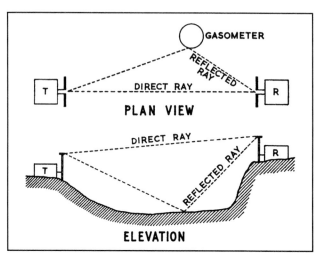

Fig 5.19. Interference between direct and indirect rays

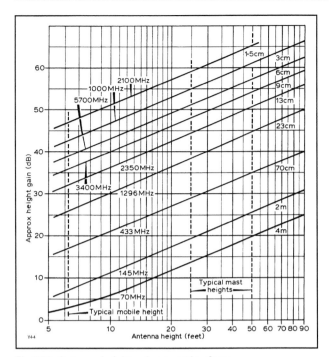

Fig 5.20. Antenna height gain correction factor

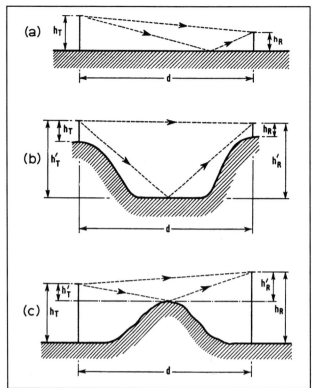

Fig 5.21. The effect of ground profile on direct and indirect rays

improves, and an additional gain of 6dB is obtained each time the antenna height doubles.

Fig 5.20 gives the approximate height gain obtained at various frequencies for various heights above ground. For heights greater than 12m, and assuming all obstacles have been cleared, a 24m (80ft) mast would be required to increase gain by a further 6dB. The additional expense for the mast may not be justified by the 6dB gain improvement, and care should be taken that losses in the additional feeder length required do not cancel out any gain that may be expected from the increased height. (See 'Coaxial lines' earlier for typical cable losses).

Should the station be well sited, on a hill for instance, increasing the mast height may make little or no improvement. The effective height above ground will relate to a point at the bottom of the hill, not the base of the mast under these circumstances. Conversely, a station in a valley or behind a hill may obtain a considerable increase in gain with height, much in excess of 6dB, as a more favourable angle to the hilltop or looking over it is achieved. A change of the vertical mounting angle (tilt) or a change of polarisation will also often provide a gain improvement.

The three basic configurations for receiving and transmitting antennas and the intervening ground are illustrated in Fig 5.21. The classic plane-earth case is shown in Fig 5.21(a), and under ideal conditions the signal received at the distant antenna follows the relationship:

$$e = \text{constant} \times \frac{h_T h_R}{\lambda d^2}$$

where h_T is the height of the transmitting antenna, h_R is the height of the receiving antenna, λ is the wavelength, and d is the distance between antennas. In this expression h_T, h_R and d must all be in the same units and d must be much larger than either h_T or h_R (by a factor of least 10) which is usually the case in practice.

From this expression it is clear that an increase in either h_T or h_R will result in a corresponding increase in e, and doubling the height will give an increase of 6dB. This is the 6dB 'height gain' rule.

Fig 5.21(b) may be that of the operator who has selected a good hilltop site for 'portable' operation. Here, the antenna height above immediate ground is relatively small compared with the effective height above ground level at the point from where the indirect ray is reflected. Now,

$$e = \text{constant} \times \frac{h'_T h'_R}{\lambda d^2}$$

where h'_T and h'_R are the *effective* heights of the two antennas. There is still height gain to be achieved by increasing antenna height locally, but not at the same rate as in the first example. To obtain a gain of 6dB it is necessary to double h'_R, and this will require a manyfold increase in h_R. In the limit it clearly is not worthwhile seeking any great antenna height improvement; this is often the case for portable stations on hilltops, when the increased loss in the feeders is less than offset by the small additional signal to be obtained by raising the antenna.

The third case, Fig 5.21(c), is that of a station whose antenna is just able to 'see' over the surrounding higher ground, and is the reverse of case (b). The effective height h'_R is much less than h_R, and only a small increase in the height of the antenna is required to bring massive improvements in signal level.

To summarise, the antenna should ideally be positioned as high as possible, whilst taking into account the additional losses of the extra feed cable required. The signal improvements can be quite large if the station is in a location masked by hills or buildings.

EMC and location

The problems in achieving electromagnetic compatibility (EMC) are becoming ever more severe as ownership of electronic devices increase, together with housing densities. The problem is no longer solely one of television interference (TVI); amateur transmissions can interfere with the operation of telephones, audio equipment, and car security systems. There is also a growing reverse problem of domestic electronics interfering with amateur reception; line timebase noise from older large-screen television sets, and more recently from personal computers, is adding to the general pollution of the RF spectrum. Whilst legislation is now in place to reduce emissions from, and the susceptibility of, domestic equipment, it will be many years before some of these equipments are replaced. In the meantime, it is prudent to design installations to minimise the mutual interference that may occur.

In positioning antennas, the following should be considered.

Avoid:

- Placing the antenna close to your neighbour's (or your own) TV antenna!
- Allowing arrays to 'stare' directly in the same plane at adjacent antennas; raising the array a few feet may reduce the potential for interference dramatically.
- Locating antennas where they can easily couple into mains wiring or plumbing.
- Placing antennas where they can couple into overhead telephone wires.
- Running feeders next to mains wiring or plumbing where coupling may occur.

Do:

- Use coaxial feeders with good screening indoors.
- Use chokes and baluns to minimise any RF on the (coaxial) feeders.
- Place the antennas as far away as is practicable from other antennas, TV feeders, mains wiring or telephone cables.
- Make friends with your neighbours and explain what you are doing – it is then easier to resolve any difficulties that occur.
- Choose materials that are electrochemically compatible to minimise corrosion and harmonic generation through the 'rusty bolt' effect.
- Overhaul antenna systems regularly to prevent 'rusty bolt' effects and deteriorating cable connections that can cause interference (also a good idea to preclude the antenna from deteriorating mechanically).

See also Chapter 6 – 'EMC'.

Installations

Internal installations

Whilst external installations are preferable, adequate VHF and UHF antenna systems can be installed successfully within a loft space. Space constraints will limit the size of antenna, especially if a rotatable array is considered, but omnidirectional antennas usually present few problems.

The roofing material can have a marked effect on signal losses, especially when wet. Slates shed water and dry out fairly quickly, but old and porous tiles, although adequately waterproof, can scatter and absorb much of the signal.

Measurements have shown a difference of more than 7dB for propagation through dry and wet weathered tiles at 435MHz.

Coupling into wiring and plumbing should be very carefully addressed and investigated with loft installations, and it is prudent to choose antennas that are not highly tuned or over-sensitive to the presence of adjacent objects.

Chimney installations

The nature of these installations is usually determined by the strength of the chimney, the courage of the erector, and his willingness to revisit the chimney regularly.

An end chimney can provide an excellent antenna site provided it is not too close to adjacent property and antennas. A short mast is usually lashed to the stack at two or three places, and a fixed or rotating array fitted immediately above. Space and safety considerations dictate the size of the antennas, and whether they are assembled *in situ*. If the chimney is relatively accessible, complex antennas and systems that require maintenance or tuning are practicable. However, simpler, fixed systems are better if the site is difficult (or expensive) to access. In choosing the antennas, the wind load and overturning moment should be carefully considered, and if in doubt, a survey of the chimney should be carried out by someone with the necessary knowledge and qualifications – this could prevent expensive roof repairs! Lightweight fixtures and fittings can be bought from television antenna supply companies. Heavier-duty fixtures are available from amateur antenna suppliers and professional antenna installers.

Masts and towers

Where suitable chimneys are not available, but wall and garden space can be used, a mast or tower may provide the best option, especially if the station is to be located in a garage or shed. Many varieties of mast are available commercially, both as free-standing and wall-mounted designs, and hardware for fastening masts to walls and footings is available from a number of suppliers.

A mast can offer the freedom to experiment with antennas if suitable equipment for raising and lowering is provided. However, planning permission is nearly always required, and considerable thought is needed before installing free-standing towers – the foundation requirements can be considerable, and are not easily relocated. If garden space permits, a guyed mast may provide a good solution, although assistance and a great deal of care is required when erecting such structures, especially when loaded with antennas. The reader is referred to the articles by G3ZPF [17] for information outlining the size of foundations and guy anchors required together with some methods for construction.

In addition, lightning protection should be installed to good earths with short, wide copper straps to minimise the current flowing into the radio equipment and house wiring if a lightning attachment does occur. Again, professional advice should be sought in this respect.

Wind loading

In all considerations for antenna design and erection, the wind loading of the array must be taken into account, so that the rotator (if used) and the supporting structures can be selected or designed to withstand the stresses to which the system may be subjected. It is prudent to allow a good margin for safety, to allow for wear and tear, corrosion and general deterioration in any calculation related to safety.

The articles by G3ZPF [17] provide the basis for estimating the loads experienced by antennas and masts. BS8100 and the earlier, but still useful, BSI CP3 Chapter 5 Part 2 provide information on basic wind speeds throughout the UK. This can be used with the given topography, ground roughness and height above ground factors to determine the dynamic pressure that is likely to be experienced by the structure under 'worst-case' conditions. Wind loading of masts and towers is now assessed under BS8100, and advice should be sought from the manufacturer for the appropriate information.

Safety

Masts and antennas are potentially dangerous structures especially during erection and dismantling. There are a number of safety rules that *must* be observed during these activities:

1. Thorough checks must be carried out to ensure that there is *no* possibility of the mast or antenna coming into contact with overhead power wires, however it may topple or collapse.
2. The job of erection or lowering must be planned carefully. Considerations must include the positioning of each part of the antenna and/or mast at every stage of the process. Enough persons should be available, wearing boots, gloves and safety helmets during the raising and lowering processes, and sufficient guiding ropes should be used to ensure control of the structure at all stages of the operation. There should be no possibility of tripping on ropes or equipment during the operation, which should not be attempted in strong winds or when it is getting dark.
3. Before raising or lowering, all components and fastenings should be double-checked for being fixed firmly and safely. The base of the mast must be firmly fixed to prevent slipping.
4. Everybody involved shall have their role clearly defined. Those not needed to assist should be kept well clear. If any children are nearby, a person should be tasked to keep them clear of the area of operations, including those areas where the mast might topple or fall, and animals should be kept under control.
5. One person should be in charge of the operation, and not take any part in the lifting activities themselves. He/she shall give clear concise instructions, which have been rehearsed before the actual lift or lowering.
6. Safety precautions must be continued until all mast fixings and guys are secured, and any temporary ropes and equipment have been removed and stowed away.
7. After erection, the mast should be inspected for tightness of bolts and for the integrity of any protective coverings. The mast and antennas should be regularly inspected for tightness of bolts, wear and/or damage to guys and fastenings, and integrity of protective coverings. The mast and antennas should be lowered for full inspection and overhaul at least every three years, or more often in exposed locations. Electrical continuity, sealing and painting/greasing should be checked, together with the replacement of items that weather or denature in sunlight (plastic covers and fittings).

Antennas – build or buy?
General considerations
A great deal of satisfaction can be obtained from building one's own antennas, either by following detailed instructions, or by experimenting with the materials available. However, as either the frequency or complexity of the antenna increases, so does the need for some test equipment or measuring facilities. There is little more frustrating than to have spent many hours in construction, and then be unable to make the antenna work.

Simple antennas such as whips and dipoles can be tuned with a low-power transmitter and VSWR meter, by 'pruning' element lengths for best VSWR.

As the frequency increases, variations in construction and the dielectric constant of materials used for insulators or spacers can have a considerable influence on the performance of antennas. Tools to at least estimate the input impedance (resistance *and* reactance) can become essential to find out exactly why an antenna is not working. Noise bridges can provide the necessary information up to the 70cm band, beyond which second-hand professional impedance bridges provide the best means for measuring antennas.

Single antennas with gains greater than, say, 10dB really require facilities for measuring changes of gain if experimentation is to be meaningful. This requires a reasonable amount of space with few unwanted reflections, and a calibrated signal generator and receiver. This is not as difficult as it may seem; the techniques, together with much other useful information on building test equipment and carrying out measurements are shown in *The Antenna Experimenter's Guide* by G3LDO [19].

Careful adherence to construction details will usually result in a working antenna with minimum tuning, so it can be well worth considering building your own if basic metal working facilities are available.

Arrays can also be assembled with a minimum of measuring equipment if ready-built antennas are obtained (all antennas in the array should be identical), and care is taken in measuring and making up the feed cables. Some manufacturers can supply ready-built (and phase matched) feeder harnesses for standard array configurations.

Decreasing cost and increasing power of personal computers has added a relatively new tool to the serious experimenter's armoury. A number of programs are available for modest cost which allow the electrical design of antennas on-screen, followed by analysis of the current distribution, radiation pattern and gain. They can be useful to evaluate the effect of changes in dimensions or configuration, or to try out completely new structures. Some knowledge of antenna theory is necessary – the 'garbage in-garbage out' syndrome certainly applies! A description of the techniques and the results that can be obtained have been described by G3SEK and G3HCT [20, 21]. Special programs are also available for optimisation of Yagi antennas.

Choice of materials
The use of dissimilar metals in an antenna system is likely to cause considerable trouble due to electrolytic corrosion. Each metal has its own electro-potential and, unless metals of similar potential are used, the difference will cause corrosion even when they are dry. When moisture is present, the effect

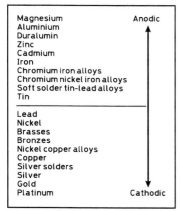

Fig 5.22. Electrochemical series for metals

will be much more severe and can be enhanced by atmospheric pollution.

If, for any reason, dissimilar metals must be used then considerable care should be taken to exclude moisture. The metals can be arranged in order of their electrochemical potential as shown in Fig 5.22.

Metals in each of the groups may be used together with little corrosive action, but metals from different groups will quickly corrode at the point of contact. The list is arranged in order, so that the greater the spacing between materials in the list, the greater the effect.

The materials in the lower part of the list will corrode those in the upper. For example, brass or copper screws in aluminium will corrode the aluminium, whereas cadmium-plated brass screws would cause less corrosion.

Corrosion can cause weakening of mechanical structures and also increases in contact resistance between elements and feeders, resulting in dissipation of transmitter power as heat. Under some circumstances, the joint between corroded materials behaves as a semiconductor, generating harmonics and intermodulation products that cause interference to other radio users, both in and out of band. For this reason, selection of materials to minimise corrosion is important, and all antenna joints and weather protection measures should be inspected and refurbished at least every two years.

DIRECTIONAL ANTENNAS FOR FIXED STATIONS
The Yagi antenna

This is one of the most useful antennas for VHF/UHF, as it can be compact, robust and provide good directivity and gain with a relatively simple structure. Unfortunately, it is also one of the most complex antenna structures to analyse, and it can be difficult to construct Yagis that really provide good performance, especially where high gain is required.

The original research was carried out by S Uda in Japan in 1926, but it was the review and translation into English by his professor, H Yagi, in 1928 that introduced the design to the West. The basic array comprises a driven dipole element with a passive dipole adjacent to it. If both elements are tuned to resonance, the currents in each element are approximately equal, and are in phase. By lengthening the passive (*parasitic*) element, the phase of the current is delayed, whilst the amplitude remains almost unchanged. When the phase delay complements the spacing between the elements, the radiated power will be directed away from the parasite, which is then known as a *reflector*. By similarly placing another, shorter *director* parasite in line with the driven element, but on the opposite side from the reflector, the directivity can be further enhanced. The principles for this phenomenon were addressed in the section on arrays.

Yagi antennas can be provided with large numbers of

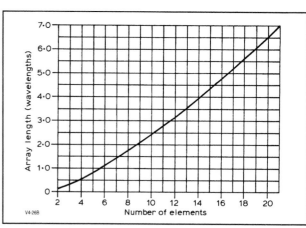

Fig 5.23. Optimum length of Yagi antenna as a function of number of elements *(ARRL Antenna Book)*

reflectors, the elements being excited by mutual coupling with the driven element and other elements according to their relative position. As the magnitude and phase of the current on each element is influenced by their relative positions and lengths, the permutations of dimensions that can produce satisfactory performance become very large.

Until relatively recently, performance of the antenna was optimised by 'cut-and-try' methods, as the mathematical analysis of the problem was too complex to afford numerical solution other than for small numbers of elements. Theoretical methods indicated the limits of performance that could be expected of the array for given constraints, eg Fig 5.23 and Fig 5.24, showing boom length and number of elements for 'optimum' arrays. However, experimental work showed that these gains were rarely realised, usually falling short by 0.5 to 1dB, and very poor performance was sometimes obtained, especially from long Yagi antennas. Many independent investigations of multi-element Yagi antennas have shown that in general the gain of a Yagi is directly proportional to the array length provided the number, lengths and spacing of the elements are properly chosen. However, to constrain the number of variables, the concept of equal-length reflectors, or equally spaced reflectors was often used for elements well removed from the driven element.

A suite of results for several antenna geometries was published by P Viezbicke for the US Department of Commerce and National Bureau of Standards in 1976 [10], and it has become a reference document for many Yagi designers. It addresses: (a) the effect of reflector spacing on the gain of a

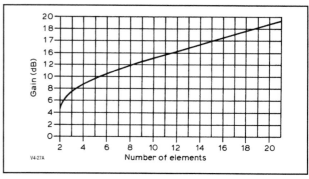

Fig 5.24. Gain (dB) over a λ/2 dipole versus the number of elements of a Yagi antenna *(ARRL Antenna Book)*

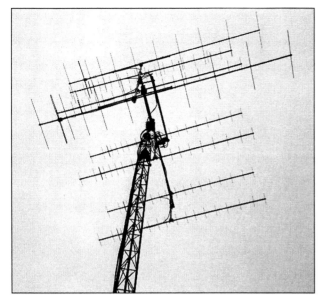

DL6WU has stacked two 11-element Yagis of his own design with six of the highly respected K2RIW 19-element Yagis for 432MHz

dipole; (b) effect of different length directors, their spacing and number on realisable gain; (c) effect of different diameters and lengths of direct, realisable gain; (d) effect of the size of a supporting boom on the optimum length of parasitic elements; (e) effect of stacking of antennas on gain; and (f) measured radiation patterns of different Yagi configurations.

However, as greater computing power has become available, it has been possible to investigate the theoretical optimisation of Yagi gain more closely, and to take into account the effects of mounting the elements on metallic and dielectric booms. Dr J Lawson, W2PV, carried out an extensive series of computations, collated in reference [11], which explain many of the disappointing results achieved by constructors. G Hoch, DL6WU, has especially studied the design and construction of long Yagis [12–14] and identified the pitfalls.

Generally, short Yagi antennas with less than six elements will perform reasonably well with a selection of materials and minor deviations from the optimum dimensions. However, higher-gain Yagis need to be carefully constructed with minimum deviation from the design if the gain is to be realised. If it is necessary to use different diameter tubing from that specified, the length of the element must be adjusted to compensate for the change in self-reactance that results. Hoch gives a formula for the reactance of an element of arbitrary length (L) and diameter (D) for a given wavelength:

$$X = \left\{ 430.3\log_{10}\left(\frac{2\lambda}{D}\right) - 320 \right\}\left(\frac{2L}{\lambda} - 1\right) + 40$$

The modified length L' for a new element diameter D' can be calculated by rearranging the formula:

$$L' = \left\{ \frac{(X-40)}{\left\{430.3\log_{10}\left(\frac{2\lambda}{D'}\right) - 320\right\}} + 1 \right\}\frac{\lambda}{2}$$

Table 5.4 shows typical component dimensions for a range of Yagi antennas for 4m, 2m and 70cm, using either open or

Table 5.4. Typical dimensions of Yagi array components

	Length		
	70.3MHz	145MHz	433MHz
Driven elements			
Dipole (for use with gamma match)	79 (2000)	38 (960)	12¾ (320)
Diameter range for length given	½–¾ (12.7–19.0)	¼–³/₈ (6.35–9.5)	¹/₈–¼ (3.17–6.35)

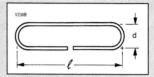

Folded dipole 70Ω feed			
l length centre/centre	77½ (1970)	38½ (980)	12½ (318)
d spacing centre/centre	2½ (64)	⁷/₈ (22)	½ (13)
Diameter of element	½ (12.7)	¼ (6.35)	¹/₈ (3.17)

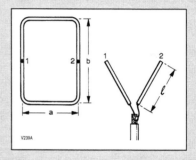

a centre/centre	32 (810)	15 (390)	5¹/₈ (132)
b centre/centre	96 (2440)	46 (1180)	152 (395)
Delta feed sections (length for 70Ω feed)	22½ (570)	12 (300)	42 (110)
Diameter of slot and delta feed material	¼ (6.35)	³/₈ (9.5)	³/₈ (9.5)
Parasitic elements			
Element			
Reflector	85½ (2170)	40 (1010)	13¼ (337)
Director D1	74 (1880)	35½ (902)	11¼ (286)
Director D2	73 (1854)	35¼ (895)	11¹/₈ (282)
Director D3	72 (1830)	35 (890)	11 (279)
Succeeding directors	1in less (25)	½in less (13)	¹/₈in less (3)
Final director	2in less (50)	1in less (25)	¾in less
One wavelength (for reference)	168¾ (4286)	81½ (2069)	27¼ (693)
Diameter range for length given	½–¾ (12.7–19.0)	¼–³/₈ (6.35–9.5)	¹/₈–¾ (3.17–6.35)
Spacing between elements			
Reflector to radiator	22½ (572)	17½ (445)	5½ (140)
Radiator to director 1	29 (737)	17½ (445)	5½ (140)
Director 1 to director 2	29 (737)	17½ (445)	7 (178)
Director 2 to director 3, etc	29 (737)	17½ (445)	7 (178)

Dimensions are in inches with millimetre equivalents in brackets.

Photo showing how a driven element and first directors are typically mounted on a boom

folded dipole elements to drive the array. As stated above, antennas of this form can be expected to work reasonably well with up to six elements (12 elements for a skeleton slot array) if the dimensions are adhered to. Longer Yagis need to be constructed exactly as described, including the boom and fastenings used to secure the elements, if claimed performances are to be realised without recourse to antenna measurement ranges. The articles by DL6WU [12–14] address the construction of such antennas.

Skeleton-slot Yagi stack

The skeleton slot provides an ingenious means to feed two stacked Yagi antennas efficiently and achieve a good impedance match. The skeleton slot can be thought of as a pair of $\lambda/2$ dipoles spaced vertically by $5\lambda/8$. Since most of the radiation is provided by the centre of the dipoles, their ends can be bent out of plane with little effect, and joined together with high-impedance feeder so that end feeding may take place. To feed both dipoles in phase, the feed point must be midway between them; the high impedance is transformed to more manageable levels by a tapered section or delta match as shown in Fig 5.25.

The overall slot Yagi structure is shown in Fig 5.26. Element dimensions are taken from Table 5.4 and the radiation pattern, together with those of other typical Yagi antennas, is shown in Fig 5.27.

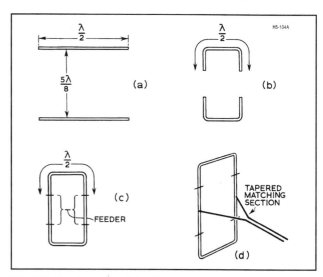

Fig 5.25. Development of the skeleton-slot radiator

Quad antennas and arrays

The quad antenna offers a useful horizontally polarised alternative to short Yagi antennas at VHF and above, being both compact and lightweight with just a driven element and reflector – see Fig 5.28. Gains of 5.5 to 6dB are readily obtained, together with good front-to-back ratio. Arrangements for two- and four-antenna arrays of quads are described below.

Typical dimensions for quad elements are shown in Table 5.5. The input impedance is strongly affected by the spacing between the driven element and the reflector, and will be between 180 and 230mm for an input impedance of 72Ω. The elements may be made from 3mm or 6mm aluminium rod or bar, and if the vertical dimensions of both elements are made the same, two short cross-pieces can be used to separate the elements and mount them to a mast. The cross-pieces may be metal so that the whole structure with the exception of the feedpoint and reflector stub (if used) can be solidly built and bonded together. A balun should be used at the feedpoint, although "this is not essential if the feeder is short and of low loss".

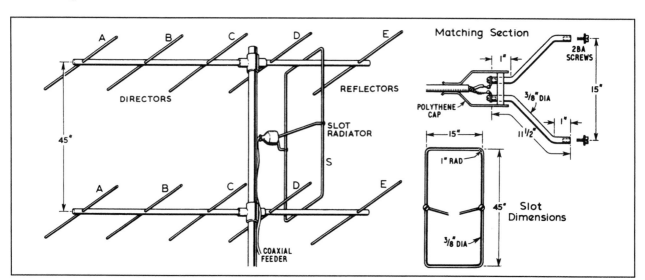

Fig 5.26. Six-over-six skeleton-slot Yagi for 2m

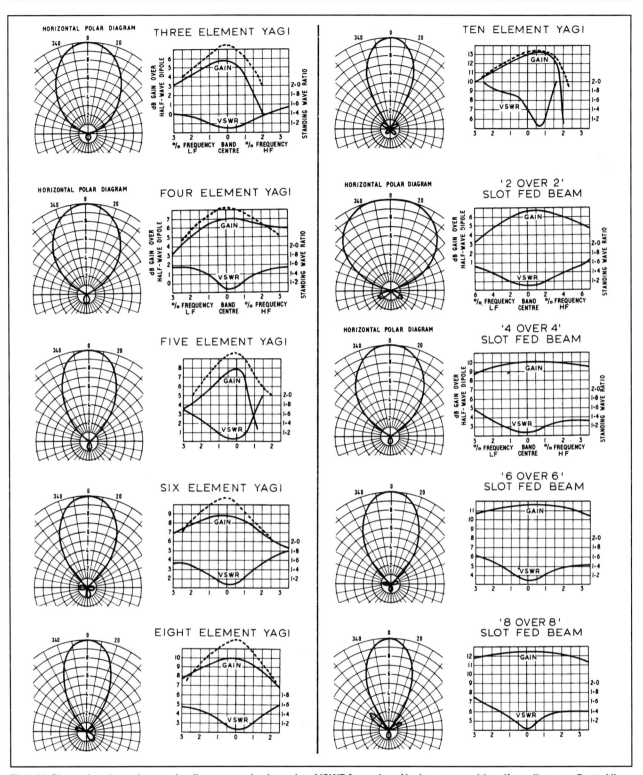

Fig 5.27. Charts showing voltage polar diagrams and gain against VSWR for various Yagi antennas with uniform directors. Dotted lines are for antennas optimised for maximum gain

The antenna can readily be configured as a two-element or four-element array. Each antenna for 144MHz has the dimensions shown in Fig 5.29, spaced 178mm between elements. Two quads stacked vertically should be spaced $5\lambda/8$ between centres and paralleled through a single $\lambda/4$, 51Ω transformer. To obtain an input impedance of 72Ω (for further baying as a four antenna array), it may be necessary to increase the separation of the reflector and driven element to 230mm to overcome the effects of mutual coupling. The pair of antennas should provide a gain of 8.2dBD (10.3dBi) with a front-to-back ratio of 20dB.

A four-antenna arrangement for the 2m band is shown in Fig 5.30. The layout is determined by the ease with which feeder cables can be run, and the minimisation of unsupported

Table 5.5. Design dimensions for 70 and 144MHz quad antennas

Band (MHz)	Reflector 1 total length	Reflector 2 total length	Director (if used)	Approx length of stubs if used Reflector s/c	Director s/c
70 (a)	173 (4390)	165 (4190)	157 (3990)	—	—
70 (b)	165 (4190)	165 (4190)	165 (4190)	8 (203)	8 (203)
144 (a)	84 (2130)	80 (2030)	76 (1930)	—	—
144 (b)	80 (2030)	80 (2030)	80 (2030)	4 (101)	4 (101)

Dimensions are in inches with millimetre equivalents in brackets.

(unguyed) sections of mast. Reflector-director spacing is 230mm, the vertical spacing remains 1650mm between centres, and the horizontal spacing is 2070mm, one wavelength in free space. The feed arrangements are shown in Fig 5.31 below. The design is based on a 72Ω main feeder; for 50Ω array impedance, the transformer in the feedline should be replaced with a 42Ω section or a 'cot transformer' as described in the section on transmission line transformers. The more readily available URM57 may be substituted for UR1 cable with minor adjustments to the antenna element spacing.

The gain of the overall array should be 13.5dBD (15.6dBi)

with a front-to-back ratio of 18dB. The radiation pattern is shown in Fig 5.32.

Quad-element Yagi (quagi)

The quad-element Yagi (Fig 5.36) offers better performance than a simple Yagi of comparable size, together with reduced sidelobes. Up to five elements will perform satisfactorily, although larger structures can be made with care. The relative performance of Yagis with circular (loop) and conventional straight elements is shown in Fig 5.33. Loop Yagis with square and circular elements have comparable characteristics. Comparative measured radiation

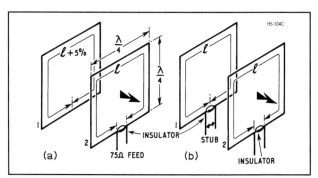

Fig 5.28. Quad antenna dimensions

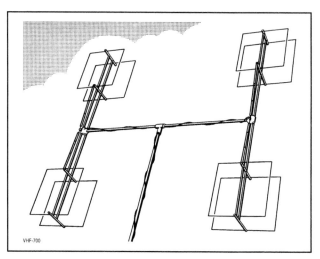

Fig 5.30. A 144MHz cubical quad array

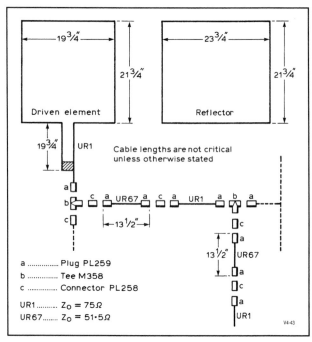

Fig 5.29. Arrangement of two- or four-antenna quad array with power divider and matching details

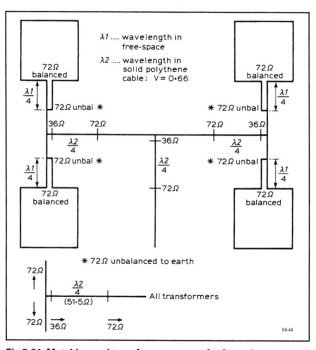

Fig 5.31. Matching and transformer system for four-element quad array

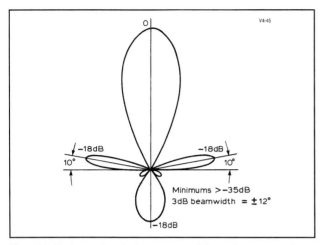

Fig 5.32. Horizontal radiation pattern of four-element quad antenna array

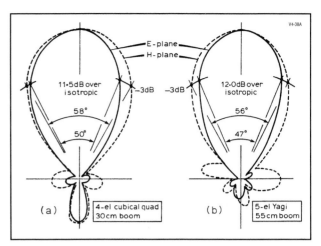

Fig 5.34. Measured voltage patterns of four-element quad and five-element Yagi showing approximately equivalent *beamwidths*

patterns for conventional and quagi antennas are shown in Fig 5.34 and Fig 5.35.

The only insulator required is that of the feed point, resulting in a simple and mechanically robust structure. 9mm aluminium rod or tube is satisfactory for elements for 144MHz and above.

Table 5.6 shows dimensions for several multi-element quagi antennas for 144MHz; dimensions can be scaled for 432MHz. This antenna is relatively easy to construct, and will work well.

A quadruple quad antenna

This collapsible antenna, designed for portable use [18] but equally useable as a fixed antenna for use indoors or in a loft, can achieve gains of between 10 and 11dBi on the 2m band. It is effectively a stacked quad using mutual coupling instead of a phasing harness to excite the outer elements. Constructional details are shown in Fig 5.37.

Each section has a circumference of around 1.04λ, which is not as would be expected for conventional quads. The dimensions are the result of experiments to obtain the best front-to-back ratio and least sensitivity to adjacent objects, which can be important for portable or loft operation, ensuring that the antenna will work without extensive adjustment.

Note that the antenna was designed for low-power (1W)

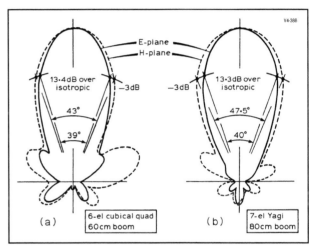

Fig 5.35. Measured voltage patterns of six-element quad and seven-element Yagi (*ARRL Antenna Book*)

operation; the ferrite bead must not be allowed to magnetically saturate, or non-linearities and harmonic generation may occur. The bead may also become hot and shatter.

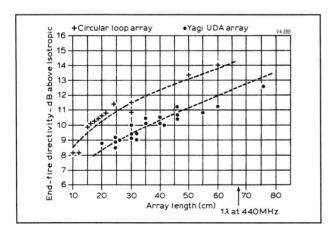

Fig 5.33. Comparative directivity of quad and conventional Yagi antennas as a function of array length (*ARRL Antenna Book*)

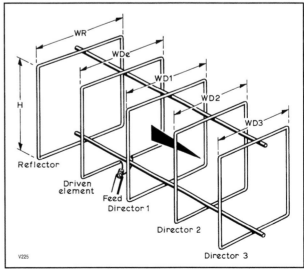

Fig 5.36. General arrangement of a multi-element quad

Table 5.6. Centre-to-centre dimensions for multi-element quad Yagi

Height H	21 (533)	21	21	21
Width reflector WR	24½ (622)	24½	24½	24½
Driven WD$_e$	20½ (520)	20½	20½	20½
Director 1 WD$_1$	—	18 (457)	18	18
Director 2 WD$_2$	—	—	16 (406)	16
Director 3 WD$_3$	—	—	—	14 (356)
Spacing				
Reflector to Driven	7 (178)	19 (483)	20 (508)	20
Driven to Director 1	—	12 (305)	14½ (368)	14½
Director 1 to Director 2	—	—	14½	14½
Director 2 to Director 3	—	—	—	14½
Approx gain (dBD)	5	7	10.5	12.5

Element diameters all ³⁄₈in (9.35mm). Feed impedance in all cases is 75Ω. Dimensions are in inches with millimetre equivalents in brackets.

Log-periodic antenna

This antenna was originally designed and proved at the University of Illinois in the USA in 1955. Since then the military, in particular, have made considerable use of it. Its particular properties are a very wide bandwidth, governed only by the number of elements used, and the directive qualities of a Yagi antenna.

Tables 5.7 and 5.8 show typical dimensions for element spacings and length for log-periodic arrays which are derived from a computer-aided design produced by W3DUQ in *Ham Radio*, August 1970. Other frequency bands can be produced by simple scaling of *all* dimensions.

The tabulated parameters have a 5% overshoot in the working frequency range at the low end and a 45% overshoot at the high-frequency end to maintain logarithmic response over the complete frequency range specified.

For higher-power operation, ferrite rings could be considered for the balun transformer, or a sleeve balun constructed as appropriate.

In log-periodic operation approximately four elements are active at any one specific frequency, hence the need for the high-frequency and low-frequency extension. The alpha or logarithmic element taper is 28° for all three antennas, which exhibit a forward gain of 6.55dBD with a front-to-back ratio of typically 15dB and a VSWR better than 1.8:1 over the specified frequency range.

The construction can be straightforward but it should be noted that the element lengths for the highest-frequency antenna were calculated for the elements to be inserted completely through the boom, flush with the far wall. The two lower-frequency antennas have element lengths calculated to butt flush against the element side of the boom. If the elements are to be inserted through the boom on the 21–55MHz and 50–150MHz antennas, the boom diameter must be added to the length of each element.

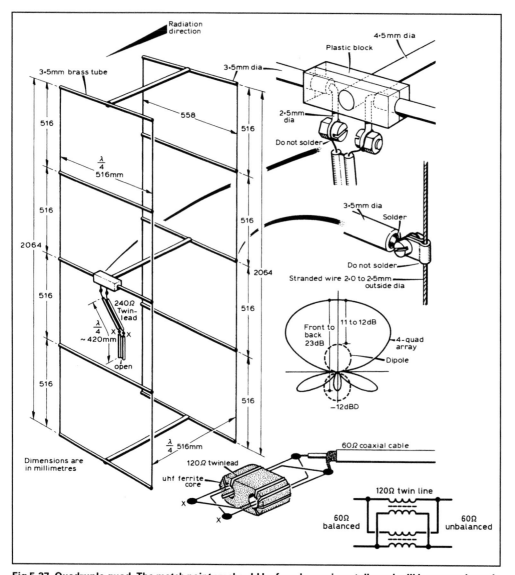

Fig 5.37. Quadruple quad. The match point xx should be found experimentally and will be approximately 200mm from the open end (*VHF Communications*)

Table 5.7. Spacing and dimensions for log-periodic VHF antennas

Ele-ment	21–55MHz array			50–150MHz array			140–450MHz array		
	Length (mm)	Diameter (mm)	Spacing (mm)	Length (mm)	Diameter (mm)	Spacing (mm)	Length (mm)	Diameter (mm)	Spacing (mm)
1	3731	38.1	1050	1602	2.54	630	535	6.7	225
2	3411	31.8	945	1444	2.54	567	479	6.7	202
3	3073	31.8	850	1303	2.54	510	397	6.7	182
4	2770	31.8	765	1175	19.1	459	383	6.7	164
5	2496	31.8	689	1060	19.1	413	341	6.7	148
6	2250	25.4	620	957	19.1	372	304	6.7	133
7	2029	25.4	558	864	19.1	335	271	6.7	119
8	1830	19.1	500	781	12.7	301	241	6.7	108
9	1650	19.1	452	705	12.7	271	215	6.7	97
10	1489	19.1	407	637	12.7	244	190	6.7	87
11	1344	19.1	366	576	12.7	219	169	6.7	78
12	1213	12.7	329	522	9.5	198	149	6.7	70
13	1095	12.7	0	472	9.5	178	131	6.7	63
14				428	9.5	160	115	6.7	57
15				388	9.5	0	101	6.7	52
16							88	6.7	0
Boom	7620	50.8	12.7	5090	38.1	152	1823	38.1	152

Table 5.8. Spacing and dimensions for log-periodic UHF antenna (420–1350MHz array)

Element	Length (mm)	Diameter (mm)	Spacing (mm)
1	178	2.1	75
2	159	2.1	67
3	133	2.1	61
4	127	2.1	55
5	114	2.1	49
6	101	2.1	44
7	91	2.1	40
8	80	2.1	36
9	72	2.1	32
10	63	2.1	29
11	56	2.1	26
12	50	2.1	23
13	44	2.1	21
14	38	2.1	19
15	34	2.1	17
16	30	2.1	0
Boom	607	12.7	

As the supporting booms are also the transmission line between the elements for a log-periodic antenna they must be supported with a dielectric spacing from the mast of at least twice the boom-to-boom spacing; otherwise discontinuities will be introduced into the feed system. Feed line connection and the arrangement to produce an 'infinite balun' is shown in Fig 5.39. Any change in the boom diameters will necessitate a change in the boom-to-boom spacing to maintain the feed impedance. The formula to achieve this is:

$$Z_0 = 273 \log_{10} D/d$$

where D is the distance between boom centres and d the diameter of the booms.

The antenna can be orientated either horizontally or vertically (if a non-metal mast section is used) to suit the

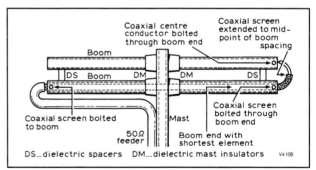

Fig 5.39. Feeding the log periodic is relatively simple. Remove the outer plastic jacket from the feedline for the entire length of the boom, so that the coaxial outer is permitted to short itself inside the boom as well as the solid electrical connections at each end of the boom (*Ham Radio*)

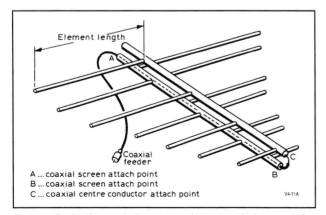

Fig 5.38. Typical log-periodic antenna. Note that the bottom is fed from the coaxial outer while the top boom is fed from the centre conductor (*Ham Radio*)

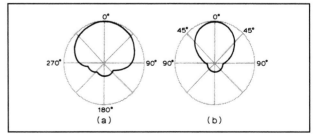

Fig 5.40. Typical log-periodic voltage radiation patterns: (a) horizontal, (b) vertical (*Ham Radio*)

50MHz and 144MHz log-periodic antennas

polarisation required. The horizontal half-power beamwidths will be typically 60° with a vertical half-power beamwidth of typically 100°.

Log-periodic Yagi bandpass antenna

This is an antenna with an interesting and useful band-pass characteristic, giving a flat response over a wide band, and significant attenuation outside. It is basically a combination of a log-periodic driven section with a parasitic Yagi section.

The prototype 50MHz design gave a gain of 12dBD and a bandwidth of 2MHz. The details given in Fig 5.41 are for 144MHz, where the bandwidth would be around 5MHz.

This type of characteristic offers obvious advantages in terms of reducing adjacent channel interference; and also giving a more constant performance over the whole 144 to 148MHz band. The simple Yagi, by comparison, is essentially a narrow-band antenna.

Dimensions and construction details for 50, 70 and 144MHz have been developed by G3FDW [22].

The corner reflector

The use of an aperiodic plane reflector spaced behind a radiating dipole has already been discussed. If this reflector is bent to form a V, as shown in Fig 5.43, a considerably higher gain is achieved. The critical factors in the design of such an antenna array are the corner angle α and the dipole/vertex spacing S. The curves in Fig 5.44 show that as α is reduced, the gain theoretically obtainable becomes progressively greater. However, at the same time

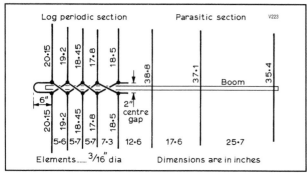

Fig 5.41. A log-periodic Yagi band-pass antenna for 145MHz

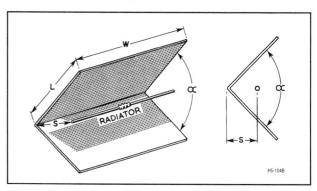

Fig 5.43. Corner reflector. The λ/2 dipole radiator is spaced parallel with the vertex of the reflector at distance S; its characteristics are shown in Figs 5.44 and 5.45

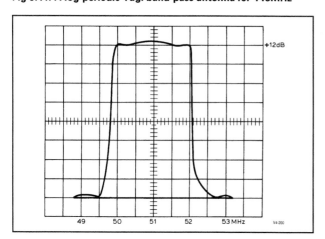

Fig 5.42. Gain versus frequency characteristic of the 50MHz log-periodic Yagi

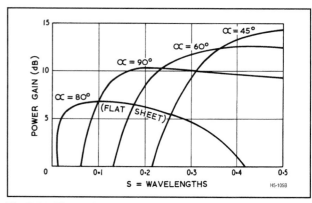

Fig 5.44. Theoretical power gain obtained by using a corner reflector with a λ/2 dipole radiator

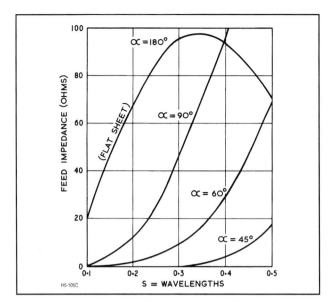

Fig 5.45. Feed impedance of a λ/2 dipole provided with a corner reflector: see Fig 5.43

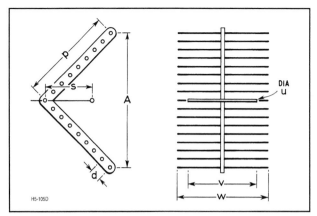

Fig 5.47. Dimensions for a 60° corner reflector antenna system giving a gain of about 13dBD. The feed impedance of the dipole radiator is 75Ω. The apex may be hinged for portable work

Dimensions in millimetres

Band	p	s	d	v	w	A	u	λ
144	2540	1016	152	965	1270	2540	9.5	2083
433	889	337	38	324	508	889	6.4	692
1296	305	114	12.7	102	203	305	3.2	232

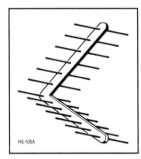

Fig 5.46. The corner reflector can be modified by using a set of metal spines arranged in V-formation to replace the sheet metal or wire-netting reflector

the feed impedance of the dipole radiator falls to a very low value, as can be seen from Fig 5.45. This makes matching difficult and hence a compromise has to be reached. In practice the angle α is usually made 90° or 60°; adjustments in a 60° corner are a little more critical although the maximum obtainable gain is higher. The final matching of the radiator to the line may be carried out by adjusting the distance S.

It does not greatly affect the gain over a useful range of variation but causes a considerable change in radiation resistance. A two-stub tuner may also prove helpful in making final adjustments.

The length L of the sides of the reflector should exceed 2λ to secure the characteristics indicated by Fig 5.44 and 5.46, and the reflector width W should be greater than 1λ for a λ/2 dipole radiator. The reflecting sheet may be constructed of wire netting as described previously or alternatively may be fabricated from metal spines arranged in a V-formation, all of them being parallel to the radiator: see Fig 5.46. The spacing between adjacent rods should not exceed 0.1λ.

A useful approximation for the power gain G referred to a λ/2 dipole is $G = 300/α$ where α is the angle between the sides measured in degrees.

The maximum dipole/vertex spacing S included in the curves shown is λ/2. Spacings greater than this would require rather cumbersome constructions at lower frequencies, but at the higher frequencies larger spacings become practicable, and higher gains than would be suggested by Fig 5.44 can then be obtained; see Table 5.9. This indicates that the corner reflector can become a specially attractive proposition for the l.3GHz band, but the width across the opening should be in excess of 4λ to achieve the results shown.

HB9CV mini-beam

An antenna that falls into the category of horizontally or vertically polarised, portable rather than mobile, or for base station use, is the HB9CV mini-beam. Similar units are the *lazy H* and *ZL special* often used on the HF bands. The HB9CV version, however, has one or two mechanical advantages which makes it particularly suitable for VHF portable use.

Figs 5.48 (taken from 'The HB9CV Antenna for VHF and UHF', H J Franke, DK1PN, *VHF Communications* February 1969) and 5.49 show two methods of construction for the HB9CV antenna. A point that should be stressed is that a *series* capacitor of 3–15pF is required to adjust finally the gamma match/phasing combination to a VSWR of about 1.3:1 against 50Ω. The dimension of the element spacing and the transmission lines, particularly the spacing (5mm), is critical for optimum impedance matching and phasing, and hence gain and front-to-back ratio.

The principle of operation is as follows. If two dipoles at close spacing, typically 0.1–0.2λ, are fed out of phase, 'end fire' radiation will occur in a direction at right-angles to the line of the dipole elements. If the dipoles are resonant at the same frequency a bidirectional pattern with a gain of typically 3dB referred to a single dipole will be realised. However, if correct phasing between the elements is used, a unidirectional or beam pattern is produced. The different lengths found on most HB9CV antennas assist with bandwidth. The end at which the beam is fed designates the direction of radiation. A theoretical gain in excess of 6dBD should be possible. However, depending on the construction techniques,

Angle α (degrees)	Value of S for maximum gain (λ)	Gain (dBi)	T (λ)
90	1.5	13	1–1.25
60	1.25	15	1.0
45	2.0	17	1.9

Table 5.9. Corner/trough reflector

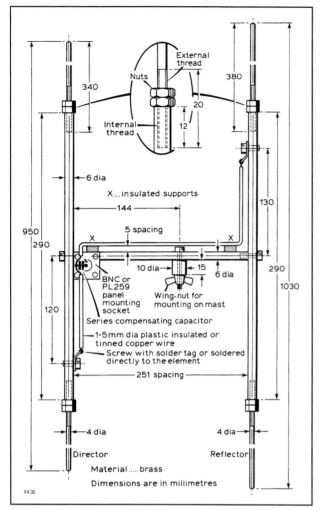

Fig 5.48. A collapsible HB9CV antenna for the 144MHz band (*VHF Communications*)

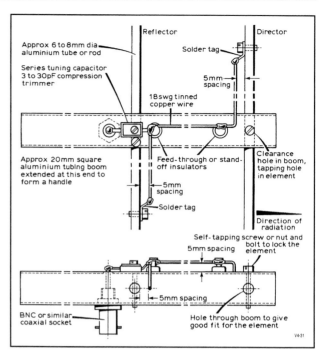

Fig 5.49. Alternative construction of the HB9CV. Dimensions as per Fig 5.48

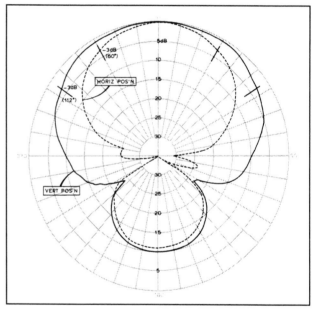

Fig 5.50. HB9CV antenna at 10m above ground

gains between 4 and 5.5dBD with front-to-back ratios between 10 and 20dB tend to be realised in practice. The radiation pattern shown in Fig 5.50 is for the antenna of Fig 5.48 which has a gain of typically 5dBD.

The HB9CV was mounted on a professional glassfibre radiation pattern measuring mast for the 10m test. This ensured a minimum disruption of the antenna radiation pattern when set up for vertical polarisation.

Crossed Yagi with adjustable polarisation

Vertical polarisation is popular for mobile operation in the UK, due to the basic fact that it is far easier to obtain omnidirectional radiation with a vertical antenna than it is with horizontal one. This is particularly important on a vehicle, where the mechanical simplicity of a short vertical rod considerably outweighs the complexity of a halo or crossed dipole, particularly when it is realised that the horizontal antenna must be at least λ/2 above the vehicle surface to ensure low-angle radiation.

Repeaters using vertical polarisation for much the same reason of simplicity of antenna design means that operation of a fixed station, either direct to mobiles or via repeaters, can only be satisfactorily accomplished if a means of changing polarisation is available. It is of course quite possible to use

two antennas, and ideally two rotating systems, but the cost becomes rather formidable.

Space communication, where control of polarisation is difficult or impossible, has forced the use of circular polarisation and it is surprising that it is not used more between fixed stations for long-distance terrestrial work. The fundamental advantage of circular polarisation is that all reflections change the direction of polarisation, precluding the usual addition or subtraction of main and reflected signal; therefore there is far less fading and aircraft flutter when circular polarisation is used at each end of the link. The use of circular polarisation at one end only, with normal horizontal or vertical at the other

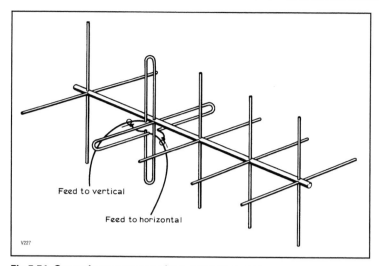

Feed to vertical

Feed to horizontal

V227

Fig 5.51. General arrangement of a crossed Yagi antenna

end of the link, naturally results in a 3dB loss, and therefore to achieve the full advantages of circular polarisation it is necessary for all stations to use it.

The usual practice when using circular polarisation for terrestrial communications is to standardise on clockwise or 'righthand' in the northern hemisphere, and this may well become standard for the amateur by its regular adoption. The direction of polarisation is referred to as viewed from the *rear* of the antenna.

Changing all VHF operations to circular polarisation is obviously not practical, but if a system of switching polarisations were in use at all stations it would soon become

evident that circular offers advantages, and there would of course be the added bonus that vertical would be available for operation with mobiles. Having used a system of polarisation switching, big variations are found in polarisation from stations, in particular mobiles. Quite often a mobile using a vertical antenna has been found to be of equal strength on all polarisations and in some cases a definite advantage for circular has been shown.

Circular polarisation normally brings to mind the helix antenna, which can only produce modes of circularity, depending upon whether the thread of the antenna element is wound clockwise or anti-clockwise. Horizontal or vertical polarisation is possible from helix antennas, but only by the use of two helices and suitable phasing, with no real means of control. The simple means of changing polarisation is to mount a horizontal Yagi and a vertical Yagi on the same boom, giving the well-known *crossed Yagi*. Separate feed to each section of the Yagi brought down to the operating position will enable the user to switch to either horizontal or vertical, but it is perhaps not generally realised that it is a relatively simple matter to alter the phasing of the two Yagis in the shack and obtain four more polarisation options, namely two slant positions (45° and 135°), together with two circular positions (clockwise and anti-clockwise) which with horizontal and vertical gives six positions altogether. This capability is also of great assistance for transmission and reception through satellites.

Although vertical polarisation is mechanically and electrically advantageous when using a simple dipole type of antenna, the presence of the mast in the same plane as the vertical elements on a Yagi considerably detracts from performance. This can be very simply overcome with a crossed Yagi with polarisation switching, mounting the antenna with elements at 45°. The mast then has little effect on the input impedance of the two Yagis, and vertical and horizontal polarisations can still be produced by feeding both antennas in the correct phase relationship.

Assuming therefore that a crossed Yagi is mounted at 45° with individual feeders to the operating position, the polarisation available and the phasing required is as follows:

Slant position 45° and 135°	Antennas fed individually
Circular positions clockwise and anti-clockwise	Both antennas fed with 90°+ or 90°− phase relationship
Horizontal and vertical	Both antennas fed with 0° or 180° phase relationship

This all sounds very complicated, but in actual fact the desired result may be accomplished relatively simply with a three-gang six-position Yaxley-type wafer switch. A coaxial switch is the 'pure' way to do the job but, considering the cost of a three-gang six-way coaxial switch together with the necessary plugs and sockets, the difference in performance is just not worthwhile on 144MHz.

The first problem to overcome is simply that of providing the correct matching for feeding two antennas in parallel. Briefly, with 75Ω antennas the two feeders are simply paralleled, giving 37.5Ω, and λ/4 of 50Ω feeder used to transform

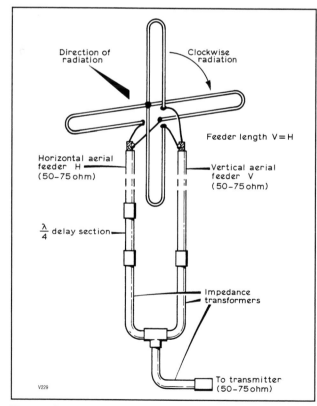

Direction of radiation

Clockwise radiation

Feeder length V = H

Horizontal aerial feeder H (50–75 ohm)

Vertical aerial feeder V (50–75 ohm)

$\frac{\lambda}{4}$ delay section

Impedance transformers

V229

To transmitter (50–75 ohm)

Fig 5.52. General arrangement of feeders with delay line (phasing) for clockwise radiation

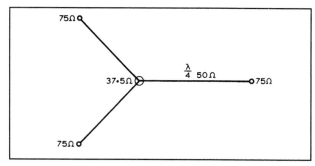

Fig 5.53. Matching two 75Ω antennas by paralleling to 37.5Ω and increasing impedance to 75Ω again

back to 75Ω, as illustrated in Fig 5.53. 50Ω antennas are treated in a slightly different way in that λ/4 of 75Ω feeder is used in each feeder to transform up to 100Ω and the two are placed in parallel to produce 50Ω again, as shown in Fig 5.54.

Phasing is simply a question of altering the length of the feeders to each half of the crossed Yagi as the polarisation is changed. Where a 90° phase shift is required, λ/4 of feeder is inserted and where a 180° phase shift is required, λ/2 feeder is inserted. The polarisation switch must therefore arrange for correct matching by switching in the appropriate λ/4 impedance transformer and correct phasing by switching in the appropriate length of feeder.

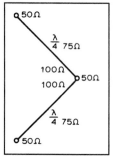

Fig 5.54. Matching two 50Ω antennas by increasing impedance to 100Ω and paralleling to 50Ω again

There is an added complication in that by no means all antenna systems are 50Ω, and a considerable number of 75Ω users still remain on VHF. 50Ω has become an international standard and is of course completely standard on low frequency; it can therefore only be a matter of time before all VHF installations are 50Ω.

Figs 5.55 and 5.56 show the necessary switching arrangements for 75Ω and 50Ω antennas respectively. The normal drawing of a switch makes the illustration of the 50Ω system extremely complicated, and Fig 5.56 is drawn as a side view of the Yaxley switch with the six contacts visible in a vertical line, the moving contact not being shown. It will be noticed that the 50Ω version is much simpler as there is no need to manufacture T-junctions in the cables.

It is very necessary for the phasing lengths of feeder to be accurately cut and this may be simply accomplished with a GDO. First, use the smallest possible diameter cable to minimise the mechanical problems of connection to the contacts of the switch. Types UR43 for 50Ω and UR70 for 75Ω are to be preferred and certainly a solid dielectric type should be used in the interests of uniformity. To obtain λ/4 of cable, cut off slightly more than the calculated length, which in the case of 144MHz will be 15in of solid dielectric cable, leave one end open-circuit, and short the other end with the shortest possible loop that will produce a dip on the GDO. It is surprising just how small that loop can be and, given a reasonably sensitive GDO, a virtual short-circuit will still couple. Check the dip frequency, which will probably be around 120MHz, and carefully clip pieces off the open end of the cable until the dip

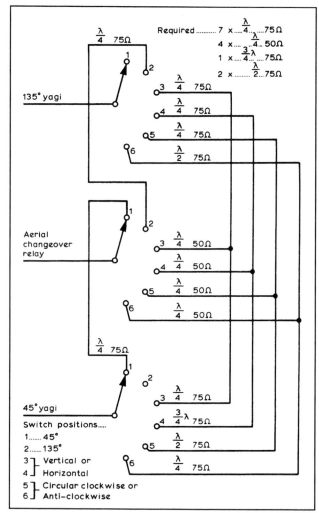

Fig 5.55. 75Ω phasing and matching switch

occurs at 145MHz. Assuming that a solid dielectric cable of similar size is used throughout the switch, there is no necessity to dip each length. The uniformity of the cable is sufficient simply to copy mechanically this λ/4 and to double or treble

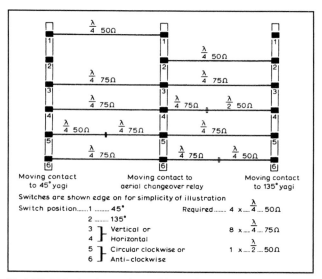

Fig 5.56. 50Ω phasing and matching switch

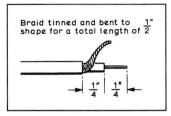

Fig 5.57. Method of 'tailing' coaxial cable

it where $\lambda/2$ or $3\lambda/4$ is required. The slight shortening of the cables when they are prepared for connection is compensated by the length in the switch contacts.

Remember when wiring the switch that every effort should be made to maintain impedance and all cable ends should be made up as short as possible to the configuration shown in Fig 5.57. All outer braids on each wafer of the switch must be joined together by the shortest possible route and not connected to the frame of the switch. The use of miniature switches with small-diameter cable makes for a beautifully neat assembly, but very great care indeed is needed to deal with the many coaxial connections in a switch of this small size. The joining of a length of 50Ω and 75Ω is important, and here every effort should be made to maintain the coaxiality of the cable by pushing the braid back away from the inner, making the inner connections carefully, taping up with polythene tape to avoid any possible short-circuit, and then bringing the braids back again over the tape and binding securely with fine wire. Any attempt at soldering will probably be disastrous, as the polythene will undoubtedly melt with the risk of short-circuit. Further protection may be given by a layer of tape over the entire joint. Similarly, the T-junctions on the 75Ω switch may be made up by cutting small triangular sections of tinplate and quickly soldering the outers of each cable to the tin; in this case short-circuits may be seen and avoided. Fig 5.58 illustrates the method.

Assuming that the switch has been satisfactorily built, there is now the problem of whether the feeders to the halves of the crossed Yagi are of the correct individual length. Ideally, these feeders should be cut mechanically and electrically to equal length before installation, and the two halves of the crossed Yagi should be in exactly the same place on the boom. While the feeders may be cut accurately, it is mechanically difficult and almost impossible to mount the two halves of the Yagi in the same place. They inevitably have to be spaced by a few inches. It is therefore necessary to correct this mechanical displacement of phase by an equal displacement of length of the feeders, and in practice it is far easier to simply connect everything up with unknown lengths of feeders and adjust the length of one or both feeders until the switch operates correctly.

A convenient method of adjustment is to receive a horizontally polarised signal of constant amplitude from a local station, ensuring that the transmitting and receiving antennas

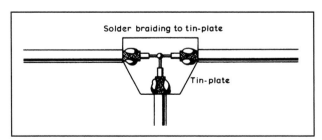

Fig 5.58. Method of joining three cables

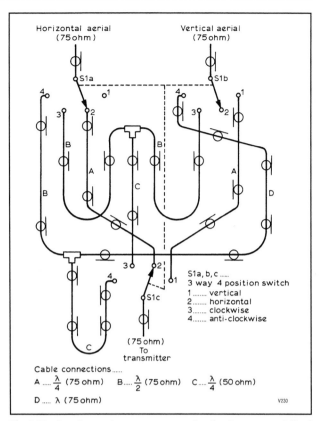

Fig 5.59. An alternative arrangement for feeding crossed Yagi antennas which provides various polarisations at the click of a switch

are beamed directly at each other. This point is vitally important – a beam antenna only radiates its intended polarisation from the main lobe – a fact which will become very evident in subsequent use of the switch. The feeder lengths should now be adjusted so that all slant and circular positions are equal, together with maximum rejection in the vertical position of the switch. The choice of which shall be the horizontal and vertical positions can now be taken. Accurate S-meter readings logged for each position of the switch after every feeder adjustment are essential. Typically, the slant or circular positions will be about one S-point down on the horizontal, while the vertical position will be some six S-points or 20 to 30dB down. To avoid the problem of the man trying to level the legs of a four-legged table and finishing up with a 3in-high table, when cutting feeder lengths cut only 1in at a time from one feeder. When the recorded readings indicate that the last cut as one too many, cut that last piece from the other feeder and the optimum situation will be restored.

With the Yagis mounted at 45°, it may appear surprising that a horizontal signal can produce differing signal strength on each antenna, but this will happen until the respective feeders are of equal length. The reason is the inevitable mismatch (sometimes deliberate to improve noise factor) which occurs at the input to the converter or receiver. Remember the object is *equal* signals, not maximum signals – converter mismatch can be compensated for and *maximum* signal strength achieved by altering the length of the main feeder after the switch, which will not affect the phase relationships between the antennas.

The question now arises as to which of the circular polarisation positions are clockwise or anti-clockwise. This subject

Table 5.10. Received signals expected with various switch connections

Switch position	Polarisation of signal (dB down)					
	Horiz-ontal	Vert-ical	45°	135°	Clock-wise	Anti-clock-wise
Horizontal	Max	20/30	3	3	3	3
Vertical	20/30	Max	3	3	3	3
45°	3	3	Max	20/30	3	3
135°	3	3	20/30	Max	3	3
Clockwise	3	3	3	3	Max	20/30
Anti-clockwise	3	3	3	3	20/30	Max

merits an entire article; it will be remembered that even the world's top telecommunication engineers got this one wrong on the first transatlantic TV broadcast via Telstar. Should the operator wish to define the circular positions, then with accurately cut equal feeders and an accurately made switch, position 5 will be clockwise and 6 anti-clockwise, providing the antenna connections are as shown in Fig 5.56. If the antenna connections are not known, then the only way to calibrate the switch is to receive a known circularly polarised signal, when the respective positions will be immediately evident.

A correctly wired and phased switch should perform as in Table 5.10.

Axial-mode helix

The helix antenna is a simple means of obtaining high gain and wide-band frequency characteristics. When the circumference of the helix is of the order of 1λ axial radiation occurs, ie the maximum field strength is found to lie along the axis of the helix. This radiation is circularly polarised, the sense of the polarisation depending on whether the helix has a right-hand or left-hand thread.

If a pick-up dipole is used to explore the field in the direction of maximum radiation, the signal received by this dipole will show no change of amplitude as it is rotated through 360°, thus indicating true circular polarisation. At any point to the side of the helix the wave will be elliptically polarised, ie the horizontal and vertical components will be of unequal strength.

A helix may be used to receive the circularly polarised waves radiated from a transmitting helix but care must be taken to ensure that the receiving helix has a thread of the same sense as the radiator. If a thread of the wrong sense is used, the received signal will be very considerably weaker.

The properties of the helical antenna are determined by the

diameter of the spiral D and the pitch P (see Fig 5.60) and depends upon the resultant effect of the radiation taking place all along the helical conductor. The gain of the antenna depends on the number of turns in the helix. The diameter of the reflector R should be at least λ/2, the diameter of the helix D should be about λ/3 and the pitch P about λ/4.

A helix of this design will have a feed impedance of about 140Ω; this may be transformed to the feeder impedance by means of a λ/4 transformer. A typical helical antenna having a seven-turn helix has a gain of approximately 12dBi over a 2:1 frequency range. However, to achieve this gain fully it is necessary to use a circularly polarised antenna (eg a helix of the same sense) for reception. If a plane-polarised antenna, such as a dipole, is used there will be a loss of 3dB.

A practical helix antenna for 144MHz

The greatest problem to be overcome in this type of antenna for 144MHz, with its relatively large helix diameter of 24½in, is the provision of a suitable support structure.

Fig 5.61 shows a general arrangement, in which three supports per turn (120° spacing) are shown, and details of suitable drilling of the central boom are given in Fig 5.62.

The helix may be made of copper, brass, or aluminium tube or rod, or coaxial cable. This latter alternative is an attractive material to use, being covered and substantially weatherproofed. If coaxial cable is used the inner conductor should connect to the outer at each end, or be removed completely.

The reflector is located at a distance a behind the start of the first turn, and is supported by crossed supports from the central boom. The material for the reflector can be any kind of metal mesh such as chicken netting or plastic-coated garden mesh.

The central boom should be sufficiently rigid to adequately support the whole structure, and should ideally at the same time be of a non-metallic material such as wood, thick-wall plastic tube or thick-wall glassfibre. Although glassfibre is

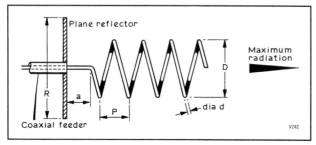

Fig 5.60. The helix antenna. The plane reflector may take the form of a dartboard type of wire grid. The dimensions given in Table 5.11 are based on a pitch angle of 12°. The helix, which may be wound of copper tube or wire, the actual diameter of which is not critical, must be supported by low-loss insulators

Fig 5.61. General arrangement of support structure for a five-turn helical antenna for 144MHz

more expensive it would undoubtedly be worthwhile for a permanent installation.

The length of the final turn of the helix can be adjusted to obtain optimum circularity. This would entail rotating a dipole set up in line with the helix at a distance of, say, 10m, to be outside the near field and clear of all objects. The signal obtained from the dipole will be constant for all points of rotation when the helix is optimised for circular polarisation. Any variation of the signal is known as the *polarisation axial ratio* or *boresight ellipticity,* and is usually expressed as a ratio or decibel figure. Helix antennas for higher frequencies are easier to construct and require little adjustment. Detailed instructions for building a 435MHz helix have been published by G3RUH [23].

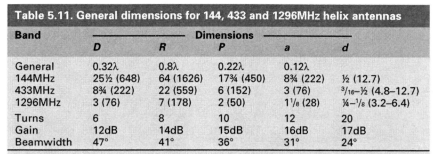

Table 5.11. General dimensions for 144, 433 and 1296MHz helix antennas

Band	Dimensions				
	D	R	P	a	d
General	0.32λ	0.8λ	0.22λ	0.12λ	
144MHz	25½ (648)	64 (1626)	17¾ (450)	8¾ (222)	½ (12.7)
433MHz	8¾ (222)	22 (559)	6 (152)	3 (76)	³/₁₆–½ (4.8–12.7)
1296MHz	3 (76)	7 (178)	2 (50)	1⅛ (28)	¼–⅛ (3.2–6.4)
Turns	6	8	10	12	20
Gain	12dB	14dB	15dB	16dB	17dB
Beamwidth	47°	41°	36°	31°	24°

Dimensions in inches, millimetres are given in brackets. The gain and beamwidth of the helical antenna are dependent upon the total number of turns as shown above.

Bandwidth = 0.75 to 1.3λ

$$\text{Feed impedance} = 140 \times \frac{\text{circumference}}{\lambda} \text{ ohms}$$

(Note: λ and circumference must be in the same units.)

$$\text{Beamwidth (degrees)} = \sqrt{\frac{12{,}300}{\text{No of turns}}}$$

OMNIDIRECTIONAL ANTENNAS FOR FIXED STATIONS

The horizontally polarised omni-V

This antenna consists of a pair of λ/2 dipoles. The ends of the dipoles are physically displaced to produce quadrature radiation and are supported on a λ/4 shorted stub. A pair of Q bars are tapped down the stubs to a point where the impedance is 600Ω so that when the two units are fed in parallel they produce an impedance of 300Ω at the centre. A 4:1 balance-to-unbalance coaxial transformer is fitted to the centre point of the Q bars so that a standard 75Ω coaxial cable feeder may be used.

A 50Ω feed can be arranged by repositioning the Q bars on the antenna stubs. This can best be achieved by monitoring the VSWR on the coaxial feeder whilst adjusting the Q bar position by small but equal amounts on both stubs.

The general arrangement is shown in Fig 5.63(a). Fig 5.63(b) shows how the antenna may be arranged to give a bidirectional radiation pattern.

Simple crossed dipoles

The ordinary turnstile, also known as *crossed dipoles,* provides a simple yet very effective horizontally polarised, omnidirectional antenna. It consists of two horizontal dipoles

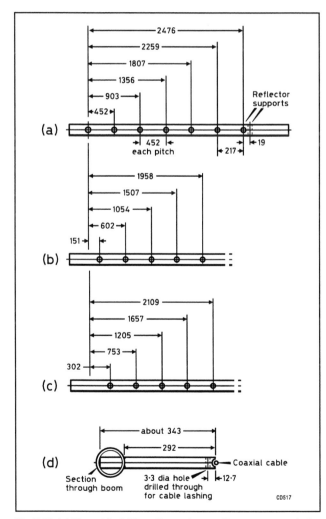

Fig 5.62. (a) First side drilling dimensions, reflector support holes are drilled at right-angles; (b) and (c) are drilled at intervals of 120° and 240° respectively from (a). (d) Cutting and filing dimensions for the element stand-offs

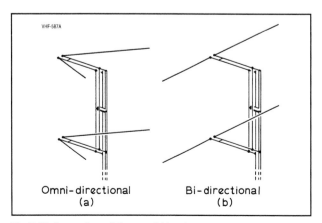

Fig 5.63. Formation of the omni-V antenna

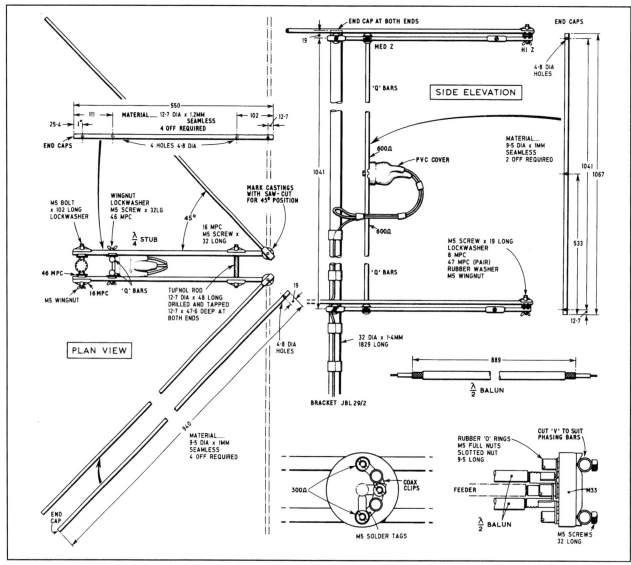

Fig 5.64. The mechanical details of the construction of the omni-V (dimensions are in millimetres)

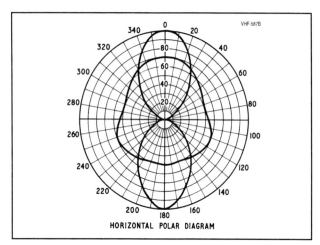

Fig 5.65. The horizontal polar diagram for an average antenna, showing both the bidirectional and omnidirectional charts

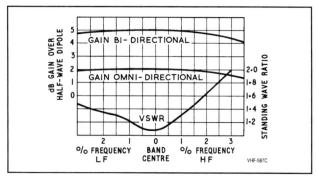

Fig 5.66. Chart showing gain versus VSWR on the omni-V just described

and with a little adjustment a very low SWR can be obtained. The radiation pattern produced tends to be square with the 'corners' at element ends being about 1dB up on a dipole's maximum radiation.

The 90° phase difference is readily obtained with a resonant λ/4 feeder between the dipoles and a further resonant

mounted at right-angles and fed with equal power but at 90° phase difference (Fig 5.67). Matching to 75Ω is quite simple

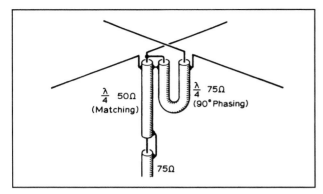

Fig 5.67. Phasing and matching arrangement of crossed dipoles

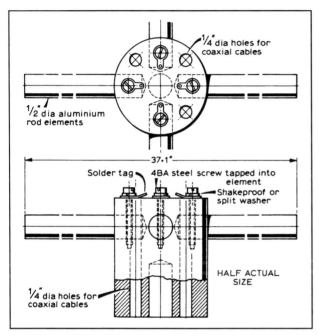

Fig 5.68. Details of central insulator

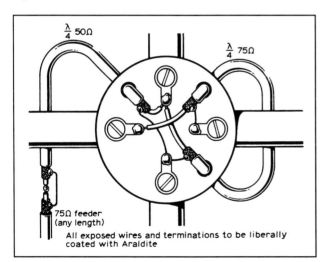

Fig 5.69. Connections of coaxial sections

series λ/4 section as a matching transformer for the characteristic line impedance. The antenna should be mounted at least 0.5λ above any conducting surface, otherwise much of the signal will be radiated upwards.

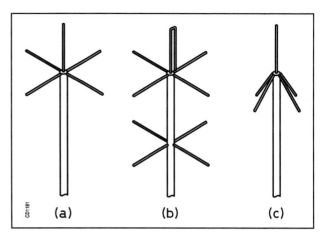

Fig 5.70. Quarter-wave ground-plane antennas. The folded monopole radiator may be used with any of the ground-plane configurations

The λ/4 ground-plane antenna

This is one of the simplest omnidirectional antennas to construct and usually yields good results. However, some unexpected effects may occur when the antenna is mounted on a conductive mast, or if RF current is allowed to flow on the outside of the coaxial feeder.

In its simplest form, the ground-plane antenna comprises a λ/4 extension to the inner of a coaxial cable, with several wires extending radially away from the end of the outer of the coaxial cable: Fig 5.70(a). The input resistance will be quite low, of the order of 20Ω, although this may be transformed to a higher impedance by using a folded monopole radiator as shown in Fig 5.70(b). Equal-diameter elements provide a 4:1 step-up ratio to around 80Ω, and a smaller diameter grounded leg can reduce the input impedance to 50Ω.

The feedpoint impedance can be modified by bending the ground plane rods downwards from the horizontal: Fig 5.70(c). If the radiating element and the ground plane rods are all λ/4 long, the input resistance is approximately:

$$R = 18(1 + \sin \theta)^2 \quad \text{ohms}$$

where θ is the ground-plane rod angle below the horizontal, in degrees. A 50Ω resistance is achieved when θ is 42°.

The ends of the ground-plane rods are sometimes joined together with a conductive ring to provide additional mechanical stability. The ring increases the electrical size of the ground plane, and the length of the radials can be reduced by about 5%.

The few rods forming the ground plane usually do not prevent current flowing on any conductive supporting mast or on the outside of a coaxial feeder. The mast or feeder can become a long radiating element which may enhance or destroy the radiation pattern of the antenna, dependent upon the magnitude and phase of the mast currents relative to that on the antenna. An example of this is shown in Fig 5.71(a), where the monopole and ground plane is mounted on a 5λ mast (about 10m). The corresponding radiation patterns without mast or cable influences are shown in Fig 5.71(b). The effects of ground reflections have been suppressed in both cases.

Some antenna designs make use of these currents to enhance the gain of the monopole; they sometimes have a second set of ground-plane rods further down the mast, tuned to

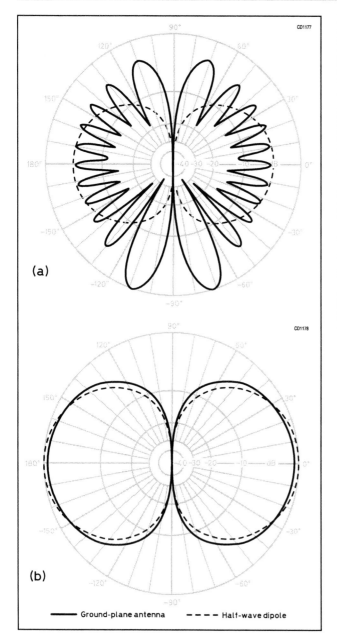

(a)

(b)

—— Ground-plane antenna   – – – – Half-wave dipole

Fig 5.71. Radiation patterns of quarter-wave ground-plane antenna. (a) On top of a 5λ (10m) mast. Note that the main lobes are directed downwards, and would be prone to pick up man-made interference. The pattern of a λ/2 dipole is shown for comparison. (b) In free space. A λ/2 dipole is again shown for comparison

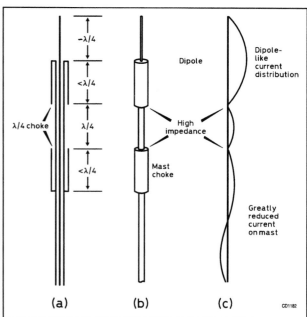

(a)   (b)   (c)

Fig 5.72. Skirted dipole antenna with mast choke. Note that the interior of the choke must be λ/4 in electrical length. Some designs use dielectric loading inside the dipole skirt to shorten its length, which can be used to adjust the impedance of the dipole as a radiator

high impedance at its lower end, reducing unwanted currents on the mast. The current is further reduced by a second choke, with its open, high-impedance end placed λ/4 below the dipole skirt for best effect. The radiation pattern of this antenna closely resembles that of a λ/2 dipole in free space.

The gain sleeve dipole (vertically polarised)
The gain sleeve dipole in Fig 5.73 is derived from the 1.8dBD shunt-feed 5λ/8 mentioned later in the mobile antenna section.

The radiating element B-B is in principle a centre-fed 1λ element but is fed coaxially to make it end fed. Having effectively twice the aperture of the λ/2 dipole, a gain of typically 2.5–3dB is achieved.

Mechanical construction is open to interpretation but a beer can or plastic water-pipe format are two solutions. It should be noted that the mounting point should be at A-A and not on the 0.25λ sleeve.

The discone
This antenna has not found too much favour with amateurs in the past, though frequently used for commercial and military purposes. Unlike many other types this antenna is not only omnidirectional but also has wide-band characteristics. It is capable of covering, say, the 70, 144 and 432MHz bands or 144, 432

present a high impedance to reduce currents flowing below that point. The mast currents can be reduced a little by using more radials in the ground plane or extending their length to around 0.3λ.

An open-circuited choke sleeve can be more effective than radial wires for mast current control. This technique is used in the skirted antenna described below.

The skirted antenna
The skirted antenna (Fig 5.72) does not require ground-plane radials, and can be mounted in a cylindrical radome for better appearance and lower wind-induced noise. The skirt forms the lower part of a λ/2 dipole and, being λ/4 long, presents a

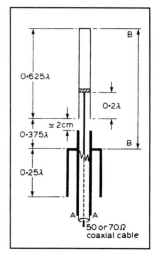

Fig 5.73. Gain sleeve dipole

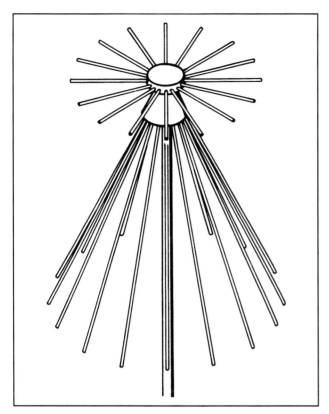

Fig 5.74. General arrangement of skeleton form of discone antenna

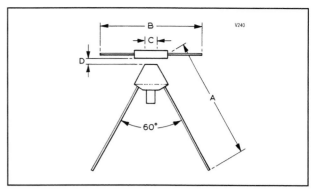

Fig 5.75. Primary dimensions of discone antenna

The detail given in Fig 5.76 of the hub construction will be suitable for any design using a 50Ω cable feed and may be taken as an example. There is likely to be some problem in producing a suitable insulator which may be made of a potting resin or turned from PTFE or other stable low-loss material.

An extension of the discone is the *helicone*. The elements of the conventional discone can be replaced with helical elements working in the normal mode as discussed later.

In its simplest form only eight elements are required for the disc and for the cone. Gain and the radiation pattern is essentially the same for both the discone and helicone but for the helicone the usable bandwidth is reduced to approximately one-third.

Collinear antennas

Communication with mobile stations is best achieved with a vertically polarised omnidirectional antenna, as there is no

and 1296MHz, although there will of course be some variation of the SWR over such a wide range.

Also, since the antenna can operate over roughly a 10-to-one frequency range, it will more readily radiate any harmonics present in the transmitter output. It is therefore important to use a suitable filter to adequately attenuate the harmonic outputs. The radiation angle tends to rise after the first frequency octave.

The discone consists of a disc mounted above a cone, and ideally should be constructed from sheet material. Many amateurs would find this impossible to realise, but with little loss the components may be made of rods or tubes as illustrated in Fig 5.74, with a minimum number of rods of eight or preferably 16. Of course, open mesh may be used as an alternative, bearing in mind the windage increase, and that the current flows radially away from the feedpoint.

The important dimensions are the end diameter of the cone and the spacing of this from the centre of the disc, so that the terminating impedance is correct, eg 50Ω.

The primary parameters are shown in Fig 5.75 with dimensions as follows:

A the length of the cone elements – these are λ/4 at the lowest operating frequency, or 2952/*f*(MHz)in.

B the overall disc diameter – this should be 70% of λ/4.

C the diameter of the top of the cone – this will be decided to some extent by the diameter of the coaxial cable but for most purposes 0.5in will be suitable.

D the spacing of the centre of the top disc to the cone top – this is 20% of C, or 0.1in for 50Ω.

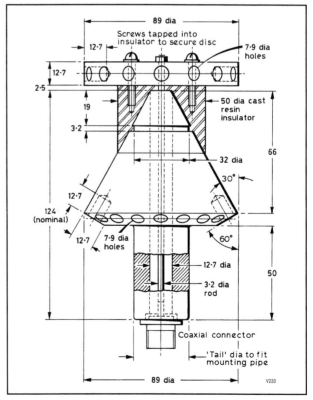

Fig 5.76. Details of a hub assembly

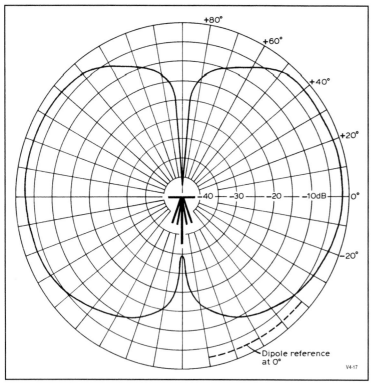

Fig 5.77. Typical discone and helicone decibel radiation pattern over the first 2:1 frequency range. As the frequency increases above 2:1 the pattern tends to rise above the horizontal level until at about 5:1 in frequency the main direction of radiation is above 45° from the horizontal

for calculating the radiation pattern of groups of elements. The radiation pattern of broadside arrays develops nulls as the elements are spaced further apart, so it is desirable to place the elements as close together as practicable, taking into account the capture area and mutual coupling effects also discussed in the section on arrays.

The current on a length of wire several wavelengths long will be distributed as shown in Fig 5.78(a). The wire shown is 2λ long. Radiation at right-angles to the wire will be poor, as the successive half-wavelength current maxima are in opposing phase, and if the currents were equal, there would be perfect cancellation of the radiation in that direction. However, if all the current maxima were in phase, the radiated fields would add, and a high gain could be achieved: Fig 5.78(b).

There are several ways of achieving this phase reversal. The simplest is to insert an anti-resonant network or a non-radiating half-wavelength of transmission line as a phasing section between the λ/2 radiating elements: Fig 5.78(c). The λ/2 transmission line can be realised as a quarter-wavelength of ribbon cable, which can be wound around the insulator between the radiating elements (see the section on mobile antennas).

A more subtle approach uses radiating elements that are a little longer or shorter than λ/2. This helps the feeding arrangements, as it will be remembered that end-feeding a λ/2 dipole is difficult because of its very high impedance. The self-reactance of the longer or shorter dipole is then used in the design of the phasing network between the elements to achieve the desired overall phase shift. The non-radiating transmission line can then often be replaced by a capacitor or an inductor in series with the residual element reactance: Fig 5.79(a) and (b). Again, a transmission line stub can be used to synthesise the required reactance, which may be more convenient or cheaper than a lumped component, especially if significant RF power handling is required: Fig 5.79(c). Sometimes a parallel-tuned

need to point the antenna in the direction of the mobile. However, a fixed station is not as constrained by mechanical considerations as a mobile, and can thus be fitted with larger, and hence higher-gain, antennas.

This can be achieved by stacking dipoles vertically above one another in a collinear array, and feeding them with cables of equal lengths, as shown for the GB2ER repeater antenna later in this chapter. Another method of achieving gain with simpler feed arrangements is discussed below.

A formula was presented in the section on antenna arrays

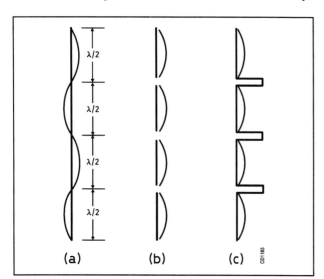

Fig 5.78. Current distributions on a wire and derivation of the collinear antenna

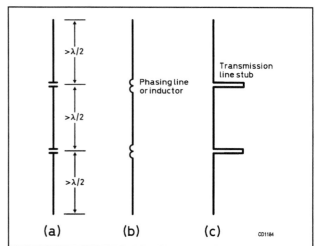

Fig 5.79. Realisation of collinear antennas. The antennas are end-fed

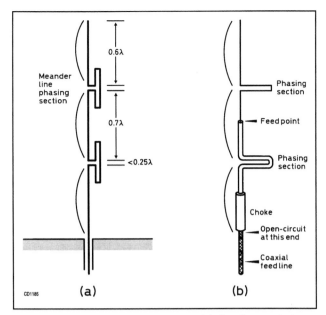

Fig 5.80. Frankin collinear antennas, end-fed and centre-fed

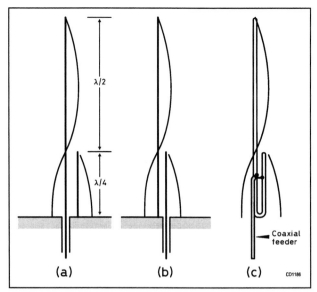

Fig 5.81. The J antenna

circuit is realised as an inductor resonated by the self-capacitance of the insulator separating the radiating elements, and on which it is wound.

A technique devised by Franklin that has been attractive to VHF antenna manufacturers folds parts of the radiating element to provide the phasing section as shown in Fig 5.80(a). Provided that the folded sections are significantly shorter than the radiating elements, the gain is not significantly degraded, although the whole structure is sensitive to capacitive loading by any housing and insulators required. The radiation pattern is frequency sensitive, and the main lobe will squint upwards or downwards as the frequency changes from the nominal. While these folded element designs look attractive for home construction, adjustments to optimise both the radiation pattern and input impedance are very difficult without proper measuring facilities. Poor gain and broken radiation patterns result if the sections are not properly excited and phased.

All these designs are end-fed, which have practical disadvantages with longer, multi-element arrays. If identical sections are used, the end elements carry less current than those close to the feed, reducing the overall efficiency of the antenna. While different length radiators and phasing elements can be used to equalise the current distribution, the design and adjustment is lengthy and definitely requires good radiation pattern measurement facilities. If the array can be centre-fed, any residual phasing errors tend to cancel out and, for a given length, the performance tends to be better because of a more uniform current distribution. Fig 5.80(b) shows one means of achieving centre feeding with a Franklin array. Note the use of the λ/4 choke section at the base of the array, which is essential to prevent current flowing down the outer of the coaxial cable and destroying the performance of the collinear antenna. The practical gain limit of the singly fed collinear antenna is around 10dBi.

Practical collinears in radio amateur use tend to use variations on Fig 5.79. The radiating elements may comprise combinations of lengths up to 5λ/8, with or without ground planes.

The presence of a good ground plane increases the gain as the image or reflection effectively doubles the length of the array (see also the section on mobile antennas). However, good results can be achieved with collinears directly mounted on pipe masts, especially if care is taken to control unwanted currents from flowing on the mast.

None of the above considers the practicalities of feeding and matching the antenna. Collinear antennas, by virtue of their operation as end-fed structures, have high feed-point impedances. A good feed arrangement, valid for both ground-plane and mast mounted antennas, is the use of a λ/4 short-circuited transmission line, as described in the section on matching in this chapter.

Fig 5.81(a) shows such an arrangement to end-feed a λ/2 dipole mounted over a ground plane. The matching section should not radiate, and the overall effect is that of a λ/2 radiator raised λ/4 above the ground plane. Either leg of the λ/4 section can be fed, leading to the structure in Fig 5.81(b), which is identical to Fig 5.81(a) in terms of current distribution, and hence radiation performance. The evolution can be taken a stage further by removing the ground plane and feeding either leg of the λ/4 section as in Fig 5.81(c); this is the *J antenna* or *J-pole antenna*, which may use different diameters of tubing for the radiator and stub.

The *Slim Jim antenna* provides an elegant solution for a simple, mechanically robust antenna made from a single piece of tubing as shown in Fig 5.82. This antenna [24] comprises a folded, open-circuit λ/2 radiator above a λ/4 transformer section, and is a derivative of the J antenna. The folded-stub characteristics of the radiator provide some control over the reactive element of the input impedance. The two ends of the tube can be joined by an insulator, eg a piece of stiff plastic tubing, to provide weather proofing and enhanced mechanical rigidity. Either balanced or unbalanced feeds can be used, tapped on to the λ/4 transformer section at the point that provides the best match to the feeder. Coaxial feeders should be strapped or bonded to the λ/4 section to reduce unwanted currents on the outer of the cable. The antenna has a maximum gain of around 2.8dBi in free space, although the main

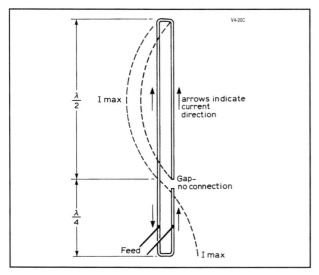

Fig 5.82. The basic Slim Jim, showing direction of current flow and phase reversal in matching stub (*Practical Wireless*)

lobe is tilted up about 10°. The main lobe can be brought to the horizontal by reducing the length of the upper section to about 0.4λ. This reduces the peak gain to around 2.5dBi, and can make the feed impedance capacitive.

Phasing sections and additional elements can be combined to produce a collinear form for the J antenna as shown in Fig 5.83(b). This antenna and that of Fig 5.83(c) have been used

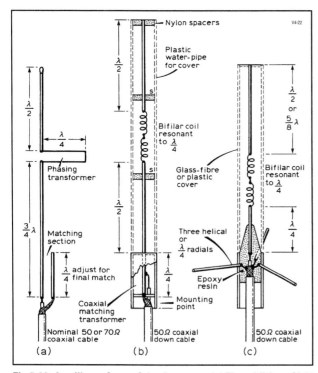

Fig 5.83. A collinear form of the J antenna. (a) The addition of λ/4 sections as suggested by Franklin. (b) Use of a coaxial short-circuit λ/4 transformer to give an unbalanced input. The tapping point in the matching transformer is approximately 0.15λ from the 'earthy' end. (c) A variant of (b) with radials. With both (b) and (c) the λ/4 phasing transformer has been 'wound up' as a bifilar coil (each coil being wound in the opposite hand). While the inductive component is cancelled, the mutual capacitance on the windings makes them physically shorter than λ/4

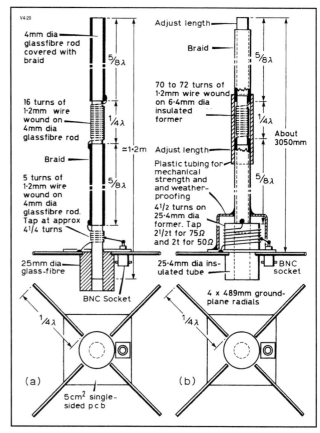

Fig 5.84. (a) A 432MHz collinear. (b) A 144MHz collinear (*UK Southern FM Journal*)

successfully to produce low-angle radiation for the GB3SN 144MHz repeater.

A variation of the techniques described but using coils as with the original Marconi concept is shown in Fig 5.84(a) for 432MHz and Fig 5.84(b) for 144MHz. The expected gain is between 6 and 7dBD.

Materials required for Fig 5.84(a) are as follows:

- One 2.5cm dia 10cm long glassfibre tube
- One 40mm dia 1.2m long glassfibre rod
- Four 20mm dia 20cm long glassfibre rods
- Length of braiding from junk multicore cable
- Length of 18 SWG wire for matching coils
- Approx 5cm square of singled-sided PCB

First, adjust the bottom 5λ/8 element to give minimum SWR; this is done by adjusting the tapping point on the bottom coil (approx 4¼ turns). A fine adjustment can be made by altering the length of the first 5λ/8 element.

Next fix on the centre matching coil and the top element. Please note that to obtain the best results both elements should be approximately 5λ/8 and within reason the same length. A good SWR is obtained by adjusting the centre matching coil (the coil is spread over λ/4).

The matching coil provides the phase change necessary to feed the top element and so adjustment is quite critical. It has been found that if the matching coil has to be 'squeezed up' to obtain a good SWR, then the coil has too many turns. The opposite is true if the coil has to be greater than λ/2 for a good SWR.

To prevent the collinear going off tune once set up, the elements were secured to the centre glassfibre rod and the matching coil taped with self-amalgamating tape. Provided care is taken in setting up, an SWR of close to 1:1 to 1 can be obtained.

Materials required for Fig 5.84(b) are as follows:

- Two ½in dia by 47½in ± ½in, 5λ/8 elements (adjustable)
- Four 19¼in rods for ground plane
- One 1in dia by 30in insulated rod
- One 1in dia insulated tube (a cotton reel can be used instead)
- 18 SWG wire for matching and phasing coils.

The diagram shows extra insulated tubing over the matching and phasing coils to give more mechanical strength and weather-proofing.

Setting up is carried out as follows. First, the length of the bottom 5λ/8 element must be adjusted to give the minimum SWR possible.

Next fix on the phasing coil and the top element which must be the same length as the bottom element. Then obtain the best SWR possible by adjusting the phasing coil.

This coil provides the phase change necessary to feed the top element; it is a length of 18 SWG wire, about 1λ long, coiled up to give 70–72 turns on a 4in former. It was found that the λ/4 spacing between the two elements is more critical than the number of turns. 68 turns gave satisfactory SWR on one version.

Some difficulty may occur in setting up the phasing coil. Before taking too many turns off, go back to the first stage to ensure that the bottom 5λ/8 element is correctly matched. If the bottom element is not correctly matched the collinear will not tune up. Careful adjustments in setting up should produce a SWR of 1:1 to 1.

A technique that has not been discussed but is widely used involves feeding conventional λ/2 dipoles in phase from a single source or adjusting the phase relationship of cable lengths between dipoles. There is a degree of interaction between cables and radiating elements but individual dipoles can be positioned to modify the pattern shape. The example given in Figs 5.85–5.87 is probably the simplest to implement and was devised for the GB3ER 432MHz band repeater.

ANTENNAS FOR MOBILE AND PORTABLE STATIONS

The choice of an antenna for mobile VHF and UHF use is dependent on several factors. As the frequency increases the aperture of the antenna decreases. This means that larger gains are required for UHF than VHF to overcome the loss of aperture as well as the radiation path loss due again to the increase of working frequency.

As the direction of a vehicle, relative to the station to which it is transmitting or receiving, is continually changing there is a need for an omnidirectional antenna system. This will mean that to achieve gain in the horizontal plane, while retaining an omnidirectional pattern, will require considerable reduction of the pattern in the vertical plane. For example an omnidirectional antenna of 6dBD gain will have a typical half-power point (−3dB) of under 30°. The narrow beam or disc that is produced will result in considerable variation in transmitted and received signal strength as the vehicle or antenna tilts or

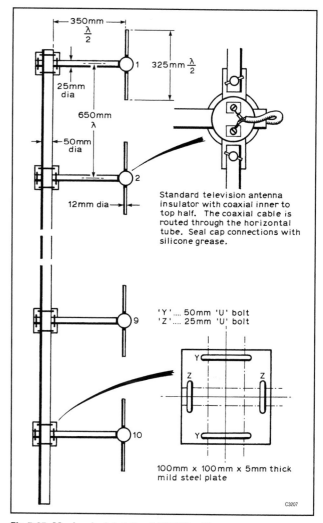

Fig 5.85. Mechanical details of GB3ER collinear

where signals are reflected, as will always be the case, from nearby objects. A compromise has therefore to be arrived at to obtain maximum gain in the best direction which gives minimum disruption of signals when mobile.

The choice of polarisation is not only dependent on compatibility with stations being received and the optimum

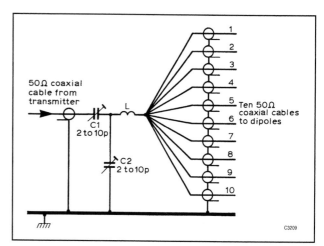

Fig 5.86. Matching unit of GB3ER collinear

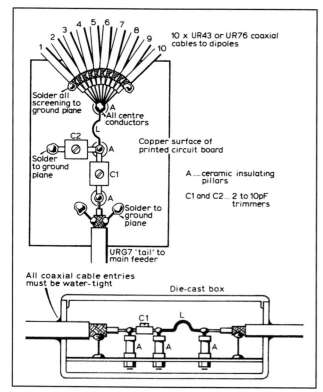

Fig 5.87. Matching unit layout of GB3ER collinear

polarisation for the propagation path concerned, but the aesthetics and mechanical complexity of the antenna used and its mounting position on the vehicle.

Antennas, particularly when vehicle-mounted, must always be considered as an integral part of the environment in which they are to be used. Radiation patterns quoted by manufacturers can be completely different when an antenna is in use. Increased gain normally means an increase in physical size. This improvement of gain can be lost, with a probable loss of omnidirectivity, if, due to its physical size, the antenna is mounted at a lower point to facilitate access to a garage, for instance. The difference in mounting an antenna on the wing or boot of a car compared with mounting it on the top dead centre of the car roof can lose at least 3dB of gain with the variations of the expected radiation patterns.

There are several antennas in current use which are worth considering. In addition one or two specialised antennas are available or can be readily fabricated by the radio amateur which also merit consideration. Mobile antennas can be considered in three basic groups:

1. Vertically polarised antennas, more often used for FM and repeaters.
2. Horizontally polarised antennas, normally used for SSB transmission.
3. Circularly polarised antennas.

together with a sub-group of low-profile antennas to produce vertical or horizontal polarisation but with physical heights below 0.1λ.

Quarter-wave whip

This is the simplest and most basic mobile antenna. It is derived from the doublet or λ/2 dipole. Marconi, by replacing

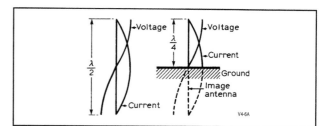

Fig 5.88. The λ/2 antenna and its grounded λ/4 counterpart. The missing λ/4 can be considered to be supplied by the image in ground of good conductivity

half of the doublet with a ground plane as shown in Fig 5.88, found that the image of the vertical λ/4 section was 'reflected' in the ground plane, producing an antenna which was substantially the same as the original dipole. The theory of operation showed that if the ground plane was infinitely large and made of a perfectly conducting material, all of the radiation associated with the lower half of the dipole was radiated by the top half giving, in fact, a 3dB improvement over the dipole. In practice the size of the ground plane and its resistive losses modify the pattern and this 3dB is never realised. Figs 5.89 and 5.90 show optimum patterns of a λ/4 whip measured on a ground plane of λ/2 sides and 1λ sides. Although the pattern is raised from the horizontal, on a medium ground plane the loss of horizontal gain is relatively small (20° and 1dB at 0° in Fig 5.89 but 40° and 6dB at 0° in Fig 5.79).

However, as the ground-plane size increases the main lobe continues to rise until the situation of Fig 5.91 occurs. When a radiator is mounted over a ground plane as described, the input impedance is typically halved. So for the λ/4 whip or monopole the input impedance is typically $36\Omega + j$, that is to say, approximately half the resistance of the dipole but with an additional reactive component.

Considering 50Ω as being the standard cable impedance used at VHF and UHF, this would produce a standing wave at the antenna base of about 1.5 to 1. The simplest way to

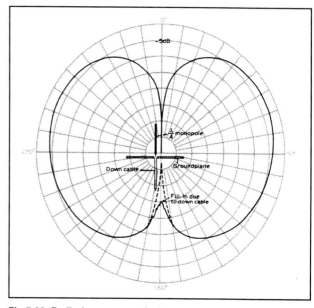

Fig 5.89. Radiation pattern of a λ/4 monopole over a λ/2 square ground plane at 145MHz

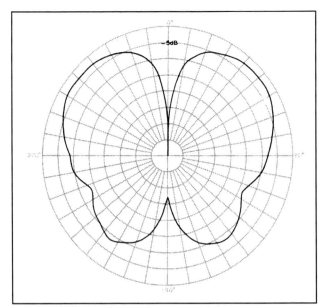

Fig 5.90. Radiation pattern of a λ/4 monopole over a 1λ square ground plane at 145MHz

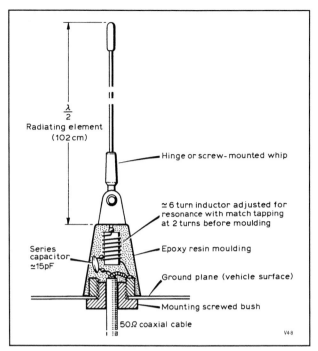

Fig 5.92. A typical home-built λ/2 mobile antenna and mount

overcome this mismatch is first to slightly increase the length of the whip to produce an inductive reactance to cancel the capacitive reactance normally obtained. In practice this also raises the resistive value of the whip and a close match can usually be obtained to 50Ω cable. Should a VSWR bridge or similar (of 50Ω characteristic impedance) be used to set up the whip, when a match has been achieved, the length of the cable should be changed and the match re-checked. If there is no change in the meter reading, then the antenna is matched to the cable. If a change does occur then the antenna/cable combination has been matched to the VSWR meter and the whip should be readjusted until changes in cable length have minimal or no effect. It is preferable that the added cable length is not an exact multiple of a λ/2 or λ/4 as this, particularly with a multiple of λ/2, will confuse the results.

The ground-plane effects and aperture size of the λ/4 whip tend to limit its use at VHF and UHF. At UHF the aperture is small and the pattern tends to be raised in the vertical plane due to the large ground-plane area. It is therefore not often used at those frequencies. At VHF, ie 144MHz, the compromise of the λ/4 whip's simplicity and size (about 49cm or 19¼in) often balances with its medium aperture and tendency on some vehicles to have a raised vertical pattern. At 70MHz the physical dimensions are such (about 102cm/40in) that this is the normal limiting factor to the use of the λ/4 whip as opposed to gain devices. The aperture of the antenna at this frequency is compatible with path-loss conditions, and the ground-plane size is such that the radiation angle when roof mounted is fairly low. However, the shape of the

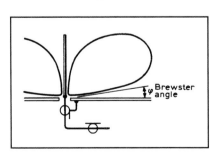

Fig 5.91. Radiation pattern of whip on large ground plane showing elevation of the main lobe

radiation pattern can have a loss of 3dB in the omnidirectivity each side of the vehicle.

The λ/2 and 5λ/8 gain antennas

Using the ground-planing techniques described for the λ/4 whip, gain antennas can be produced. If the λ/2 dipole is extended in length, maximum forward gain (before the pattern divides into several lobes) is obtained when the dipole is about 1.2λ. This becomes the maximum length of 5λ/8 for a ground-plane antenna. A natural extension to the λ/4 whip is the λ/2 whip. However, such a radiator fed against a ground plane has a high input impedance. On the other hand, a 3λ/4 radiator fed against a ground plane has a resistive input of almost exactly 50Ω but is above the optimum length for a reasonable pattern shape.

If the λ/2 whip could be made to look like a 3λ/4 radiator then it would be possible to obtain a 50Ω resistive input. A series coil at the ground-plane end of a λ/2 radiator can be used to resonate it to 3λ/4, but the input is still fairly high impedance and reactive. If, however, the coil is shorted to the ground plane a tapping point up the coil will provide the required impedance and the addition of a non-critical capacitor in series will compensate for the reactive components. Fig 5.92 shows details of such an antenna.

As the aperture of the antenna has been doubled compared with the λ/4 whip, twice the effective radiation is obtained, ie approaching 3dB gain. This assumes however, that there is minimum resistance in the radiating element, ie it must be copper-plated or similar.

The maximum radiator size of 5λ/8 for a single-lobe pattern can also make use of the impedance characteristics of the 3λ/4 radiator. Construction is in fact simpler than the λ/2 antenna. If the radiating element is made 5λ/8 with a series coil equivalent to λ/8 at the ground plane end, an input impedance very close to 50Ω can be obtained. With correct materials a gain close to 4dBD can be achieved by the increase in aperture

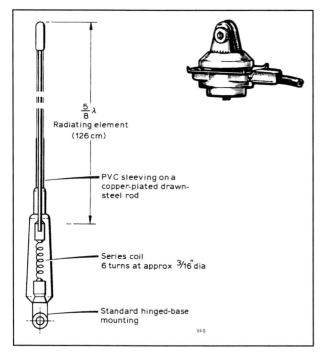

Fig 5.93. A typical commercial 5λ/8 mobile antenna and mount (top right)

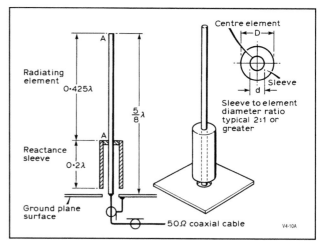

Fig 5.94. The reactance-fed 5λ/8 monopole. Typical gain is +1.8dBD (Ham Radio)

Other antennas with similar properties but different in construction are the 'J' and 'Slim Jim'. These were described earlier in this chapter.

7/8λ whip antenna

This is a variant of the 5/8λ antenna and its current distribution is shown in Fig 5.95. This antenna uses the principles of the collinear antennas shown earlier in this chapter, using either a

over the λ/2 antenna. The radiation pattern is often raised more than that of a λ/2 antenna so the slightly improved gain of the 5λ/8 may not always be realised.

Fig 5.93 gives details of the series 5λ/8 whip. One other advantage of this antenna is that over a wide range of mounting and ground-plane conditions it will self-compensate for impedance and resonance changes. It is preferable for both the λ/2 and 5λ/8 antennas to be on a hinge mount, particularly if roofmounted, to enable folding or 'knock' down with obstructions like trees and garages.

Various gain figures have been given for the 'five-eighth-wave'. Unfortunately not all antennas use optimum materials. As previously stated, the DC resistive losses of the radiator must be a minimum, and in addition the use of a glassfibre rod changes the resonant length because the dielectric material changes the velocity factor by as much as 20%. This means the radiator has to be cut shorter than 5λ/8 with the accompanying loss of aperture.

Incidentally, the series coil with the true 5λ/8 whip must be held rigidly as movement of the coil turns will change the antenna's resonance, giving apparent flutter. With certain transceivers with VSWR-activated transmitter close-down this can produce a situation where the power output of the transmitter is continually being turned down or switched off, producing extremely severe 'flutter'.

Apart from the above reasons for different gain figures, several ground-plane antennas discussed in articles about the 5λ/8 system are in fact discussing antennas which are not truly of this nature. One of these devices worth considering for its own merits is that shown in Fig 5.94. It consists of a 5λ/8 vertical element with a reactive sleeve of 0.2λ at the ground-plane end of the vertical as shown. The gain obtained from this antenna is typically 1.8dBD and, as can be seen, the actual radiating element A-A and therefore its aperture is under that of a λ/2 antenna.

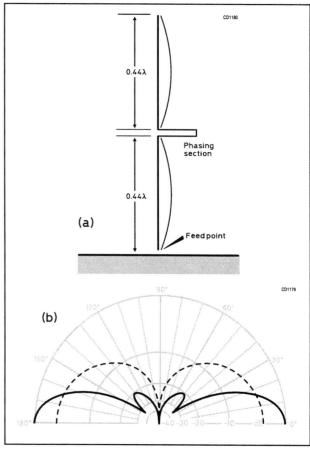

Fig 5.95. 7/8λ whip antenna with theoretical current distribution and radiation pattern on infinite, perfectly conducting ground plane. λ/4 whip pattern shown for comparison

phasing section or a series capacitor to ensure that the radiation from the upper and lower elements is approximately in phase. A stub phasing section, if properly adjusted, can enhance the gain by approximately 0.5dB over the capacitor variant, and can be realised as a short-circuited piece of ribbon cable wrapped round the insulator separating the upper and lower elements. Phasing can also be achieved with a wound section along the lines discussed in the section on collinear antennas. Care should be taken in designing this insulator if the whip is for use on a vehicle, as it must withstand drag of the upper element at speed and the shock loads of the whip snapping from side to side.

For the dimensions shown, the stub length should be approximately 0.245λ. If a capacitor is used, it should present an impedance of around 500Ω at the working frequency (about 2.2pF at 145MHz). The base impedance will be high, between 200 and 400Ω, and capacitive. Base matching arrangements similar to those of the 0.5λ whip are suitable, although the series capacitor should not be necessary. Component values will depend on the materials and construction used, especially around the mounting base.

Low-profile antennas

An alternative to vertical ground-plane antennas are devices to reduce the physical size of the system. The reduction of physical size normally implies loss of aperture and therefore gain. However, of the antennas discussed in this section, one in fact produces a gain referred to a dipole of +1dB.

The λ/2 ring radiator

Although called a 'ring' radiator, in fact radiation is produced by the slot formed between the horizontal λ/2 ring and the ground plane.

Consider a λ/2 slot in a metal sheet. If the sheet is rolled

Table 5.12. λ/2 ring radiator dimensions				
		Theoretical	VHF measurement antenna	UHF measurement antenna
Frequency	f MHz		145MHz*	433MHz
Diameter D	52°		298mm	100mm
Height H	8°		39mm	15.5mm
Diameter d	nom. 1–2°		15mm 20 SWG strip	10mm 20 SWG strip
Match M	5° for 50Ω		28.7mm	9.7mm
Tuning capacitor C	To give capacitive reactance, nominally 250–500Ω		2–5pF	0.5–2pF

* Tuneable 137–148MHz.

into a cylinder such that the two ends of the slot come together, an omnidirectional vertically polarised radiator is produced. As with the conventional λ/2 slot an impedance match can be obtained by tapping along from one end. Also, if the slot is just under λ/2 a capacitor across the centre will resonate it to λ/2 again. As with the skeleton slot developed by G2HCG, if the ground-plane sheet at the top of the slot is reduced to produce a ring and the lower ground-plane section is bent into the horizontal plane the low profile of Fig 5.96 is produced. Dimensions in terms of electrical degrees and specific sizes for optimum performances for 144MHz and 432MHz are shown in Table 5.12. Halving the dimension H or the loop diameter D (with the necessary increase of capacitance and match point to re-tune to frequency) will halve the radiation capability.

The λ/2 ring radiator is a fairly high-Q antenna and has therefore a reduced bandwidth compared to a dipole (typically 3% compared to 10% for a monopole). Gain is 1dBD. If the ground plane is completely reduced, as was the top section previously described, a double ring radiator is produced. Both ring radiators lend themselves to discreet fixed antennas.

Normal-mode helix

Typically less than 0.1λ high, this is described in the next section.

The normal-mode helix antenna

Much has been said for and against what is termed the *normal-mode helix* as used on hand-held transceivers. Unfortunately the method of operation and the results obtainable for this type of antenna have been much misunderstood by amateurs and professionals alike. Most theoretical papers only consider the helical equivalent of the λ/4 whip while most users of this antenna are in fact using the equivalent of a physically reduced 3λ/4 whip.

A helix will work in the normal mode when the diameter and pitch of the helix is less than 0.1λ. When working in this mode the radiation is from the side of the helix, and when the diameter is considerably less than 0.1λ the resultant 'spring' has a radiation pattern similar to a short vertical monopole or whip.

A 3λ/4 whip over a moderate ground plane has a resistive match very close to 50Ω. If this whip is coiled into a helical spring as previously described it will resonate to approximately 50Ω but at a somewhat lower frequency. If the spring

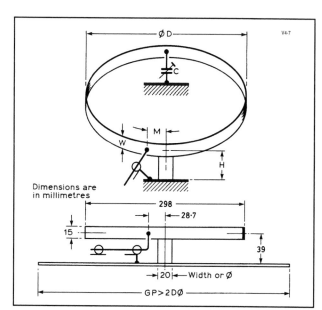

Fig 5.96. A low-profile vehicular antenna with vertical polarisation. Gain is 1dBD, termination 50Ω

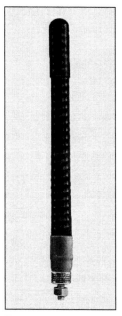

Fig 5.97. A typical commercial helical antenna with screw mounting facility

is trimmed to the original frequency the result will be an antenna of about 0.1λ long matching to approximately 50Ω. The actual wire length tends to be around λ/2 to 5λ/8 long at the working frequency. The capacitance formed between the turns of the spring has 'loaded' the antenna such that it still resonates as a 3λ/4 antenna. This capacitance also tends to modify the matching under various conditions.

Because of its construction, the spring is very reactive off-resonance and this makes it very important that it be resonated for the specific conditions that prevail in its working environment.

Fortunately it is only necessary to change the number of turns to resonate the spring over such diverse conditions as a large ground plane and no ground plane at all. However, the match referred to 50Ω can vary between about 30 and 150Ω at the extremities. Under typical hand-held conditions, however, and depending on the frequency of operation, the spring tends to be fairly close to a 50Ω impedance match. This is shown in Fig 5.98 which also gives an indication of the number of turns required for a typical 9mm diameter helix for 3λ/4 resonance.

An important consideration is that since the helix is a reduced size and aperture antenna two factors arise. First, the radiation resistance is lower than the equivalent linear whip so the choice of a good conducting material is important to minimise resistive losses. A steel spring compared with a brass or copper-plated helical can waste 3dB of power in heating up the spring. The aperture of the helical is a third the physical size of the λ/4 whip and would moreover indicate a loss of 4.77dB. However, results obtainable with copper-plated, Neoprene-sheathed helical antennas, correctly matched to a hand-held transmitter at 145MHz, are at worst −3dB and at best are +1dB compared to the equivalent λ/4 whip (which is −6dB compared to a λ/2 dipole). One thing that will be seen however is that the top of the spring on a hand-held transceiver will often need to be raised to a position corresponding to the top of the equivalent λ/4 whip to receive or transmit the maximum signal strength.

A similar device resonated on to a λ/2 square ground plane could give results 2–3dB below a λ/2 dipole. An alternative arrangement using a bifilar wound helix gives identical results (within 0.2dB) to a λ/2 dipole.

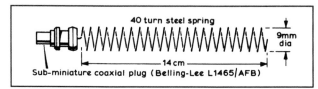

Fig 5.98. Details of a home-made helical whip for 145MHz. A BNC plug could also be used

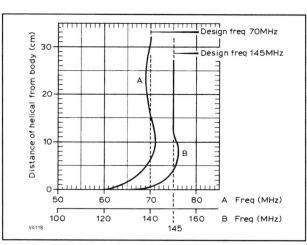

Fig 5.99. Frequency shift of a helical antenna on a typical hand-held transceiver for various distances from the body

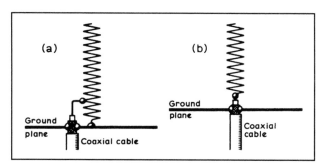

Fig 5.100. Two ways of feeding a helical antenna: (a) shunt feed, (b) series feed

The helical or spring has an interesting and difficult operating characteristic when supported close to the body, particularly at the higher frequencies. Fig 5.99 shows the typical results of a 145MHz or high-band spring and a 70MHz or low-band spring as it is brought closer to the body. The interesting effect which occurs at several centimetres from the body can be seen, where the resonance of the spring, instead of continuing to decrease due to body capacitance, suddenly increases the frequency of resonance. At 2cm and closer the operating frequency suddenly decreased due to body capacitance. Unfortunately this very changeable area occurs at the typical mounting distance of a body-worn transceiver. However, many transceivers are required to be raised to the mouth when transmitting and this puts the antenna back to its best operating conditions.

The normal-mode helical antenna can be vehicle or ground-plane mounted if desired. The height is typically less than 0.1λ and the gain is around to 2–3dB below a dipole. An acceptable match to 50Ω can often be achieved by simply trimming the resonant length. Alternatively, a small inductance or capacitor across the base or a shunt feed as shown in Fig 5.100 will provide the required matching.

The halo and super turnstile

Horizontally polarised antennas for a mobile station become complex and bulky when gain is required. A simple antenna which produces an almost omnidirectional horizontal radiation pattern is the *halo* in its various forms. Basically this is a λ/2 dipole, often gamma matched, which is bent round into a

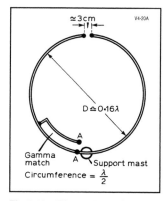

Fig 5.101. Dimensions of the λ/2 halo

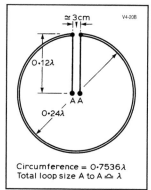

Fig 5.102. Dimensions of the lambda loop

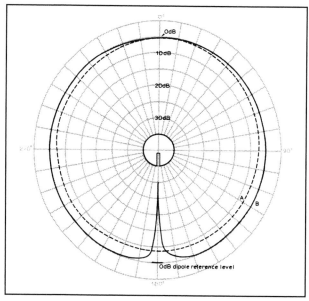

Fig 5.103. Decibel radiation pattern comparison of halo (A) and lambda loop (B) antennas

circle or square. As can be seen in Fig 5.101, when correctly resonant the resultant radiation pattern is somewhat offset in favour of the direction of the gap. Best results are obtained when mounted at a minimum height of 70cm, 0.34λ at 144MHz, above the ground plane produced by the vehicle roof.

An extension of the λ/2 halo is the full-wave or *lambda loop*. A 1λ loop is drawn in at one point to the centre to produce both a support and a match transformer, to approximately 50Ω (see Fig 5.102). The addition of a 1:1 Pawsey stub or similar balun (see earlier section on matching) produces a near-omnidirectional pattern with a unity gain relative to the maximum radiation of a dipole. A comparison of the halo and the lambda radiation patterns are shown in Fig 5.103.

Further extension to three loops can be produced to form the *super turnstile* but the complexity and sheer physical size tends to limit this sort of structure to only the most daring mobile radio amateur.

Both the lambda loop and the super turnstile require to be at least 0.34λ above the ground plane surface to work satisfactorily.

Turnstile antennas along the lines of the crossed dipoles shown in the section on antennas for fixed stations were at one time popular for mobile operations, typically mounted on a λ/2 mast above the vehicle bodywork. However, the aerodynamic drag, wind noise, higher vehicle speeds and the danger of injuring pedestrians (the elements were often around eye height) have all discouraged the use of this and other horizontally polarised antennas for mobile use.

ANTENNAS FOR SATELLITE OPERATIONS

For the average radio amateur satellite antennas fall into two groups, both of which are *ground-station antennas*, that is, those on the ground rather than on the satellite itself. The two groups are *steerable*, which enable the passage of the satellite to be tracked across the sky, and *fixed* which, as they in the ideal case have a hemispherical radiation pattern, receive the satellite signals equally in any direction and do not require to track the satellite's passage. The tracking antennas are usually of high gain while the fixed antennas are usually relatively low gain due to the hemispherical coverage required. Fortunately, as signal losses between ground and satellite are low, being mostly line-of-sight path with no obstructions, relatively low-gain antennas of the fixed variety are often acceptable for reception of amateur or weather satellites.

However, as the satellite tends to rotate, both groups of antennas are normally circularly polarised, right-hand by convention, to compensate for variations in polarisation.

Of the higher-gain tracking antennas, crossed Yagis and the helix are used in the main, with the crossed Yagis probably the easiest to construct and most readily available commercially. The sections on pp5.31 and 5.30 give details of crossed Yagis and the helix respectively.

For fixed or low-gain steerable antennas, several variations of crossed dipoles can be used and also the *volute*, which is a fractional turn four-element helix that can be made to give either directional gain or hemispherical circular polarised coverage (see later). It is worth noting that a conventional single-element helix requires two or more complete 'turns' to obtain circular polarisation.

Crossed dipoles over a ground plane

Fig 5.104 shows a simple arrangement of crossed dipoles above a ground plane. This type of antenna can be scaled for use at 29, 145 or 432MHz. A suggested version for 145MHz is shown in the figure. Mechanical problems may make the reflectors inadvisable in a 29MHz version. The height above ground can be about 2m for 145MHz and 3m for 29MHz. Typical dimensions are:

29MHz	driven elements	(λ/2)	188in	477.5cm
145MHz	driven elements	(λ/2)	38in	96.5cm
	reflectors		40.5in	103cm
	spacing	(0.3λ)	24.5in	62.2cm

The phasing line comprises λ/4 of 72λ coaxial cable, and the matching section λ/4 of 50Ω cable.

When calculating the length of the λ/4 sections, the velocity factor of the cable must be taken into account. Typically this is 0.8 for cellular and semi-airspaced types, and 0.66 for solid dielectric cables, but verification of the correct figure for the cable used should be obtained. As an example, a matching section of RG59/U would be 13in (33cm) in length. To obtain a 50Ω input impedance, the 50Ω transformer section

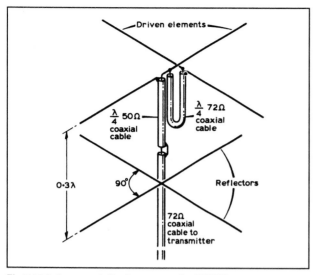

Fig 5.104. A crossed-dipole antenna for 145MHz

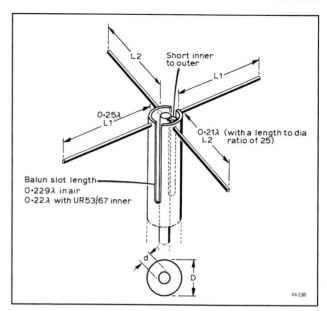

Fig 5.106. A starpole turnstile. D/d = 1.86 for 75Ω and 1.5 for 50Ω

should be replaced by two pieces of 95Ω cable, λ/4 long, connected in parallel.

It is preferable to have a 1:1 balun included at each dipole centre to ensure a consistent pattern through 360° of azimuth. Dependent on the spacing between the dipoles and ground plane the radiation pattern can be made to be predominantly to the side for satellites low on the horizon or up for overhead passes. By drooping the dipole elements at 45° and with a spacing of approximately 0.4λ of the dipole mounting boss about the ground plane, a compromise radiation pattern can be achieved that tends to be hemispherical. As horizontal and vertical polarisation is affected differently by ground reflections, low-to-horizon flight paths will not produce circular polarisation. This is due both to ground scatter from the satellite and ground reflections at low levels of incidence at the receiving antenna and its ground plane.

Circular polarisation is normally produced by feeding one dipole 90° out of phase to the second dipole by means of a phasing harness containing an extra λ/4 on one side.

An alternative approach to this method of phasing is to utilise the phase properties of a capacitive or inductive reactance. Suppose, for example, that the length and diameter of the dipoles are made to give a terminal impedance of 70 − j70Ω (capacitive). By introducing a series reactance (inductive) of +j70Ω at each terminal of one of the dipoles (Fig 5.105) the terminal impedance of this dipole becomes 70 + j70Ω. With

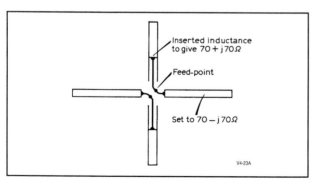

Fig 5.105. Achieving phase quadrature by introducing a reactance in one arm

the two dipoles connected in parallel the current in each dipole is equal in magnitude but, due to the opposite phase differences of 45° in each dipole, a total phase difference of 90° (phase quadrature) is achieved which produces circular polarisation.

The two impedances in parallel become 70 + j0Ω so the addition of a 1:1 balun provides a direct match to a 70Ω coaxial line. If the impedance of the balun is correctly proportioned this match can be to the standard 50Ω coaxial line. Radiating elements can be drooped as previously described to improve the hemispherical coverage. An easier way of introducing the series inductance is simply to make one dipole long, therefore inductive, at the working frequency, and one dipole short, therefore capacitive at the working frequency.

Fig 5.106 shows a working example of the *starpole turnstile* arrangement. The reactive components were chosen as ±25Ω and dimensions were based on the reactive information for dipoles as shown in Fig 5.107.

Volute antennas

The volute can also make use of both phasing line or the reactance method to produce circular polarisation. The number of 'turns' or part turns of the radiating elements combined with their length can be used to produce various radiation patterns. Radiation patterns produced for several combination of turns and resonant lengths are shown in Figs 5.107(a) to (d) with general details of the volute in Figs 5.108 and 5.109 [25, 26]. It must be noted that elements that are multiples of λ/4 have open-circuit ends, while the elements that are multiples of λ/2 can be short-circuited to the mounting structure.

REFERENCES

[1] *Antennas*, J D Kraus, 2nd edn, McGraw-Hill, 1988, pp70–73.
[2] *The ARRL Handbook for the Radio Amateur*, any edition after 1986, antennas section.
[3] *Antennas*, J D Kraus, 2nd edn, McGraw-Hill, 1988, Chapter 4.

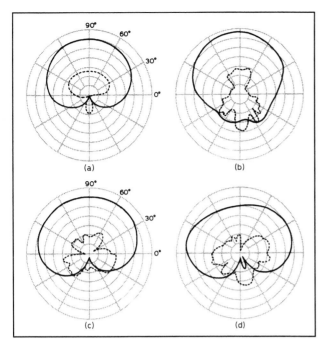

Fig 5.107. Volute radiation patterns. (a) Three-quarter-turn λ/4 volute. (b) Three-quarter-turn λ/2 volute. (c) Three-quarter-turn 3λ/4 volute. (d) Three-quarter-turn 1λ volute (*Microwave Journal*)

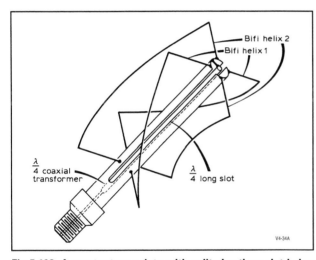

Fig 5.108. A quarter-turn volute with split sheath or slot balun (*Microwave Journal*)

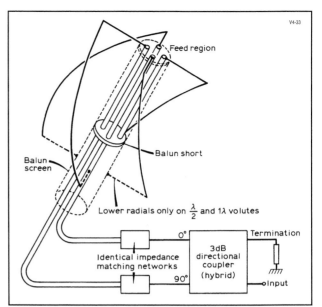

Fig 5.109. The general arrangement using Pawsey stub baluns. A half-hybrid or λ/4 phasing harness as used for the crossed dipoles can be used in place of the directional coupler (*Microwave Journal*)

[4] *Antenna Theory, Analysis and Design*, Constantine A Balanis, Harper and Row, 1982, pp204–243.

[5] 'In Practice – Finding coax impedance', I White, G3SEK, *Radio Communication* February 1995, pp40–41.

[6] 'In Practice – Precise coax lengths', I White, G3SEK, *Radio Communication* July 1995, pp60–61.

[7] *Electronic Applications of the Smith Chart*, Phillip H Smith, McGraw-Hill, 1969.

[8] *VHF Line Techniques*, C S Gledhill, Edward Arnold Publishers, 1960.

[9] 'The transmission line explained', Clive Smith, G4FZH, *Radio Communication* April 1994, pp54–57, 61.

[10] *Yagi Antenna Design*, P Viezbickie, National Bureau of Standards Technical Note 688, 1976.

[11] *Yagi Antenna Design*, J L Lawson, ARRL, 1986.

[12] 'Yagi antennas – principle of operation and optimum design criteria', G Hoch, DL6WU, *VHF Communications* 3/1977.

[13] 'More gain from Yagi antennas', G Hoch, DL6WU, *VHF Communications* 4/1977.

[14] 'Extremely long Yagi antennas', G Hoch, DL6WU, *VHF Communications* 1/1982.

[15] 'Stub filters revisited', J Regnault, G4SWX, Radio Communication November 1994, pp46–48.

[16] 'Diplexers for the VHF bands', J Regnault, G4SWX, *Radio Communication* March 1996, pp63, 65 and April 1996, pp61–63.

[17] 'Wind loading', D J Reynolds, G3ZPF, *Radio Communication* April 1988, pp252–255 and May 1988, pp340–341.

[18] 'A quadruple quad antenna – an efficient portable antenna for 2 metres', M Ragaller, DL6DW, *VHF Communications* 2/1971, pp82–84.

[19] *The Antenna Experimenter's Guide*, P Dodd, G3LDO, 2nd edn, RSGB, 1996.

[20] 'Antenna modelling on a PC', I White, G3SEK, *Radio Communication* August 1993, pp39–41.

[21] 'Antenna modelling with ELNEC', J Bazley, G3HCT, *Radio Communication* August 1993, pp41–42.

[22] 'The VHF log-periodic Yagi', M Gibbings, G3FDW, *Radio Communication* July 1994, pp13–17.

[23] 'Helical antennas for 435MHz', J Miller, G3RUH, *Electronics and Wireless World* June 1985, pp43–46.

[24] 'Slim Jim antenna', F C Judd, G2BCX, *Practical Wireless* April 1978, pp899–901.

[25] 'Resonant quadrifilar helix design', C C Kilgus, *Microwave Journal*, Vol 13-12, December 1970, pp49–54.

[26] 'Shaped-conical radiation pattern performance of the backfire quadrifilar helix', C C Kilgus, *IEEE Trans Antennas and Propagation* May 1975, pp392–397.

6 EMC

ELECTROMAGNETIC compatibility is the desirable situation where nearby electronic equipment is not affected by amateur transmissions and does not unduly affect amateur reception. Further information on EMC for radio amateurs is given in references [1] and [2]. This chapter also deals with interference to amateur reception by non-radio equipment, particularly a computer in the shack.

If amateur transmissions affect a neighbour's TV or other electronic equipment, there are three possible causes:

(a) The affected equipment has insufficient immunity to the fundamental frequency of the transmitter.
(b) A harmonic or other unwanted emission from the amateur transmitter is not sufficiently well suppressed.
(c) A non-linear device somewhere else is receiving the amateur signal and re-radiating a harmonic.

The most common reason is (a), while (b) is less likely and (c) is rare. If the affected equipment is a TV, video recorder or some sort of radio receiver then it is important to establish whether the cause is (a) or (b). If the amateur transmitter is producing an unwanted signal then adding a filter at the TV cannot remove it! Conversely, if a TV or other affected equipment has insufficient immunity to the fundamental frequency of the transmitter then the problem cannot be solved by filtering at the transmitter! If the affected equipment is an audio amplifier, wired telephone or other equipment which is not intended to receive radio signals at all, then clearly the problem is not due to harmonics.

Even if harmonics etc are not causing a problem, it is wise to ensure that they are adequately suppressed in case of a visit from the Radiocommunications Agency. It is also important to realise that a VHF or UHF amateur station may be able to generate very high field strengths nearby.

GOOD RADIO HOUSEKEEPING

The Schedule of the *Terms, Provisions and Limitations Booklet BR68*, which accompanies the full UK Amateur Licence 'A' or 'B', lists a maximum output power level of 26dBW (400W) on most bands but this is subject to certain other conditions such as Note (l) which states:

> "In densely populated areas sufficient separation of amateur equipment from surrounding transmitters, receivers and electronic equipment may not be possible to permit the amateur to operate with high power without the high probability of causing interference."

The above statement emphasises the need to plan with EMC in mind where an amateur station is to be installed in a typical urban environment in close proximity to neighbours. The RF from the transmitter should be kept under reasonable control,

---

WARNING – Protective multiple earthing (PME)

Many houses in the UK, particularly those built or wired since the middle 'seventies, are wired on what is known as the *PME system*. In this system the mains earth of the house wiring is bonded to the neutral where the supply enters the building. In the event of certain rare fault conditions it is possible for the earth and neutral conductors all over the house to rise to a voltage significantly above that of the true earth (ie the earth out in the garden). In extreme cases the earth neutral voltage could be the full mains voltage above true earth. For this reason the supply authorities advise certain precautions regarding the bonding of metalwork inside the house.

WHERE A HOUSE IS WIRED ON THE PME SYSTEM, DO NOT CONNECT ANY EXTERNAL (ie radio) EARTHS TO APPARATUS INSIDE THE HOUSE unless suitable precautions are taken. (See reference [1] or [2]).

---

with the highest possible percentage going where it is wanted (in the direction of the distant station) and as little as possible going into the local environment. This is sometimes known as *good radio housekeeping*. Fortunately, installations designed to achieve this are also likely to minimise the pick-up of locally generated interference.

Antennas

It is always good practice to erect any antenna as far from houses as possible, and as high as practical, subject to planning constraints. If possible, VHF/UHF beams should be located so that most of the power is beamed over the roof tops towards the horizon rather than towards neighbouring buildings or TV antennas. A mast away from the house (and neighbouring houses) is preferable subject to considerations of feeder loss.

Coaxial feeder should be well screened with good-quality woven braid to minimise RF leakage into and out of the cable. When a balanced antenna is fed by coaxial cable, a balun should be used to minimise RF radiation from the braid of the cable. Any remaining RF currents on the braid of the cable can be reduced by passing the latter through some large ferrite beads or clip-on ferrite chokes near the antenna.

Earths

Most VHF or UHF antenna systems do not require an RF earth for EMC reasons but don't forget the need for lightning protection. It should also be borne in mind that when antennas are mounted on an earthed tower, the braid of the coaxial feeder entering the radio shack is likely to be earthed via the antenna to the tower. In such cases, it is important to consider PME (protective multiple earthing) – see the warning panel on this page.

Field strengths

Note (l) in the BR68 booklet mentions excessive field strength from an amateur station. It is therefore useful to be able to calculate the electric field strength generated near a transmitting antenna. The electric or E-field strength at a certain distance is given by equation 6.1 which assumes far-field 'free space' conditions.

$$E = \frac{\sqrt{49.15P_d}}{d} \qquad (6.1)$$

where E is the electric field strength in volts/metre, d is the distance from the antenna in metres and P_d is the effective radiated power.

It should be noted that P_d is ERP, ie the input power to the antenna multiplied by the gain of the antenna relative to a dipole, not an isotropic radiator.

Fig 6.1 shows the field strength generated by an antenna radiating between 1W and 4kW ERP at distances between 1m and 100m. For example, 100W (20dBW) into an antenna with a gain of 10dBd gives an ERP of 30dBW or 1kW. At a distance of 10m, this would produce a field strength of 22V/m in the direction of maximum radiation. This example shows that a high-power VHF/UHF amateur station can easily generate a field strength which is higher than nearby electronic equipment can reasonably be expected to withstand. Field strength is also mentioned in leaflet RA234 (see below). It may therefore be necessary to avoid using maximum power in certain directions in order to avoid generating excessive field strengths in neighbours' premises. In any case, it is good practice to use only as much power as necessary for a contact. In the case of local contacts, the power necessary may only be one watt or less.

RF IMMUNITY STANDARDS

The UK EMC Regulations (Statutory Instrument 1992 No 2372) came into force on 1 January 1996. Almost all electronic equipment manufactured since that date must meet certain requirements for RF immunity and emissions and must also carry the CE mark to indicate compliance with all applicable European Directives.

This was a major step forward in EMC, as previously there was no requirement for consumer electronic equipment to meet any immunity standard in the UK. Nevertheless, the standards only set a basic level of immunity compared to the possible field strengths from an amateur station. In some cases it is argued that if immunity problems arise when an amateur station generates field strengths in excess of the levels specified in the relevant immunity standard, the amateur should take steps to reduce the field strength. In such cases, it is worth noting the standard, IEC 1000-2-5, *Electromagnetic Compatibility (EMC) – Part 2: Environment – Section 5: Classification of Electromagnetic Environments*. This lists various sources of RF fields (and other types of electromagnetic phenomena) which may exist in various classes of location including residential (urban), residential (rural), commercial etc. In most of these environment classes including residential (urban), the standard states that field strengths of up to 10V/m may be encountered in locations which are at least 20m from the nearest amateur radio transmitter.

Selected information about the RF immunity requirements of some CENELEC harmonised European immunity

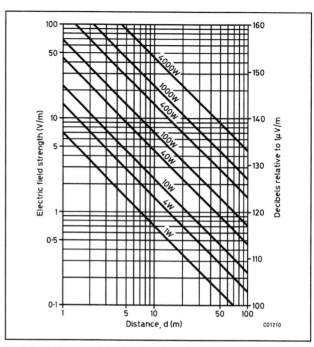

Fig 6.1. Field strength in the direction of maximum radiation from an antenna radiating from 1W to 4kW ERP into free space.

standards is given below. As standards are revised from time to time, this information may not apply to future editions. For further details, an up-to-date copy of the relevant standard should be consulted. These are often kept by university or college libraries and by learned societies such as the IEE.

EN 55104 : 1995 EMC – immunity requirements for household appliances, tools and similar apparatus

This standard specifies immunity requirements which are generally less demanding than the Generic Standard. It is expected to be replaced with EN 55014-2 : 1996.

EN 55020 : 1995 Immunity of broadcast receivers and associated equipment

This is applicable to television broadcast receivers, sound broadcast receivers and associated equipment such as audio systems. Radio and TV equipment without a connection for an external antenna or without a mains power connection is not required to meet this standard.

The standard specifies various tests for immunity to radiated and conducted signals. For UHF TV receivers, VHF Band II (87.5–108MHz) sound broadcast receivers and audio equipment, the radiated immunity is tested up to 150MHz at a field strength of 125dB(μV/m) (1.78V/m) (carrier) with 80% AM at 1kHz. The modulated signal therefore has a peak envelope voltage (PEV) of 3.2V/m. There are some exclusion bands around IF frequencies and the tuned frequency. Long-wave, medium-wave and short-wave sound broadcast receivers are only tested for immunity to common-mode conducted currents on the antenna terminals (if any) at 26–30MHz.

Draft CISPR 24 Ed. 1 : Information technology equipment – immunity characteristics – Limits and methods of measurement

CISPR 24 will form the basis of EN 55024-1 and requires similar levels of immunity to the 1996 draft Generic standard. Although the title refers to information technology equipment, this standard also applies to Telecommunications Terminal Equipment (TTE) such as telephones. Until EN 55024-1 is issued, however, a manufacturer can CE mark a telephone by testing it to the Generic Immunity Standard, EN 50082-1 : 1992. Fortunately, the immunity of many CE-marked telephones exceeds this minimum requirement.

EN 50082-1 : 1992 EMC Generic Immunity Standard – Part 1; residential, commercial and light industry

The Generic Standard EN 50082-1 : 1992 can be applied if no product-specific standard exists although it may not be appropriate for all cases. This is a 'watered-down' version of the 1990 draft, prEN 50082-1. The 1992 edition references the IEC 801-3 standard for immunity to radiated fields but only tests from 27–500MHz at 3V/m with an *unmodulated* carrier. Immunity tests below 27MHz are not required and neither are tests for immunity to RF signals picked up on cables.

A new edition of the Generic Standard BS EN 50082-1 : 1996 was published on 1 June 1997. This is a great improvement on the 1992 edition but equipment can still be tested to the weak 1992 standard until 1 July 2001 which is the date of withdrawal. The 1996 draft references the EN 61000 (IEC 1000) series of standards and specifies tests which are broadly similar to the 1990 draft. These include conducted immunity tests on interconnecting cables and mains cables with a 3V signal from 0.15–80MHz and radiated immunity tests at 3V/m from 80–1000MHz. In each case, a 3V or 3V/m carrier is modulated with 80% AM at 1kHz. The PEV (peak envelope voltage) on modulation peaks is therefore 1.8 times higher at 5.4V or 5.4V/m. There is also a new test at 900MHz with 200Hz pulse modulation to simulate GSM cellular telephones.

Section 3 of prEN 50082-1 : 1996 includes the following statements:

"The immunity requirements have been selected so as to ensure an adequate level of immunity for apparatus at the locations described. The levels do not however cover extreme cases which may occur in any location but with an extremely low probability of occurrence."

"In special cases, situations will arise when the level of disturbance may exceed the levels specified in this standard; for example, a hand-held transmitter used in close proximity to an apparatus. In these instances special mitigation measures may have to be applied."

prETS 300 683 EMC Standard for Short Range Devices

This is an ETSI (European Telecommunications Standards Institute) standard for short-range radio devices which includes specifications for RF immunity. Such devices include baby alarms, cordless household alarm systems etc. Immunity to radiated fields is not tested at 3V/m with 80% AM except within an exclusion band of ±5% of the receive frequency as performance within this range is considered to be a 'spectrum utilisation parameter' rather than an 'EMC parameter'. Narrow-band spurious responses (such as image frequencies) can be declared outside the ±5% exclusion band.

BREAKTHROUGH OF AMATEUR TRANSMISSIONS
Television and video

If breakthrough occurs with a UHF TV set connected directly to an antenna, a suitable high-pass filter should be plugged in

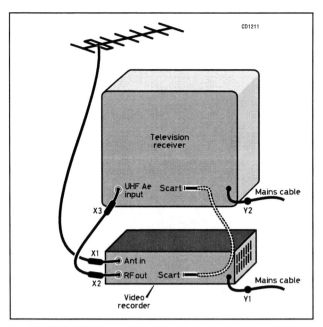

Fig 6.2. Fitting filters to a TV with video recorder

at the TV antenna socket. If the problem cannot be cured by filtering the antenna input, it is possible that winding the mains cable through a ferrite core close to the TV set may help. At VHF, however, direct pick-up in the TV set itself may occur and cannot be cured by external filtering. Possible causes include pick-up in the vision IF amplifier circuitry or pick-up in the internal loudspeaker cable. In the case of TV sets with external speakers, pick-up in loudspeaker cables can be tackled in the same way as for audio systems (see below).

If breakthrough occurs when a TV is connected to a video recorder as in Fig 6.2, the first thing to establish is whether the TV set alone is immune. The addition of a video recorder makes breakthrough more likely because most video recorders contain a VHF/UHF amplifier with a bandwidth of typically 40–860MHz. A high-pass filter should be fitted at X1 and another may be required at X2 or X3. In some cases, winding the mains cable through a ferrite core at Y1 or Y2 may help. If the TV and video recorder both have a SCART connector, the use of a SCART cable (shown dotted) provides a direct 'base-band' audio and video connection on playback which bypasses the UHF modulator in the video recorder and the tuner and IF stages in the TV. This generally improves picture quality on video playback and also reduces the possibility of RF breakthrough. If the tuner or IF stages in the TV are susceptible to breakthrough but the video recorder is immune, it is possible to receive off-air UHF signals without using the tuner and IF stages in the TV. The channel tuned on the video recorder can be viewed on the TV via the SCART connection. The only exception to this is when recording one channel while watching another.

Satellite TV

In a satellite television receiving system, the LNB (low noise block converter) in the dish is unlikely to be affected by amateur signals directly, except on the 10GHz amateur band. The output of the LNB is at the first intermediate frequency covering 950–1750MHz or 950–2050MHz so there is a possibility of 23cm amateur signals causing IF breakthrough.

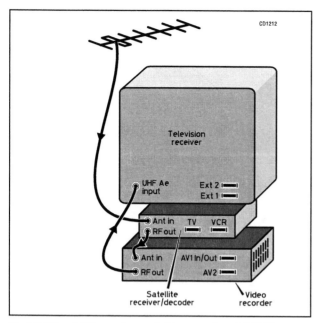

Fig 6.3. TV, satellite receiver and video recorder with UHF connections only

Fortunately, the cable between the LNB and the indoor receiver unit is normally quite well screened with foil and braid which minimises the possibility of IF breakthrough. Nevertheless, common-mode signals can be picked up on the braid of the cable to the dish which may require a common-mode ferrite choke.

The indoor satellite receiver unit normally contains a broadband amplifier and UHF modulator for use with UHF connections as shown in Fig 6.3. Such a set-up may suffer breakthrough of amateur signals due to the cascaded broad-band amplifiers in the satellite receiver and video recorder.

Fig 6.4 shows a possible set-up which should reduce the chance of RF breakthrough while providing improved picture

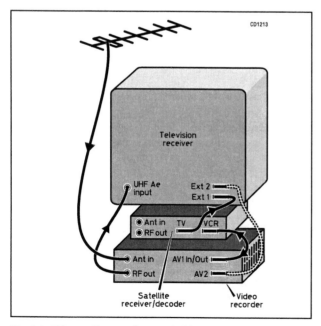

Fig 6.4. TV, satellite receiver and video recorder with SCART connections

quality for satellite reception and video playback. With some satellite receivers, video playback via the SCART lead can pass through the satellite receiver to the TV but, if this is not possible, a third SCART cable (shown dotted) is required for video playback.

TV mast-head preamplifiers

In a fringe area or where a long feeder cable is necessary, a TV masthead preamplifier can give a significant improvement in reception. Nevertheless, mast-head preamplifiers are sometimes used inappropriately in areas of adequate reception in an attempt to compensate for a low-gain antenna and/or poor-quality feeder cable. The use of a mast-head preamplifier increases the chances of breakthrough of out-of-band signals from amateur transmitters or other radio transmitters nearby. Older preamplifiers may be unscreened and have broad bandwidth which can lead to breakthrough problems on any VHF/UHF amateur band. If strong amateur signals are picked up by the TV antenna and cause breakthrough, a filter is required at the input to the TV antenna but unfortunately, this is not easy to install with a mast-head preamp! In such cases, the only solution may be to install a new preamplifier which is CE marked, adequately screened and covers UHF only.

TV distribution amplifiers

Indoor or loft-mounted TV distribution amplifiers are available with two, three, four or more outputs. If any of the amplifier outputs are not used, these should be terminated with a 75Ω load otherwise the gain of the amplifier is increased. Distribution amplifiers are available in two types: broad-band and UHF only. The broad-band type, which typically covers 40–860MHz, can distribute 88–108MHz Band 2 FM broadcast and Band 4/5 UHF TV signals simultaneously. In installations where the Band 2 capability is not used, a UHF high-pass filter may be required at the input to the amplifier. If UHF TV and Band 2 antennas are both connected, a combiner is required and any UHF high-pass filter must be fitted at the UHF input to the combiner. The Band 2 antenna may pick up 50, 70 or 144MHz amateur signals, in which case an 88–108MHz band-pass filter is required at the VHF input to the combiner. Non-CE marked amplifiers in unscreened cases may also be susceptible to picking up signals via the mains cable or directly in the amplifier itself. Such effects may be reduced by fitting the amplifier in a screened box grounded to the coaxial braid or by fitting a ferrite ring to the mains cable.

Fig 6.5 shows a 'worst case' configuration from the EMC point of view. This configuration allows multiple TV sets to select the currently tuned satellite channel, video playback or any terrestrial channel. Band 2 FM signals are also distributed by the same broad-band amplifier and output cables. With three wide-band amplifiers cascaded, the probability of breakthrough is clearly increased. To solve a problem with this type of set-up, it is advisable to start with the satellite receiver feeding the TV alone and to cure any breakthrough problem. This may require a high-pass filter at the input to the satellite receiver. The video recorder should then be connected, followed by the distribution amplifier alone. Finally, the combiner and Band 2 FM antenna should be added. It may be necessary to fit additional filters at the input to the video recorder or distribution amplifier and an attenuator may also be required to reduce the total gain.

Cable TV

The introduction of new cable television (CATV) systems may reduce TVI problems because neighbours who subscribe to the cable system no longer need to use their UHF TV antenna. There are, however, some potential EMC problems due to signals leaking into and out of CATV systems (known to cable TV companies as *ingress* and

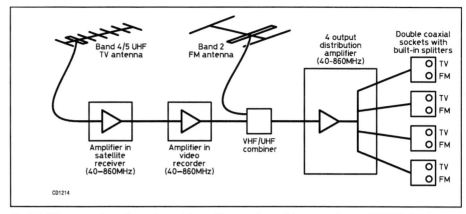

Fig 6.5. 'Worst case' configuration with satellite receiver, video recorder and TV/FM distribution amplifier

egress respectively). Many systems use harmonically related vision carriers on multiples of 8MHz, for example from 128 to 560MHz or higher with an FM sound carrier 6MHz above each vision carrier. Some systems use a vision carrier at 432MHz with sound on 438MHz. Although some UK cable TV operators avoid the use of 144MHz as a vision carrier, others use it for a leakage detection test signal or for programmes. This may lead to 144MHz breakthrough problems even with low power.

For cable TV systems, the permitted levels of radiated emissions are defined in the Radiocommunications Agency standard MPT 1510. This standard prohibits the use of certain frequencies and specifies low levels of leakage in certain bands including 50–54MHz, 144–146MHz and 432–440MHz [8]. It is anticipated that this standard will eventually be withdrawn and replaced by a harmonised European standard.

FILTERS FOR RADIO AND TV RECEIVERS

The details below relate to filters for reducing breakthrough of 6m, 4m, 2m and 70cm amateur band signals. For details of filter performance on the HF bands and a filter which also rejects the 23cm band, see Appendix 3 of reference [1] or [2]. All the filters listed below are for use in the antenna input of TV and FM radio receivers and allow UHF TV signals to pass through. As with any filter, there is a small loss in the pass band. Only the HPF2 allows both VHF/FM broadcast radio (Band 2, 88–108 MHz) and UHF TV (Bands 4/5) to pass through.

Unwanted pick-up of amateur signals by a UHF TV antenna system can occur in two different ways. The first is where the TV antenna itself picks up VHF or UHF amateur signals which pass along the inner of the coaxial cable and return via the braid in the normal way. This is most likely to occur at 432MHz where a UHF TV antenna still has a moderate gain but it can still be a problem at 144MHz. Pick-up by the UHF TV antenna itself tends to be less significant on 70 and 50MHz, however. The second type of pick-up is where the whole TV antenna with its downlead acts as a receiving antenna, resulting in signals which are on the braid and inner together relative to earth. If such signals cause breakthrough, some sort of 'braid breaker' is required. There are four types, the transformer type such as the BB1 or HPFS, the capacitive type such as the HPF1, the resonant type such as the TNF range and the ferrite common-mode choke.

HPF1 high-pass filter and braid breaker
Pass band: UHF TV.

Stop band: All bands up to and including 144MHz (good performance on 50 and 70MHz, some effect on 144MHz).

'Braid breaking': Capacitive braid breaking at HF, some effect on 50MHz but little effect on 70 and 144MHz.

Remarks: The HPF1 is not stocked separately by RSGB but is included in the RFK1 filter kit (see below).

HPF2 High-pass filter (RSGB order code Filter 2)
Pass band: FM radio broadcast (88–108MHz) up to UHF TV.

Stop band: All HF bands plus limited effect at 50MHz.

'Braid breaking': None.

HPF6 high-pass filter (RSGB order code Filter 8)
Pass band: UHF TV.

Stop band: All bands up to and including 430–440MHz.

'Braid breaking': None.

Remarks: This high-performance six-section filter has a very sharp cut-off below 470MHz and is primarily intended for rejecting the 430–440MHz amateur band. It also offers a high degree of rejection at 144MHz and below.

BB1 braid breaker (RSGB order code Filter 1)
Pass band: All VHF/UHF amateur bands plus FM Band 2 (88–108MHz), and UHF TV.

Stop band: The BB1 does not give any rejection of any VHF/UHF amateur band as it is a 'braid breaker' rather than a filter.

'Braid breaking': A 1:1 transformer type braid breaker. Moderately effective on 50 and 70MHz, limited effect on 144MHz.

Remarks: A BB1 on its own is only likely to be useful where the pick-up is primarily on the braid of the coaxial cable. It can be cascaded with other filters such as HPF2 or HPF6 which do not have any braid-breaking action, although this increases the total pass-band loss.

HPFS high-pass filter (special) (RSGB order code Filter 3)
Pass band: UHF TV.

Stop band: All bands up to and including 144MHz.

'Braid breaking': Includes 1:1 transformer type braid breaker (see BB1 above).

Remarks: The HPFS is a BB1 combined with a high-pass filter. Due to the relatively high pass-band loss, it is not suitable for areas where the TV signal strength is low.

RBF1/70cms notch filter (RSGB order code Filter 5)

Pass band: UHF TV

Stop band: 430–440MHz.

'Braid breaking': None.

Remarks: The RBF1/70cms is pretuned to reject 435MHz although the HPF6 is more effective on the 430–440MHz band. The RBF1/70cms also has a high-pass action with some rejection at 70MHz and below.

TNF2 tuned notch filter range (VHF types)

Type	RSGB order code
TNF2/145	Filter 4, notch tuned to 145MHz
TNF2/70	Filter 7, notch tuned to 70MHz
TNF2/50	Filter 6, notch tuned to 50MHz

Pass band: UHF TV.

Stop band: Only the specified band.

'Braid breaking': Only on the specified band.

Remarks: These filters are designed to provide rejection of one particular amateur band. They have a parallel L-C notch (band-stop) filter in series with the inner conductor and with the braid. The manufacturers state that these notch filters are unsuitable for use with some TV distribution amplifiers.

Ferrite rings and cores

Unwanted breakthrough of RF signals into electronic equipment can occur in two ways. RF signals may be picked up directly inside the affected equipment or they may be conducted in via external cables such as loudspeaker cables, antenna cables and mains cables. If the pick-up is on cables, it can often be reduced or eliminated by winding the affected cable onto a suitable ferrite core. This forms a 'common-mode choke' which presents a high impedance to unwanted RF signals without affecting the wanted signals. A common-mode choke can also be used as a 'braid breaker' for a TV or FM radio coaxial antenna cable. Compared to other types of braid breaker, it has the advantage that it introduces little or no loss to the wanted signal and maintains the integrity of the braid of the coaxial cable.

For the best chance of success, it is important to use a suitable grade of ferrite and a suitable number of turns in order to achieve the highest possible impedance at the frequencies of interest. Ferrite rings available from RSGB are made in the USA by Fair-Rite Corporation in type 43 material. The inside diameter is 22.85mm (0.9in) and the width is 12.7mm (0.5in). They are equivalent to FT140-43. These rings give good results at VHF whereas some other grades of ferrite are poor at these frequencies.

At 50 or 70MHz, an impedance of 3kΩ or more can be obtained using 12 turns on two Fair-Rite grade 43 ring cores wound separately, although in many cases one ring is sufficient. At 144MHz, six turns are recommended on a ring core. Further details of the characteristics of various ferrite rings are given in reference [3]. Stray capacitance between the ends of the winding core is critical at VHF and, in the case of a ring core, this should be minimised by keeping the ends of the winding separated and securing them to the core with cable ties. If the cable is very thick, if it has connectors which cannot easily be removed or if it is not long enough, the best solution is usually to make up a short extension lead by winding a length of the thinnest suitable cable through a ferrite core and then fitting suitable connectors. This also has the advantage that it simply plugs in which is much more satisfactory when dealing with neighbours' equipment.

Normal TV coaxial cable has a minimum bending radius of typically 26mm so it should not be wound tightly through a ferrite ring otherwise it may collapse internally and short-circuit. Instead, a one metre length of miniature 75Ω coaxial cable can be wound onto a ring core or a clip-on core and fitted with coaxial connectors. Suitable cable is available from Maplin Electronics (Stock No XR88V). To ensure that the cable grip in the coaxial plug grips reliably, sleeving or PVC tape should be fitted to the end of the cable to increase its outside diameter to 5–6mm.

Various types of clip-on core are available but the type with 'U' shaped cores is not particularly effective unless four pairs of 'U' cores are stacked together. For best results, the core aperture should have a length which is two or three times its diameter. The split bead type of clip-on ferrite core is available from several sources including Maplin Electronics (BZ34M), Farnell Components (535-904) or RS Components (779-813 or 779-863). With such cores, three turns are recommended for all VHF bands.

Audio systems

A common cause of RF breakthrough in audio systems is RF being picked up in the loudspeaker cables and fed into the power amplifier where it is detected and comes out again as audio. A symptom of this effect is that turning the volume down does not reduce the breakthrough but it disappears if the speakers are unplugged and headphones are used. This effect can often be reduced by fitting suitable ferrite ring cores or clip-on chokes to the loudspeaker cables close to the outputs from the amplifier. RF may also get in to the amplifier inputs, in which case the breakthrough is affected by the setting of the volume control and may affect only one source such as cassette. In hi-fi systems composed of separate units, a plug-in filter may be required for the appropriate audio input.

Telephones

There are large variations in RF immunity between different models of wired telephone. If RF breakthrough occurs on a telephone which is rented from BT, the customer should ask to have it exchanged for another model with better RF immunity. In many cases, breakthrough at VHF is caused by direct pick-up in the telephone itself or in the handset cable so that it cannot be cured by means of a line filter. In any case, at the time of writing, telephone line filters which are available in the UK and are BABT approved are not suitable for VHF use. For example, the BT 'Freelance' RFI filter LJU 10/14A and the BT80A/RF2 filtered junction box contain chokes with a self-resonant frequency of around 1.3MHz for filtering medium-wave broadcast signals and are little use at VHF.

As telephones used on the UK public telephone system require BABT approval, they should not be modified to improve RF immunity and neither should home-constructed telephone line filters be used. There is, however, no objection to winding the cable of the telephone through a ferrite core which may reduce RF breakthrough if this is caused by common-mode RF signals on the cable. In the case of answering machines, fax machines or modems, a ferrite ring may also be required on the power supply cable or other cables.

Low-power devices

Various low-power devices, also known as *short-range devices* (SRDs) are exempt from UK licensing provided they are UK type-approved. Some devices such as vehicle radio keys or baby alarms operate on frequencies in or near amateur bands and can be susceptible to breakthrough.

Vehicle keys

Most radio-controlled car alarms and immobilisers made since mid-1994 operate on a harmonised European frequency of 433.92MHz which is allocated to them on a secondary unprotected basis. Some cars contain superhet receivers whose local oscillator radiates a detectable signal at around 433.275–433.475MHz. These receivers use an IF centre frequency of approximately 500kHz and earlier types have no image rejection so they can be blocked by UK 70cm repeater output frequencies. Some types have a SAW RF bandpass filter to provide some image rejection.

Another type of receiver is the super-regenerative. Some types may have a SAW stabilised oscillator or SAW bandpass filter but those without either have a −6dB bandwidth of typically 6MHz.

In some systems, the radio key only controls central locking whereas in other systems, it also operates the immobiliser. If an amateur receives a complaint about blocking of vehicle radio keys by 70cm transmissions, the first thing to find out is whether there is an alternative way of disarming the immobiliser, for example by entering a code number manually. If there is no alternative to the radio key then it could be argued that the designers of such a system have used an unprotected frequency allocation for an unsuitable purpose.

Baby alarms

Devices which are UK approved to MPT 1336 are allowed up to 10mW ERP from 49.82–49.98MHz although many have an ERP of 1mW or less. This frequency allocation is used for wireless baby alarms, licence-exempt walkie-talkies and cordless headphones. The receivers used in these low-cost devices may have poor rejection of signals in the 50MHz amateur band, and in some cases only a few watts on 50MHz can cause breakthrough up to 100m away [4]. Some baby alarms have a switch to select one of two frequencies but this is unlikely to make much difference to breakthrough from 50MHz amateur signals. A few models have sockets to allow a cable to be connected between the units.

Users of wireless baby alarms should be aware that they are using an unprotected radio service. Models which are also sold in the USA include an FCC statement in the instructions stating that the device must accept any interference received, including interference that may cause undesired operation. The instructions for CE-marked baby alarms may include a statement about possible interference from a nearby transmitter.

Intruder alarms and security lights

If RF triggering of a neighbour's intruder alarm system occurs, the radio amateur is in a strong position technically, particularly if the alarm installation is claimed to meet BS4737 which refers to the "environmental conditions" at the protected premises. As these conditions include "electrical interference", a system which complies with BS4737 should be immune to radio signals from licensed transmitters nearby.

The most likely cause of RF triggering of an intruder alarm is insufficient immunity of PIR (passive infra-red) sensors [5]. These use high-gain operational amplifier circuits whose DC bias conditions may shift slightly when an RF carrier is keyed on or off. Most types use some form of pulse counting and can be set to count two, three or more pulse edges within about 5–10 seconds before sounding the alarm. This also provides some degree of immunity to RF triggering by an FM voice transmission but if the basic RF immunity is insufficient, amateur SSB, CW or packet transmissions will soon exceed the pulse count and trigger the alarm.

It is not advisable to attempt any modifications to PIR sensors in a neighbour's intruder alarm and in any case, improving immunity at VHF may require changes to the PCB layout. Fitting filters or ferrite rings to the cables is unlikely to give a significant improvement in immunity so in most cases, it will be necessary to replace the PIR sensors with a more immune type. If the make and model of the PIR sensor can be identified, it is worth approaching the manufacturer or importer to see whether they have a more immune model which they may be prepared to supply in exchange for the existing PIRs. Even if new PIRs are purchased, these need not be expensive as some low-cost types are available with high RF immunity. Unless the system is a DIY installation, the replacement normally needs to be done by the installer, possibly under a maintenance contract.

PIR sensors used in security lights work on a similar principle to intruder alarm PIRs but generally have lower RF immunity and no pulse counting. On most types, the DC power supply to the electronic circuitry is not isolated from the mains so great care is required if modifications are attempted. Further details on how to improve the RF immunity of PIR security lights is given in reference [6].

SPURIOUS SIGNALS FROM AN AMATEUR TRANSMITTER

The majority of amateur radio EMC problems are caused by the affected equipment having insufficient immunity to the fundamental frequency of transmission but it cannot be assumed that this is true in all cases. If interference occurs due to insufficient suppression of transmitter harmonics or other spurious outputs, it is likely to affect certain specific TV channels or FM broadcast stations. Every receiver within a certain distance is likely to be affected, although this depends on the directional properties of the transmitting and receiving antennas. Spurious emissions may also be generated if an RF power amplifier is unstable or has been incorrectly tuned. In the latter case, frequency halving may occur leading to strong spurious signals at half and 1.5 times the carrier frequency.

Harmonics

Clause 4.(1) of the UK Amateur Radio Licence (A) or (B) *Terms, Provisions and Limitations Booklet BR68* states:

"The Licensee shall ensure that: (a) the emitted frequency of the apparatus comprised in the station is as stable and as free from Unwanted Emissions as the state of technical development for amateur radio apparatus reasonably permits;"

In the USA, the FCC spectral purity regulations for VHF amateur equipment which reached the market since 1978 require spurious emissions at VHF to be at least 60dB below the level of the carrier (−60dBc) for power levels of 25W or more.

For commercially available amateur radio equipment manufactured or imported into Europe since 1 January 1996, the EMC standard ETS 300 684 specifies levels of emissions and immunity. Section 8.1.3 defines limits for unwanted emissions from the antenna port when the transmitter is active. From 50–1000MHz, the limit is of −36dBm (0.25µW) or −60dBc, whichever is higher.

Even if all harmonics and other unwanted emissions are at least 60dB below the carrier level, this may not be sufficiently low for all situations. In the case of the 50–52MHz band, suppression of the second harmonic at 100–104 MHz is particularly important. For example, even with only 10 nanowatts ERP of second-harmonic power, equation 6.1 shows that at a distance of 10m this would produce a field strength of 70µV/m or 37dB(µV/m). Within the service area of an FM broadcast transmitter, the field strength should be at least 54dB(µV/m) at a height of 10m above ground. Towards the edge of the service area, a spurious signal of 37dB(µV/m) within the passband of the FM broadcast receiver would be more than enough to cause noticeable interference. Clearly, effective low-pass filtering together with a second harmonic trap is required for 50MHz. It is also important to avoid any radiation of second harmonic from sources other than the antenna, for example from a power amplifier with insufficient screening or decoupling.

It is advisable to identify all FM broadcasts between 100 and 104MHz which are intended to serve your area and to check that you can transmit on or near half the frequency without causing interference. If sufficient suppression of the second harmonic is still not achieved after all possible steps have been taken, it will be necessary to avoid transmitting on or near certain frequencies.

In the case of the 144–146MHz band, the fourth harmonic falls at 576–584MHz in UHF TV channels 34 or 35. The fifth harmonic falls at 720–730MHz and could interfere with UHF TV channels 52 or 53. In areas where the above UHF channels are used, additional low-pass or band-pass filtering may be required at the amateur transmitter.

However, it should be noted that, if a sufficiently high level of amateur signal is received by a TV antenna amplifier or the front end of a TV or FM receiver, this can cause harmonics to be generated *within the antenna amplifier or receiver* even though the amateur signal itself may be free of them.

Frequency synthesiser lock-up

When constructing a synthesised transceiver or modifying synthesised ex-PMR equipment, attention should be paid to the lock-up characteristics of the synthesiser, particularly if the transceiver is to be used for packet radio where it is likely to transmit frequently for short periods. With most VHF transceivers, the PLL (phase-locked loop) synthesiser must get into lock on switching from receive to transmit or vice versa. While it is locking, RF drive to the transmit amplifier chain must be inhibited for long enough to avoid a full-power transmitted signal sweeping rapidly across other frequencies inside or outside the amateur band.

In a synthesised transceiver, out-of-lock detection should also be considered. If the VCO (voltage-controlled oscillator) cannot reach the frequency required by the synthesiser IC, the loop fails to lock, resulting in an unstable transmission on an incorrect frequency. There are two reasons why a synthesiser may fail to lock. The first is if the VCO frequency range is incorrectly adjusted and the synthesiser is programmed for a frequency which the VCO cannot reach. The second, which could affect a serially programmed synthesiser, is if the microprocessor fails to program the synthesiser when switching to transmit, leaving the synthesiser programmed to an incorrect frequency. To protect against such error conditions, the out-of-lock condition should be detected and should inhibit transmission. Frequency synthesiser ICs intended for use in transceivers normally have a lock detector output but devices such as the Philips TSA 6057 which are intended for receive-only applications have no lock detector which makes their use in a transceiver inadvisable.

INTERFERENCE TO AMATEUR RECEPTION

In most cases where nearby electronic equipment causes RFI on amateur bands, the equipment complies with any RFI standards which were required at the date of manufacture and the owner is not obliged to take any action unless reception of a protected service UHF TV broadcasting or FM radio is also affected. There is, however, a possibility that a fault has developed, that screening/suppression components have been removed during servicing or that the equipment was not intended for the European market and was imported by the owner.

The first thing to check is whether any interference can be seen on TV or heard on FM radio when using a satisfactory receiving antenna within the intended service area of the broadcast transmitter. If so, the matter can be referred to the local office of the UK Radiocommunications Agency using form RA179 (see below). In such cases, it is worth trying to locate the source so that the unpaid service can be used.

In most cases, only amateur bands are affected and the RFI can only be reduced if the owner of the equipment in question is prepared to co-operate, so a diplomatic approach is recommended. In any case, it is difficult to be certain of the source unless the owner is prepared to co-operate in doing tests. Any RFI reduction should be restricted to measures which can be fitted by the owner without the need for you to touch or dismantle the equipment in question.

It is worth trying to find out details of the make, model number and date of purchase of the equipment so that a complaint can be made directly to the manufacturer or importer. A polite and technically well-informed approach is recommended when dealing with manufacturers. The most effective approach is to phone first to find out the name of the person responsible for EMC then follow up the phone call with a letter, fax or e-mail. It is also worth finding out whether a newer model with reduced RFI is available. In some cases, the manufacturer may be prepared to exchange the equipment in question for a newer model at a reduced price.

In cases where it is not possible to reduce the RFI,

cancellation techniques may be used. See for example, reference [7].

RF emission standards

Radio amateurs might wish for nearby electronic equipment to be so well screened and suppressed that it emits no detectable signals in any amateur band but existing RF emission standards fall far short of this ideal. At VHF, emission standards were designed primarily to protect broadcast radio and TV reception with an outdoor antenna at a distance of 10m from the source of the emission. Consequently, they allow levels of RFI which are far higher than radio amateurs would like. Nevertheless the situation has improved for electronic equipment manufactured since 1 January 1996 because previously many types of electronic equipment were not required to meet the relevant emission standards in the UK.

Radiated emissions above 30MHz are covered by BS EN 55 022 which applies to information technology equipment. This not only includes computers but also other equipment containing microprocessors. Various other standards such as the Generic Standard EN 50081-1 are based on EN 55022. The EN 55022 Class 'B' limits are specified as a field strength of 30dB(μV/m) at a distance of 10m over the range 30–230MHz, increasing above 230MHz. This is a very large signal compared to the minimum discernible signal in VHF/UHF amateur bands, but in practice the situation is seldom as bad as it might appear because emissions near the limit are only likely to be found at a few frequencies and in most cases these are not in an amateur band. Further information on RF emission limits in relation to received amateur signal levels can be found in reference [8].

For a VHF/UHF amateur station with a high-gain antenna and low-noise preamp in a quiet rural area, the MDS (minimum discernible signal) for 144MHz SSB corresponds to a field strength of about −30dB(μV/m). In an urban area, the MDS is likely to be higher on certain beam headings due to man-made broad-band noise sources. At certain spot frequencies, there may be significantly stronger narrow-band signals from nearby electronic equipment.

Computer RFI reduction

Although many laptop computers generate little RFI at VHF, other types of computers and associated equipment can be a major source of RFI. The RFI reduction measures described below are primarily intended for desktop PC-type computers used in the radio shack but similar principles can be applied to other types of computer and to digital electronic equipment in general. Clearly, internal modification of a computer or monitor should not be attempted on someone else's computer or one which is still under guarantee. Further details of computer RFI reduction are given in reference [9].

If a computer is used in the radio shack, the antenna and computer should obviously be as far apart as possible. It is also worth checking that the RFI disappears when a dummy load is plugged into the antenna socket, proving that it is not getting into the radio by some other route.

A computer may contain many different clock oscillators, for example for the CPU, graphics controller, disc drives, keyboard, mouse etc. Most of these oscillators are divided down to lower frequencies which can in turn produce many other harmonics. Some frequencies commonly used in digital

electronic equipment include 4, 6, 8, 12, 16 and 24MHz, and unfortunately all of these have harmonics at 144.0MHz. Another frequency found in virtually all PC-compatible computers is 14.318MHz (±25kHz or so). This is four times the NTSC colour TV sub-carrier and may be used to synthesise other frequencies such as the clock for the CPU and the pixel clock for the graphics card. For 486 and Pentium processors, a clock frequency of around 30 or 33MHz is commonly used and is multiplied up on the CPU chip to 66, 90, 100, 133 or 166MHz etc.

Reducing RF leakage

Unwanted emissions may escape from a computer or other digital equipment via a number of routes so a step-by-step approach is normally required. It is best to monitor the level of RFI with an indoor antenna 2–3m from the computer, using an SSB receiver with an S-meter if possible. Displaying a graphics screen with a lot of fine detail is recommended as a 'worst case' test even when testing without the monitor. The starting point is to unplug the video lead from the computer, switch off the monitor and unplug the keyboard, mouse and all other interface cables. Any remaining RFI is likely to be a radiated emission due to insufficient screening of the case or a conducted emission via the mains cable. The latter is more likely to affect the HF bands than VHF.

On a CE-marked computer, the case normally has several features to improve screening as shown in Fig 6.6. Arrows 'A' indicate lugs or 'pips' at intervals of about 50mm on the base or cover to ensure good electrical contact at many points. Holes for unused disc drive bays are usually filled with a metal blanking plate ('B'). The wires to LEDs and switches on the front panel come through the metal case ('C') and could cause a slight leak. In practice, however, the shielding of the case may not be the limiting factor so a metal case without these features may be adequate if there is good electrical contact between the lid and the base all around the joints. If not, it may be necessary to add extra fixing screws.

Keyboard

On a PC, the keyboard cable can radiate RFI if the shell of the keyboard connector is not solidly grounded to chassis. Although PC main boards nearly always use four or more layers with power and ground plane, there can still be a small RF potential difference between 'ground' at the shell of the keyboard socket and ground at the back of the case. The fixing hole on the main board nearest the keyboard socket ('D' in Fig 6.6), should be grounded via a metal pillar to minimise common-mode emissions. On CE-marked PCs, the shell of the keyboard DIN socket is normally grounded directly to the back of the case using four spring fingers ('E' in Fig 6.6).

Another way of tackling common-mode emissions is by means of a common-mode choke using a ferrite core on the cable ('F' in Fig 6.6). Most keyboard cables already have one of these moulded on but with only one 'turn' – they introduce a series impedance of only about 100–200Ω. Up to four times as much impedance can be introduced by threading the cable twice through a clip-on ferrite core with 13mm inside diameter.

In some cases, the keyboard itself may radiate a harmonic in an amateur band. As the clock normally uses a ceramic resonator rather than a crystal, it may be possible to move the

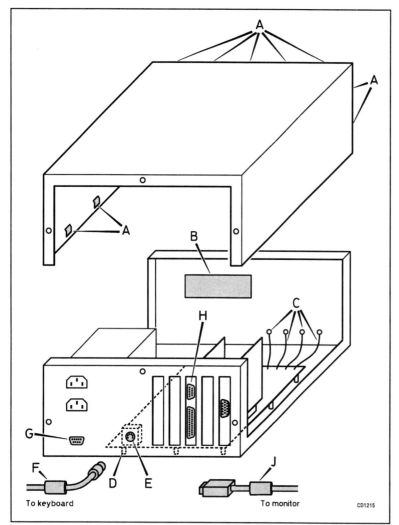

Fig 6.6. A typical PC case showing features which can affect EMC

harmonic out of the band by 'pulling' the frequency of the resonator by increasing its loading capacitors. If this is not successful, it may be necessary to substitute a new keyboard as it is not easy to screen a keyboard effectively.

Serial and parallel I/O ports

Any unscreened serial or parallel interface cable can radiate RFI due to unwanted coupling inside the computer. Where possible, a screened cable should be used with the screen well grounded to the metal connector shell. For a computer mouse, however, unscreened cable is normally used and a clip-on ferrite choke or a filtered connector may be required. A filtered 'D' type connector can be made by soldering a 1nF or 4.7nF ceramic capacitor from each pin to the connector shell. Filtered 'D' connectors or adaptors with built-in feedthrough capacitors are available ready made from suppliers such as RS Components or Farnell Components but are relatively expensive.

A filtered connector on a cable will only be effective if there is good electrical contact between the two halves of the connector shell which requires 'dimples' on the male 'D' type connector. The shell of the plug on the computer must also be well grounded to the case of the computer. This is likely to be true of connector 'G' in Fig 6.6 but connector 'H' may not be

well grounded because it is on an expansion card.

For a computer with an internal modem, the unscreened telephone cable can radiate or pick up RF, especially if connected to an overhead telephone line. The only feasible way of filtering the telephone line where it leaves the modem card is by means of a ferrite ring or clip-on choke. Connecting series inductors or shunt capacitors directly to the telephone line is not permissible as it would invalidate BABT approval for the modem.

Graphics card

It is important that the shell of the video connector on a PC graphics card is well grounded to avoid a VHF common-mode emission from the braid of the video cable. The shell of the video output connector is grounded to the mounting bracket but this is only grounded to chassis with one bolt at the top. If possible, the graphics card should be fitted in one of the end slots where grounding to the back panel is better. Some good-quality cases for CE-marked PCs have spring fingers around the expansion slots on the back panel to improve grounding but, if these are not fitted, RF grounding can be improved by bolting or clamping the mounting bracket of the video card to the back panel close to the connector. Another way of reducing RFI from a video cable is to clip on a ferrite choke ('J' in Fig 6.6) if one is not already fitted.

Computer monitors

Following the above steps should lead to a fairly quiet computer at VHF, until the monitor is switched on. RFI from a monitor may have definite peaks at certain frequencies or may be broad-band noise. There are large variations in the amount of VHF RFI emitted by different models of computer monitor. To reduce RFI from a monitor at VHF, it is normally necessary to make internal modifications to circuitry which operates at a high voltage. Such modifications should only be attempted by those with sufficient experience. Note that ferrite is conductive and any ferrite cores should be fitted so as to avoid causing a short-circuit or flashover.

In many computer monitors, the switching frequency for the power supply is synchronised to the line timebase frequency which can make it difficult to distinguish between power supply harmonics, line timebase harmonics and video amplifier harmonics. If turning the brightness and contrast right down give a large reduction in RFI, this could be due to reduced loading on the power supply, reduced loading on the line output stage or reduced output from the video amplifiers. The switch-mode power supply in a monitor may be on an unscreened PCB in a plastic case leading to direct radiation, in which case adding additional mains filtering is unlikely to give much improvement at VHF.

The line output stage can radiate harmonics up to VHF due to the fast switching of the output transistor. As the collector of the line output transistor is usually connected directly to the 'hot' side of the line scan coils, these coils and associated wiring can act as a radiating antenna. The only effective way of reducing VHF harmonics of the line timebase is usually to cut the track to the collector of the line output transistor and put in a series choke consisting of 2–3 turns on an FX1115 ferrite bead. As the added inductance in the collector could alter the operating conditions of this highly stressed device, such modifications should be regarded as experimental. A similar modification can be applied to the main switching transistor in the switch-mode power supply if necessary.

If the video amplifiers are radiating, displaying a screen with a lot of fine detail will produce more RFI than a plain screen of the same brightness. The video output transistors are nearly always mounted on the base if the CRT on a small PCB with a tinplate screen. This screen should be grounded to the chassis by two short lengths of braid. The video cable from the computer should have its braid solidly grounded to chassis where it enters the monitor. Some CE marked monitors have two large ferrite beads on the video cable, one each side of this ground point.

Although it would be possible to coat the whole inside of a monitor's case with nickel RF shielding spray grounded to chassis, this is not recommended for several reasons. First, there are high voltages on the PCB which may flash over to any conductive coating inside the case. Secondly, the conductive paint may find its way through ventilation slots so that it can be touched from outside. This presents a shock hazard if part of the coating inside comes into contact with a high voltage. A third problem is that the coating may not adhere well to certain types of plastic unless a special primer is used. If the coating flakes off, this could cause short circuits.

Even the software set-up of a PC can affect the emissions from a monitor. For example some Cirrus Logic VGA video cards operating in the 800×600 resolution modes use a pixel clock frequency of 36.088MHz or 72.176MHz. This produces a second or fourth harmonic at nominally 144.352MHz with sidebands either side. A VGA utility program such as CLMODE can be used to demonstrate the various graphics modes and identify any differences in RFI.

Other RFI sources

There are many possible sources of unwanted signals in the VHF and UHF bands apart from computers and associated equipment. Other domestic products which generally incorporate a microprocessor include intruder alarms and fax machines. Satellite TV receivers and decoders, video recorders and TV sets with NICAM stereo or digital signal processing can also generate RFI in the VHF bands. Many consumer products use a ceramic resonator rather than a crystal in the clock oscillator for the digital circuitry. Harmonics of ceramic resonators tend to drift with temperature and they may even be microphonic where nearby sound or other vibrations cause slight frequency modulation.

Some types of heating thermostat may develop a fault causing them to arc for several seconds or even tens of seconds when the contacts open. This may occur every few minutes and tends to occur more frequently in cold weather. In some cases, the same type of thermostat may have been installed in a number of houses and there could be several arcing thermostats.

Equipment in nearby commercial or industrial premises which may radiate RFI at VHF includes arc welders, computers and computer networks using unscreened twisted pair (UTP) rather than coaxial cable or optical fibre. Some types of fire alarm systems can also be a problem, particularly the 'analogue addressable' type if these are wired with unscreened cable.

A broad-band noise source which can affect all or part of the 70cm band is a super-regenerative receiver on 433.92MHz. With a high-gain 70cm antenna and low-noise preamp, some types within 30–50m can cause a substantial degradation of signal-to-noise ratio. Noisy 433.92MHz super-regenerative receivers are found on some after-market car alarms manufactured in 1994 and 1995. Receivers manufactured from 1996 onwards have to meet ETS 300 220 and are therefore much quieter. Some particularly poor 173MHz garage door openers sold in the late 'eighties also produced high levels of noise on 70cm and up into the UHF TV band.

RFI from noisy super-regenerative receivers can take two forms. In the absence of a signal, they radiate broad-band noise, possibly covering tens of megahertz. When the super-regenerative receiver detects a carrier somewhere near its operating frequency, its emission changes to a number of discrete frequencies spaced at intervals of the quench frequency which may be around 800kHz. These emissions drift and are modulated by signals from other radio services such as radio paging. They can give the misleading impression that a paging transmitter has spurious outputs or that an amateur receiver has spurious responses.

Other radio users

If signals from other radio services such as radio paging or PMR are heard on a receiver tuned to an amateur band, a likely cause is a spurious response in the amateur receiver or overloading of any preamplifier. In particular, some 144MHz amateur transceivers with extended receive coverage can be susceptible to breakthrough of nearby radio paging signals at around 138 or 153MHz. This problem can often be cured by means of a 144–146MHz bandpass filter or a notch filter tuned to the pager frequency [10].

It is possible for radio paging transmitters to develop a fault which produces a number of unstable spurious frequencies either side of the carrier and, if this occurs, the interference typically drifts up or down the amateur band. Note, however, that similar symptoms can be produced on 70cm by some types of super-regenerative garage door receiver nearby re-radiating pager signals.

If it is suspected that another radio service is radiating spurious signals in an amateur band, it is advisable to obtain conclusive proof of this before proceeding further.

DEALING WITH NEIGHBOURS

With some amateur radio EMC cases, the technical problem is easy to solve but applying the solution is difficult because of a social problem. If relations deteriorate too far, even a simple matter like getting a plug-in filter fitted could become a major issue. *It is therefore well worth trying to maintain friendly relations even if the neighbour's initial approach is unfriendly.* The neighbour's point of view may be that they have bought a good-quality product which works perfectly well when the radio amateur is not transmitting, so they blame the amateur. The radio amateur's point of view is that he or she is operating within the terms of the amateur licence so the problem is caused by shortcomings in the neighbour's equipment.

To explain your point of view to a neighbour may not be easy and a diplomatic approach is called for. If you take the view that it is not your problem, there is a risk of a much bigger problem later on! Even if your station is 'in the clear' technically, an unco-operative or, worse still, an alienated, neighbour could make life very unpleasant. Some radio amateurs have even resorted to moving house in such a situation.

It is wise to be prepared for the possibility of a breakthrough complaint before it happens. First of all, make sure your own house is in order by solving any EMC problems with your own domestic electronic equipment as far as possible. Being able to show that your TV/video recorder/hi-fi/telephone does not suffer breakthrough when you are transmitting should convince anyone that your transmitter is not at fault. Interference-free radio and TV reception in your own house is also an additional check that any spurious outputs from your transmitter are adequately suppressed. It does not prove this conclusively, however, due to the directional properties of transmitting and receiving antennas.

Solving any breakthrough on your own domestic electronic equipment is also good practice and means that you will probably have a selection of suitable filters or ferrite rings to hand. Even if none are required for your own equipment, it is advisable to keep an 'EMC first aid kit' consisting of at least one suitable TV filter together with a few ferrite rings. It is also worth having at least one RF immune telephone available even if your own telephone is never used while you are transmitting.

If a neighbour reports a problem, this could be your only chance to negotiate so *great diplomacy is necessary.* If there is any doubt about whether your station is the cause of the problem, you could ask the neighbour to keep a written log of dates and times when breakthrough occurs but they may be unwilling to do this so it is worth offering to conduct test transmissions immediately. If possible, the breakthrough should be solved promptly using a filter which you already have.

You are under no obligation to pay for filters for neighbours' TVs etc but in many cases, the neighbour is unwilling to pay, so it is in the interests of good relations to provide a filter on loan for as long it is needed. A small neat label with your name and address makes the point that it remains your property rather than being a gift (which might be taken as an admission of liability). It may also reduce the chance of a TV service engineer taking it away.

REGULATORY ISSUES

The Radiocommunications Agency of the DTI produces a leaflet RA234, *EMC and the Radio Amateur.* This is available from the RA Document Distribution Centre and also via the World Wide Web (http://www.open.gov.uk/radiocom/ra234.htm). RA234 states the following:

"**What is EMC?**
EMC, short for electromagnetic compatibility, is the capacity of equipment to function without causing excessive interference and without being unduly affected by emissions from other apparatus.

Why is EMC important?
Amateurs are privileged in being allowed to operate at high power levels in residential areas. This privilege brings responsibility. Interference can be immensely annoying. As a responsible amateur you will naturally take care not to interfere with television and radio reception, for example. Apart from general considerations of good neighbourliness, there are conditions in the Amateur Radio Licence on interference. In addition from 1 January 1996 an EC Directive will impose new EMC standards on virtually all electrical and electronic equipment.

Does the Directive apply to amateur equipment?
Self-built amateur equipment is not covered by the Directive but it will still be necessary when using it to abide by the Licence conditions on interference. Commercially available products will have to comply and carry the CE mark to show compliance.

What happens if an interference problem arises?
If a problem arises, as a first step, the amateur should check that his or her own equipment is not at fault. Poor immunity is often to blame for reception problems and it may be necessary to take steps to improve the immunity of the affected installation. The amateur should co-operate with the neighbour and/or the dealer to identify and resolve the problem. But, if this does not work, the Radiocommunications Agency is likely to become involved.

What happens then?
The Agency is empowered to vary the amateur's permitted power so that the amateur does not cause excessive interference. Before resorting to this, the Agency will take all relevant circumstances into account, including the immunity of the affected installation. In the final analysis, however, the Agency will be guided by the immunity required by the relevant European Standard. If poor immunity is not to blame and other steps to reduce interference have failed, the amateur may be required to take steps to stop the field strength exceeding the level that the relevant European standard requires the affected installation to be able to withstand."

Another useful RA publication is RA323, *Guidelines for Improving Television and Radio Reception.* It consists of 16 pages plus a colour section with photos showing various types of TV interference. It is primarily intended for radio and television dealers, service engineers and antenna installers rather than for the general public. Topics of particular relevance to amateur radio include TV antenna amplifiers, CE marking and effects due to lack of immunity.

Radiocommunications Agency involvement

The following information is believed to be correct at the time of writing (late 1997) but may be subject to change.

If a UK householder experiences a reception problem with UHF television, a video recorder or FM radio, they can refer the matter to the RA using form RA179, *Advice on Television and Radio Reception.* It is useful to keep an up-to-date copy of RA179 in case of a complaint from a neighbour. Copies are available from the Radiocommunications Agency Document Distribution Centre but are no longer available from Post Offices. RA179 is only applicable to domestic complaints. If a businesses is affected, there is a different procedure, details of which are available from the local offices of the RA.

Part A of form RA179 is used when reporting a known or suspected source of interference for possible investigation by the RA. There is no charge for reporting a source but the RA does not visit the complainant to investigate the affected equipment. If a radio amateur is nominated as a source of interference, it is likely that the local officers of the Radio-communications Agency (previously known as the 'Radio Investigation Service' or 'RIS') would visit the amateur's station. Such a visit may include checking for spurious emissions and ensuring that the station is being operated within the terms of the Amateur Licence. In some cases, the field strength produced by the amateur station could be measured.

Part B of form RA179 is used by a householder to request a visit from the RA to investigate the affected equipment. There is a charge (£45 at the time of writing) which includes the supply of any necessary filters.

Form RA179 states that the paid service is only available for UHF televisions, video recorders or FM radios. It does not cover long-wave and medium-wave radios, satellite TV, cable TV, telephones, fax machines or answering machines. Neither does it cover other equipment not intended to pick up radio such as record players, CD players, tape recorders, electronic keyboards, baby alarms, computers or monitors. PIR security lights and intruder alarm systems are not specifically mentioned but appear to come under the category of 'other equipment'.

REFERENCES

[1] *The Radio Amateur's Guide to EMC*, Robin Page-Jones, G3JWI, RSGB, 1992.

[2] *RSGB Guide to EMC*, Robin Page-Jones, G3JWI, RSGB, to be published 1998.

[3] *RSGB Yearbook*, EMC section.

[4] 49MHz baby monitors item in 'EMC' column, *Radio Communication* June 1996, p74.

[5] Alarm PIR sensors item in 'EMC' column, *Radio Communication* December 1994, pp75–77.

[6] PIR lights item in 'EMC' column, *Radio Communication* April 1994, pp76–77.

[7] 'Two metre interference reduction system', T Day, G3ZYY, *Radio Communication* April 1992, pp48–50.

[8] RF emission standards item in 'EMC' column, *Radio Communication* June 1995, pp76–77.

[9] Computer RFI reduction items in 'EMC' column, *Radio Communication* December 1996, pp77–78, and February 1997, pp 80–81.

[10] 'Intermod – A modern urban problem', E Hare, KA1CV, *QST* August 1996, pp40–43.

7 Data modes

DATA modes can mean a variety of modulation modes, from Morse (which is arguably the simplest form of data transmission using on-off keying) to advanced error correcting (eg packet radio) and direct-sequence (eg spread-spectrum) modes. The commonly used modes are:

1. Data networking, eg AX25 packet and TCP/P.

2. Weak-signal modes, eg Morse, PACTOR, CLOVER etc. It must be said that, with the exception of Morse, these are much less used at present at VHF/UHF than at HF.

3. Digitised speech, image and multimedia. This series of modes are still in their infancy at the time of writing (late 1996) and will not be dealt with further.

DATA NETWORKING
AX.25 packet radio

The overwhelmingly most popular data mode on VHF/UHF at present is packet radio, used with an FM transceiver. Unlike weak-signal modes such as PACTOR, CLOVER etc (see later) as well as visual modes such as fax and SSTV, AX.25 packet uses a amateur protocol derived from X.25, defining the content, format and the handling of packetised data. Information on AX.25 and other amateur packet protocols is extensively covered in other RSGB publications [1, 2] as well as the ARRL Computer Network Conference documents, so only a brief description is given here, concentrating instead on the 'physical layer' and user operation.

HDLC

Packet radio uses high-level data link control (HDLC) to handle the forwarding of error-free frames of data over a communications link. The transmission is based upon a series of 'packets' of data, each packet containing a portion of the transmitted information preceded by routing information and ending with a cyclic redundancy check (CRC), which is a value calculated by the sending station based upon the content of the information in the transmitted packet.

At the receiving end, each packet is automatically checked for correct and valid information content. If a valid packet is received, an 'ACK' (acknowledgement) is sent by the receiving end station to acknowledge that the packet has been received without errors. Otherwise, the transmitting station automatically repeats the transmission of that data packet.

By the use of this protocol, a number of packet radio stations may all use a common frequency, with individual data packets 'interleaving' with others as required. Packet addressing, by callsign or a short 'alias', ensures that the desired receiving station is correctly addressed, with each station ignoring packets not intended for that station's callsign or alias.

TCP/IP

A progression from AX.25 is TCP/IP, also used in other data systems such as the Internet. Like AX.25, TCP/IP (Transmission Control Protocol / Internet Protocol) is similarly used for packet processing, formatting and routing. However, TCP/IP differs from AX25 in that it automatically adapts to system network delays, lengthening transmission delay times accordingly to provide the best overall system throughput performance.

The various protocols in TCP/IP include:

FTP (File Transfer Protocol) – used to exchange data or binary files with another FTP user on the network.

Telnet – allows person-to-person keyboard communication, together with remote log-in facilities to any other computer system on the network.

SMTP (Simple Mail Transfer Protocol) – used to send messages to other TCP/IP users on the network, the message being stored locally with SMTP automatically feeding it to the network for onward forwarding.

POP (Post Office Protocol) – a mail handling facility which is a variant of SMTP, where a remote system is used as a 'post office' for the storage and onward transmission of mail.

PING (Packet INternet Groper) – used to check if a given remote user is on air, and the 'return trip time' for a response.

A packet TNC is used in 'KISS' (ie 'Keep It Simple, Stupid') mode for TCP/IP, with appropriate software running on the PC. This system is *NOS* (Network Operating System), originally developed by Phil Karn, KA9Q – subsequent derivations have included *GRINOS, JNOS, TNOS* and *MFNOS*. Before you can use TCP/IP on the air, you'll need to contact your local TCP/IP co-ordinator for a numeric 'address', which consists of a four-part number, for your station.

TERMINAL NODE CONTROLLER

To handle the AX.25 protocol, as well as providing a platform for TCP/IP, a terminal node controller (TNC) is typically used. This is a self-contained unit comprising a modem and microprocessor-based control system with the operating firmware typically stored in a plug-in erasable programmable read-only memory (EPROM) IC. This allows firmware changes or upgrades to be accomplished as needed.

For the 'user interface', the TNC has an RS-232 serial data connector for connection to a terminal. This may either be a 'dumb terminal', a computer operating in terminal emulation mode, ie running the Windows Terminal program, or a computer running a dedicated packet radio program to give added operating features such as automatic connections, logging,

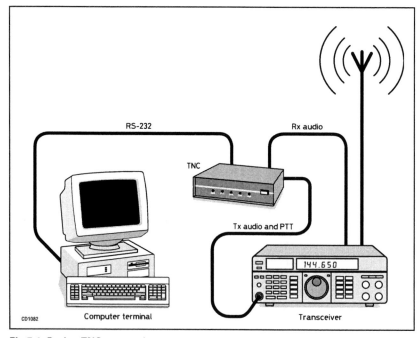

Fig 7.1. Packet TNC connections

mailbox facilities etc. For personal use, many TNCs also have a self-contained message 'mailbox' to provide storage facilities of personal messages to and from the TNC user.

For the radio interface, the TNC connects directly to your VHF/UHF transmitter/receiver although, depending upon the packet radio data rate, differing connections are required. Typical packet data rates used by individual amateurs are 1200 baud and 9600 baud, although 'backbone networking' data rates typically use 9600 baud, 56 kbaud, 64 kbaud, or higher speeds still (eg 2Mbits/s) on the microwave bands. Note that the terminal baud rate you select for use between the TNC and your terminal does *not* affect the radio baud rate, the latter being dependent upon the type and speed of modem used within the TNC.

See Fig 7.1 which shows these connections diagrammatically.

Multiple users

The TNC receives audio from the packet station receiver, and on a given frequency used by a number of packet stations this

Fig 7.2. Here's what's inside a TNC

is usually a sequential combination of many individual packets from differing stations, as well as packets from individual stations intended for a number of other 'connected' stations. Up to 26 different connection 'streams' can be handled by each TNC. In 'monitor' mode, the TNC decodes all received packets, and transfers the decoded information to the RS-232 terminal port for subsequent display and optional processing. However, in communication or 'connected' mode, it still decodes all received packets but typically only transfers to the RS-232 port packets addressed to the callsign or alias the user has manually stored (again via the terminal) into the TNC. It also automatically waits until the frequency is clear before transmitting a packet, to prevent interference to other packet stations on the same frequency. Pseudo-random 'wait' timings prior to transmission give a degree of protection in preventing 'collisions' of packets due to simultaneous transmissions from different stations on a given frequency.

HARDWARE

TNC kits of parts are available from groups such as MAXPAK in the UK to allow you to build a TNC-2 'clone', ie a 'generic' TNC which uses a plug-in EPROM common to many other TNCs. The TNC-2 clone is the type required if you intend to substitute the normal plug-in user EPROM with EPROM-based firmware for dedicated network node operation.

A wide variety of commercial ready-built TNCs are of course available. Many of these are based upon a TNC-2 clone (eg some PacComm and AEA TNCs) whilst others use proprietary firmware to provide additional features (such as some Kantronics TNCs).

TNC connection and operation

The TNC requires a suitable RS-232 connection link to your terminal for operation. Note, however, that some TNCs may employ otherwise unused connections on the 25-way D-type connector for other purposes, eg alternative supply voltage input, test points etc. If in doubt, follow the instructions supplied with your TNC. Tables 7.1 and 7.2 show the most-commonly used connections required for typical TNCs, and Figs 7.6 and 7.7 the serial port connector wiring diagrams.

It is beyond the scope of this chapter to describe the many TNC operational commands due to the wide variety of firmware versions available (see your TNC firmware manual or a dedicated packet radio handbook [1, 2] for these), although TNCs commonly use a pre-defined set of LED indicators on the front panel, which give the operator a degree of information about the status of the TNC at any time. These are:

PWR   Power on
RCV   Off-air signal data being received
XMIT TNC in transmit mode
CON   TNC in 'Connected' mode
STA   Unacknowledged packets outstanding

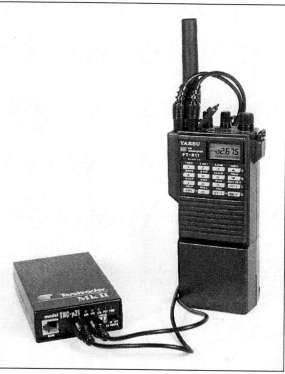

Fig 7.3. Typical factory-built packet TNCs: the DPK-2 (top left), the Sprint-2 (left) and the TNC-μ21 (above)

TRANSCEIVER CONNECTION

For *1200 baud* packet, the TNC transceiver interface may connect simply to the receiver external speaker audio and to the transmit microphone and PTT connections. Unless your TNC has a 'software DCD' incorporated and enabled, ie it has intelligent data detection of packet data to differentiate from receiver squelch noise and other signals, you should ensure that your receiver squelch is suitably adjusted. This is because

Table 7.1. TNC-2 'clone' RS-232 connections (25-pin D type)

Pin	Function	Signal direction
1	Frame Ground (FG)	Common
2	Transmit data (TXD)	PC o/p
3	Receive Data (RXD)	TNC o/p
5	Clear To Send (CTS)	TNC o/p
6	Data Set Ready (DSR)	TNC o/p
7	Signal Ground (SG)	PC o/p
8	Data Carrier Detect (DCD)	TNC o/p
20	Data Terminal Ready (DTR)	PC o/p
22	Ring Indicator (RI)	Not usually connected

Table 7.2. PacComm Tiny-2 connections (nine-pin D type)

Pin	Function	Signal direction
1	Data Carrier Detect (DCD)	TNC o/p
2	Receive Data (RXD)	TNC o/p
3	Transmit data (TXD)	PC o/p
5	Signal Ground (SG)	PC o/p
6	Data Set Ready (DSR)	TNC o/p
7	Request to send (RTS)	PC o/p
8	Clear To Send (CTS)	TNC o/p
9	Ring Indicator (RI)	Not connected
Shell	Frame Ground (FG)	Common

Fig 7.4. A plug-in PC card TNC can be used – this one has modems for 1200 and 9600 baud operation

Fig 7.5. The KAM is a popular multimode data controller

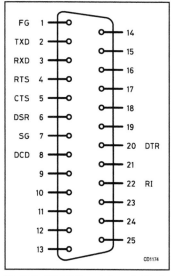

Fig 7.6. IBM PC serial port 25-pin connector

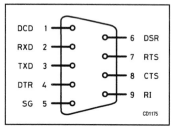

Fig 7.7. IBM PC serial port nine-pin connector

Fig 7.9. Rear-panel connections on the TNC interface to your radio and RS-232 terminal

the TNC will not otherwise transmit if the TNC's front panel 'DCD' LED is illuminated, this being controlled by the detection of a received signal by the TNC modem.

9600 baud packet requires connection to the 'flat', ie unprocessed, audio points in your transceiver. On receive, this typically means the receive audio needs to be taken directly from the receiver discriminator, prior to any audio de-emphasis filtering. On transmit, an audio response down to a few hertz, preferably down to DC, is required, together with an essentially 'flat' (ie unprocessed) transmitted frequency response. Some commercially available FM transceivers are fitted with 9600 baud packet data jack connections for this. However, many amateurs also use dedicated low-cost crystal-controlled transceivers, often ex-PMR equipment, for packet radio use, to avoid permanently tying up a high-value commercial transceiver on a given BBS or DX cluster frequency (see the RSGB's *PMR Conversion Handbook* [3] for more details on typical equipment and comprehensive conversion information). Transceiver connections for both 1200 and 9600 baud are shown in Fig 7.8 and a typical FM modulator modification circuit in Fig 7.10.

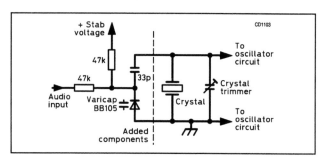

Fig 7.10. Typical 9600 baud direct FM modulator

PACKET DIGIPEATERS AND NODES

For individual one-to-one amateur communication via your terminal you simply issue a 'connect' command to your TNC to directly link to the intended station, who is operational on the same frequency and in communication range of your station. A typical command would be 'CONNECT GB7SMC' (or 'C GB7SMC') if I wished to connect to my local DX packet cluster node.

However, the AX.25 protocol also allows 'digipeating', where a third-party packet station can automatically re-transmit packets by remote command. Thus, 'CONNECT GB7DXW VIA G0SBV' would attempt a link to GB7DXW, using the packet station of G0SBV as an intermediate digital 'relay'. Up to eight intermediate digipeaters may be used for this. Any error-checking here is performed at the 'far end' of the link though, individual digipeaters simply retransmitting the packet information to the next station along. The digipeater facility is an inherent feature in every current packet TNC, although it may be enabled or disabled by the TNC operator as required.

A packet 'node' goes one step further, by employing local error checking and repeat transmission requests. A simple node facility is occasionally also an inherent feature of some TNCs, eg the 'KA-Node' on Kantronics TNCs. One stage further is that of a 'network node', which usually uses dedicated firmware or a PC running appropriate node software such as that written by John Wiseman, G8BPQ.

A network node system has automatic networking abilities, including automatic routing using the best possible transmission quality path between two remote points. A typical network node station arrangement could use multiple transceivers and TNCs, eg operating on 4m, 2m, 70cm and 23cm, with the TNCs locally

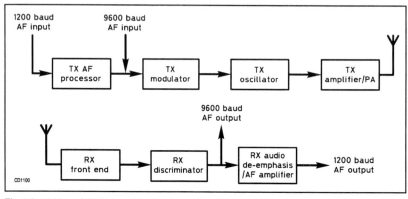

Fig 7.8. 1200 and 9600 baud transceiver connections

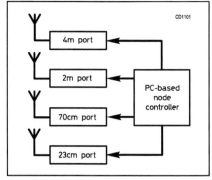

Fig 7.11. Typical network node arrangement

interconnected either via an RS-232 matrix or with the host computer running appropriate node software (Fig 7.11). In the latter case, the individual TNCs are commanded to run in 'KISS' mode, with the computer handling packet routing.

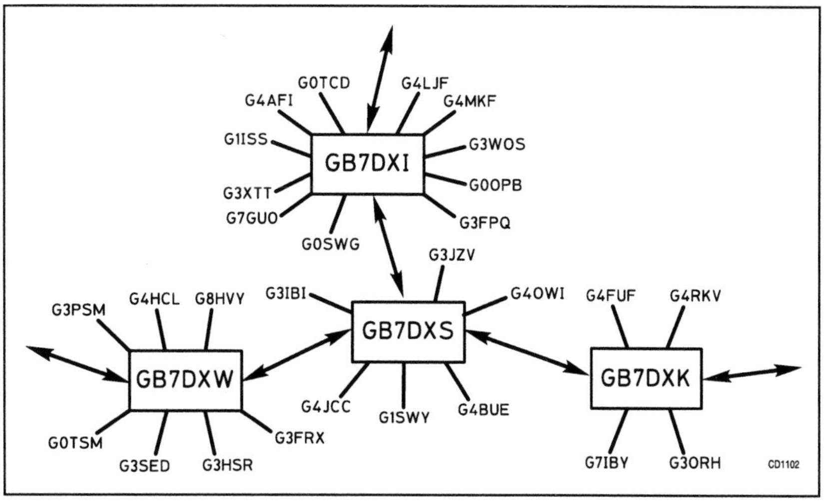

Fig 7.12. Typical DX packet cluster configuration

BULLETIN BOARDS

Although individual contacts are made using packet radio for live 'chats', the most common use of packet radio is by the use of a bulletin board system (BBS). These systems consist of a computer running appropriate BBS software, linked to the packet radio network, usually through individual TNCs and radios at the BBS station.

Two common types of BBSs are in use, the 'normal' BBS and, of greater interest to the DX operator, the DX packet cluster system.

Network BBS

Differing from the 'personal' BBS you may have in your TNC or computer software, which is used for personal messages to and from your station only, a network BBS operates as a linked national and international message storage and forwarding system for third-party messages and bulletins to and from radio amateurs. Some overseas BBS also have facilities for Internet links.

After you have connected to your local BBS, you can then list message titles, either all stored messages or to any given subject, callsign, or whatever, view and download message texts and stored files, as well as uploading files of interest to others, and enter messages addressed to other amateurs. Each BBS is part of the worldwide network, linked via nodes on HF, VHF and UHF, as well as via store-and-forward amateur satellite gateway stations. Thus, you can send and receive messages worldwide, the BBS network routing your messages to the intended recipient. You may read and send general 'bulletins', subject to licensing restrictions, which are intended for general reading, eg to seek help or information on a given subject from other amateur on the packet network.

Each BBS is normally run by an individual, or occasionally by a club, with all running costs being met by him or her and not by any national

organisation. This is worth bearing in mind as, due to current UK licensing conditions, the BBS system operator (sysop) usually refrains from directly soliciting donations to pay towards the running costs.

DX packet cluster

A DX packet cluster is a network of interconnected individual DX cluster 'nodes', each of which is located in a given area to serve a local amateur population. Similar in many physical respects to a network BBS, the controlling PC instead runs specialised DX cluster software which has enhancements for DX station activity reporting, propagation information etc. A typical area configuration is shown in Fig 7.12, with local stations each connected to their local DX cluster node, which are in turn linked to each other, and to those further afield (not shown here) either via dedicated RF links or via the national and international AX.25 packet network.

In operation, the users are all part of a shared information resource, where one station can enter an 'announcement', ie a DX 'spot' with DX station details, operation frequency and a short comment, usually when he's heard or worked a station worthy of reporting to others. This announcement is then forwarded throughout the DX cluster system and passed to all other connected stations. A 'filter' is available, where if you wish you can choose to only receive announcement 'spots' relating to certain bands, eg the VHF/UHF bands, you are specifically interested in, or indeed any combination including HF.

The UK is extensively covered by linked DX cluster nodes, which are often also linked to those in other European countries. This system can be an excellent way of obtaining and

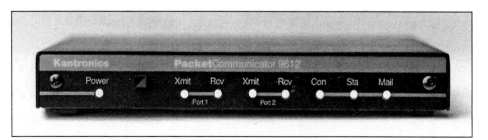

Fig 7.13. This KPC-9612 TNC combines 1200 and 9600 baud packet operation

Fig 7.14. The DB0RGB multi-frequency packet radio node site

Typical 2m DX packet cluster 'spots'

144080.0	VE7BQH	3-Nov-1996	0921Z	EME 529	\<PA0JMV\>
144112.0	DK9IP/P	3-Nov-1996	0918Z	JN48GT	\<DF2UU\>
144081.0	TM6P	3-Nov-1996	0915Z	JN19pg	\<F6HPP\>
144015.0	DF0CK	3-Nov-1996	0917Z	cq contest from jo50an	\<DG00PK\>
144099.9	F6DJB	3-Nov-1996	0915Z	jn03cl best dx 956 km !	\<PA3BAS\>
144092.0	G3JRM	3-Nov-1996	0911Z	jo02-jo60 559qsb	\<DK0SAX\>
144100.0	F5KHG/P	3-Nov-1996	0913Z	ae52b	\<PA3BAS\>
144067.0	GM0CLN/P	3-Nov-1996	0830Z	io85	\<G4WOX\>
144096.3	DL0KM/P	3-Nov-1996	0815Z	JO31BC-JN03CF 559 983km!	\<F6BOL\>
144096.3	F6BOL/65	3-Nov-1996	0812Z	JN03CF-JO31BC 559/559	\<DF2JQ\>

Typical 6m DX packet cluster 'spots'

50024.0	9H1SIX/B	21-Oct-1996	2128Z	JM75>JN18 559	\<F6FLV\>
50111.8	9H1AW	21-Oct-1996	2045Z	59 jn08>>jm75	\<F1LLS\>
50110.0	SP2NJE	21-Oct-1996	2121Z	Es again !	\<PA0RDY\>
50112.0	9H1AW	21-Oct-1996	2120Z	Alan GW3LDH	\<G00FE\>
50112.0	9H1AW	21-Oct-1996	2112Z	jm75>io91 59+	\<G4RGK\>
50112.0	9H1AW	21-Oct-1996	2053Z	57 >IO83 QSB	\<G0JHC\>
50112.0	9H1AW	21-Oct-1996	2039Z	JM75>IO92	\<G0PQO\>
50120.0	F6HTJ	21-Oct-1996	2023Z	JN12 > JO01	\<G8RZA\>
50112.0	EH1EH	21-Oct-1996	2011Z	IN82 cq cq	\<OZ5AGJ\>
50110.0	F6HTJ	21-Oct-1996	2009Z	59 JN12	\<G0JHC\>
50117.0	EH1TA	21-Oct-1996	2010Z	in53>jo32	\<PA2TAB\>
50125.0	EH7AH	21-Oct-1996	1957Z	IM67-JN67 still 59	\<OE2UKL\>
50112.0	EH1EH	21-Oct-1996	1935Z	IN82 > JO01	\<G8RZA\>
50112.0	EH1EH	21-Oct-1996	1925Z	in82>io92	\<G4VPD\>
50029.5	CT0WW	21-Oct-1996	1920Z	5/5 beacon in61ge	\<PA0PAU\>
50125.0	EH7AH	21-Oct-1996	1920Z	59 IN JN47	\<OE9PTI\>
50113.0	EH4EHI	21-Oct-1996	1913Z	59 IM68-IO80 RARE SQUARE	\<G4HBA\>
50112.8	EH4EHI	21-Oct-1996	1902Z	5/7 im68tv- jo22nw	\<PA0PAU\>

sharing 'real-time' information on sporadic-E or tropospheric activity with other amateurs, as well as arranging skeds for meteor scatter, EME etc, for example with other European stations.

As with network BBSs, each DX cluster node is usually financed by an individual amateur or local club, which should be borne in mind if you are a regular user of a particular one.

MULTIMEDIA DATA COMMUNICATION

The near-universal use of PCs for amateur data communication together with increasing PC processor speeds has significantly obviated the earlier need for dedicated terminal units for modes such as SSTV. Software-based signal processing within the PC, often using programs written by amateurs, allows the computer to perform the hard work of modulation, demodulation, and signal processing, together with data storage and retrieval facilities.

At the time of writing, amateur freeware and shareware programs are readily available (eg JVFAX, HamComm, MSCAN, EZSSTV etc) for SSTV, fax, CW, RTTY transceive, and PACTOR and packet receive, all using an extremely simple interface which is used between the transceiver and the PC's RS-232 port.

SIMPLE OP-AMP INTERFACE

The circuit given in Fig 7.16 is suitable for use with a variety of readily available programs, and provides a simple, easy-to-build interface for data modes. Received audio from the transceiver is shaped in the

Table 7.3. Typical DX packet cluster commands

BYE	Bye, disconnect from the packet cluster
CONFERENCE	Enter conference mode on the local cluster node
CONFERENCE/FULL	Enter conference mode on the full cluster
DELETE	Delete mail message
DIR	List active mail messages on the local node
DIR/ALL	List all active mail messages on the local node
DIR/BULLETIN	List active messages addressed to 'ALL'
DIR/n	List the last n active messages
DIR/NEW	List active messages added since you last used the DIR command
DX	DX spotting info announcement
DX x y z	Announce DX station of callsign x on frequency y with comment z
EXECUTE	Execute your personal command procedure
FINDFILE	Locate file(s) on the system
HELP or ?	Help (displays a short command listing)
HELP x	Display help for command x
KILL x	Delete mail message x
LIST	List active mail messages
QUIT	Bye, disconnect from the packet cluster
READ n	Read message numbered n
REPLY	Reply to the last-read mail message
REPLY/D	Reply to and delete the last-read mail message
SEND	Send a mail message
SEND/P	Send a personal mail message
SEND/NOP	Send a public mail message
SET	Set user-specific parameters
SET/NEED x	Store prefix x that you need in the cluster's database
SHOW/C	Display full packet cluster configuration
SHOW/CL	Display shortened packet cluster configuration
SHOW/DX	Show last reported DX spots
SHOW/DX/x y	Show last x number of reported spots on band y
SHOW/H x	Show heading and distance to country prefix x
SHOW/LOC x	Display the latitude and longitude of station callsign x
SHOW/M x	Show maximum usable frequency to country prefix x
SHOW/QSL x	Show QSL information for station callsign x
SHOW/U	Show callsigns of stations connected to local cluster node
SWITCH	Change to alias call
TALK x	Enter 'talk' mode to station with callsign x
TALK x y	Send one-line message y to station with callsign x
TYPE	Display a particular file on the packet cluster
UPDATE	Update a custom database
UPLOAD	Upload a file to the packet cluster
WWV	Log/Announce WWV propagation information
WX	Announce weather conditions

Fig 7.15. A simple one-IC interface can be used for data modes

op-amp to provide a rectangular waveform, and fed directly to one handshake line (DSR) of the PC serial port. For this, the 741 operates as a limiting amplifier with full open-loop amplification. The circuit is powered directly from the PC RS-232 port, where the RTS and DTR lines are used to serve as a power supply to the op-amp, the diodes and capacitors in the interface being used for voltage smoothing. Note that the RS-232 interface boards of some computers may not provide sufficient output here for a standard 741 IC – in these cases the use of a CMOS 741 or the pin-compatible TL071 op-amp may be usefully substituted.

On transmit, the rectangular waveform from the PC's RS-232 TXD line is initially limited by the resistor and back-to-back diodes. This is followed by a passive two-stage low-pass RC filter to filter the resultant square wave, prior to application to the transceiver microphone input, a potentiometer providing a level-setting adjustment. Transmit/receive switching is provided by the RS-232 RTS (Request To Send) line – when this goes high it drives the base of the NPN switching transistor to place the collector/emitter into conduction, the collector driving the transmitter PTT.

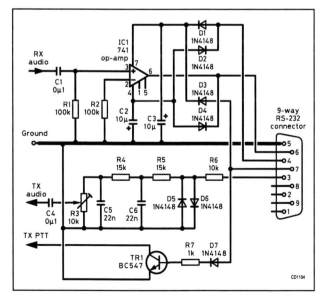

Fig 7.16. Simple SSTV/fax/packet/PACTOR interface

As the PC is used to perform signal processing, the timing is particularly sensitive, and slower computers, such as early 8086/88 XTs, may prove a limitation, although all 'current specification' PCs should be more than adequate. Furthermore, this method in some cases conflicts with some memory managers such as EMM386. (However, most interestingly, not on every machine!) Results obtained with such a 'software demodulation' are from very poor up to excellent.

OTHER INTERFACES

Using the same program but with differing interfaces, the four RS-232 input handshake lines, DCD, RI, CTS and DSR, can be used to provide a 4-bit parallel input port. To expand the data input capability from these 4 lines to 8 bit, a multiplexing technique can also be used by the program if it supports this, where the software initially reads in the four most significant data bits with the RTS line set to 'high'. The RTS line is then toggled to the low state and after a timed delay the lower four bits are read. Alternatively, the PC parallel port may be used to provide greater flexibility, again with alternative interfaces. These are available from commercial suppliers, and construction details for home-made designs are available in specialist amateur publications such as the quarterly journals of the British Amateur Radio Teledata Group (BARTG) and the Remote Imaging Group (RIG).

Packet modems

A popular solution to providing packet radio operation is by use of a BayCom modem for either 1200 baud or 9600 baud packet, together with the use of appropriate PC software such as that also offered by BayCom. The BayCom team is a group of German amateurs, and their modem designs are available either ready-built from commercial suppliers (eg Siskin Electronics and J&P Electronics in the UK) or in kit form from groups such as MAXPAK (Midlands AX.25 Packet group) and the NWPUG (North West Packet Users Group).

The 1200 baud modem is based upon a TCM3105 modem IC which, although reportedly no longer available in the UK, can be obtained from Germany. The interface connects to the PC's RS-232 port, and requires the use of appropriate software to provide the AX25 packet processing – a standard terminal emulator will not suffice. A commercial ready-built 'MiniPak' circuit for this system is available in surface-mount form – this is entirely contained within the shell of an RS-232 connector but kits using discrete components are also readily available.

The PAR96 is a 9600 baud modem, also from BayCom, again using the same BayCom PC software. This is again available either in kit form or ready-built. The circuit design for this unit, including PCB etc, has been published in the German amateur radio press.

PC sound card

At the time of writing, a number of data mode systems are available using PC software together with a standard PC sound card for the audio interface. These currently include CW, SSTV, FAX, AMTOR, RTTY etc as well as for DSP filtering implementations. As technology and PC processing power increases, the use of this type of interface for amateur data modes is likely to grow significantly.

Note, however, that a typical PC modem, designed for

Fig 7.17. 9600 baud modem from BayCom in kit or ready-built form

landline use, is usually not suitable for data-over-radio use, ie for direct connection to an amateur transceiver for packet radio etc. The use of PC-based TCP/IP programs, similar to those used for landline-based Internet connection, is however possible for use with amateur-based TCP/IP radio networks, providing sufficiently high-speed radio links are available. At least one UK TCP/IP group have this facility available for the use of amateurs. A further progression from this is the use of digital speech over TCP/IP.

Here is a quotation from a 1988 article by James Miller, G3RUH, designer of the famous G3RUH 9600 modem used worldwide terrestrially and on amateur satellites: "Who will predict that one day even our voice repeater links will be entirely digital. I will!"

In 1992, the BayCom team demonstrated digital speech via a packet radio store-and-forward system between remote 'speech mailbox' repeaters. In 1996, the Internet was first used with 'RepeaterLink' and 'Iphone' software to provide remote simplex transceive speech operation for amateurs on a number of FM VHF/UHF repeaters around the world. Its use via amateur radio-based TCP/IP networks is certainly possible, again given suitably fast links. We are seeing the gradual merging of data modes with other operation modes, and there may soon be no difference.

WEAK-SIGNAL MODES

These typically use FSK (direct frequency shift keying, or audio frequency shift keying on SSB), and PSK (phase shift keying) of a transmitter.

CLOVER is a proprietary mode, developed in the USA by Hal Communications. It uses PSK with full duplex simulation, where data is transferred between two linked stations, with automatic data link direction changeover. External data compression is used to increase data throughput, and the timing and modulation mode are automatically changed to suit the prevailing propagation conditions.

PACTOR-1 was developed by amateurs in Germany and is an FSK mode. It is increasingly found included as 'standard' on a number of commercially available multimode data controllers, and the hardware design of a PACTOR controller for home construction has been published in the German amateur press. Adaptive Huffman data compression is internally and automatically used, together with variable 100 baud or 200 baud speeds in the controller to improve throughput depending upon the prevailing propagation and signal conditions.

'Memory ARQ' using an internal 8-bit A/D converter is used in the original modem design, which has been adopted by a number of commercial TNCs but not by all, thus offering differing performance based upon the actual modem used. The A/D unit converts received 'packets' into a data stream, and subsequent identical packets (automatically repeated under weak signal conditions) are added to this to eventually 'build up' a valid frame whilst the background noise reduces towards zero. In this way, PACTOR can be successfully used in signal conditions where the wanted data signal is significantly below the level of unwanted noise and interference, even to the point of complete inaudibility by the human ear.

PACTOR-2 is a PSK mode, and is 'backwards-compatible' with PACTOR-1 as it uses the same handshaking protocol. The additional use of DSP techniques provides greater throughput and operation under even weaker signal conditions than PACTOR-1. A combination of Huffman and Pseudo-Markov adaptive automatic software compression is used to further increase throughput. The modulation is automatically changed to suit the prevailing propagation conditions, ie DQPSK, D8-PSK, D16-PSK etc.). It has the ability to employ automatic frequency tracking with fine-adjustment capability, via up/down fine frequency control output lines to your transceiver.

GTOR is a further proprietary mode, developed in the US by Kantronics. It is an FSK mode offering a high data transfer rate given reasonable signal conditions. Software compression is inherent in this mode to improve throughput.

The most common implementation of the above modes in the amateur radio station is by the use of a commercially available multimode data controller, connected to a transceiver with a terminal or PC employed for control. A number of such controllers also feature multiple ports, eg one for weak signal modes as above and often combining CW, RTTY and AMTOR (all used with a transceiver in SSB mode), plus a further port for packet radio (using an FM mode transceiver).

Frequency stability requirements

Unlike other modes, PSK used by CLOVER and PACTOR-2 requires a high degree of frequency stability, with stations 'netted' to typically within 10Hz, although the auto-tracking in PACTOR-2 can cope with up to 100Hz offset drift. This is rarely a problem on HF with current TCXO (temperature

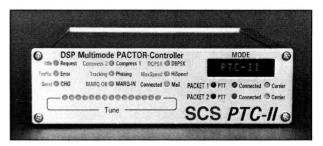

Fig 7.18. The SCS PACTOR-2 DSP Multimode Controller

compensated crystal oscillator) technology, but additional care must be taken on VHF and UHF to ensure accurate frequency netting.

CONTACTS

MAXPAK: Richard Nichol, G1NZZ, 37 Thicknall Drive, Stourbridge, West Midlands, DY9 0YH. Tel: 0973 262287 evenings/weekends. Email: richard@g1nzz.demon.co.uk.

Siskin Electronics: SM House, School Close, Chandler's Ford Industrial Estate, Eastleigh, Hants, SO53 4BY. Tel: 01703 255111. Fax: 01703 263507. Email: siskin@smc-comms.com.

J&P Electronics: Unit 45, Meadowmill Estate, Dixon Street, Kidderminster, DY10 1HH. Tel: 01562 753893.

NWPUG (North West Packet Users Group): W Bateman, Ingleside, Waterloo Whixall, Whitchurch, Shropshire, SY13 2PX.

BARTG (British Amateur Radio Teletype Group): Peter Adams, 464 Whippendell Road, Watford, Herts, WD1 7PT. Tel: 01923 20774 evenings/weekends.

RIG (Remote Imaging Group): Ray Godden, G4GCE, Wayfield Cottage, The Clump, Chorleywood, Herts, WD3 4BG. Tel/fax 01923 720714. Email: 101602.376@compuserve.com.

REFERENCES

[1] *Your First Packet Station*, Steve Jelly, G0WSJ, RSGB, 1996.

[2] *Packet Radio Primer*, 2nd edn, Dave Coomber, G8UYZ, and Martyn Croft, G8NZU, RSGB, 1995.

[3] *PMR Conversion Handbook*, Chris Lorek, G4HCL, RSGB, 1997.

8 Amateur television

OF all our senses, sight is probably the most precious to us. Almost every activity we involve ourselves in has a degree of searching, moving and manipulating which require visual cues or feedback at some point. It seems logical that visual communication using television, which has become so much a part of our domestic lives, should also be applied to amateur radio. Listen to any voice conversation on the amateur bands and before long you will hear someone describing a piece of equipment in their shack or asking if anybody knows what a "grey thing with an odd-looking connector in the top corner" is. It's much easier to explain the gadget in your hand when you can hold it up to a camera and let the other person see it for themselves. The adage "a picture is worth a thousand words" is proven true with amateur television (ATV).

The majority of ATV contacts are picture and sound in one direction with 'talkback', usually on 144.750MHz in the UK, in the return direction. Full duplex operation (sound and vision both ways simultaneously) is becoming more popular as activity grows and repeater coverage is extended.

WHAT GETS BROADCAST?

As in the case of voice communication, ATV tends to be unprepared and unrehearsed. Some people use television as an extension of photography – their interest lies in the picture content and production rather than its technical aspects. Others are experimenters, preferring to try new electronic techniques and exotic components. The blend of art and technology works well and provides a wide variety of enjoyable material.

Local shows and events are often tape recorded with camcorders and replayed to an audience over the air – occasionally, depending primarily on location, the transmissions are sent 'live'. Having an ATV station at a public event always attracts attention and is a good way of introducing newcomers to the hobby. The view through a camcorder lens will often make a more rewarding transmission than one from a professional camera team or editing suite.

Of course, many ATV transmissions are simply 'shack shots' with the camera pointing at the operator – this may not always be the prettiest of sights but at least it adds a more personal touch to the contact. There are a few ATVers who prefer not to send camera shots at all and concentrate their efforts on transmitter and video circuitry design – the only evidence on-air of these devotees is an occasional test card transmission.

Like other aspects of amateur radio, TV has its contests and contest groups. The challenge in UK ATV contests is to send a four-digit number over the greatest distance and receive confirmation of its total from the recipient. The numbers themselves are never repeated back in case they are overheard by other competitors but they are entered in the contest log sheets for checking by the adjudicator. Some contests allow slow-scan television (SSTV) on the HF bands, while others only allow normal fast-scan TV on 70cm and above. Either way, striving to exchange pictures as well as voice enhances the competition. Picture quality reports are also exchanged using the 'P' system, where P0 corresponds to an unrecognisable picture through to P5 for a perfect, blemish-free picture.

A CLOSE LOOK AT A TELEVISION SIGNAL

Unlike a voice transmission which only carries a single modulation at audio frequencies, TV signals are a composite of several different component parts. Before getting too deeply involved in transmitter and receiver functions, let's look at exactly what these video components are and their purpose.

The intention is to measure the amount of light falling at each point in the source image and faithfully recreate it on a screen some distance away. Two of the requirements are already defined: a way of measuring the intensity of light and some way of defining its position within the image. If colour is being used, a third signal is needed – this is itself a composite of two *colour difference* signals modulated onto a common carrier. This method of carrying colour information ensures compatibility with monochrome monitors which can simply ignore the colour difference signals and use the intensity (also called *luminance*) signal alone.

In the camera, the source image is focused by a lens and made to illuminate a light-sensitive pick-up. In older cameras this was a sensitised layer which was electrostatically charged – some of the charge was displaced when hit by light. The layer, or *target* as it is correctly named, was also hit by an electron beam which was magnetically or electrostatically scanned to make it sweep side to side and top to bottom over the image area. You may find it useful to think of the scanning process as moving your eyes over these lines of text. The combination of electron beam, fixed charge and light impact made the target voltage change according to the light intensity at the point hit by the beam, and after amplification this was used as the video signal.

More modern cameras use charge-coupled devices (CCDs) to convert the image to an electrical signal. The image is focused onto the CCD which consists of an array of photo-sensitive cells – the charge on the cell depends upon the amount of light falling onto it. To retrieve the image as a usable voltage, the cells are read sequentially, usually as a long shift register (aka *bucket brigade*). The process is analogous to the electron beam scanning in an older camera in that at any point in time the signal from the CCD corresponds to a particular position in the image.

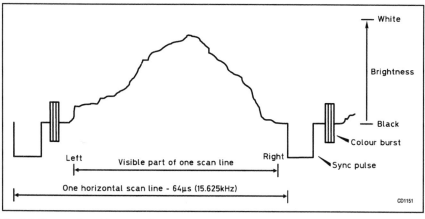

Fig 8.1. Composite video waveform

Once a video signal has been generated, it can be used to modulate a carrier and be sent over the air. At the receiving station, the signal can be demodulated to recover the original voltage. The final step is to use the video signal to change the intensity of a dot of light on the monitor screen.

If the position of the dot and its intensity match that generated in the camera, the image has been successfully reproduced. The process of ensuring the same position within the image is being used at the sending and receiving stations is called *synchronisation* or 'sync' for short. The sync pulses are generated in the camera at the sending end and are included in the transmitted waveform. There are two main types of sync pulse – one occurs just before the start of the horizontal sweep and the other before the vertical sweep – and they can be distinguished by their lengths. Horizontal sync pulses are relatively short compared to the vertical ones, and the difference in length is used in the monitor to decide which sweep should be reset to its start position.

The combined video and sync pulses is known as *composite video* and is shown diagramatically in Fig 8.1. Also shown is a part of the signal called the *colour burst* – this is only present when colour information is present in the picture. The burst is a 10-cycle-long sample of the colour subcarrier oscillator from the camera's colour encoder. It is used to ensure the colour demodulator at the receiving end stays in exact phase lock with the sending one. Inside the monitor, a timing circuit triggered by the horizontal sync pulse opens a gate allowing only the colour burst through. It is then compared to the phase of the monitor's own colour decoder oscillator and any phase errors between them are detected and eliminated. As an extra precaution, the phase of the burst signal is shifted +45 then −45° relative to centre on alternate lines. The monitor averages the phase shift to derive a single central phase for demodulating and uses the instantaneous difference in phase to decide the polarity of one of the colour difference signals. This system is called *phase alternation line* (PAL). The advantage of PAL over the North American NTSC colour system, which does not alternate the burst phase, is that phase errors taken over any two-line average tend to cancel out. Phase errors manifest themselves as shifts in the hue of the colour, for example making flesh tones take on a green or blue tinge. This can be quite important in ATV where poor signal paths are common and can cause considerable distortion to both amplitude and phase. The full process of encoding and decoding colour information is beyond the scope of

this text – see the references at the end of this chapter for further reading on this subject.

The final component added to the composite video before transmission is the sound carrier. Audio is first pre-emphasised by increasing the volume of its high frequencies while at the receiving end these higher frequencies are attenuated to bring them back to their original levels. This roll-off of the frequency response also reduces the effect of noise from other sources, thus improving the overall signal-to-noise ratio. The transmission audio is used to frequency modulate a carrier at a nominal 6MHz. This carrier is then added at low level to the picture signal and the total is then used to frequency modulate the transmission carrier. The carrier-in-a-carrier principle is called *intercarrier sound*. In the receiver, the 6MHz is recovered

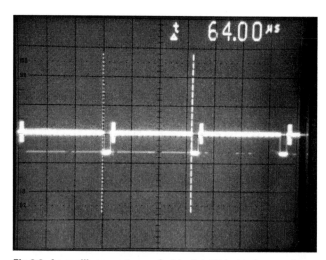

Fig 8.2. An oscilloscope trace of a blank (all-black) picture, showing sync pulses (to the right of the dotted time marker) and the colour burst (to the right of the sync pulse). The time markers are 64μs apart, corresponding exactly to the UK standard 625-line format

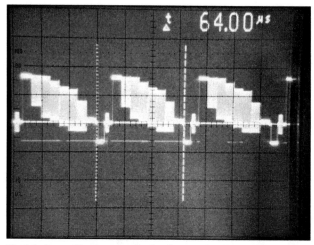

Fig 8.3. An oscilloscope trace of a display of 75% saturated colour bars. The sync pulses and colour burst are still clear

from the demodulated video, filtered and fed to its own amplifier and demodulator.

VIDEO EQUIPMENT

The vast majority of ATV operators rely on commercially available cameras and monitors so the complications of generating the composite video source are largely circumnavigated. One area where home-brew video is still the norm is the test card. Most operators use an electronic test card generator to identify themselves. Typically this will have a callsign in large letters, the operator's name and locator square. Many fancy and varied designs can be seen on the air, originating from a variety of electronic designs and sometimes generated by computer.

A typical ATV station consists of a camera, test card generator, a video and sound source switch, a TV and of course a transmitter and receiver. Some operators utilise more advanced gadgets such as video effects and 'wipe' generators or units to display one picture in another. Almost all the commercially available home-video equipment can be applied to ATV use as the transmission standards used are almost the same as those of domestic broadcast television. The narrower bandwidth used on the 70cm band does not permit colour or sound to be sent but on higher frequencies amateur TV sound and picture quality can surpass that of professional broadcasters. It follows that on the 70cm band a low-pass filter must be employed to ensure the transmission bandwidth is restricted to prevent out-of-band radiation from the signal sidebands. Even with the reduced bandwidth, perfectly acceptable pictures can be sent. For those of us who can remember 405-line television, the 70cm band can still give picture quality superior to a good VHF BBC signal!

ATV REPEATERS

Although a great deal of point-to-point operating goes on, particularly during contests, the majority of ATV activity is through repeaters. The directional nature of long Yagi arrays and dishes makes it difficult to find new contacts unless locations and headings are known before hand. Repeaters provide a central target to aim at and their omnidirectional output ensures their reception in the widest possible area. Unlike voice and data repeaters, ATV repeaters are normally operational all the time. Instead of shutting down when not in use, they show a test card (Fig 8.5) or page of descriptive text instead. The presence of a steady constant signal is an enormous help when setting up a receiving system, making it easy to optimise antenna position and receiver tuning. Some repeaters have facilities for reporting the strength of incoming signals, displaying a graphic S-meter to assist with transmitter alignment. The wide separation between repeater input

Fig 8.4. Typical ATV shack

and output frequencies, usually 50MHz or more, also makes it fairly easy to filter out transmitted RF from the receiver input, allowing 'look-through' while sending.

Repeater input and output signals are horizontally polarised, generally using Alford slot antennas, although some allow the selection of a directional antenna to improve reception at the repeater by sending command tones (usually telephone dialling tones) over the sound channel.

ATV TRANSMITTERS

The methods employed depend upon the band being used. On the 70cm band, where space is very limited, transmissions are normally amplitude modulated and ideally will have one of the sidebands reduced in amplitude by filtering – this asymmetrical spectrum is called *vestigial sideband*. Sound

Fig 8.5. Off-air capture of the Bristol 24cm repeater test card over 25km distance

and colour carriers are normally not used on 70cm because they would result in sidebands spreading wider than the band allocation allows. Control of the final amplifier supply voltage is normally used to achieve the amplitude modulation of the carrier. On the higher-frequency bands, FM is the predominant mode of operation, the combined composite video, colour and sound signals being used to directly control the transmission frequency. Some operators have experimented with reduced bandwidth FM in the 70cm band and achieved good results but unfortunately the techniques used are somewhat incompatible with domestic television sets and are therefore not very popular.

ATV construction guidelines

The frequencies present in a video waveform span DC up to about 5MHz and therefore need to be treated rather like a HF band signal. Screening is important, not only to prevent pickup of magnetic or radio signals but to prevent radiation of the same. A strong signal entering the video signal chain will show as a pattern overlaid on the picture – this may be stationary or random depending on the type of interfering signal. Interference escaping from video circuitry manifests itself as a buzzing sound on nearby radio receivers. The level and harshness of the buzz changes with the picture content.

Always use screened cables to carry video signals – 75Ω cable is generally used rather than the 50Ω type used to carry RF. Unfortunately, the quality of domestic UHF TV feeder cables leaves a lot to be desired and in many cases is unusable. Use a cable with a properly woven braid to ensure signal leakage is minimised. Cables should be correctly fed and terminated with resistive loads – mismatch causes standing wave problems which show as 'ghosts' or repeated images side by side as the signal bounces back and forth along the cable. Very short reflections can cause phase cancellation of certain frequencies which may result in loss of colour or sound subcarriers.

Most ATV stations will have more than one video source on hand, probably at least one camera and a test card generator. Because these are most likely not synchronised with each other, if any cross-coupling occurs between them, the weaker signal will probably appear as a faint image drifting slowly through the dominant one. Care is needed to minimise this breakthrough, particularly in source-switching or mixing units. Standard CMOS signal switch ICs can be used at video frequencies but grounding and decoupling needs to be very efficient to keep the signals apart. Note also that switching between unsynchronised signals will almost certainly cause monitor 'jump' until the new sync pulses are recognised and cross-fading will wreak havoc while two sets of sync pulses appear together.

Unlike audio where a potentiometer can control the volume, video fading requires the reduction of the visible part of the waveform while leaving the sync pulses and colour burst at the same amplitude. Reducing sync level will result in an unlocked picture, while reducing burst level will cause severe colour noise and eventually no colour at all. Several designs for video faders or 'fade to black' units are available from sources listed later. Basically they use the sync pulses to operate a changeover switch – syncs pass straight through while the picture information alone is routed through an attenuator. The two paths are then recombined.

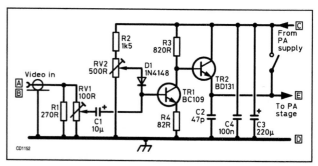

Fig 8.6. 70cm AM modulator. BD131 will require a small heatsink (minimum 10°C/W)

Practical design for an AM modulator

The circuit shown in Fig 8.6 is a simple AM modulator for use in the 70cm band and can be used to convert a low-powered (no more than 3W) conventional voice rig to transmit ATV. Ideally the rig should use CW mode but FM will work just as well if the microphone audio is disconnected. Although a small amount of audio frequency deviation will not affect the picture, it will be receivable on a conventional FM receiver. To use the modulator, the power supply to the PA stage (and possibly driver stage) is redirected through TR2. The switch across TR2, when closed, will restore normal operation so the transmitter can be used as before when not using ATV mode. Before adding the circuit, it will be necessary to locate and disconnect any large-value decoupling capacitors which will almost certainly be present across the PA supply lines. A small capacitance, no more than 470pF, should be left in place to provide a low impedance to RF and to help attenuate any high frequencies in the video signal. Component and PCB layouts are given in Appendix 1.

Adjustment is straightforward. Initially set RV2 to mid-position and tune the rig to the desired frequency – 435.5MHz is a commonly used frequency but avoid moving too close to the band edges as sidebands will start to radiate out of band. With the switch closed, check that the rig is working normally. If all is well, open the switch – the output power should drop and be adjustable by setting RV2. Apply a video signal, preferably of a stationary image or test card, and set RV1 to mid-position. While monitoring on a receiver, adjust RV2 for optimum picture – at one end of its range the sync pulses will

Table 8.1. Component list for 70cm AM ATV modulator		
Component	**Value**	**Maplin order code**
R1	270R	M270R
R2	1k5	M1K5
R3	820R	M820R
R4	82R	M82R
RV1	100R	UF97F
RV2	470R	UF99H
C1	10μ	AT98G
C2	47p	WX52G
C3	220μ	AT41U
C4	100n	YR75S
D1	1N4148	QL80B
TR1	BC109	QB33L
TR2	BD131	QF03D
Heatsink for TR2	—	JW29G

Note: Heatsink is suitable for rigs up to 1W – a larger heatsink may be needed if the modulator is used with more powerful rigs.

Fig 8.7. Photo of modulator board

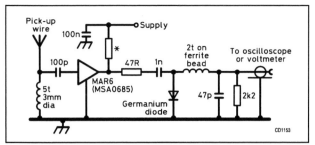

Fig 8.8. Simple RF pick-up probe and detector. * Use 330R for 12V supply – reduce to 270R for 9V battery

'crush', causing the monitor to lose synchronisation. At the other end the brightest parts of the picture will 'wash out', rather like the appearance of an over-exposed photograph. The correct setting is midway between the onset of each symptom. Once the optimum setting is established, adjust RV1 for best contrast – its setting will have some effect on RV2 so it may be necessary to repeat both adjustments until best results are obtained.

If an oscilloscope is available, the circuit in Fig 8.8 will help with the alignment. It is a simple RF pick-up probe and detector. If used, the oscilloscope should display the same video waveform as the one fed into the modulator. This circuit can also be used as a field-strength meter by connecting a millivolt meter instead of the oscilloscope and will work over frequencies from about 10MHz up to about 1GHz.

As with all transmitters, before connecting the antenna, check for spurious emissions and that the signal is confined within the band edges. If the sidebands are wide enough to reach the band edges, a low-pass filter should be fitted in line with the video input – a roll-off starting at about 2.5MHz should be adequate. Remember the filter response must be relatively flat right down to DC to avoid video

distortion. Use a linear amplifier after the rig to boost the power output if necessary – one suitable for SSB should do the job but under no circumstances use one designed for FM only. 70cm ATV transmissions are AM, so linearity is important.

23/24cm (1.3GHz) transmitter designs

Several excellent and inexpensive kits are available for this band, and it is doubtful if one could be built with better quality and lower price than these kits offer. A list of some kit suppliers is given later.

Most designs use a varactor diode (varicap) to tune a VCO at the transmitted frequency. The alternative of using a lower-frequency oscillator and passing it through frequency-multiplying stages is sometimes used but the relatively wide deviation can cause problems, especially as the deviation is multiplied along with the carrier. After the oscillator there is usually a buffer stage and then a modular power amplifier block. Several amplifiers are available at affordable prices. Mitsubishi make one capable of producing 20W when adequately heatsinked. Frequency stability is usually controlled by using a PLL and frequency divider (normally in one IC) – the Plessey SP5060 and SP5070 are popular, containing the phase detector, a divide-by-256 prescaler and the reference oscillator circuits. For example, a crystal cut to

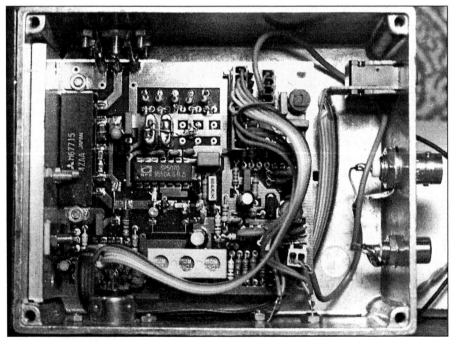

Fig 8.9. 1.5W 24cm ATV transmitter designed by G8OZP

Fig 8.10. A typical 23/24cm transmitter and test-card generator unit at GW6BWX. The transmitter is on the right in the die-cast box and is the GB3VR group design as mentioned in the text under 'Kits'. The PCB to its left is a home-brew testcard generator. The front-panel switches allow either normal operation or link the test-card generator to the transmitter so it can send identification without a camera attached.

4.902MHz will result in a carrier 256 times higher in frequency on the 1255MHz simplex TV frequency.

ATV RECEIVERS

As with transmitters, receiver techniques depend very much on the band being used. On the 70cm band, where AM is the predominant mode, most stations use up-converters to shift the band so it can be received on a normal UHF broadcast TV. Some televisions and VCRs will tune low enough to receive the band without any additional converter or modification but the later-generation synthesised tuners are less generous when it comes to out-of-UHF-band reception. Some manually tuneable TV sets have a resistor in series with the low-voltage side of the tuning control, and shorting it out will usually allow the bottom end of the tuning range to extended down to the ATV frequencies. Domestic terrestrial broadcasts in the UK are AM so the mode used commercially and in 70cm ATV are completely compatible.

On bands above 70cm the mode usually used is FM which makes a separate receiver mandatory. This isn't as bad as it first sounds because domestic satellite broadcasts are FM and surplus receivers are inexpensive and only require minor modification before being usable for ATV. To see what changes are needed to convert a satellite receiver it is first necessary to understand how one works. In essence they are nothing more than a normal superheterodyne receiver with a tuneable IF and an additional intercarrier sound demodulator.

Fig 8.11 shows the structure of a typical system – the satellite signal is typically in the 11GHz (K) band and is down-converted inside the LNB by mixing with a 10GHz local oscillator and filtering to accept the subtractive product. After amplification, this signal is sent down a coaxial cable to the indoor unit which is tuneable across the filter bandwidth, typically 750MHz to 2GHz. Sometimes the LNB local oscillator can be switched to different fixed frequencies so a wider range of input bands can be converted to the same IF. Note that the whole of the 23/24cm band falls within the tuning range of the indoor unit – many receivers even give a direct frequency readout of the IF and therefore the frequency being received.

Satellite units can be used without any modification at all but performance can be significantly enhanced by making a few small changes. First, a warning. When used for satellite reception, the DC supply to the LNB is fed from the receiver via the coaxial cable. If an antenna utilising a looped dipole or balun is directly attached it will short out the supply and may cause damage. There are several ways to avoid this problem – the simplest is to cut the supply feed wire inside the receiver but alternatively a small capacitor can be wired in line with the input socket. If a capacitor is used, make sure it is a type suitable for use at UHF or losses will be incurred.

Probably the most satisfactory solution is to use the feed to power a preamplifier because, as receivers are normally preceded by an LNB which provides 50dB or more gain, they

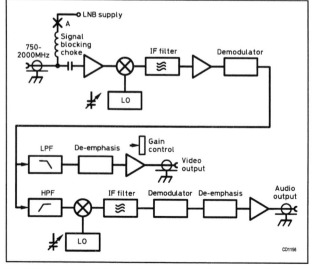

Fig 8.11. Functional blocks of a typical satellite receiver. Cut at 'A' to isolate voltage from input socket if connecting antenna directly

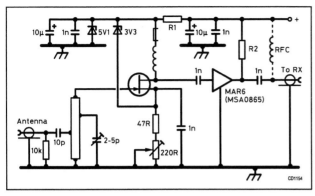

Fig 8.12. High-gain 23/24cm preamp using GaAs FET and MMIC from dismantled LNB. For 12V operation, R1 = 150R (0.5W) and R2 = 330R (0.5W). To power from satellite receiver, R1 = 270R (1W), R2 = 560R (0.5W) and connect RFC (5t on 3mm former) as shown to link receiver supply from coaxial output cable

Fig 8.14. Photo of amplifier board

are relatively insensitive when used alone. Many designs for preamps exist – the single GaAsFET followed by a MMIC seems popular and yields excellent results. If the preamp includes a filter, it should have sufficient bandwidth to allow a 12MHz-wide TV signal through. A narrow-band filter will result in poor sound and colour performance because both of these use the higher-frequency contents of the video signal.

A simple and inexpensive design is illustrated in Fig 8.12. The GaAsFET and MMIC devices can be salvaged from a broken LNB – typically there are three low-noise FETs and two MMICs inside an LNB so they make an excellent source of RF amplifier components, yet are usually thrown away when they break down. A trip to the local TV dealer to ask for discarded LNBs can be very rewarding. Before removing semiconductors from an LNB, mark them to identify the input pin, for once removed it can be difficult to tell their original orientation. Hint: use sharp scissors to cut the PCB around the component before unsoldering, it reduces the heat dissipation into the board and shortens the time the component is heated by the soldering iron.

It should be noted that satellite broadcasts use a much higher modulation index than used in ATV and this will result in a lower-than-expected video voltage from the demodulator. Almost all satellite receivers have an internal video gain control which can usually be advanced to maximum to increase the video level. There may be a penalty to pay for increasing the

level control – the amplifier stage in some receivers will exhibit poor HF response due to bandwidth reduction as more gain is demanded. If this happens, little can be done with the existing amplifier and another stage will have to be added in series – this can be in-line with the video output socket and external to the receiver if desired.

A suitable external amplifier with two identical output channels is shown in Fig 8.13. Component and PCB layouts are given in Appendix 1. Deriving a split-polarity supply from a DC-DC inverter unit eliminates the need for coupling capacitors, so ensuring a near-perfect LF response. Do not be tempted to use normal op-amp ICs in this application – purpose-designed video amplifier ICs have a wide bandwidth, low phase distortion and are designed to feed 150Ω loads (75Ω in series with the cable and 75Ω terminating load at the far end). Also, note that large-value coupling capacitors should normally be used to carry video signals – the relatively low impedance used and requirement to convey frequencies close to DC makes a low reactance essential. It is also a good idea to connect a low-value ceramic capacitor in parallel with large-value electrolytic capacitors as their internal inductance can reduce their effectiveness at carrying high frequencies. Poor low-frequency response will be seen as a brightness gradient across large areas of dark or light picture and in extreme cases will lead to poor vertical synchronisation or field roll. A poor high-frequency response causes a loss of definition and makes the picture appear smudged.

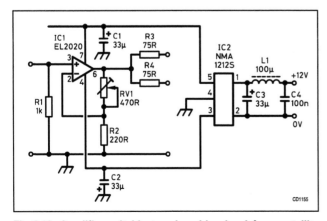

Fig 8.13. Amplifier suitable to raise video level from satellite receiver

Table 8.2. Component list for video amplifier		
Component	Value	Maplin order code
R1	1k	M1K
R2	220R	M220R
R3, R4	75R	M75R
RV1	470R	UF99H
C1, C2, C3	33μ	AU00A
C4	100n	RA49D
L1	100μ	WH41U
IC1	EL2020	UR06G
IC2	NMA1212S	AH17T

Some older satellite receivers expect fixed sound carrier frequencies, usually 6.5MHz, but modern ones are tuneable usually between 5.5MHz and 8MHz. If the frequency is fixed, the sound IF filter needs to be replaced – they are all a standard size and 6MHz ones, as used in domestic TV sets, are inexpensive and easy to obtain. Obviously, satellite receivers are not ideal for ATV use but they are inexpensive and make a good 'base' system on which to build. Experience shows that the performance of a 'hotted-up' satellite receiver is almost indistinguishable from a purpose-designed ATV receiver.

OPERATING TIPS

To check for local activity, try calling on 144.750MHz – it's used throughout the UK and much of Europe as a 'talkback' frequency so it is likely to be monitored by active ATV stations.

When sending live pictures, try to send sound with them, particularly when talking to the camera. Do this even if you are also using a separate 'voice' transmitter to talk to another station – watching someone's lips moving but not hearing what they are saying is impolite to say the least. Remember there could be people watching who cannot hear the voice transmission.

Try to keep the camera in the same line of view as the monitor – if possible place it immediately above the centre of the monitor screen as a slight downward glance while you watch the picture is hardly noticeable. If the camera and monitor are spaced too far apart, there is a natural tendency to look toward the monitor rather than the lens. At the receiving end this looks like the conversation is with someone out of camera view in the shack instead of the station in contact.

Be aware of the background – avoid bright lights or reflections which can result in flare or a silhouette image. The rules are pretty much the same as with photography – keep the light source behind the camera, not behind the subject.

If the camera is in a position where other members of the family can be seen, make sure they are aware that they can be observed and overheard by a third party. Embarrassing situations when people are unaware of the camera being used are not uncommon!

FURTHER INFORMATION

The BATC (British Amateur Television Club), affiliated to the RSGB, exists for the benefit of ATV enthusiasts. It has about 2000 members and issues a quarterly colour magazine called *CQ-TV*. Membership is currently £12 per year. Details from: The Membership Secretary, 'Grenehurst', Pinewood Road, High Wycombe, Bucks, HP12 4DD.

The BATC also publish several ATV books and offer an extensive library of technical publications to members. They can also provide printed circuit boards and components for many of the projects featured in their magazine. They organise an annual ATV rally and a biannual ATV convention.

KITS

23cm transmitter kits are available from:
Worthing & District Video Repeater Group, GB3VR, c/o 21 St. James Ave, Lancing, Sussex, BN15 0NN. This is a 1W design, priced at £80.

Bob Platts, G8OZP, 220 Rolleston Road, Burton upon Trent, Staffs, DE13 0AY. This is a slightly more powerful design using a PLL and incorporating video and audio filters. It produces 2W and is priced at £125.

23cm antennas are available from:
Severnside Television Group, 18 Linnet Close, Patchway, Bristol, BS12 5RN. They sell three types: a trough reflector design for £19, an 18-element Yagi for £15 and a 38-element Yagi for £26. The 18-element unit can be converted to the 38-element type with a conversion kit also sold by this group.

All the prices quoted are correct at the beginning of 1997 but should be confirmed before ordering. Please send an SAE with enquiries as some of these suppliers are non-profit making organisations, manned by volunteers to raise funds to keep ATV repeaters on the air.

9 Satellite communications

AMATEUR active satellites have been on the scene since the first OSCAR (orbiting satellite carrying amateur radio) launched in 1961. They have been likened to amateur repeaters. They *do* receive a signal on one frequency and transmit it on another but there the similarity ends.

Terrestrial repeaters are at a fixed point and do not need steerable antennas to track them. Most repeaters use FM and most satellites use Morse or SSB. Terrestrial repeaters cost a few thousand pounds to build and support and can be serviced or replaced without much effort. Satellites, on the other hand, cost upwards of £300,000 to design, build and launch, plus a few thousand pounds a year to command into the correct orbit. For the Phase 3 D satellites, it is at present about £2,500,000 (1996 prices).

Orbiting satellites cannot be serviced with new hardware once in orbit and, to date, battery supplies have been provided with solar energy to maintain control and transponder output.

Satellites have a shortish life span of five to 10 years before decay or mishap cause their demise. Generally they operate on a bandpass of a few hundred kilohertz in the internationally allocated Amateur Satellite Service bands using Morse or SSB and providing a worldwide service. A few operate in digital modes.

There are a number of current satellites which are divided into four classes:

1. Those with transponders, receiving on one band and transmitting on another. These are the 'conventional' satellites and use Morse or SSB.

2. Those which receive digital signals, store them and retransmit them later on interrogation. These are the so-called *forward store and retrieve* satellites.

3. Those which contain scientific apparatus and send out data signals for reception only, eg the UOSAT series.

4. Occasionally there are radio amateurs in orbiting spacecraft. Information is usually broadcast by the RSGB with the bands to be used, the times of operation and the modes. These occur every day when the amateur is on board.

Most satellites contain beacons, reception of which is a good indication that the satellite is within range. They always carry information of the condition of the satellite, ie telemetry.

Since there are a large number of active satellites, and they are being added to regularly, no list is given here. Data is available in the *RSGB Yearbook* or, in a more up-to-date form, from AMSAT UK [1]. There are currently (1996) 19 active satellites in orbit.

Table 9.1. Satellite operating modes

Mode	Input ('uplink') (MHz)	Output ('downlink') (MHz)
A	145	29
B	435	145
J	145	435
K	21	29
L	1269	435
S	435	2401
T	21	145

BAND PLANS

Most satellites are built and recommended for use with a low duty cycle. This means that Morse or SSB are the normal modes with recommended use as follows:

Morse: The lower one-third of the received signal section.

Mixed Morse/SSB: The middle one-third of the band.

SSB: The upper one-third of the receive section.

MODES

Modes are the names of the system of input and output frequencies used in each satellite. They are shown in Table 9.1.

A frequency list of all current amateur satellites is available from [1] together with a satellite information package. Each costs £1.94 at present (1996).

ANTENNAS

As will be realised, the best communication is obtained from beam antennas for each band which are fully steerable both in azimuth and elevation.

In some cases, simple dipoles for 145MHz and 29MHz running east-west should enable the satellite to be used for 80% of each pass. This is especially true for LEO (low earth orbiters) devices.

WHERE TO FIND ORBITAL INFORMATION?

The Oscalator and Orbital Calendar are all that is required to find a particular satellite. A computer is not necessary. These are available from [1] at a small charge of £3.00 for *two* months or £18.00 for a year to members of AMSAT-UK. At present (1996), membership costs a minimum of £13.50 per year. This just covers costs and more would be very welcome.

A more complex method using *Kepler elements* [2, 3] is also available from the same source together with tracking software for the IBM PC. Books on the subject are available

Code of practice for satellite users

1. Ensure that your down link is the best possible. No other factor will help more than a really low-noise, high-sensitivity receive system (see Chapter 4). Use the best, lowest-loss, feeders and the shortest runs possible for the up-link and down-link systems. Every decibel counts if the signal has to travel 40,000km *and* back! It should be easy to hear the up-link signal on the down-link without using excessive power (see below).

2. Use the *absolute minimum* of power (ERP is meant here) to make the contact. The return signal should be *no stronger* than the beacon when that is available. No attempt to use the satellite should be made unless the beacon can be heard. Some satellites need as little as 10W ERP. Do not attempt satellite communication unless good power control is possible with the transmitter in use.

3. Observe the amateur code of politeness. Listen before transmitting and be sure that the channel is clear. Join others on the frequency if appropriate. Please do not put out a long CQ call because that is unlikely to be answered.

4. If you are in doubt or requiring help, there are many users who will be glad to help. To find one, listen to the AMSAT net on 144.280MHz in many parts of the UK or the net on 3.780MHz at 10.15 local time on Sunday or 19.00 local time on Monday or Wednesday or ask AMSAT UK [1].

from the RSGB or from AMSAT-UK. An SASE or some IRCs will bring lists and an application form to join AMSAT-UK.

GETTING STARTED

With modern transceivers for the modes to be used, the only other requisite is an antenna system. As mentioned above steerable beams are preferred, but access can be achieved using simple crossed dipoles at least for the lower frequency bands (21, 28 and 144MHz). The need is for a system which has either circular polarisation (see Chapter 5) or has changeable polarisation because polarisation of signals from the satellite are variable by nature and, in any case, may change on transmission through the ionosphere. A start can be made by listening on the beacon frequencies (listed in the data from [1]) which are lower than the downlink frequency by 50–100kHz. Having found the downlink frequency, listen to the traffic and get used to the change of frequency caused by the Doppler effect – the frequency is higher when the satellite is approaching, it falls at its nearest point and is lower when it is going away.

Having become accustomed to the various effects, make an attempt to join a QSO at a suitable break, bearing in mind the suggestions above in the code of practice.

REFERENCES

[1] Contact AMSAT-UK via Ron Broadbent, MBE, G3AAJ, Hon Sec, AMSAT-UK, London, E12 5EQ. Tel: 0181-989 6741 (+44 181-989 6741 for overseas readers). Compuserve ID: 100024,614. Internet at: rbroadbent@ee.surrey.ac.uk.

[2] *Radio Communication Handbook*, ed Dick Biddulph, G8DPS, RSGB, 1994, Chapter 18.

[3] *Space Radio Handbook*, John Branegan, GM4IHJ, RSGB, 1992, Chapter 4.

10 Repeaters

REPEATERS have been described as the second greatest development in amateur radio since the Second World War. The first was, of course, the advent of SSB which is firmly established as the speech DX mode on all bands.

What is a repeater? A repeater is analogous to the talk-through systems of the user services. In commercial two-way radio systems the base station and the mobile station are allocated different transmit frequencies so that any eavesdropper can only hear half the conversation. In commercial circles talkthrough is often a luxury in that it allows mobile-to-mobile communication rather than the more normal mobile-to-base traffic.

In the Amateur Service mobile-to-mobile contact is very common but the difficulty is that range is restricted – why not put a base station on the biggest hill in the county so that many mobiles can make contact through it? See Fig 10.1.

A repeater is a device which will receive a signal on one frequency, and simultaneously transmit it on another frequency. Careful design has meant that repeaters can receive and transmit on the same band, and this means that the same antenna can be used for both reception and transmission. In effect, the receiving and transmitting coverage of the mobile station becomes that of the repeater and, since the repeater is favourably sited on high ground or a tall mast, the range is greatly improved over that of unassisted, or *simplex* operation. The coverage areas of two mobile stations continually change shape, whereas the coverage of a repeater will stay constant, and can even be published (Fig 10.2).

The Amateur Service has specific bands and repeaters are confined to fairly small segments of these bands by international agreement so that the needs of all users can be accommodated in the limited amount of spectrum available. The repeater uses two frequencies simultaneously, one for transmit and one for receive.

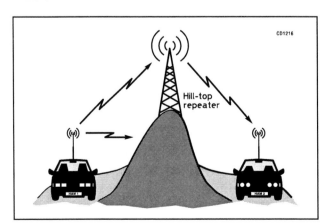

Fig 10.1. A repeater on a hill being used by two mobile stations

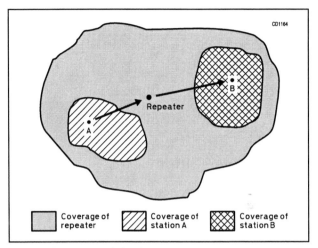

Fig 10.2. Repeater and simplex areas

Repeaters are operational in the UK on all of the VHF bands except for the 70MHz one because the small amount of space available means that it is not able to accommodate any. The difference between receive and transmit frequency is 500kHz on 50MHz, 600kHz on 145MHz, 1.6MHz on 432MHz and 6MHz on 1.3GHz. Channel spacings are 10kHz, 25kHz (soon to become 12.5kHz), 25kHz and 25kHz respectively. On the 50 and 433MHz bands the input frequency is higher than than the output frequency but in the other bands it is lower.

During the late 'sixties and early 'seventies FM came into widespread use on the VHF bands mainly because of its cheapness and the ease of construction of FM equipment compared with that for SSB. Surplus ex-private mobile radio (PMR) equipment was cheaply available and this was frequently converted from high-band PMR use to FM on the amateur 2m band.

The improvement to mobile communications system performance is quite dramatic because although the range is potentially less, the quality of reception is much better. This is because of the limiting effect of an FM signal which eliminates much of the ignition noise from surrounding vehicles. Although an individual may have satisfactorily suppressed his/her vehicle the problem is all those other unsuppressed vehicles around. It is also advantageous for the repeater in that when a receiver is close in frequency to an adjacent transmitter a lot of amplitude noise is generated which is easier to eliminate in an FM system by the nature of the limiting action of the FM detector.

Because of the limited spectrum available in the amateur bands it is customary to use a much narrower spacing between the receive (input) and the transmit frequency (output) compared to commercial systems, eg on the 430MHz band

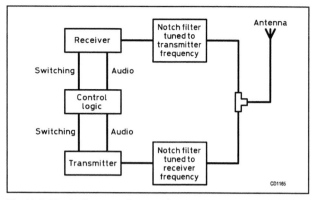

Fig 10.3. Block diagram of parts of a repeater

the spacing is 1.6MHz and on 144MHz band is 600kHz. There are nearly 300 repeaters in the UK, comprising approximately 80 VHF repeaters, 170 UHF repeaters, and 25 repeaters on the 1.3GHz band including 12 TV repeaters. There are also four TV repeaters operational on the 10GHz band. Some of these repeaters are extremely popular and are in use for many hours a day whereas the corresponding PMR system might only be in use for a few minutes per hour. This continuous service aspect of repeaters makes greater demands on power supplies and other components which have to be continuously rated rather than for intermittent use. Further information on these repeaters is available in the *Amateur Radio Operating Manual* [1], in a computer listing available from RSGB [2], in the *RSGB Yearbook* [3] as well as in the *Amateur Radio Diary* [4], all published by the RSGB. A list is also available on the Internet [5].

The fact that large numbers of amateurs use any repeater system means that the coverage area of the unit is very quickly established. This large number of users highlights another problem. How do you share out the available air time to all potential users on what is basically a single-channel device? Although many can listen, only one person at a time can transmit. In order to provide an incentive for short transmissions it is normal to provide a limitation to the talkthrough time permitted. After a given period of time, usually one to two minutes on the busiest VHF repeaters and five minutes on the UHF repeaters, the user *times out*, ie the repeater will no longer relay the input signal.

The simplest sort of repeater needs an antenna or antennas, a receiver, a transmitter, something to control it (usually referred to as the *logic*), and an arrangement of filters to enable it to receive and transmit at the same time. A further difficulty for the would-be repeater builder is that the DTI have stipulated that repeaters should not be triggered by a spurious transmission on their input frequency. Access to the repeater, ie the switching on of the transmitter, is accomplished by either a short tone burst of 1750Hz or by the transmission of a sub-audible tone. This is often called

CTCSS which stands for 'continuous tone-coded squelch system'. The user has to transmit a tone which is below the audible range all the time. The CTCSS frequency used depends on the area and has the advantage of preventing a station accessing a repeater out of its area except in exceptional conditions. For example, all the London repeaters have the same CTCSS tone (82.5Hz) but the Brighton repeater (GB3SR) on the same frequency as the East London repeater (GB3EL) would not be accessed at the same time because its tone is 88.5Hz. For convenience of mobile users, repeaters that are using the sub-audible tone transmit an appropriate letter after their callsign in Morse code to indicate which tone should be used. The tones used and the geographic areas are co-ordinated by the RSGB's Repeater Management Committee. They are shown in Fig 10.4.

If the repeater receiver hears a valid tone on its input frequency it will relay the transmission. If either the carrier or sub-audible tone ceases then after a short time the transmitter will send a 'K' or 'E' in Morse which is a signal that the input of the repeater is clear and is an invitation for another user to make a transmission. If no further valid transmission is received then after a short period of time the repeater will close down. Also the repeater transmitter must identify itself in Morse code at intervals not exceeding 15 minutes. Often

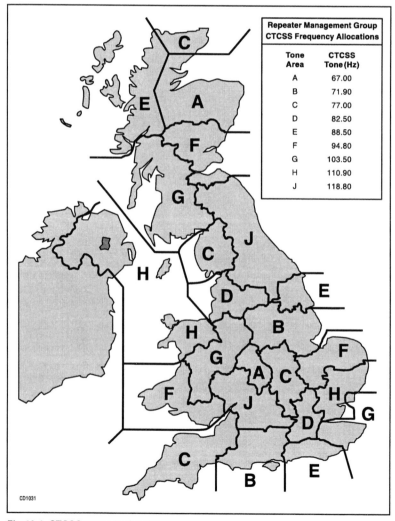

Repeater Management Group CTCSS Frequency Allocations	
Tone Area	CTCSS Tone (Hz)
A	67.00
B	71.90
C	77.00
D	82.50
E	88.50
F	94.80
G	103.50
H	110.90
J	118.80

Fig 10.4. CTCSS tones in the UK

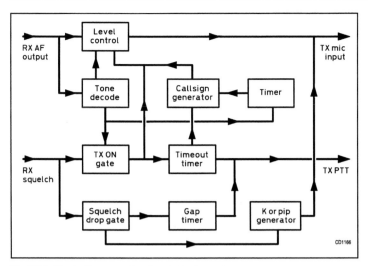

Fig 10.5. Block diagram of a simple logic system

repeaters respond with their callsign when accessed. Thus the repeater needs to be able to decide whether suitable conditions have been met before it can relay an incoming transmission, to know when to send an identifying callsign and when to close down.

As the repeater has to respond to these various situations it needs to be able to 'think' for itself especially as quite often it is remotely located. This means therefore that a logic system has to be built into it. This is often referred to simply as *the logic* by the repeater users. The control of the repeater can be accomplished by several sorts of logic systems. Some simple and very reliable circuits have been published in *Radio Communication* [6, 7]. There are other more sophisticated systems available and in operation such as the G8CUL and G1SLE logic systems. Many groups have built up their own logic systems.

Other more sophisticated techniques are beginning to appear which are microcomputer based and these can offer many other features such as remote control facilities. At least one group is using an elderly BBC microcomputer to control its repeaters including a very sophisticated interference rejection system and remote control.

HOW A SIMPLE LOGIC SYSTEM WORKS

The block diagram shows the simplest sort of repeater logic system which provides the basic minimum to cover the mandatory requirements for a working repeater as well as a user-friendly system that is simple to understand. Here is a general description of what it does. The receiver audio is fed to the toneburst decoder, producing an output which:

1. keys the transmitter;
2. feeds audio to the transmitter via the audio control;
3. starts the time out timer; and
4. activates the callsign timer.

When the user has finished talking the receiver squelch closes:

1. activating the 'K' or 'pip'
2. activating a timer determining the interval after which a callsign will be sent; and
3. resetting the timeout timer.

Thus the repeater will send a 'K' and may send a high-level

callsign if there is no receiver audio present and close the repeater transmitter down. If a further transmission takes place after the 'K' then once again the timeout timer begins to time the length of the transmission. The callsign will be sent at a time governed by the callsign timer at low deviation so as not to interrupt the audio through the repeater. Many repeaters also send what is known as a *beacon callsign* when they are not in talkthrough mode which serves to notify listeners that they are within range of a particular repeater. This is relatively simple to incorporate as there is already the timer and the callsign generator available. Repeaters may send other information such as their location and signal strength of received signals, or even a busy tone to indicate that a user has timed out but is still transmitting. There are numerous possibilities including speech messages but before incorporating any of these ideas a prospective repeater builder must seek the advice of the Repeater Management Committee of the RSGB which handles repeater applications on behalf of the Radiocommunications Agency. For further information see reference [8].

Many repeater builders make some of these parameters variable so that they can tailor the repeater to the needs or wishes of local users. It has to be pointed out that the vast majority of UK repeaters conform to the pattern of logic outlined above and this has evolved after many years of experimentation by repeater builders and users. VHF repeaters tend to be very busy devices and the timeout is almost universally set at one or two minutes. It can all be summed up in the KISS acronym – "Keep it simple, stupid!" The system outlined is easy to understand and logical to use!

HOW A REPEATER TRANSMITS AND RECEIVES AT THE SAME TIME WITHOUT DESENSING ITSELF

Desensing or *desense* is a term referring to the problem of a receiver trying to listen in the same band as the local transmitter. A transmitter never transmits a single frequency but a range of frequencies distributed either side of the carrier frequency. This results in wide-band noise which is received by the adjacent receiver and prevents it from receiving any but the very loudest signals.

This desensitisation of the receiver is usually referred to as *desensing*. How is this problem overcome? The answer is to use very selective filtering, not only in the receiver but also in the transmitter. The filtering system is usually called a *duplexer* and the process as *duplexing* as the filters allow the transmitter and receiver to operate on their two separate frequencies simultaneously, ie duplex operation, as opposed to simplex operation where the receiver or transmitter cannot operate simultaneously.

A typical duplexer is made up of three cavity filters or *cavities* in the receiver input and three cavities in the transmitter output (see Fig 10.6). Each cavity is basically a very-high-Q filter which therefore has a very high loss either side of its resonant frequency. See Fig 10.7.

The three cavities in the receive leg are tuned to the transmitter frequency so as to give maximum rejection of the transmitter. This ensures that the receiver front-end circuits are not driven into overload by the strong carrier. The transmit

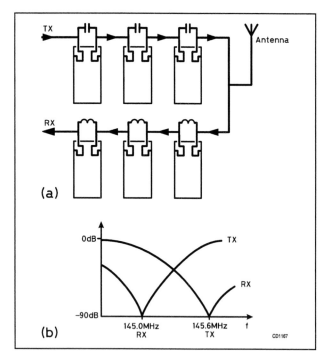

Fig 10.6. (a) Block diagram of duplexer, three-cavity receive/three-cavity transmit. (b) Response curves

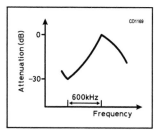
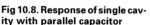

Fig 10.8. Response of single cavity with parallel capacitor

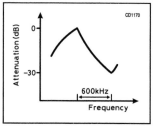

Fig 10.9. Response of single cavity with parallel inductor

USING REPEATERS

Using repeaters involves *duplex* operation where you transmit and receive on different frequencies, and most available transceivers have this facility built in. There is a user's code of practice. First, repeaters are primarily intended for *mobile* or *portable* users. It is definitely unacceptable to 'hog' them for long lengths of time. Always welcome newcomers to join in, encourage membership of the group, and remember your normal amateur codes of practice are as valid on repeaters as on simplex operation (use of callsign, courtesies etc).

Before attempting to transmit, ensure that:

(a) Your transmitter and receiver are on the correct frequencies (remember the repeater split).
(b) Your tone access (if fitted) is operating correctly.
(c) Your peak deviation is set correctly (some repeaters will not relay your signal if this is incorrect!)

Any adjustments you have to make should be done into a dummy load, *not on-air!*

Avoid using the repeater from your base station; it is really intended for the benefit of local mobile and portable stations. If you really do intend to try it from a fixed station, then use

cavities are tuned to the receiver frequency so that they attenuate the wideband noise generated by the transmitter as much as possible on the receiver input frequency. This enables the receiver to hear weak signals.

Fig 10.6(b) shows the response curve of each set of cavities at the receive and transmit frequencies. For the purposes of this diagram it has been assumed that the repeater receiver frequency is 145MHz and the transmitter frequency is 145.6MHz. However, there is a slight difference in the set of cavities used in the receive leg compared with those used in the transmit leg. Those in the transmit leg are wired up with a capacitor in parallel whilst those in the receive leg have an inductor in parallel. These additional

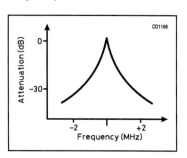

Fig 10.7. Response of a single cavity

components have the effect of skewing the filters' skirts so that the attenuation effects can be adjusted to allow little or no attenuation of the transmit frequency by the transmitter cavities and little or no attenuation on the receiver input frequency by the cavities in the receiver input. In practice this is usually adjusted on site to give the performance necessary. See Figs 10.8 and 10.9.

As a typical receiver sensitivity is of the order of −130dBm and the transmitter generates noise on the receiver frequency at about −40dBm it is necessary to achieve an attenuation of about 90dB, ie −130 − (−40) = −90 in order for the receiver to be able to receive as well as when the transmitter is off.

In practice each cavity is capable of producing a rejection notch of 30dB so the repeater needs three in each leg to provide approximately 90dB. See Fig 10.10.

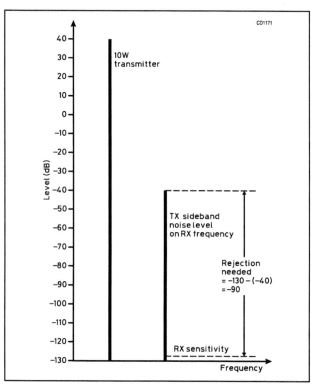

Fig 10.10. Transmitter-receiver levels for a repeater

the lowest power to get into the repeater (under 1W is acceptable in the majority of situations where you can hear the repeater well).

Always listen before transmitting. Unless you are calling another specific station, simply announce that you are "listening through", eg "GM8LBC listening through GB3CS". On the other hand, if you are responding to someone specific, try something like "GM0ZZZ from GM8LBC".

Once contact is established:

(a) At the beginning and the end of each over, you need give only your own callsign, eg "from GM8LBC".

(b) Change frequency to a simplex frequency at the first opportunity, especially if you are operating from a fixed station.

(c) Keep your overs short and to the point, or they may time out, and do not forget to wait for the 'K' or 'blip' if the repeater uses one.

(d) Do not monopolise the repeater when busy; others may be waiting to use it.

(e) If your signal is very noisy into the repeater, or if you are only opening the repeater squelch intermittently, finish the contact and try again later.

JOINING UP

Repeaters have initiated many newcomers to the amateur radio hobby. Repeater outputs can be monitored easily, either using widely available amateur equipment, or perhaps by a scanner. Repeater groups themselves have been able to join up prospective users and, through local meetings or contact, newcomers have been shown how to proceed. Many amateurs use repeaters in addition to their other amateur activities, perhaps using their local repeaters whilst travelling to and from work, then doing something entirely different in the evenings!

If you enjoy operating through your local repeaters then remember that they do cost money to run and this is done on a purely voluntary basis, sometimes by individuals but mostly by groups who would appreciate contributions towards the cost of running the repeater. Apart from the initial costs of the equipment there are the on-going costs of electricity and site rental. Site rentals for advantageous sites such as those of the BBC and NTL can cost several hundreds of pounds a year even at the favourable rates negotiated either by the local repeater group or by the RSGB.

References [1] to [5] give details of the repeater keeper who is the person to contact to offer your help to.

Amateur radio 'purists' have, particularly in the early years of repeater growth, shunned their existence, believing them not to be truly in the 'ham spirit'. Twenty-five years on, this is very much a minority view. The presentation of so many strands for devotees to find their niche is a strength of our hobby. Repeater builders are amongst the most technically competent and experienced people in amateur radio, and many are professionally employed in PMR or other professional communications. Repeaters are often co-sited with other major broadcasters or PMR users, and so have to be of a sufficient technical standard to co-exist.

Repeaters have sometimes become the target for abuse, generally by men with limited vocabularies (using profanities) or with strange voices, ('squeakies'). There have been no female abusers to our knowledge. The only way to treat the abuse in whatever form it takes is to ignore it completely. Any attempt to remonstrate with them encourages them since they know they have an audience. If possible, take a bearing on the repeater input frequency, make a tape recording of the abuser and note the time, date, frequency etc. This information should be sent to the Repeater Abuse Co-ordinator at RSGB Headquarters. Further information on how to deal with abuse problems is available from the same address.

If you feel there is a need for a repeater in your area then make sure you contact the Repeater Management Committee of the RSGB, c/o RSGB HQ and read reference [8] before you do anything else.

REFERENCES

[1] *Amateur Radio Operating Manual*, 4th edn, ed R Eckersley, G4FTJ, RSGB, 1995.

[2] *The Repeater List*, a printout from the RSGB HQ computer containing the very latest information (updated monthly).

[3] *RSGB Yearbook*, 1998 edn, ed B Rider, G4FLQ, RSGB, 1997.

[4] *The Amateur Radio Diary 1997*, ed M Bamber, G0SHY, Bambers, 1996.

[5] An Internet link to RMC Online is given in the RSGB web site at www.rsgb.org.

[6] A J T Whitaker, G3RKL, *Radio Communication* 1980, pp34–42; A J T Whitaker, G3RKL, *Radio Communication* 1982, pp30–31.

[7] A J T Whitaker, G3RKL, *Radio Communication* 1983, pp882–885 and pp990–993.

[8] *The Guide to Repeater Licensing*, 1997 edn, RMC, RSGB, 1996.

11 Test equipment, methods and accessories

IN the VHF region and above there is still a fair amount of scope for experimentation and home construction as well as the use of the so-called 'black box'. There are many items of ex-commercial equipment that can be obtained at reasonable prices for adaptation.

In the case of a receiver, where low noise is of paramount importance, it is extremely difficult to adjust an input stage or preamplifier for the best signal-to-noise ratio unless a noise generator is used.

Details of these and other useful devices are described in this chapter. They are generally straightforward and, provided care and attention to detail is taken, satisfactory and reliable performance should be achieved. Readers are also referred to *Test Equipment for the Radio Amateur*, published by the RSGB [1], which gives details of other test equipment.

ANTENNA MEASUREMENTS

To keep the performance of any VHF/UHF station as near optimum as possible the antenna system should be properly tuned to start with and maintained in that condition.

To tune up any antenna system, it is essential to keep it away from large objects such as buildings, sheds and trees, and the array itself should be at least two wavelengths above the ground. It is useless to attempt any tuning indoors since the change in the surroundings will result in a completely different performance when the array is taken outside.

Undoubtedly the most effective apparatus for tuning up any antenna system is a standing-wave indicator or reflectometer. If there is zero reflection from the load, the standing-wave ratio (SWR) on the antenna feeder is unity (1:1). Under this condition, known also as a *flat line*, the maximum power is being radiated. All antenna matching adjustments should therefore be carried out to aim at a standing wave better than about 1.5:1 (some 4% reflected power). Many modern transceivers have SWR protection circuits built-in and these may cut in and start to limit power output. Consult the manual for your equipment if in doubt.

If suitable apparatus is not available, the next best course of action is to tune the antenna for maximum forward radiation. A convenient device for this is a field-strength meter comprising a diode voltmeter connected to a $\lambda/2$ dipole placed at least 10λ from the antenna. When adjustments have resulted in a maximum reading on the field-strength meter, the SWR may not be unity and therefore some power may be wasted. However, if the best has been done with the resources available it is highly likely that good results will be achieved.

Reflectometer for VHF

When power at radio frequency is fed into a transmission line which is correctly terminated at its far end, this power is

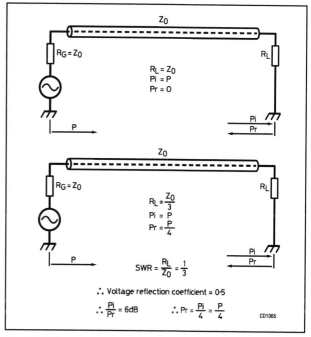

Fig 11.1. Effects of mistermination on a transmission line in terms of the incident and reflected power at the load

propagated along the line in terms of voltage and current waves and is all absorbed in the load at the far end of the line. This represents the ideal condition for the transfer of power from a transmitter to an antenna system. Such a condition is rarely, if ever, achieved due to the impossibility of presenting the transmission line with a perfectly matched load. In practice, it is possible only to terminate the line with an antenna or load which approaches the perfect condition. Under these circumstances a certain amount of power is reflected at this mistermination and is propagated back down the line again by means of further waves of voltage and current travelling in the opposite direction, to be either absorbed or re-reflected at the generator according to whether the generator impedance terminates or misterminates the line.

The amount of power reflected from the antenna or load mistermination is directly proportional to the magnitude of the mismatch on the line. Therefore, the mismatch on the line, or in more practical terms, the standing wave ratio, may be expressed in terms of the ratio of the forward or incident and the backward or reflected powers (Fig 11.1).

If the SWR = S, then the voltage reflection coefficient K is given by:

$$K = \frac{S-1}{S+1}$$

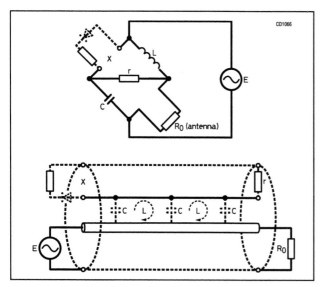

Fig 11.2. Maxwell bridge representation of transmission line coupler

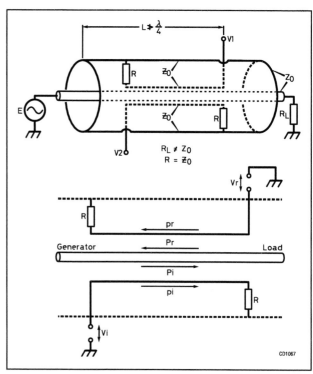

Fig 11.3. Arrangement of sampling lines to respond respectively to incident and reflected powers

Clearly, if a device can be constructed which will differentially respond to power in terms of direction, then it can be used directly to measure standing wave ratio, and the ratio M of incident to reflected power is given by:

$$M = 20 \log_{10} 1/K \text{ dB}$$

It can be shown that if a line whose length is short compared with a wavelength is introduced into the field of, and parallel to, another line which is carrying power, then an amount of power is coupled into the secondary line which is directly proportional to the magnitude of the power travelling in either or both directions on the main line. The configuration of main and sampling lines may be regarded as a Maxwell bridge, the reactive arms of which are provided by the distributed capacitance C and mutual inductance L of the coupled lines, and the effective load on the bridge is r (Fig 11.2). Then, if $r^2 = L/C$ the bridge is effectively balanced at all frequencies, and now power from the generator E appears in the load r, but a proportion appears in the detector load.

If two such subsidiary lines are coupled to a main transmission line carrying power and are respectively terminated at opposite ends, an output can be taken from each line which is respectively proportional to the incident and reflected power in the main line.

This is the principle behind the reflectometer – Fig 11.3. The accuracy of such an instrument depends on the correct termination of the sampling lines. Any mismatch on those lines will result in a standing wave along them, and consequently the RF voltages appearing at their output terminals will not be proportional to the forward and reflected powers. This parameter of performance is termed the *directivity* of the reflectometer, and is measured as the ratio of the voltage developed on the backward sampling line, when the instrument is itself correctly terminated, to the voltage on the same line when the instrument is reversed. The directivity is usually expressed as a ratio in decibels (dB).

Design aspects

Before the details of construction can be finalised, it is necessary to consider one or two design aspects of the instrument itself. It has already been shown how two voltages may be obtained which are proportional to the forward and backward components of power respectively. However, these voltages are still of a radio frequency nature and it is necessary to convert them to DC before they can be used to drive a moving coil meter.

If the forward voltage is arranged to produce a full scale deflection of the meter, then clearly the meter can be calibrated directly in SWR by observing the deflection produced by the backward voltage and making due allowance for any differences in coupling between the two sampling lines and the main line. The calibration will be valid independent of the actual transmitted power, since in each case the meter is adjusted for FSD.

In practice, it is easier to arrange for identical sampling lines, in which case the calibration of the meter becomes a simple question of the ratio of RMS voltages applied to the rectifier diodes. This places an inherent limit on the sensitivity of the instrument at low SWR. However, provided that the relative couplings can be measured, it is possible to improve the overall sensitivity for a given power and meter sensitivity by arranging for an appreciably greater degree of coupling on the backward sampling line than on the forward, and thus providing an immediate improvement of x dB in the lowest SWR which can be measured for a given deflection of the meter (Fig 11.4).

Care must be exercised that the coupling from either line is not increased to the point where the presence of the sampling line distorts the electromagnetic field around the inner of the main line sufficiently to cause an effective change of Z_0 of the main line and hence introduce an inherent SWR in the instrument itself.

As a general rule the coupling should not be greater than

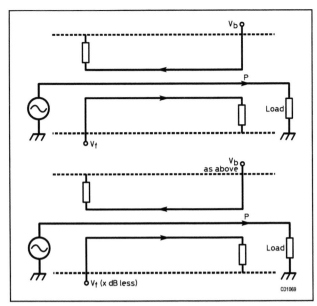

Fig 11.4. Instrument sensitivity and coupling ratios. (a) Sampling couplings equal. V_f gives meter FSD, so V_b/V_f (say y dB) which corresponds to a given meter deflection. (b) Sampling couplings different by x dB. V_f gives meter FSD less x dB for same power, SWR V_b/meter FSD, so for same deflection as (a) SWR = $x + y$ dB

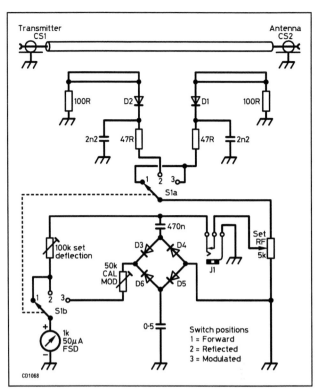

Fig 11.5. Circuit diagram of the reflectometer. D1, D2: OA91; D3–D6: 1N4148. D3–D6 should be bypassed by 1nF ceramic capacitors across each diode

30dB to maintain an inherent reflection coefficient of less than 3–4%.

When the main line is carrying power which is subject to amplitude modulation, then the sampling voltage from the forward (and backward) line will also be subject to amplitude modulation at the same modulation depth. Since this voltage has already been rectified and arranged to deflect the meter to full scale, then if a rectified (or detected) signal is once more rectified, a DC voltage will be obtained which is proportional to the audio frequency voltage modulating the carrier. This voltage can then be used to deflect the meter and this can be calibrated directly in percentage modulation. This calibration will also, to a first order, be independent of the transmitted power, since the meter has been adjusted for FSD on the sampled detected carrier.

In practice it is necessary to resort to full-wave rectification of the detected carrier, although this does not really provide sufficient DC voltage to cause large excursions of the meter reading under full modulation conditions, ie it is not possible to advance the meter to FSD for 100% modulation. It is recommended therefore that the 'modulation meter' aspect of the instrument be regarded only as of an arbitrary quantitative nature.

A circuit diagram for a typical reflectometer is given in Fig 11.5. The diodes used *must* be capable of the frequency range the instrument is to cover.

The introduction of the instrument into a transmission line requires the use of plugs and sockets, and this in turn will lead to a discontinuity in the lines at the ends of the reflectometer proper due to the sudden transition from the relatively large inner of the instrument line to the inner of the coaxial fitting. The size of the inner conductor of the instrument must be large to maintain the line characteristic impedance while at the same time providing sufficient room to accommodate the sampling lines between the inner and out conductors, ie

this is a physical requirement. These discontinuities are of the right-angled step type (Fig 11.6), and there is an optimum arrangement of dimensions to provide minimum reflection at the step for any given characteristic impedance and inner conductors ratio. There is no simple arithmetical formula relating the step-length a to these parameters.

Construction

The design is based on a die-cast box $114 \times 89 \times 55$mm (formerly $4\frac{1}{2} \times 3\frac{1}{2} \times 2$in), with a partition running the length of the box to form an almost square cross-section (51×51mm) into which the trough line is assembled. Any other spacing may be used but this complicates the calculation of Z_0 of the line.

The characteristic impedance of a coaxial line with a cylindrical inner conductor and a square outer is given by:

$$Z_0 = 138 \log_{10} L/d$$

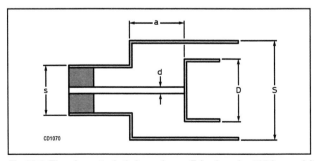

Fig 11.6. The characteristic impedance Z_0 is given by $138 \log_{10} s/d$ which is also $138 \log_{10} S/D$. The optimum step-length a is a function of Z_0 and D/d

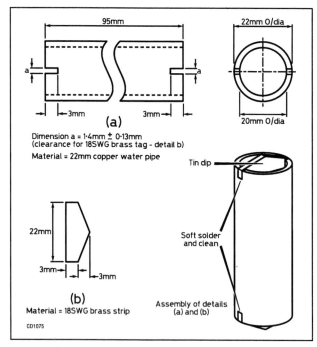

Fig 11.7. Construction of main line inner conductor

where L is the length of the side and d is the diameter of the inner conductor. It is assumed that $L/d > 1.5$. For a 50Ω line, substitution of 51mm in this formula gives $d = 22$mm.

The RF connections to the box can be made from N-type, BNC, TNC or SO239 type connector, the last being a non-constant impedance type. When soldering to these it is wise to insert a plug into them – this will hold the middle pin central as prolonged soldering usually softens the surrounding insulation.

The sockets are mounted centrally at each end of the 51mm square section of the box, and their spigots are cut down so that the overall dimension from the inside face of the box to the end of the spigot is about 6.5mm. The inner conductor detail (Fig 11.7, detail a) is slotted at each end for a depth of 3mm and wide enough to accept 18 SWG (1.4mm) brass sheet as a tight fit. It is important to ensure that the slots at each end lie in the same plane.

The small end pieces (Fig 11.7, detail b) are cut from 18 SWG (1.4mm) brass sheet and pushed into the slots at each end as shown and soldered in position. The pointed end of each tab is then tinned, any surplus solder being removed in order to keep the cylindrical shape at the ends. The inner assembly may then be rested between the spigots of the coaxial sockets and soldered into position (Fig 11.8).

The sampling lines are formed from a strip line of 18 SWG (1.4mm) brass lying parallel to the partition. The formula for the characteristic impedance of a strip line over an infinite plane is:

$$Z_0 = 230 \log_{10} 4D/W$$

where D is the distance from the plane, W is the width of the strip and the ratio D/W has a value between 0.1 and 1.0. As already explained, it is necessary to terminate the sampling lines correctly in order to preserve the directivity of the instrument, and a characteristic impedance of 100Ω is used, based upon the use of available 100Ω, 2% tolerance 0.5W

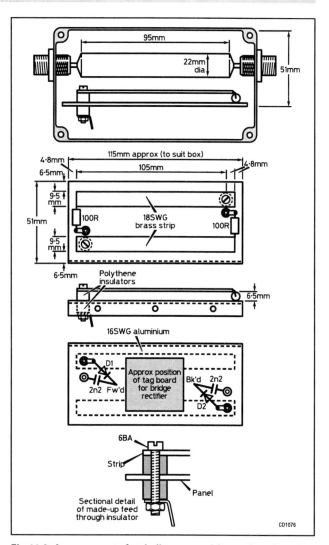

Fig 11.8. Arrangement of strip line on partition and tag board

resistors as the terminating loads. This figure substituted in the above expression gives a value of D/W of 0.68. This provides a whole possible range of dimensions for the strip line and in order to achieve the required degree of coupling to the main line a value of $D = 6.5$mm and hence $W = 9.5$mm was chosen by experiment. The sampling lines were made as long as conveniently possible, care being exercised to make them as near as physically identical as possible.

The partition is made from 16 SWG (1.6mm) aluminium sheet and the sampling lines mounted in the positions shown in Fig 11.8. The spacing of the sampling lines may be trimmed by adjustment at the terminated end when the instrument is being set up. The partition is assembled with sampling lines, tag board on the rear, and all components, before being fitted in the box. Connections from the other side of the partition to the various controls are made up as short flying leads to facilitate this assembly. An alternative and neater solution would be to mount most of the components on a PCB instead of the tag board, but keeping D1, D2, C1 and C2 in approximately the positions shown.

The position of the various potentiometers and switches is not critical, and some alteration to the suggested layout is permissible. Alternatively there is no objection to extending

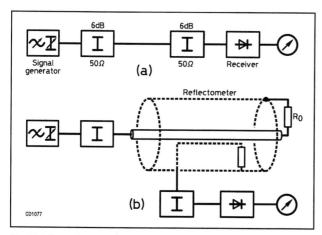

Fig 11.9. Insertion method for measuring coupling. (a) Set a signal generator to give an arbitrary deflection K on receiver meter. Note the signal generator attenuator setting, say x dB. (b) Repeat the exercise with reflectometer in circuit and readjust the signal generator to give the same deflection K on the receiver meter. Read the attenuator setting, say y dB. Then the coupling of the main line to the sampling line is x − y dB

Table 11.1. Reflectometer calibration figures (72Ω)			
Meter reading			
Forward	Backward	Level (dB)	SWR
50	50	0	∞
43	44	−2	8.8
37	36	−4	4.4
30	29	−6	3.0
23	21	−8	2.3
18	17	−10	1.92
14	13	−12	1.67
11	10	−14	1.5
8	7	−16	1.37
6	5	−18	1.29
4	3	−20	1.22
3	2	−22	1.16
2	1	−24	1.13

the DC outputs of D1 and D2 via a three-core cable to another position. D1 and D2 must be fitted as per Fig 11.8.

Calibration

Accurate calibration of the reflectometer requires a signal generator with calibrated output, a receiver with some form of carrier-level meter, and a load of known reflection coefficient suitable for direct connection to either end of the reflectometer test line (this load should be as near matched as possible). The procedure is then as follows.

First terminate the antenna end of the instrument and measure the coupling of each sampling line in turn by the insertion method (Fig 11.9). Adjust the sampling line spacing for identical coupling.

Then, using the signal generator injecting directly into each sampling diode in turn (with sampling lines disconnected), calibrate the indicating meter in terms of decibels relative to the injection voltage for FSD.

This provides also a check on the match of the diode characteristics of each sampling circuit. These must be matched if the instrument is to read accurately at all transmitted power levels. Two diodes at random from the box provided the results quoted for the prototype.

The instrument is then calibrated directly in terms of the ratio of backward to forward voltages, expressed in decibels, for all transmitted powers, provided it is always adjusted to FSD on the forward position using the SET RF control. (The SET DEFLECTION control should be set, for any particular meter, to such a value as to allow the SET RF control to function over the whole range of transmitted powers expected.)

Many amateurs will, of course, not have the necessary test equipment outlined above available to them. However, this need not detract greatly from the appeal of the instrument since, even without any calibration at all, the output from the backward line will usually reduce as the SWR on the main line is reduced. Thus the reflectometer may be used qualitatively to indicate best SWR when adjustments are being made to, say, an antenna system.

It is possible, without any test equipment other than a low-power transmitter, to make some basic checks on the instrument as follows.

With an open-circuit on the antenna end of the instrument, vary the power from the transmitter in steps, and take at each level the forward meter readings with the instrument connected normally, and then the backward meter readings with the instrument reversed. This will check the characteristics of the diodes, and also enable slight adjustments to be made to the sample lines to equalise the coupling. The latter adjustment should be carried out at the normal transmitter power only, for the best performance in practice.

Care must be exercised, when carrying out such checks, to avoid damaging the output PA device through excessive dissipation on no load. Provided that the dimensions given have been followed closely, the errors introduced due to stray differences in the final instrument should not be more than 2–3dB. Inspection of the calibration table shows that for the lower values of SWR such an error results in a very small error in SWR, this becoming increasingly worse as the SWR gets larger. Therefore, an uncalibrated but carefully built instrument can be expected to indicate SWR to an accuracy of ±0.5 up to values of 2:1, becoming as poor as ±1.0 at 4:1. This should be quite adequate for most amateur uses.

The SWR of column of Table 11.1 represents the conversion of backward meter readings for a forward reading of 50. For a given input level, the difference between the lines was less than 1dB over the full range. Zero level is equivalent to 1V RMS in 100Ω.

Power limitations

The sensitivity of the instrument is such as to provide FSD on a 50μA meter for a carrier power of 5W. The upper limit is set by the dissipation in the resistors terminating the sampling line. These are rated at 0.5W and, since the forward line is dissipating power 32dB down on the incident transmitted power, the maximum transmitted power should not exceed 500W carrier.

Frequency range

The performance of the instrument is constant over the 144MHz band. The sensitivity will fall linearly with decrease of frequency since the coupling lines are short. The impedance match of the instrument itself will deteriorate with increasing frequency due to the presence of the step discontinuities and

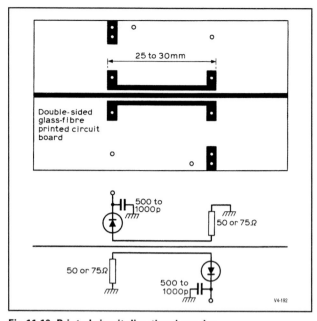

Fig 11.10. Printed circuit directional coupler

also the variations in the terminating loads on the sampling lines, which will become increasingly reactive.

Printed circuit directional coupler

A simple method of constructing a directional coupler is by use of a printed circuit board as shown on Fig 11.10. The line impedance can be made in accordance with the design information given in 'Tuned circuits' in Chapter 3. The coupling

lines may be of any convenient length to suit the meter in use but they should be short compared with λ/4.

The diodes should be a signal type such as a silicon Schottky barrier type (eg BAT83, 1N6263 etc) or a germanium type (eg OA47, OA91 etc) which have low forward voltage drop and suitable for the frequency range concerned. The terminating resistors should be as far as possible non-inductive types of good stability. The bypass capacitors may be disc, plate or feedthrough type, the latter having the advantage of providing a terminal for connection to the meter. It is important that the actual value should be suitable for the frequencies to be used.

General-purpose directional coupler

A reliable directional coupler can be made employing readily available items as an alternative to the above PCB type and without recourse to machine tools. A short section of air-spaced coaxial line is used with the coupling loops inserted into the line through the slots in the outer tube.

The general arrangement is shown on Fig 11.11. The whole unit is assembled on a piece of single-sided, copper-clad PCB made to fit a die-cast box, say, 92 × 38 × 31 mm (eg Eddystone 27969P). The size is not too important but should be kept small. The outer of the coaxial line is made from a piece of 8mm copper tube with its ends opened out by cross-sawing and slitting. This is attached to the copper side of the PCB. The inner conductor is made from a piece of brass or copper rod/tube – for 50Ω use 3.5mm rod and for 75Ω use 2.5mm.

The coupling loops are made from 24 SWG (0.5mm) brass or copper strip mounted on four small stand-off insulators. The spacing between them and the inner line should be equal and adjusted so that each provide the same readings when used either way it is connected. This should be carried out with the output socket connected to an appropriate dummy load.

Resistive VSWR bridge

Measurement of VSWR below about 450MHz can often be accomplished more conveniently by the use of a resistance bridge rather than a slotted line which is cumbersome at VHF. This method is also suitable when using other test equipment of only low power.

As already discussed in this chapter, VSWR measurements are most frequently associated with antenna and feed systems yet it could also be that the input impedance of an amplifier or similar equipment needs to be examined. It becomes more important as frequencies are increased and where impedance discontinuities give rise to unexpected losses.

A home-constructed bridge

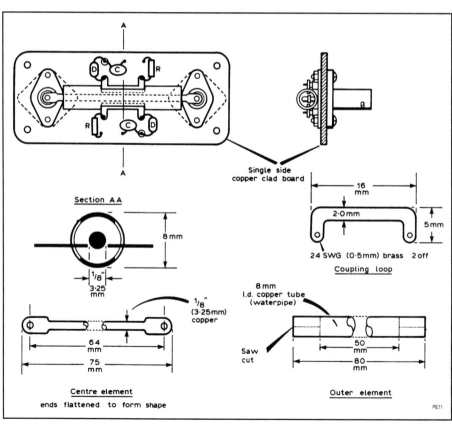

Fig 11.11. General-purpose directional coupler

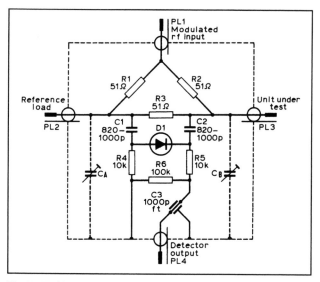

Fig 11.12. Circuit diagram of VSWR resistive bridge

can be built without difficulty, but for best performance some care in detail is needed, notably in the choice of matched resistors R1 and R2. Their installation is as far as possible identical both in respect of their lead length (which should be kept to a minimum) and their location (their relation to the ground plane and connections).

The circuit diagram of the bridge is shown in Fig 11.12, while in Fig 11.13 two methods of construction are shown, both based on a small die-cast box. In method (a) the BNC connectors are attached to the sides of the box and the circuit components fitted to a single-sided, copper-clad, glassfibre PCB. The PCB is positioned so that it is at the level of the insulation projecting from the BNC connectors so that the important resistors R1, R2 and R3 rest on the copper ground plane when soldered in position. If necessary stand-offs can be used for the junctions of components.

In method (b) the whole assembly is fitted to the lid of the die-cast box with the copper-clad PCB fitted within the raised edge of the lid. In this form it is easier to make good

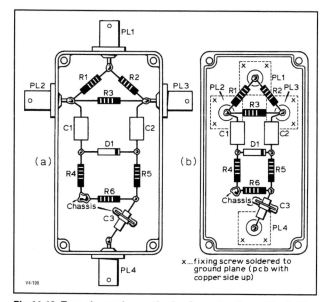

Fig 11.13. Two alternative methods of construction of the bridge

connections between the board and the four connection sockets, which may be soldered in position.

In order to test the bridge, a modulated RF signal is connected to port PL1 and an audio detector to PL4. Then, with two reference loads of the same impedance (in this case 50Ω) connected to PL2 and PL3, the output detector should read a very low value. If there is any significant output, a small capacitor (such as a ceramic plate soldered close to either PL2 or PL3 as indicated by CA or CB) should be added and adjusted to obtain balance and reduce any residual signal. Once substantial balance has been obtained, the next step is to remove one of the two reference load resistors from PL2 or PL3 – the detected output should rise by some 30dB. If the reference loads to PL2 and PL3 are interchanged no difference should be detected.

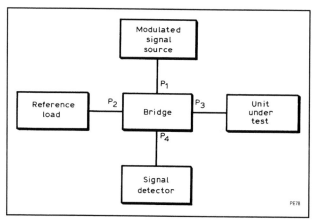

Fig 11.14. General set-up of the bridge

For a 50Ω bridge, it is useful to have one or two fixed-value mismatch loads available such as a 75Ω one for 1.5:1 VSWR, a 25Ω one for 2:1 and a short-circuit for infinite VSWR.

Operation of the bridge is readily appreciated from Fig 11.14. If identical reference loads are connected to PL2 and PL3, signals will be equal and in phase so that no output should be observed at PL4. When the unit under test at PL3 is different from that of the reference load a difference signal will be observed at PL4 which is proportional to this difference.

The bridge resistors R1 and R2 may be any appropriate value such as 50Ω or 75Ω; 50Ω is of more general application.

MEASUREMENT OF RF POWER

The UK Amateur Licence requires that you should be able to measure output power. Power is normally first assessed when running into a resistive dummy load which presents the correct load to the transmitter. Such a load is required in any case to permit non-radiating adjustments to be made to the transmitter.

Power measurements when running into a dummy load can be made directly using RF voltmeters, oscilloscopes etc, taking into account their frequency limitations. The use of reflectometers is preferable for monitoring power when coupled to an antenna system as they also give an indication of what is happening on the feed system – these are covered earlier in this chapter.

Definitions of power

The following information is taken from the *Amateur Radio Licence Terms and Limitations Booklet* BR68 [2]. Only the relevant paragraphs have been included.

Notes to the Schedule

(a) *Maximum Power* refers to the RF power supplied to the antenna. Maximum power levels will usually be specified by carrier power. For emissions having a suppressed, variable or reduced carrier, the power will be specified by the *peak envelope power* (PEP) under linear conditions.

(e) Interpretation

(i) *Carrier power:* The average power supplied to the antenna by a transmitter during one radio frequency cycle taken under the condition of no modulation.

(iv) *Mean power:* The average power supplied to the antenna by a transmitter during an interval of time which is sufficiently long relative to the lowest frequency encountered in the modulation taken under normal operating conditions.

(v) *Peak envelope power (PEP):* The average power supplied to the antenna by a transmitter during one radio frequency cycle at the crest of the modulation envelope taken under normal operating conditions.

The effect of modulation on power output

This section deals with the basic measurement of power, without specifying measuring equipment, of either basic transmitters or an amplifier. For measurement of modulation parameters the reader is referred to later in this chapter.

In a carrier-wave situation (CW) or with a frequency-modulated signal, the output is of constant amplitude and so it is relatively easy to measure the output power. Key the transmitter and determine the RMS voltage (V_{RMS}) of the resulting carrier across a dummy load (R). The power is given by:

$$P = V_{RMS}^2/R \quad \text{watts}$$

If the signal is amplitude modulated (double sideband with carrier) then the overall output power increases. The power is divided between the sidebands and the carrier component. With 100% modulation the output power increases to 1.5 times the unmodulated condition – the power contained in each of the two sidebands is one quarter that in the carrier. It is suggested that for this form of modulation the carrier power is measured (ie with no modulation) as described above. This value can be multiplied by 1.5 to give the maximum output power available.

With single sideband modulation, no power is output until modulation is applied. The output envelope is non-sinusoidal in appearance. The normal method for measuring output power is by observation of the modulation envelope and determination of the peak envelope power – this is the parameter defined by the licensing authority. Equipment for making these measurements is described in the following sections.

Dummy loads

A dummy load is a resistor (or group of resistors) which has the same resistance value as an antenna system. It should be purely resistive and so should provide an SWR of 1:1. The dummy load is normally constructed so that it provides minimal radiation when a transmitter is operated into it. Transmitters should always be set up into dummy loads before connecting them to the antenna system.

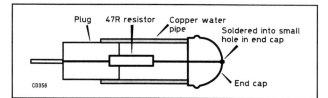

Fig 11.15. Typical construction of low-power dummy load

A resistor, no matter what type, will always have associated with it inherent inductance and capacitance, and the way it is mounted will also affect these values. The ideal resistor is one which has no associated capacitance and inductance, and is also one which does not change its value appreciably with frequency and power dissipation. This is unfortunately difficult to arrange in the real world, and the best one can do is to choose a resistor which minimises these adverse effects. In practice, impedance presented by the dummy load changes with frequency and hence will not provide an SWR of 1:1 – this effect is more pronounced as frequency increases. This is why any dummy load which is purchased should have some information included with it concerning frequency range and expected SWR values.

The best type of resistor to use is that made from carbon. Unfortunately it is becoming increasingly difficult to obtain power ratings in excess of 2W from distributors but tubular carbon resistors of higher power ratings will often be seen at rallies. *Never use wirewound resistors for RF*. However, these may be adequate for measuring AF power.

A low-power dummy load can be made from a single 47Ω resistor with surrounding shield as shown diagrammatically in Fig 11.15, and this is obviously easier for those with mechanical skills and some ingenuity. To increase the power dissipation it would be possible to make the metal container a tight fit around the resistor. However, this may pose problems if conduction can occur from the resistor case. Providing a small clearance can be ensured around the resistor, then the space could be filled with heatsink compound which is thermally but not electrically conducting. Alternatively one could fill the case with cooling oil and/or put fins onto the outside of the case. The use of the metal shield prevents unwanted radiation and also provides a low-inductance path.

To increase the power rating it is possible to use resistors in parallel – Fig 11.16 shows a typical arrangement. These should, if at all possible, be encased in a metal shield to prevent unwanted radiation, possibly a perforated shield to permit air

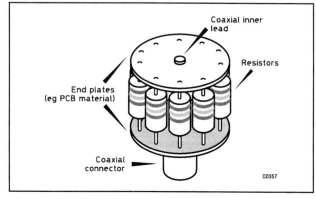

Fig 11.16. A multi-resistor dummy load

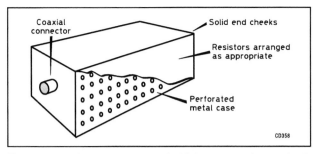

Fig 11.17. Possible construction of a higher-power dummy load

flow – see Fig 11.17. It might even be possible to build an RF probe and/or attenuator for measurements as suggested elsewhere in this chapter.

The characteristics can be improved by arranging the resistors in a coaxial manner. Ideally the pitch circle of the resistors and centre coaxial conductor should be carefully calculated but, as this arrangement tends to be very short compared to a wavelength, non-adherence has little effect until the higher frequencies are reached. The characteristic impedance can be calculated using:

$$Z_0 = 138 \log_{10}(D/d)$$

where D is the pitch diameter of the resistors and d the diameter of the inner coaxial connector. Typical arrangements to make approximately 50Ω are shown in Table 11.2.

The overall power rating is the sum of the power ratings of each resistor used.

To obtain higher power ratings it may be possible to place the load resistors in a perforated screened container and air blow them. This could be accomplished by placing a thermal switch on the resistors and using it to switch a fan on once the temperature has risen above a certain point.

Sometimes large tubular carbon resistors come onto the surplus market, eg from firms such as Morganite. These can make excellent dummy loads. Try to form them in a coaxial manner with the feed up the centre. Again, air blowing can be used to increase the power dissipation.

When using a dummy load, remember that it may be possible to dissipate a much higher power for a short period of time, providing a long cool-down period is allowed between applications of power. A commercial dummy load may often be provided with advice on this method of use.

An interesting development is the production of power film resistors in TO-126 and TO-220 packages with power ratings of 20W at +25°C case temperature when mounted on a heatsink of some 6°C/W. These resistors show good characteristics up to at least 300MHz. Typical of these are the MP820/821 from Rhopoint Ltd. Lead impedance is estimated to be 0.39 to 0.47nH per millimetre. These are also produced by other manufacturers such as Welwyn and Meggitt CGS.

Table 11.2. Resistor values for 50Ω dummy loads

Resistance (Ω)	No. in parallel	Approximate value
100	2	50
150	3	50
390	8	49
560	11	51
1000	20	50

For the type quoted above, the equivalent series inductance of the internal resistance film is about 7nH and has a shunt capacitance of about 1pF. These values will be effected to some extent when the device is mounted on a heatsink. Table 11.3 gives typical design guidelines and assumes the leads are terminated 2.5mm from the body of the resistor.

Table 11.3. Typical impedances of MP820/821 resistors

R (Ω)	10MHz	100MHz	500MHz
10	10 + j0.43	10 + j4.3	10 + j21.7
25	25 + j0.4	25 + j4	24.8 + j20
50	50 + j0.3	50 + j2.8	48.4 + j14.3
75	75 + j0.09	74.8 + j0.9	69.9 + j5.3
100	100 – j0.2	99.6 – j1.9	91 – j6.6
120	120 – j0.5	119.3 – j4.6	105 – j17.6
150	150 – j1	148.7 – j9.6	122.5 – j35.8

These figures are courtesy of Rhopoint Ltd

Use of RF voltmeters and/or probes

You can obtain an RF voltmeter, eg as surplus equipment, or make a probe as suggested in the next section. In fact, the commercial instrument may well use a probe. However, the measuring equipment *must* cover the frequency range in which the power measurements are being undertaken. If a peak reading voltmeter is being used do not forget to convert the peak voltage to RMS voltage by dividing by √2 before using the formula given in the earlier section 'The effect of modulation on power output'. *Don't forget to take into account any attenuators used*. This method of measuring power should be used for carrier power only. Fig 11.18 shows the basic arrangement for these measurements.

RF diode probe

This device allows the scope of a DC voltmeter to be extended to measure AC voltages in the VHF range, and by careful construction probably higher. The probe essentially rectifies the AC immediately and then only has to pass a DC voltage to the meter. The diode is often the limiting factor; to get high-speed operation the diode junction must be narrow and hence this reduces the breakdown voltage. Using a BAT46 Schottky barrier diode the maximum input voltage is about 35V RMS; with the 1N914/1N4148/OA91 it is about 45V RMS. Using a Schottky or germanium diode the forward voltage drop is of the order of 0.2 to 0.3V but with a silicon type it is about 0.6V. The probe should be mounted in a small metal cylinder which is well screened and the resulting DC signal fed via a coaxial cable to the DC meter – see Fig 11.19.

A typical circuit is shown in Fig 11.20 with component values for feeding a 50µA meter movement. The advantage of arranging the capacitor and rectifier in this manner is that the capacitor also acts as DC blocking.

An alternative when the circuit is to be fed into a high-input-impedance DC voltmeter such as an electronic analogue

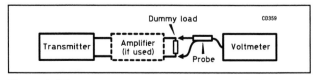

Fig 11.18. RF power measurement using probe and voltmeter

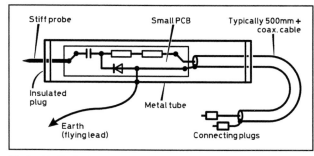

Fig 11.19. Typical construction of an RF probe

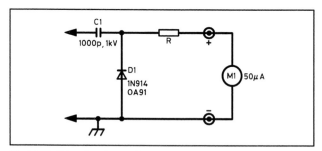

Fig 11.20. RF probe circuit. For R = 270kΩ + 12kΩ, the meter scaling is 0–10V, and full-scale power in 50Ω is 2W. For R = 820kΩ + 27kΩ, the meter scaling is 0–30V, and full-scale power in 50Ω is 18W

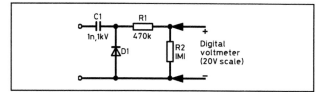

Fig 11.21. RF probe for digital voltmeter

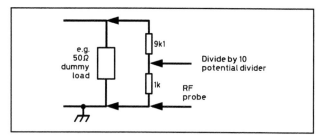

Fig 11.22. Suggested method for higher voltages

meter or a digital meter is shown in Fig 11.21. The input resistance of the meter should be such that it is 10 times the value of R2. Also, the value for the series resistor (R1) should be approximately 41% of the combined resistance R2 in parallel with the meter input resistance. This then allows the meter to read the RMS value of the RF signal. The values shown are suitable for a meter with an input resistance of at least 10MΩ. For a meter of input resistance of 1MΩ, reduce the values of R1 and R2 by a factor of 10.

To measure higher voltages and hence higher power levels, one suggestion is to use a resistive divider across the load – using resistors suitable for the frequencies encountered. Fig 11.22 shows a divide-by-10 unit suitable for a 50Ω system. Remember, the actual voltage is 10 times the value as read on the meter.

An RF millivolt probe

The RF diode probes previously described are limited to voltages in excess of about 1V as a result of the diode forward voltage drop. A method to extend measurements down to a few millivolts is to use the IC transistor array CA3046 which has a minimum gain-bandwidth product of 300MHz. The concept is to amplify the RF signal before detection.

The suggested arrangement is shown in Fig 11.23. The 14-pin DIL device should be mounted in a small screened case with a probe for the RF input in the usual manner. Every effort should be made to keep stray capacitance to a minimum and no IC socket should be used. The input impedance should be about 50kΩ in parallel with 3pF. With the arrangement of two symmetrical DC Darlington pairs the maximum offset voltage will be less than 1mV.

The working range will be from about 1mV to 4V and the device is intended as an add-on unit for

a voltmeter. Calibration can be carried out in the several-volt region. Useful measurements should be possible to frequencies in excess of 100MHz.

Alternative ICs that could be considered for the probe are the SL560C (at least 300MHz) and the MAR series (up to 1000MHz) by Mini Circuits. However, these are low-input-impedance types. Good VHF/UHF constructional techniques should be used.

QRP wattmeter

The wattmeter described here will read up to a maximum of 3W and a frequency well in excess of 30MHz; it should therefore be useful for the 50MHz and 70MHz bands and, with careful construction, the 144MHz band. It is in essence a peak-reading voltmeter with internal 50Ω dummy load and is not designed to read standing wave ratios. Sufficient information is given for the design to cope with varying meters and full-scale power levels.

Circuit description

The circuit of the complete unit is given in Fig 11.24. Resistor R1 forms the dummy load, D1 provides rectification, C1

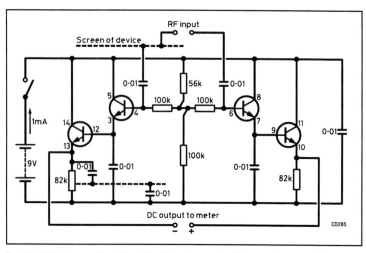

Fig 11.23. Peak-reading RF millivoltmeter probe. All capacitors are disc type. The numbers refer to pins on the CA3046 which is a 14-pin DIL device

smoothing, R2 is to limit the current through the meter M and C2 provides RF decoupling.

The dummy load should be made from carbon resistors and be of adequate rating to cope with 5W. As a minimum, use 1W resistors – three of 270Ω and two of 220Ω will give a load of 49.5Ω. Another arrangement would be four of 330Ω and three of 390Ω, giving an equivalent resistance of 50.5Ω. Other arrangements are of course possible.

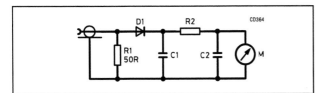

Fig 11.24. Circuit diagram of QRP wattmeter. C1 and C2 are 1000pF ceramic

The diode needs a little consideration – it must be capable of high-speed working, have a minimum PIV of 23V and as low a forward drop as possible in order to minimise errors at the low-power end. Although the ubiquitous 1N914/1N4148 is more than adequate, a lower forward voltage drop can be obtained from a Schottky diode such as the BAT85. For higher power levels use the 1N914. Both capacitors should be of the ceramic type with at least a 30V rating.

Resistor R2 can be calculated to cope with various sensitivity meters. Use a meter of between 50µA and 1mA sensitivity. Neglecting the meter resistance, R2 is given by:

$$R_2 = \frac{V}{I_{FSD}}$$

where V is the peak value of the rectified sine wave and I_{FSD} is the sensitivity of the meter. V is calculated from:

$$V = \sqrt{(100P)}$$

where P is the power being measured.

Thus for a 100µA meter and full-scale deflection for 5W, R = 223.61kΩ (220kΩ + 3.6kΩ) and the meter resistance of about 1kΩ is negligible compared to this. Assuming the meter has a linear scale, then the current corresponding to a given power is given in Table 11.4.

Construction

It is suggested that the whole unit is mounted in a metal box with some ventilation for the dummy load. The circuit from diode to meter should be kept as far away as possible from any circuits carrying RF, and be shielded if at all possible. Use a BNC or SO239 socket for connection.

Table 11.4. Power indicated by current readings for the QRP wattmeter	
Power (W)	Current reading (µA)
0.1	14
0.5	32
1.0	45
2.5	71
5.0	100

Below 0.1W the forward voltage drop of the diode becomes significant.

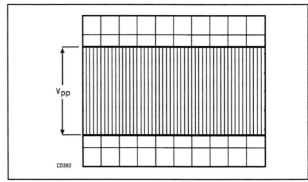

Fig 11.25. Oscilloscope display for carrier only

Use of the oscilloscope for power measurement

This requires the use of an oscilloscope with a timebase or a CRT monitor. It should be stressed, however, that oscilloscopes working into the VHF range are expensive. This section deals solely with the measurement of power, eg voltage display on an oscilloscope. An oscilloscope/CRT can also be used for some modulation measurements. At 100W (CW) the peak-to-peak voltage across a 50Ω dummy load is 200V and at 400W PEP, the maximum peak to peak voltage that will be measured is about 400V! *You have been warned.*

As with the RF voltmeter, the most straightforward measurement is of carrier power which is obtained from the key-down condition for CW operation or the constant amplitude of a frequency-modulated signal. Connect an oscilloscope instead of a voltmeter (Fig 11.18) bearing in mind any frequency or voltage limitations of the oscilloscope and probe. Measure the peak-to-peak amplitude V_{pp} (Fig 11.25) across the known dummy load R. The average power is then calculated from:

$$P_{avg} = \frac{V_{pp}^2}{8R} \text{ watts}$$

The same physical connections are made across the dummy load with the oscilloscope for PEP measurements, but the transmitter should be driven by a two-tone oscillator – see Fig 11.26. The output of the oscillator should be fed into the microphone socket and be of amplitude equivalent to that from the microphone.

Set the timebase on the oscilloscope to be in the audio range and a waveform similar to that shown on Fig 11.27 will be obtained. Measure the peak-to-peak voltage V_{pp} at the peak of the envelope (as shown) – the power is given by the same formula as above.

The input capacitance of an oscilloscope can start to have an appreciable effect at 30MHz – the reactance of 25pF is 212Ω at 30MHz, and obviously affects the readings. It may then be better to use a divide-by-10 probe that will decrease the parallel capacitive loading to about 12pF. This still represents

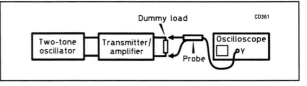

Fig 11.26. RF measurement for SSB work

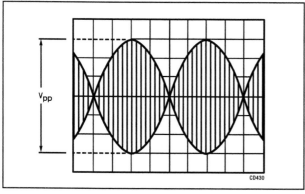

Fig 11.27. Two-tone test display

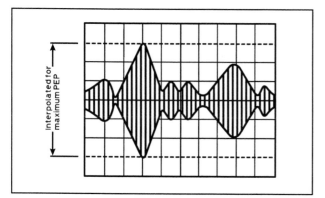

Fig 11.28. Speech waveform and interpolated maximum PEP

a capacitive reactance of 442Ω at 30MHz and the voltage read from the screen will be lower than in reality. To reduce these effects some high-quality oscilloscopes have 50Ω inputs – use these at higher frequencies *but remember that these will have significant loading on a circuit* and may have to matched into the latter.

If the same oscilloscope is continually used to monitor output power on SSB, then note should be made on the graticule or display of the positions corresponding to various power levels. The peak of the speech modulated waveform should then never exceed the maximum permitted level – see Fig 11.28.

If it is possible to feed the Y signal directly to the plates, then the capacitive loading is much smaller, the readings are therefore more accurate and it will be possible to use the oscilloscope to higher frequencies.

REPRESENTATION OF AN ANTENNA SYSTEM USING CIRCUIT COMPONENTS

An antenna system (including feed cable if necessary) represents an impedance at the feed point to whatever is driving it. This can either be considered as being made of a series circuit or a parallel circuit as shown in Fig 11.29.

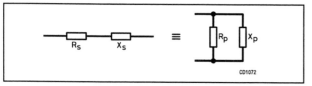

Fig 11.29. Series and parallel equivalence

It is possible to convert between these circuits, the equations being given below. Please note that these values are only true at one particular frequency.

$$R_p = \frac{R_s^2 + X_s^2}{R_s}$$

$$X_p = \frac{R_s^2 + X_s^2}{X_s}$$

$$R_s = R_p \times \frac{X_p^2}{R_p^2 + X_p^2}$$

$$X_s = X_p \times \frac{R_p^2}{R_p^2 + X_p^2}$$

For optimum power transfer, the resistive part should equal the source resistance and the reactive part should cancel with the source reactance – in effect the condition for resonance. Thus it is important to be able to make these measurements at the frequency of concern. Remember also that power can only be dissipated in a resistive element.

Thus, if serious work is to be undertaken on antennas, it is important to determine feed-point impedances. Commercial equipment to perform this function is quite expensive but the following two circuits will give a good indication of conditions.

Also, don't forget that what the transmitter 'sees' is an impedance represented by the antenna and the associated transmission line. If, and only if, the transmission line is a multiple of half-wavelengths (taking into account cable velocity factor) will the feed point impedance be that of the antenna. Ideally measurements should be made directly at the antenna terminals if at all possible.

An RF bridge

This is a Wheatstone-type bridge suitable for use on frequencies up to the 70cm band (430–440MHz). It requires care in construction to ensure absolute symmetry of the component layout together with the use of miniature components and matched pairs where necessary. This will then give a bridge which has an accuracy of the order of ±1% of full-scale deflection of the meter which is good enough for practical purposes and should fulfil most amateur needs.

The circuit of the bridge shown in Fig 11.30 is given in the same form as shown in Fig 11.31 and is self-explanatory.

The whole unit, which uses an external meter, should be built in the smallest-size die-cast box. The component list is given in Table 11.5.

Table 11.5. Component list for RF bridge	
R1, 2	100R ±1% metal oxide
R3, 4	4k7 ±1% metal oxide
R5, 6	100R
VR1	50k miniature pot
VR2	2k5 miniature pot
C1, 2	1000p ceramic disc
C3–9	10n ceramic disc
D1	OA91, CV2290, BAT85 (low-voltage-drop diode, suitable for frequency range)
Z_{known}	50R, fitted in coaxial plug

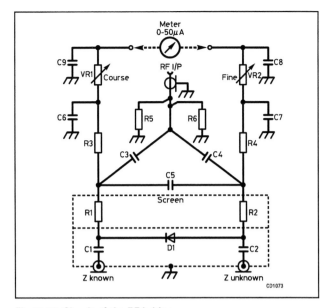

Fig 11.30. Circuit of the RF bridge

Operation

The method of operation with this bridge is to start with the value of impedance known and adjust the length of stubs, matching device etc until a balance is achieved.

This unit will be found ideal for cutting coaxial cable to quarter- and half-wavelengths, where the known Z is either an open-circuit or a short-circuit.

RF noise bridge

The circuit described here is from reference [1]. It is a useful circuit for measuring the R and X components of an impedance or antenna system at a given frequency. It also allows a modulated signal to be obtained, if desired, by pulsing the supply to the noise generator. Such modulation may aid detection of the balance point, especially if an AM receiver is used. The circuit consists of a wide-band noise generator

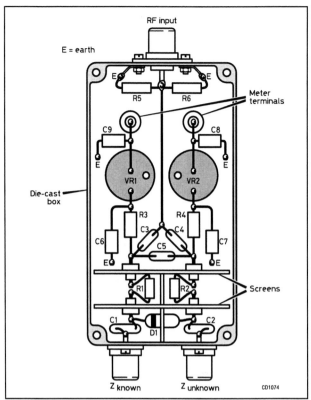

Fig 11.31. Component layout of the RF bridge

followed by a bridge for making the measurements. The bridge allows the measurement of the parallel components of an unknown impedance to be measured. The circuit requires 9V DC at about 25mA.

Circuit description

The circuit is shown in Fig 11.32. The white noise is generated by the zener diode D1 operating at low current. It may be possible to maximise the noise by suitable choice of the

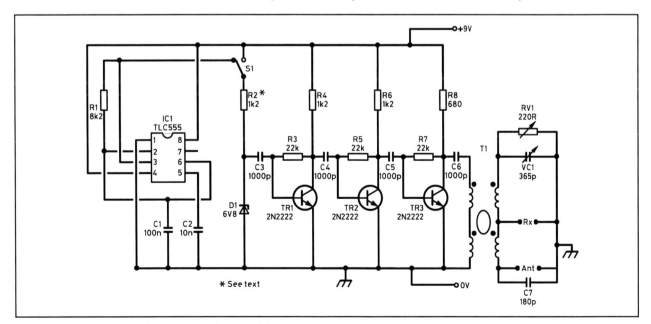

Fig 11.32. Circuit diagram of modulated RF noise bridge

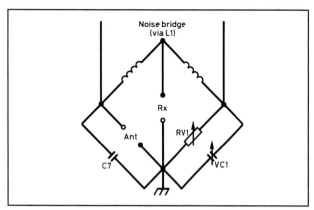

Fig 11.33. Diagrammatic representation of noise bridge

Table 11.6. Components list for the RF noise bridge	
R1	8k2
R2, 4, 6	1k2
R3, 5, 7	22k
R8	680R
RV1	220R pot (see text)
C1	100n, 50V ceramic
C2	10n, 50V ceramic
C3–6	1000p, 50V ceramic
C7	180p, silver mica
VC1	365p Jackson type 01 gang
D1	6V8 zener, 400mW
TR1-3	2N2222
IC1	TLC555
S1	SPCO switch
T1	T50-6 dust iron core, 4 windings, each 14t or 596100001 ferrite core, 4 windings, 6t each

Resistors are 0.25/0.5W, ±5% unless stated otherwise

zener diode and R2. The frequency range of this noise should extend up to at least 200MHz. The noise source is followed by a three-stage wide-band amplifier to raise the noise level to the order of 100µV, and this enables a receiver to be used as a null indicator.

The noise output from the amplifier is applied to a quadrifilar-wound toroid which forms the transformer T1. This provides two arms of a bridge circuit which has a variable resistor and capacitor in the third arm to obtain a balance against the impedance (eg antenna system) in the fourth arm. The bridge circuit is shown diagrammatically in Fig 11.33.

When the noise across the RV1/VC1 arm equals the noise across the antenna/capacitor combination, the bridge is said to be 'balanced', and this occurs when the received noise signal is at a minimum. The values can be obtained from the settings of RV1 and VC1. The inclusion of C7 allows an offset to be used so that inductive reactance can be measured. The mid-point setting of VC1 is equal to zero reactance. If a noise bridge is only required to measure the resistive part of the antenna impedance then omit C7 and VC1.

Timer IC1 is in astable mode and runs at about 850Hz with a 50% duty cycle, and this can be used to provide current for the zener circuit via S1, so modulating the noise source. The zener diode can be alternatively fed from the constant-voltage power supply line.

Construction

The component list is given in Table 11.6. The toroid transformer consists of a dust-iron core, type T50-6, which is wound as follows. Cut four lengths of 26 SWG enamelled copper wire about 120mm long, twist them together and then thread them through the toroid to give 14 turns and evenly spaced to cover the circumference. Divide the turns into two pairs, each pair consisting of two windings connected in series, the end of one winding connecting to the start of the other – be careful. Check that the two pairs are insulated from each other. Endeavour to keep the lead lengths in the bridge as short as possible and symmetrical. The variable resistor RV1 should be of high quality and with a carbon, cermet or conductive plastic track – *not wirewound!*

When constructing the circuits, ensure that the noise generator and amplifiers are well away or screened from the bridge transformer and measuring circuit. The potentiometer case should not be earthed and, if it has a metal spindle, this should be isolated from the user and should not contact ground.

The complete circuit should be mounted in a screened box such as a die-cast type with appropriate connectors – eg UHF type or BNC. In order to avoid coupling into the measuring circuit of noise by way of current in earth loops, the earthed side of the noise source should not be joined to the general chassis earth of the bridge but should be taken by an insulated lead to the frame of the variable capacitor.

As in all high-frequency measuring circuits, lead inductance should be kept to an absolute minimum and, where any lead length more than a few millimetres is unavoidable, copper foil at least 6mm wide should be used. All earth returns should be taken to the capacitor frame. Capacitor C7, which should be silver mica, can be soldered directly across the UNKNOWN socket.

A suitable PCB pattern and component layout is given in Appendix 1.

Calibration

Connect a test resistor (of a carbon type) across the UNKNOWN socket with the receiver tuned to 3.5MHz. Adjust RV1 and VC1 to give a null. The value of RV1 is at the position equal to the test resistor and the capacitor should be at approximately the mid-mesh position or the zero reactance condition – mark these positions. Repeat with different values of test resistor up to 220Ω in order to provide a calibration scale for RV1. Repeat this operation with known values of capacitance in parallel with the test resistor, up to a maximum value of 180pF. Mark the corresponding null positions on the VC1 scale with the value of this capacitance. Repeat this procedure at 28MHz to check the accuracy of the bridge. If the layout has been carefully attended to there should be little difference in the null positions.

To calibrate VC1 for negative capacitance values (ie inductance) it is necessary to temporarily place given values of capacitance in parallel with VC1. Gradually decrease the value of these capacitors (CT) from 150pF towards zero, obtaining null positions and marking the VC1 scale with the value of −(180 − CT) pF, ie if 100pF is substituted then the negative C value is 80pF.

Using the noise bridge

For work on an antenna, a noise bridge should ideally be connected across the antenna terminals. This is usually not practical, in which case a noise bridge should be connected to the antenna by a length of line which is a multiple of a half-wave-length at the frequency of interest (taking into account the velocity factor of the cable).

Connect the impedance to be measured to the UNKNOWN socket, switch on the noise generator and tune the receiver to the frequency at which the test is to be made. Use RV1 and VC1 to obtain a minimum noise reading on the receiver S-meter. The values must now be converted to circuit components. The value recorded from RV1 is the resistive part of the impedance. The value from VC1 is the parallel reactive component of the impedance and, depending on the sign, is either inductive or capacitive. If it is positive, then the value of shunt capacitance is read directly from the VC1 scale. If it is negative, the VC1 reading represents the value of the shunt inductance and must be calculated as below.

If a negative value of capacitance (C) is obtained this can be converted to an inductance value using the formula:

$$L = \frac{1}{4\pi^2 f^2 (180 - C)}$$

where f is in megahertz and C in picofarads.

This can be accomplished with the following BASIC program:

```
10   REM Noise Bridge Inductance Calculation
20   CLS
30   C=180
40   INPUT "Negative C Value in pF",CV:
     CV=ABS(CV)
50   INPUT "Working Frequency in MHz",F:
     F=F*1000000
60   K=1/(4*3.14159^2*F^2)
70   L=K*1/((C-CV)*1E-12)
80   L=L*1000000
90   PRINT "Inductance in uH is ",L
100  END
```

ATTENUATORS

The need for good attenuators capable of working at frequencies up to several hundred megahertz or higher often arises. These are relatively easy to construct out of standard resistors and can be put to a variety of uses. For example, attenuators at RF can be used as pads between interacting stages, eg varactor multipliers, or to follow noise or signal sources to bring their output close to 50Ω. At IF they can be used for calibrating attenuators, since their attenuation is fairly predictable at lower frequencies. They may also be used for calibrating S-meters etc, and as a reference for noise measurements, eg Sun and ground noise. An attenuator might also be useful between a transmitter and transverter.

Design and construction of simple attenuators

Attenuators are normally made from T or pi networks – see Fig 11.34. For this exercise it is assumed that load and source impedances (R_0) are equal and resistive. The design of these is covered by the following formulae.

T network

$$\text{Attenuation (dB)} = 20 \log_{10} \left(\frac{R_0 + R_1}{R_0 - R_1} \right)$$

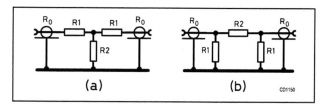

Fig 11.34. (a) T-type attenuator. (b) Pi-type attenuator

when:

$$R_2 = \frac{R_0^2 - R_1^2}{2R_1}$$

Pi network

$$\text{Attenuation (dB)} = 20 \log_{10} \left(\frac{R_1 + R_0}{R_1 - R_0} \right)$$

when:

$$R_2 = \frac{2R_0^2 R_1}{R_1^2 - R_0^2}$$

The greatest problem in constructing a good attenuator is the radiation and leakage of signals from within the unit. Because of this, the attenuator should consist of a good RF-tight metal box with high-quality connectors.

Two methods of construction are illustrated in Fig 11.35. A pi-type is shown at (a) and the T-type at (b), but either type could be used in either design. The resistors should be a low-inductance type, the common form of carbon film resistors being particularly suitable. Lead lengths should be as short as possible. For higher-power attenuators at lower frequencies, parallel combinations of 0.5W carbon resistors can be used to increase dissipation. A 10dB attenuator built in this way to handle 10W measures 9.5dB attenuation at 432MHz with low SWR.

Provided that care is taken, these attenuators can be used up to 1–2GHz. The biggest error is likely to arise in the higher-value attenuators, where stray coupling may reduce the attenuation below the expected value. For this reason it is better to use several low-value stages in cascade when a high value of attenuation is required.

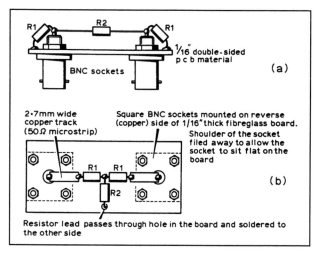

Fig 11.35. Methods of constructing attenuators: (a) below 500MHz, (b) above 500MHz

Two computer programs are given below [3] for assistance as the calculation is somewhat tedious but there is also Table 11.7 for those who do not want to use a computer.

For the pi-attenuator network use the following program:

```
10   PRINT "RESISTIVE PI ATTENUATOR CIRCUIT"
20   DEF FNA(X)=INT(X*100+.5)
30   DEF FNB(X)=LOG(X)/LOG(10)
40   DIM P(12)
50   FOR I=1 TO 12:READ P(I):NEXT
60   DATA 1.2,1.5,1.8,2.2,2.7,3.3
70   DATA 3.9,4.7,5.6,6.8,8.2,10
100  INPUT "CIRCUIT IMPEDANCE (OHMS) ";Z
110  INPUT "ATTENUATION (DB) ";DB
120  V=10^(-DB/20)
130  A=Z*(1+V)/(1-V)
140  B=Z*(1-V*V)/(2*V)
150  PRINT "OPTIMUM VALUES:"
160  PRINT "SIDES: ";A;" OHMS"
170  PRINT "  TOP: ";B;" OHMS"
180  R=Z:GOSUB 500
190  PRINT "NEAREST PREFERRED VALUES: "
200  PRINT " SIDES    TOP    DB      Z"
210  R=A:GOSUB 600:AL=L:AH=H
220  R=B:GOSUB 600:BL=L:BH=H
230  A=AL:B=BL:GOSUB 400
240  A=AL:B=BL:GOSUB 400
250  A=AL:B=BL:GOSUB 400
260  A=AL:B=BL:GOSUB 400
300  INPUT "SIDE RESISTORS ";A
310  IF A<0 GOTO 100
320  INPUT "TOP RESISTOR ";B
330  GOSUB 400
340  GOSUB 500
350  GOTO 300
400  R=A*Z/(A+Z):V=R/(R+B)
410  R=A*(R+B)/(R+A+B)
420  DB=20*FNB(V)
430  PRINT A;TAB(8);B;TAB(16); FNA(DB)/100;
     TAB(24);FNA(R)/100
440  RETURN
500  P1=R/A:P2=P1*V*V:PB=R*(1-V)*(1-V)/B
510  PRINT "POWER:  INPUT ";FNA(P1);" %"
520  PRINT "TOP ";FNA(PB);"%","OUTPUT ";
     FNA(P2);"%"
530  RETURN
600  I=1:M=10^INT(FNB(R)):L=M
610  H=M*P(I)
620  IF H>R THEN RETURN
630  I=I+1:L=H:GOTO 610
```

For T-attenuator design, replace the appropriate lines in the above program by the following:

```
10   PRINT "RESISTIVE T-ATTENUATOR NETWORK"
130  A=Z*(1-V)/(1+V)
140  B=(Z*Z-A*A)/(2*A)
150  PRINT "OPTIMUM VALUES:"
160  PRINT " ARMS: ";A;" OHMS"
170  PRINT " BASE: ";B;" OHMS"
180  R=Z:GOSUB 500
190  PRINT "NEAREST PREFERRED VALUES:"
```

Attenuation (dB)	T-type		Pi-type	
	R1	R2	R1	R2
1	2.9	433	870	5.8
2	5.7	215	436	11.6
3	8.6	142	292	17.6
4	11.3	105	221	23.9
5	14.0	82	178	30.4
6	16.6	67	150	37.4
7	19.1	56	131	44.8
8	21.5	47.3	116	53
9	23.8	40.6	105	62
10	26.0	35.1	96	71
12	30.0	26.8	84	93
14	33.4	20.8	75	120
16	36.3	16.3	69	154
18	38.8	12.8	64	196
20	40.9	10.0	61	248
25	44.7	5.6	56	443
30	46.9	3.2	53	790

Table 11.7. Design data for 50Ω T-type and pi-type attenuators

```
200  PRINT " ARMS    BASE    DB      Z"
300  INPUT "ARM RESISTORS ";A
310  IF A<0 GOTO 100
320  INPUT "BASE RESISTOR ";B
400  R=B*(Z+A)/(B+Z+A):R=R+A
500  H=V+V*A/Z:P1=R*(1-H)*(1- H)/A:
     P2=R*V*V*A/(Z*Z):PB=R*H*H/B
```

Switched attenuator

A switched attenuator has a number of applications in the amateur station; it may be made either wide or limited range depending on the intended application.

The simple three-section unit illustrated (Fig 11.36) is intended for use between the output of a VHF transceiver having an output in the range 10–20W PEP and a following linear amplifier. With the three stages of 2, 4 and 8dB available, various levels between 0 and 14dB are available.

In an attenuator which is to be used with a power source such as a transceiver, it should be remembered that a significant proportion of the input power will be dissipated in the resistors in the attenuator. The proportion is increased with the level of attenuation. In this case 2dB attenuation will dissipate 36% of the input power, 4dB 52% and 8dB 84%. Therefore adequately rated components are essential if the unit is to be used continuously.

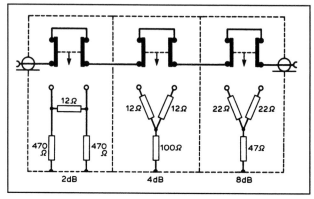

Fig 11.36. Circuit of switched attenuator

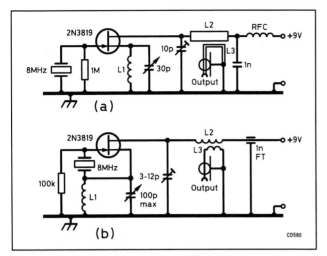

Fig 11.37. Two alternative simple VHF signal sources. Inductor details for (a) are: L1, 20t 8mm dia; L2, 120mm long by 3mm dia; L3, output coupling loop, 16 SWG wire; RFC, 35t 6mm dia. Inductor details for (b) are: L1, 28t 28 SWG wire, 6.5mm dia; L2, 4t 18 SWG wire, 12.7mm dia; L3, output coupling, 1t 18 SWG wire

For a continuous carrier input of 10W, after a 2dB attenuation 6.3W is available to the next stage, after 4dB there is 4W, after 6dB there is 2.5W and after 8dB just 1.6W. The remaining power is dissipated within the attenuator.

Although the switched attenuator may be used, for normal general-purpose operation a single-stage fixed type is more likely to find favour once the degree of attenuation has been established. Such a unit can more readily be built using suitable components and where necessary adequate heat-dissipating construction.

SIGNAL SOURCES

A reliable signal source is a useful adjunct for setting up receivers and converters. This is useful for both the setting of newly built equipment and the repair of equipment – both homebrew and 'black box'. Once the equipment has been aligned on a signal source it is worthwhile trying to tune to a distant beacon or repeater and again trying to optimise reception.

A simple signal source

Fig 11.37 shows two possible crystal oscillators with the appropriate tuned circuit, and both use 8MHz range crystals. The output should be checked with an absorption wavemeter to make sure that the correct harmonic of the crystal frequency has been selected. The possibility of error would be reduced if a higher-frequency crystal were used: this would be particularly desirable if the output circuit were modified to give an output on 432MHz.

In construction it is desirable for the unit to be completely enclosed so that output is only obtained from the output socket – this will largely eliminate unwanted signals and also allow some control of the level. The power supply should be very well decoupled *or* a battery used in the same enclosure.

Dual output signal source

A useful signal source having outputs at 144 and 432MHz can be constructed readily using the familiar Butler crystal oscillator and multiplier circuit with a fifth-overtone crystal of 103MHz – see Fig 11.38.

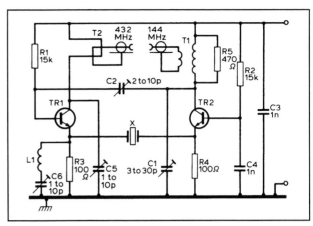

Fig 11.38. Circuit of dual-output signal source

The circuit uses a series-resonant crystal but the two different frequency output tuned circuits are connected to the respective collectors of the transistors in order to obtain the maximum output from the 432.6MHz side. A series resonant circuit (L1/C6) tuned to 288.4MHz is connected in the emitter circuit of TR1. An output power of 30mW is obtainable on 144.2MHz and 10mW on 432.6MHz for an input power of 120mW.

The outputs are inductively coupled and suitably supported and adjusted. The transformer T1 for 144.2MHz output consists of four turns of 0.5mm wire wound with 7mm internal diameter, 9mm long and with a two-turn link output coil. T2, the 432.6MHz output circuit, consists of 43mm lengths of wire formed into suitable loops. The 288MHz idler circuit (L1/C6) is formed of a coil of three turns of 0.5mm wire, 6mm internal diameter, 10mm long and tuned by a 1–10pF trimmer.

The transistors used are BFY90 or equivalent; types such as BSX20 will also be satisfactory, although somewhat lower output will be achieved.

Variable signal source for 144 and 432MHz

The signal sources so far described have been based on crystal oscillators to give high stability. Sometimes a variable frequency oscillator together with variable output level control is more useful. The harmonics of the oscillator are of sufficient strength to give outputs at 144 and 432MHz. Such a circuit is shown in Fig 11.39.

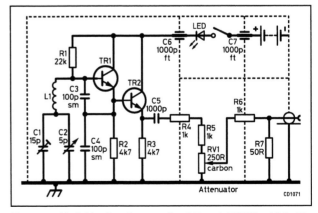

Fig 11.39. Variable signal source for 144 and 432MHz. L1 is 60–70nH

The circuit consists of a VFO (L1/C1/C2) and TR1 followed by a buffer TR2. The output is taken from R5 and goes to a variable level control (RV1). Transistors similar to those in the previous section can be used. The whole unit should be mounted in a metal box to minimise stray pick-up. Internal screening should be used as shown around the various parts of the circuit.

The unit may be battery powered but increased stability is likely if the power supply to the circuit is regulated and well decoupled.

ABSORPTION WAVEMETERS

Two important uses of an absorption wavemeter are checking:

1. that the correct harmonic is selected for driving the next stage in circuits such as multipliers; and
2. for the presence of harmonics in the output of a transmitter stage.

An absorption wavemeter provides an unambiguous frequency measurement and it is also a requirement of the UK amateur licence to check regularly the harmonic output.

In the UK, on both 50 and 70MHz the second and third harmonics fall into other user's bands, the second harmonic being in a broadcast band. For the 144MHz band the second harmonic falls in another user's band, and the third harmonic falls in our own 432MHz band. At 432MHz the second harmonic is just above a TV band whilst the third harmonic is 1296MHz – in one of our bands!

The generation of the second harmonic is often too easy, for example, it is often heard that by a little 'tweaking' with the output tuning adjustment a significant increase in output can be obtained – very often the majority of the apparent increase is second harmonic with very little increase in the fundamental.

A good absorption wavemeter should have at least a two-to-one frequency coverage, preferably without switching bands. With care this can readily be attained, although many commercial types do not tune above about 250MHz.

Two designs [4] are described here, one for general purpose use, the other for insertion into the coaxial line. Both types cover a frequency range of 125–350MHz and are sufficiently sensitive to obtain a reasonable indication of the fundamental frequency of a FET dip oscillator having an output of 3–5mW at a distance of 100–125mm. As outputs of appreciably higher levels than this are likely to be involved, the full sensitivity may not always be needed, and a shunt across the meter is provided with a press-to-open switch to give full sensitivity.

General-purpose wavemeter

In this design an edge-mounted meter has been used. There is, however, some advantage in this method insofar as in use it is almost always necessary to 'bend over' to be able to see the meter whereas with it in the end of the box direct observation is possible.

In order to obtain an adequate inductance for coupling to the circuit under test while being small enough to reach the top frequency, it is necessary to make the external loop and the connections to the tuning capacitor of material with low

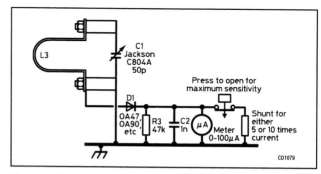

Fig 11.40. Circuit diagram of general-purpose wavemeter

inductance per unit length. The external loop also needs to be mechanically rigid to avoid damage or calibration changes. To avoid restriction of the top frequency the material used for mounting the external loop needs to be of low dielectric constant. The most suitable material for this purpose is PTFE or an equivalent. The circuit diagram of the unit is shown in Fig 11.40.

The construction of the wavemeter is straightforward and is shown in Fig 11.41. The external loop is attached to the internal connections by 4BA (or metric equivalent) brass cheesehead screws and the strip connections to the capacitor are soldered directly to the slots in the heads of the screws. The detector diode (BAT81/83/85 or OA47/90 or equivalent) is connected to one of the screws, thereby providing a tapdown of about 25% of the total inductance and avoiding undue damping of the circuit.

Calibration can readily be carried out by use of a suitable dip oscillator, the actual frequency of which can be verified by a digital frequency meter.

If it is desired to cover 50MHz and 70MHz, then a substantially larger inductance will be needed but this reduces the top frequency. This may take any convenient form – a suitable coil that covers 48–130MHz consists of four turns of 16mm ID of 3.25mm copper close wound with 25mm tails. With this much larger inductance the tapping point of the diode detector will be very much lower down and therefore the full sensitivity of the indicating meter will be required.

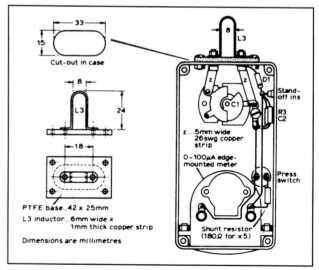

Fig 11.41. Arrangement of components of general-purpose wavemeter

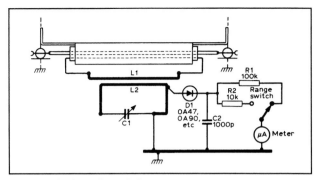

Fig 11.42. Indirect through-line wavemeter

Through-line type wavemeters

This type is intended for connection in the coaxial cable, either between an exciter or the antenna feeder. In the latter case some care is needed to ensure that the unit is not damaged when used with a high-power amplifier, and it should be used with a T connector and a suitable terminating resistor.

The main element of this type of wavemeter is a short section of coaxial line within the unit to which is coupled the tuned circuit.

The dimensions for both types are given for fitting in a die-cast box which is 60mm wide externally (eg Eddystone type 27134P). Adjustments will have to be made to suit other widths of box.

Indirect method

As shown in the circuit diagram (Fig 11.42), the tuned circuit is coupled to the inner of the coaxial line through an intermediate loop. The loop consists of a fine wire inserted in the coaxial line and is connected to a short length of more rigid wire to which the tuned circuit loop is coupled.

In constructing the line within the unit it will be found more convenient to fabricate this from a short piece of semi-air-spaced cable and replace the outer braid with a short length of copper or brass tube of the same diameter as the original braid in order to maintain the correct impedance – see Fig 11.43.

The cable used in the prototype had an insulation diameter of 6.35mm (¼in) which was replaced by a copper tube. If it is required to change the impedance from 50Ω to 75Ω it is only necessary to replace the inner conductor with a thinner wire (the size can be either calculated or obtained from the relevant chart elsewhere in this book).

Fitting the coaxial element into the case (Fig 11.44) requires the ends of the tube to be shaped and bent so that the

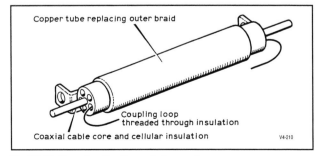

Fig 11.43. Coupling for through-line meter

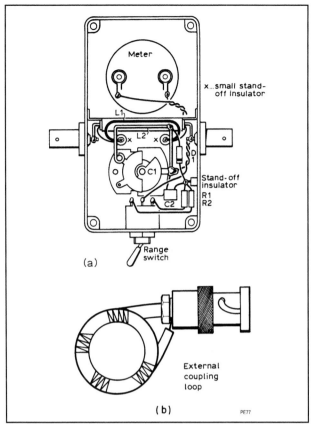

Fig 11.44. (a) Arrangement of components of indirect through-line wavemeter. (b) External coupling loop

lugs thus produced can be fixed to the box by the screw holding the connector. BNC sockets have been used in the design shown. Component arrangement is clearly shown in Fig 11.44 and should present no problems – the connection of the diode should be 20mm from the ground end of the tuned loop.

Direct method

In this form, as mentioned earlier, the intermediate coupling loop is avoided, and there is direct coupling of the tuned circuit to the inner conductor through a slot in the coaxial outer.

Details of a suitable slotted line are given in Fig 11.45. The tuned circuit inductance consists of a simple U-shaped piece of 18 SWG (1.25mm) enamelled copper wire to which the detector diode is connected at a point 20mm from the earth end. Spacing the loop from the inner conductor is important and should be within the field of the outer of the coaxial line. To assist alignment the slot is arranged to be vertical and this means that the fixing lugs of the tube forming the outer of the line must be at 45° to the slot to enable the line to be fixed by one of the screws holding the coaxial socket.

The general layout for this type of meter is shown in Fig 11.46.

Wide-range UHF cavity wavemeter

Measurement of frequencies above 500MHz becomes difficult using conventional lumped-circuit type wavemeters, so that it is an advantage to use a cavity design. Cavity wavemeters are often constructed to cover relatively narrow bands but for amateur purposes it is desirable to cover several bands,

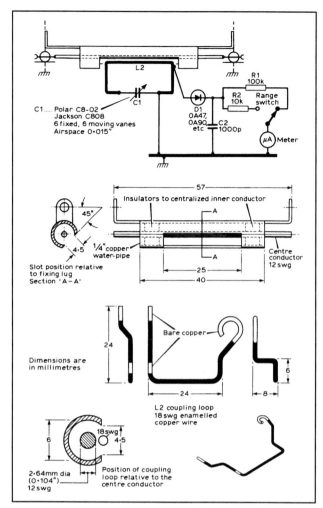

Fig 11.45. Direct through-line wavemeter

if possible, thus providing continuous coverage and allowing their use for second harmonics. The wavemeter described here has been designed to cover from around 400MHz to 2.5GHz

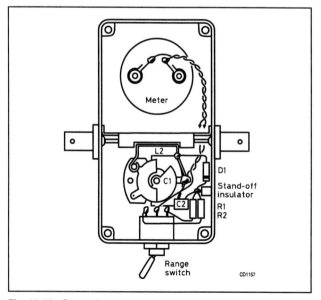

Fig 11.46. General arrangement of through-line wavemeter – direct type

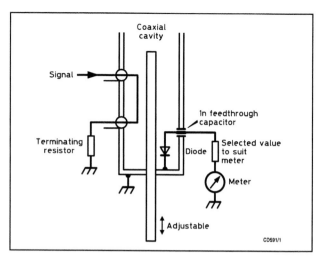

Fig 11.47. Generalised circuit arrangement

using a single cavity with an adjustable inner quarter-wave ($\lambda/4$) element.

Basically, the direct measurement of a $\lambda/4$ element represents the wavelength to which it is resonant. An equivalent circuit of the wavemeter is shown in Fig 11.47. It consists of input coupling, a resonant circuit formed by the $\lambda/4$ line/cavity and output coupling with detection and meter drive (output probe).

When a $\lambda/4$ circuit is energised, a current maximum will occur at the shorted end and a voltage maximum at the open end as shown in Fig 11.48. A current resonance indicator must therefore be coupled to the low-impedance end of the circuit, ie as near as possible to the shorted end. Also, as the input will normally be the output of an oscillator or transmitter, this will also dictate coupling at the low impedance end, ie near the short-circuit.

Both these couplings should be relatively loose so as not to foreshorten the length of the inner conductor by capacitive loading so that the mechanical length of the inner conductor is substantially the electrical length of $\lambda/4$. There will, however, be some apparent shortening of the inner conductor compared with the free-space value due to the stray field from its end to the continuing outer cylinder. This will be most noticeable at the highest frequencies and may be as much as 4mm at 2.5GHz.

The characteristic impedance of the cavity is of no significance in the case of a frequency meter and may be of a value convenient to the materials available. It may be either circular or square in section. The sensitivity will naturally depend to a large extent on the meter used. With a 50µA FSD meter

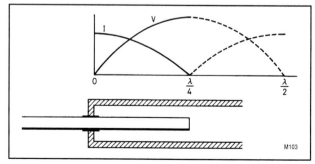

Fig 11.48. Current (I) and voltage (V) in a $\lambda/4$ cavity

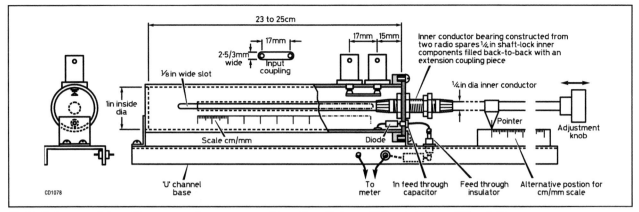

Fig 11.49. Layout of the wide-range cavity wavemeter. Note: 1in = 25.4mm, 1/8in = 3.175mm, 1/4in = 6.35mm

satisfactory indications at levels down to 5mW may be observed.

In the design illustrated in Fig 11.49, the outer consists of a 25mm inside diameter tube with an adjustable length inner conductor of 6.35mm (0.25in) diameter. The outer in this case has a narrow slot running most of the outer tube length so that the position of the inner conductor may be observed directly; the calibration scale can be fixed along the slot (similar to a slotted line). An alternative method of fitting a calibration scale to the extension of the inner conductor outside the cavity is also indicated on the diagram.

Construction

As mentioned, the precise dimensions of the cavity are not critical though, if materials permit, it can be made for 50Ω or 75Ω and may be either round or square in cross-section.

For convenience, the inner conductor should be 6.35mm in diameter and the outer tube 25mm inside diameter. The material may be copper or brass but the latter is more rigid and may be more suitable for the inner conductor. The outer may be for preference copper as it may well be made from a length of water pipe. It is important to provide a reliable sliding contact for the inner conductor. If 6.35mm material is used then two conventional shaft locks should be connected back to back, preferably with an extension tube between them, to provide a long bearing. The input coupling is at the shorted end and consists of a strip drilled and then soldered directly to the connectors.

Using the wavemeter

For frequency measurement, the indicator should be connected to one port of the wavemeter and the other port connected to the output of the source whose frequency is to be measured. In the case of a source that is likely to be sensitive to load impedance it may be preferable to connect the wavemeter via an attenuator or directional coupler since the wavemeter, when tuned to frequencies other than that of the source output, will appear as a variable reactance.

Slide the inner of the wavemeter slowly out whilst watching the indicator for a peak reading. In the case of a wavemeter that is poorly constructed there may be a residual reading whilst still far off the resonant frequency. This is usually due to over-coupling between the input and output circuits. The resonance peak will, in this case, be preceded by a sharp dip in this residual reading.

It is possible with this type of wavemeter to obtain more than one indication due to the wavemeter resonating not only at a quarter-wavelength but also at all odd multiples of a quarter-wave. For example, when measuring the output of a 1296MHz source a reading will also be obtained when the wavemeter is tuned to 432MHz. This characteristic can be used when calibrating the wavemeter since it is possible to obtain several calibration points. These can be plotted on a graph and, by interpolation, the frequencies between can be calibrated. Obviously the more frequencies available when calibrating, the more accurate the overall calibration will be.

DIP OSCILLATORS

A dip oscillator (the valve versions were called *grid dip oscillators*) is an essential tool for the construction of VHF/UHF equipment.

In its simplest form it consists of a stable LC oscillator covering a wide range of frequencies. Depending on the actual range, the inductance will be cut to an appropriate size and will normally be a plug-in type. Some form of indicator, such as a meter, is required to show when the dip oscillator is tuned to the circuit under test.

For VHF and UHF dip oscillators, FETs are normally used in a push-pull circuit. With circuits of this type oscillators for use up to 500MHz are practical with careful mechanical layout so that connecting leads between the plug-in coil and the tuning capacitor are short and of as low inductance as possible.

Plug-in coils for the higher frequencies are usually made of sufficiently substantial material to be self-supporting. If, however, any support is needed a low-dielectric-constant material such as PTFE should be used. Sockets for the coils should be mounted on similar material and adequate clearance for the sockets from the box should be provided. These precautions assist in the attainment of the highest frequencies.

The indicator may be either a low-reading microammeter or a more robust instrument operated by a simple amplifier. The tuning control should for preference be driven by a slow-motion dial, although a large-diameter dial operated by the thumb has some merit in this type of instrument.

A VHF dip oscillator

This dip oscillator [5] covers the band 29–460MHz in four overlapping ranges with plug-in coils. The ranges are:

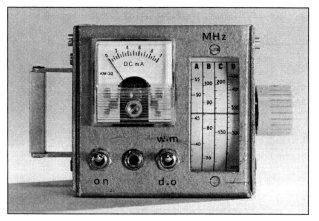

Fig 11.50. VHF dip oscillator: front panel (above) and inside view (right)

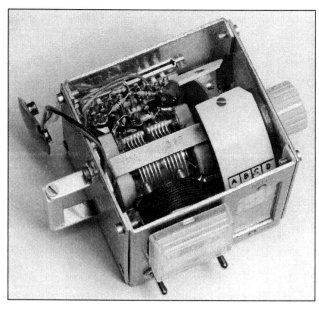

Range A	29 to 55MHz
Range B	50 to 109MHz
Range C	97 to 220MHz
Range D	190 to 460MHz

It is shown in the photograph (Fig 11.50).

Circuit description

The circuit is based around a Kalitron oscillator formed by two junction-type FETs TR1 and TR2 – see Fig 11.51. The frequency-determining components are the split-stator capacitor C1 and the plug-in coil L1. The resulting RF signal is then detected by a balanced diode detector D1 and D2, and used to drive meter amplifier TR3. The original design used either 2N5245 or TIS88 for TR1 and TR2 but these are no longer available. These can be substituted by a BF256A or similar N-channel junction FET.

The power can be turned off to convert the instrument to a sensitive absorption wavemeter, or when headphones are plugged into the jack J1 it becomes a modulation monitor.

In this design the existence of spurious dips and 'suck-outs' in the various ranges is very much associated with the quality of the two RF chokes L2 and L3. These are each of 15µH.

If troubles of this kind are experienced, other inductors can be tried. It is very difficult to find components with no strong resonance over the whole of a wide band, but nevertheless the prototype instrument using the inductors with the two series damping resistors R4 and R5 seemed to minimise the problem.

Power supply

This is normally provided by a PP3 battery, the current drain being about 10mA (including the LED). A PP3 replacement mains supply could be substituted.

Construction

Construction can either be on tag strip (Fig 11.52) or using a PCB as given in Appendix 1. The most important points are to keep the leads to the tuning capacitor as short as possible, using copper strip to keep the inductance low. Also keep all other RF leads short, especially any that are associated with the sources of TR1 and TR2.

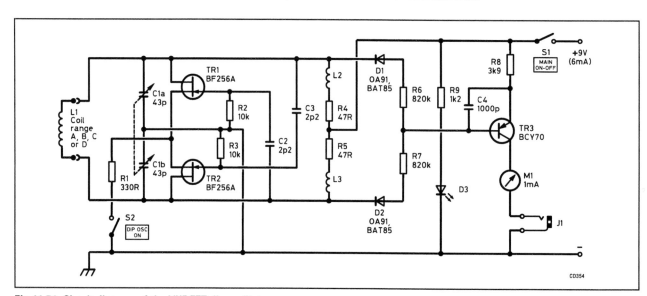

Fig 11.51. Circuit diagram of the VHF FET dip oscillator

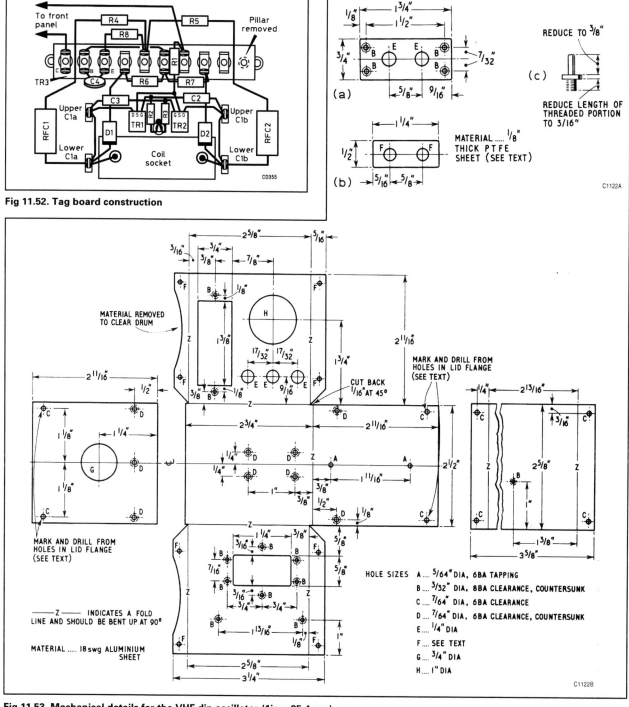

Fig 11.52. Tag board construction

Fig 11.53. Mechanical details for the VHF dip oscillator (1in = 25.4mm)

HOLE SIZES A .... 5/64" DIA, 6BA TAPPING
B .... 3/32" DIA, 8BA CLEARANCE, COUNTERSUNK
C .... 7/64" DIA, 6BA CLEARANCE
D .... 7/64" DIA, 6BA CLEARANCE, COUNTERSUNK
E .... 1/4" DIA
F .... SEE TEXT
G .... 3/4" DIA
H .... 1" DIA

—Z— INDICATES A FOLD LINE AND SHOULD BE BENT UP AT 90°

MATERIAL ..... 18 swg ALUMINIUM SHEET

MATERIAL ..... 1/8" THICK PTFE SHEET (SEE TEXT)

The original version, as shown in the photographs, was constructed in an aluminium box forming about a 50mm (2in) cube and a design for making this is given in Fig 11.53. Following this construction is, however, a matter of personal choice.

The tuning capacitor C1 with a tuning scale drum is driven by a 6:1 reduction drive. A home-made 22mm (0.875in) wide card or plastic scale is fitted to the drum.

The coil socket and the coil mounting strips are made from 3mm (0.125in) thick PTFE sheet, although polythene or even polystyrene is acceptable (Fig 11.53). Two Belling-Lee 4mm

sockets (similar to O-Z pattern) are mounted on the socket strip.

Coil construction

The coil (see Table 11.9) for the lowest frequency range, A, is wound on a short piece of 12.5mm (0.5in) diameter polystyrene rod and then glued in place. Connecting and supporting legs (each 44.5mm or 1.75in long) are made from 14 SWG enamelled copper wire. The next range coil, B, is self supporting and wound directly with 14 SWG wire, also with connection pieces 44.5mm (1.75in) long.

Table 11.8. Component list for the VHF dip oscillator	
R1	330R
R2, 3	10k
R4, 5	47R
R6, 7	820k
R9	1k2
C1	43p + 43p variable
C2, 3	2p2 ceramic
C4	1000p ceramic
D1, 2	OA91, BAT85
D3	Low-current red LED
TR1, 2	BF256A or similar – see text
L1	See text
L2, 3	15µH
M1	1mA FSD meter
S1, 2	On/off switch
J1	Jack socket to suit
PP3 battery connector	
Belling-Lee 4mm OZ similar plugs and sockets	
Resistors are 0.25/0.5W, ±5% unless stated otherwise.	

Table 11.9. Coil details for the VHF dip oscillator		
Range A	29–55MHz	12t 22 SWG enam copper wire on 12.5mm (0.5in) polystyrene rod 25mm (1in) long, 44.5mm (1.75in) legs 14 SWG
Range B	50–109MHz	8t 14 SWG enamelled copper wire wound on 9.5mm (0.375in) drill, 44.5mm (1.75in) legs
Range C	97–220MHz	16mm (0.625in) wide, 73mm (2.875in) long loop of 13 SWG enamelled copper wire
Range D	190–460MHz	8mm (0.3125in) wide, 17.5mm (0.6875in) long 26 SWG (or near) copper or beryllium/copper strip soldered directly across plug ends

Range C has a simple rectangular loop of 13 SWG enamelled copper wire, whilst the highest frequency range D requires the two plug sections to be further shortened (see Fig 11.53) and then a strip of copper foil or beryllium/copper sheet is soldered straight across their ends.

Calibration of dip oscillators

The easiest way to check the calibration of a dip oscillator is to listen for the output on a general-coverage receiver, an amateur receiver or scanner. (*Note:* When the signal is found, especially with scanners which are of very wide bandwidth, check that there is no response at one-half, one-third or one-fifth of the frequency in case the fundamental has not been found.)

This probably allows a good check on the calibration into the VHF range. Additional points can be found by using the second-channel response provided that the IF is known (the second channel response is $2 \times$ IF removed from the normal response).

Another method is to use the resonances of lengths of feeder cables, providing that the velocity factor for the particular cable is known, so that the physical length corresponding to the wanted electrical half- and quarter-waves can be found.

Using the dip oscillator

Although the dip oscillator has a wide range of uses for measurements on both complete equipment and individual components, these all rely on its ability to measure the frequency of a tuned circuit. In use, the coil of the dip oscillator is coupled indirectly to the circuit under test with maximum coupling being obtained with the axis of the oscillator coil at right-angles to the direction of current flow. Coupling should be no greater than

that necessary to give a moderate change on the dip oscillator meter. These requirements are shown diagrammatically in Fig 11.54.

If the tuned circuit being investigated is well shielded magnetically (eg a coaxial line) it may be difficult to use inductive coupling. In such cases it may be possible to use capacitive coupling by placing the open end of the line near to one end of the dip oscillator coil. A completely enclosed cavity is likely to have some form of coupling loop and the dip meter coil can usually be coupled inductively by means of a low-impedance transmission line such as a twisted pair with a coupling loop.

When used as an absorption wavemeter, the oscillator is not energised and the tuned circuit acts as a pick-up loop. This arrangement is useful when looking for harmonic output of a multiplier or transmitter or for spurious oscillations.

Determination of the resonant frequency of a tuned circuit
The resonant frequency of a tuned circuit is found by placing the dip oscillator close to that of the circuit and tuning for resonance. No power should be applied to the circuit under test and the coupling should be as loose as possible consistent with a reasonable dip being produced on the indicating

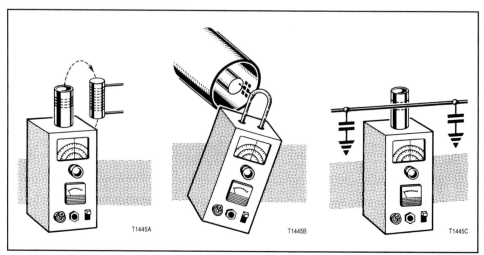

Fig 11.54. Using the dip oscillator

meter. The size of the dip is dependent on the Q of the circuit under test, a circuit having a high Q producing a more pronounced dip than one only having low or moderate Q.

Absorption wavemeter

By switching off the power supply in the dip oscillator and then using in the normal way, the instrument may be used as an absorption wavemeter. In this case power has to be applied to the circuit under test. Resonance is determined by maximum deflection on the meter caused by rectifying the received RF.

The absorption wavemeter can also be used to check for harmonics and spurii.

Capacitance and inductance

Obviously, if an instrument has the ability to measure the frequency of a tuned circuit, it can also be used for the determination of inductance and capacitance providing that one of these components is known or a substitution made. If one component is known then use of the resonance formula is all that is required, ie:

$$f = \frac{1}{2\pi\sqrt{LC}}$$

Otherwise, carry out the following steps. To measure capacitance connect a close-tolerance capacitor C_s (eg 1%) in parallel with a coil (any coil will do providing it will resonate at a frequency within the range of the dip oscillator). This circuit is coupled to the dip oscillator and its frequency f_1 megahertz noted. The unknown capacitor C_x is then connected in place of the known value and the new resonance f_2 megahertz noted. The unknown capacitance is then given by:

$$C_x = \frac{f_1^2 C_s}{f_2^2}$$

A similar substitution can be made for inductance, assuming a known close-tolerance inductor is available. In this case replace C_s and C_x by L_s and L_x respectively.

Signal generator

For receiver tuning, the dip oscillator may be used to provide an unmodulated carrier wave by tuning the oscillator to the desired frequency and placing it close to the antenna terminal. The amplitude of the signal may be controlled by adjusting the distance of the dip oscillator from the antenna terminal.

Checking crystals

The frequency at which a crystal is oscillating can be checked by using the dip oscillator as an absorption wavemeter as described above. It is also possible to check in a similar manner the harmonic on which a crystal is oscillating.

SPECTRUM ANALYSIS

Spectrum analysers are perhaps one of the best ways of examining the performance of filters, transmitters, receivers etc. They allow us to look at the frequency response in a pictorial manner. Fig 11.55 shows a typical display. From this we can see that the frequency is displayed on the horizontal axis whilst the response (or output) of a circuit is shown on the vertical axis.

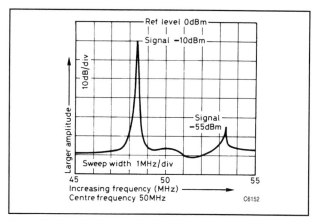

Fig 11.55. A typical screen display of a spectrum analyser

Unfortunately spectrum analysers tend to be quite expensive, although some can be picked up on the second-hand market. An excellent unit to build at home was described in *Radio Communication* [6] but its top frequency range is about 90MHz. This is satisfactory in examining the modulation of 50 and 70MHz signals but we should ideally be able to examine up to about the third harmonic in an item such as a transmitter; if only the modulation pattern or a frequency response of a filter is required we may manage with much less.

An alternative approach to a self contained spectrum analyser is the use of an add-on to an oscilloscope, where the oscilloscope display becomes the spectrum analyser display. These require an oscilloscope with X, Y mode facilities but the bandwidth of the oscilloscope is not important – that is taken care of in the add-on unit. These usually have a lower frequency limit (eg 400kHz), the upper limit being dependent on type, eg 100, 250, 500MHz. They come in formats from a large probe to a stand-alone box and prices vary from about £250 to £1000 (1997 prices).

DIGITAL FREQUENCY COUNTERS

This type of frequency meter utilises integrated circuits to count electronically the number of cycles of an input waveform in a given counting period. Although these digital integrated circuits are themselves complex, the principle of operation of the digital frequency meter (DFM) is quite simple; it consists of five major circuits, *the input wave shaping circuit, clock, gate, counter* and *display.*

The input wave shaping circuit takes the input waveform, amplifies it and converts it to a rectangular waveform of sufficient magnitude to operate the counting circuits.

The clock produces a series of pulses which determine the basic counting period of the DFM. The pulses are typically 10ms, 100ms or 1s long and are derived from a crystal-controlled oscillator (typically 1MHz or 5MHz). The pulses are thus of high accuracy and applied to the gate which can be considered as on on/off switch operated by the clock.

When the clock pulse opens the gate, an input train of pulses from the wave-shaping circuit is sent to the counting circuits. The counting circuits count the number of input pulses for the duration that the gate is open; this count is then frozen and the binary count decoded and used to drive decade displays.

The accuracy of a DFM depends on the accuracy of the internal clock signal. Accuracy can be increased if the clock

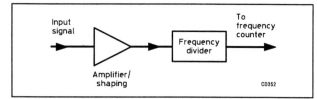

Fig 11.56. Prescaling

oscillator is housed in a crystal oven (thermostatically controlled) and compared with a standard frequency source for calibration. The resolution of a DFM is the smallest digit a display exhibits, usually 1Hz. The resolution will change according to the frequency range in operation and the length of the clock signal.

The DFM can also be made to display the period of an input waveform. In this case one period of the input allows the number of standard pulses to be counted (eg 1μs or 1ms). The number counted in one period is then the time for a period.

Prescalers

To increase the frequency range of a DFM it is common to put components that perform prescaling ahead of the input – Fig 11.56. This consists of an amplifier, wave shaping circuit and high-speed frequency divider (the prescaler). Prescaling will divide the input frequency by a known amount (eg 2, 10, 64 or 100) and the resulting signal is then applied to the basic frequency counter. It should be borne in mind that prescaling reduces the resolution of the counted frequency. For example, a frequency counter without prescaling may measure to 1Hz – if prescaling of 10 is introduced then the same counter will only read to 10Hz.

There are various prescalers on the market and Table 11.10 gives just a representative sample. The devices can have either ECL, TTL or both outputs.

The counter following has prescaling which extends its limit up to 600MHz. For prescalers and amplifiers to extend the frequency range above this the reader is referred to reference [7] or any of the typical data sheets/application notes produced by the various manufacturers. As with all VHF/UHF

Table 11.10. Typical prescalers available

Device No	Man	F_{max} (MHz)	Division ratio	V_{cc} (V)
CA3179	H	1250	64/256	5
CXA1541M	S	1100	64/65, 128/9	5
MC1690	M	2500		
MC12023	M	225	64	3.2–5.5
MC12073	M	1100	64	5
MC12074	M	1100	256	5
MC12090	M	750	2	5
SP8629	P	200	100	
SP8660	P	150	10	5
SP8680B	P	575	10/11	5
SP8704	P	950	64/65, 128/129	3–5
SP8713	P	1100	64/65 or 72	2.7–5
SP8714	P	2100	32/33, 64/65	2.7–5
SP8715	P	1100	64/65, 128/9	2.7–5
SP8718	P	520	64/65	5
SP8755	P	1200	64	5
SP8799	P	225	10/11	5.2 or 6.8–9.5
SP8830	P	1500	10	5
U666BS	T	1000	256	5

H – Harris, M – Motorola, P – GEC Plessey, S – Sony, T – Telefunken

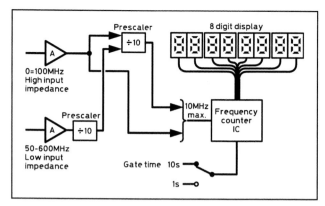

Fig 11.57. Block diagram of frequency counter

circuits, great care should be taken with layout – always use an earth plane. Care should be taken in the choice of capacitors – these should be, in order of preference, ceramic chip, silver mica and ceramic disc.

A 600MHz digital frequency counter

This frequency counter is capable of operating up to about 600MHz with a sensitivity of 50mV or better. It is based on an eight-digit frequency counter IC which will count to 10MHz. The range is increased by the use of prescalers which divide the incoming frequency down to the 10MHz range. Fig 11.57 shows a block diagram of the system. It offers three input ranges, 0–6MHz (typically 10MHz), 0–60MHz and 0–600MHz. It is possible to build a 0–60MHz counter and then add the additional components later to increase the capability to about 600MHz.

The gate time, ie the count period, can be switched between 1s and 10s. At the 1s position the counter offers a seven-digit display, while at the 10s position the counter provides an eight-digit display. The decimal point is switched to denote the megahertz position, all digits to the left of it representing megahertz. The supply requirement is 5V at approximately 300mA.

References [8], [9], and [10] provided the basic information for the design; for extension in frequency ranges and sensitivity the reader is referred to [7].

Input circuit up to 60MHz

The circuit diagram is shown in Fig 11.58. The input impedance is approximately 1MΩ, with junction FET TR1 acting as a buffer. The signal is then fed to IC3 which contains a group of transistors capable of operation up to 1GHz. This provides amplification and an output capable of driving logic circuits. The output transistor, TR2, is a high-speed PNP switch which translates the ECL output logic level of IC3 to a TTL compatible level.

Input circuit 10–600MHz

This circuit is shown in Fig 11.59 and has an input impedance of approximately 50Ω. IC1 is a monolithic amplifier with 50Ω input and output impedances and operates up to 1GHz with a gain of some 16dB. The resulting output is fed to IC2 which is a high-speed divide-by-10 counter capable of operating up to at least 575MHz (typically more than 600MHz) with a sine-wave input. The output selected is TTL compatible.

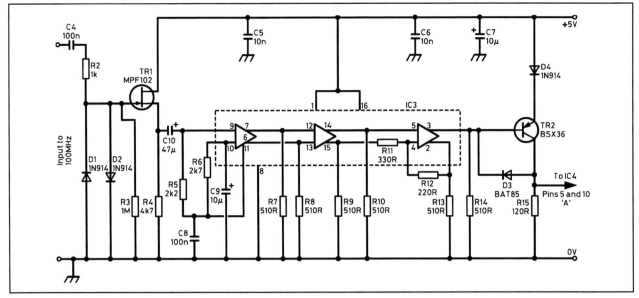

Fig 11.58. Input circuit (up to 60MHz)

The circuit will operate without IC1 but is not as sensitive. Although a Mini-circuits monolithic broad-band amplifier is used it is possible to use those from other manufacturers such as Avantek.

Control, counter and display circuit

Fig 11.60 shows all of the remaining digital side of the frequency counter and displays. The initial stages of the frequency counter consists of the input selection and prescaling circuits.

IC4 and IC5 are both 74F 'FAST' TTL in order to cope with the speed. IC4 is a multiplexer which is controlled by DC signals supplied via S1a and determines the route of signals from the input amplifiers to the counter IC. IC5 is a divide-by-10 circuit which provides prescaling for all signals above 10MHz. IC6 is the heart of the digital frequency meter and provides all the count circuits, decoders and drivers for the eight-digit LED display. Timing is derived from a 10MHz crystal oscillator.

Switches S1b/c determine the position of the decimal point in conjunction with the gate time selection switch (S2) for the various inputs. PB1 is a reset button for the counter.

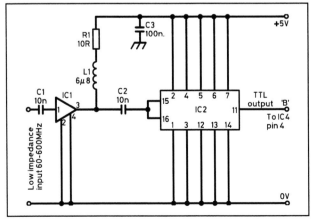

Fig 11.59. Input circuit (10 to 600MHz)

Construction

The components required are listed in Table 11.11. A double-sided PCB and component layout is provided in Appendix 1.

Table 11.11. Component list for 600MHz digital frequency counter

R1	10R
R2, 16, 17	1k
R3	1M
R4	4k7
R5	2k2
R6	2k7
R7–10, 13, 14	510R
R11	330R
R12	220R
R15	120R
R18, 20	10k
R19	22M
R21	100k
R22	3k3
C1, 2, 5, 6	10n ceramic disc
C3, 4, 8, 11, 14, 15	100n ceramic disc
C7, 9	10µ,16V tantalum
C10	47µ, 6V tantalum
C12	47p polystyrene or ceramic
C13	100p polystyrene or ceramic
VC1	65p trimmer
L1	6µ8 RF inductor
D1, 2, 4	1N914, 1N4148
D3	BAT85
TR1	MPF102
TR2	BSX36,2N5771, fast PNP switch
IC1	MAR-1
IC2	SP8680B
IC3	MC10116
IC4	74F153
IC5	74F160
IC6	ICM7216D
XL1	10MHz crystal
LD0–7	Double 7-seg LED (4 off), CC, 0.5in
S1	4p, 3w rotary
S2	DPDT toggle, PCB mounting

Resistors are 0.25/0.5W, ±5% unless stated otherwise.

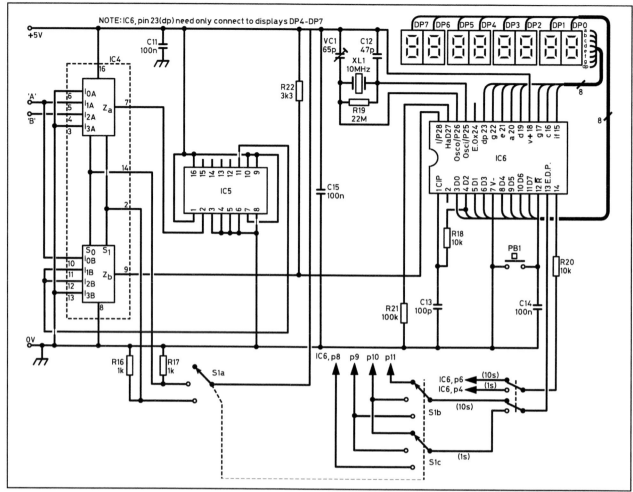

Fig 11.60. Control, counter and display circuit

If you wish to make your own, it is essential that an earth plane is provided on the copper side for the two input circuits on Fig 11.58 and Fig 11.59. It is wise to use good layout practice for the digital circuits, especially where they can run up to 100MHz. Adequate decoupling is also essential.

Do not use IC sockets for IC1, IC2, IC3, IC4 and IC5. The dual LED displays should be mounted on single-row sockets. The PCB is double sided – through connections are made mainly via component leads and this includes IC sockets. The sockets may therefore have to stand off the board slightly in order to solder 'on the top side'. It is suggested that turned pin sockets are used. There are three through connections to be made with wire links. Where necessary, clearance must be made around holes on the earth plane where connection is not made to the earth plane – use a sharp drill or cutter for this.

If a counter is only required up to 10MHz then the output of the circuit of Fig 11.58 can be fed straight to pin 28 of IC6, omitting IC4 and IC5 and the range switch S2. If an input is required only up to 60MHz then omit the components associated with the 600MHz input amplifier and alter the stop on S1 for only two positions.

Calibration

Using a highly accurate frequency counter which is calibrated against a standard, feed the same input signal into both counters and adjust VC1 for the same reading.

HF/UHF DEVIATION METER

The HF/UHF deviation meter described herein by G3BIK [11] is simple to construct, of relatively low cost and based on readily available components. It is housed in a small RF-shielded plastic enclosure. It can be used with FM signals over a wide frequency range from about 3MHz to 450MHz. The power supply requirement is 15–20V DC at about 50mA – see later.

Fig 11.61 shows the block diagram of the instrument, the interconnections and signal routing, Fig 11.62 gives the circuit diagram, and the components are specified in Table 11.12. A PCB pattern and component layout is given in Appendix 1.

Fundamentally the circuit is a type of superheterodyne receiver with an FM demodulator output which is displayed on a moving-coil meter showing kilohertz deviation. The instrument can also be used to monitor the demodulated audio signal on a small internal loudspeaker, and provision has been made for external access to the pulsed RF harmonics of the VFO as a simple source of test signals, extending up to VHF, which could be useful for calibration or general receiver testing.

Circuit operation

A restricted-range signal f_2 (1.5MHz) is generated by the Colpitts oscillator (VFO) formed by TR1 and associated components. The variable-capacitance diode in conjunction with

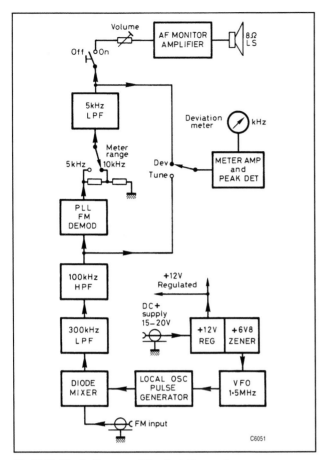

Fig 11.61. Block diagram of the deviation meter

RV1 allows variation of this frequency by about ±100kHz. The sine-wave output from this oscillator is buffered by TR2 and then amplitude limited by TR3–5 and D3. It is then differentiated by TR6 and TR7 which results in a train of sharp pulses at the VFO repetition rate.

The pulses are applied to a fast-switching diode (D4). The action of the diode causes current pulses through the primary of pulse transformer T1. These current pulses are rich in harmonics and extend well up into the VHF region. *Note*: the usable upper frequency is to a large extent determined by the switching diode. A microwave step-recovery diode would probably extend the frequency range but these devices are not cheap. Transformer T1 is wound in bifilar manner, it being important to get the phasing correct.

The two phase-related outputs from the transformer are applied to the diode bridge mixer formed by D5 and D6 and here mixed with the FM signal (f_1) being measured. The mixing products are developed across R41 and the signal $f_1 - f_2$ (harmonic) filtered by the action of the various constituents of IC1 (range 100–300kHz). This signal is then demodulated by the phase-locked loop of IC2. The output at pin 7 of the PLL is a true replica of the input modulating signal and this is attenuated by R57/RV3 for the two meter ranges. The output is selected by S1 and then amplified by a low-pass active filter IC3a. With S2 in the TUNE position, the IF signal at about 150kHz is passed to the meter amplifier IC3b/c. Diode D7 with capacitor C58 acts as a peak detector and the resulting DC drives the meter. With S2 set to DEV, then the demodulated signal is applied to the meter circuit.

An AF monitor is provided (IC4). The drive to this is via a push switch (S3) so that the user is deterred from using the monitor during measurement of deviation.

Power supply

A single supply philosophy is adopted for the deviation meter via an on-board 12V regulator, thus ensuring stability of deviation calibration and flexibility in the choice of external voltage supply.

All of the discrete transistors are fed from the full +12V regulated rail except the VFO which is further stabilised by a 6.8V zener diode. Split-voltage supplies for IC1, IC2 and IC3 are provided by resistive dividers R50/51, R52/55 and R71/72 and well decoupled.

Adequate decoupling of the DC supply connections is of the utmost importance in this circuit because of the pulsed nature of the local oscillator and mixer signals – hence the provision of low-value decoupling capacitors to filter out the higher frequencies from the supply rails and larger capacitors (microfarads) to deal with the lower frequencies.

Construction

The prototype circuit was constructed on SRBP copper stripboard of 0.1in hole spacing and dual parallel planes were allocated on the stripboard for each of the several DC supply and return rails.

Component layout is not critical provided that, as with any HF circuit, due attention is given to the shortness of component leads and interconnecting wires, and to mechanical rigidity. Sub-miniature 50Ω coaxial cable is employed for the interconnection between signal input socket and mixer, and miniature screened cable is used between all other panel-mounted components and the circuit board.

The RF screened enclosure is electrically bonded to the negative supply terminal, shown on the circuit diagram as the 0V rail, and the decoupling capacitors associated with the integrated circuits should be connected directly between the supply pins of the appropriate IC.

The panel-mounted miniature volume control was found to be not really necessary in practice, so this could be replaced by a presettable potentiometer mounted internally on the circuit board.

As the upper operational frequency limit of the instrument is largely determined by the performance of the local oscillator harmonic-generator diode D4, pulse transformer T1 and the D5/D6 diode mixer circuit, particular care should be taken to ensure shortness of component leads and symmetry of component layout for this section of the circuit.

Setting up

Before any attempt is made to use or calibrate the instrument the free-running frequency of the phase-locked loop VCO must be set to 150kHz.

Connect a frequency counter to either pin 4 or 5 of IC2 and adjust RV2 until the frequency is virtually 150kHz.

Calibration

As for the calibration of most measuring instruments the crunch comes with the requirement for a signal source of known accuracy. The ideal source for this particular application would be an RF signal generator with a frequency range of 2–450MHz, and a frequency modulation facility with

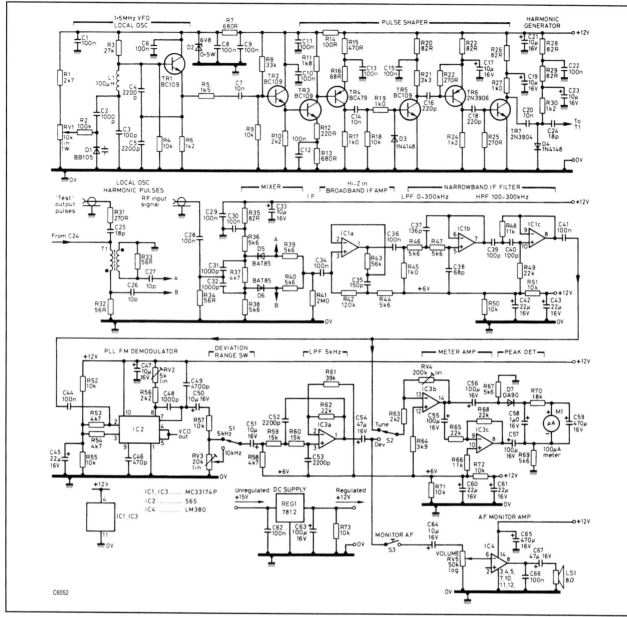

Fig 11.62. Circuit diagram of the deviation meter

calibrated deviation from zero to 30kHz at an audio frequency of 1kHz. Output attenuation down to 5μV PD across a 50Ω load is also required.

With the deviation meter switch turned ON, set switch S2 (TUNE/DEV) to TUNE. Connect the signal generator to the input of the deviation meter, and set the frequency of the generator to 50MHz with an output of 50μV PD and zero deviation. Rotate the VFO knob slowly until a maximum deflection is obtained on the meter. If the meter deflection is greater than full-scale adjust the signal generator attenuator to bring it back on to scale.

A number of maxima of differing amplitudes will be observed as the VFO knob is rotated, the choice of which is not critical. It is sufficient to opt for one which appears to be dominant, then carefully tune for the peak. Switch from TUNE to DEV (S2) and the meter reading should fall to zero (no deviation on input signal).

Set the deviation switch of the meter (S1) to the 5kHz position. Frequency modulate the signal generator with a 1kHz signal at 5kHz deviation. The resultant meter deflection can now be adjusted with preset resistor RV4 until the meter reads full-scale. Now switch S1 to the 10kHz setting and the meter will take up a lesser deflection. Adjust RV3 until a mid-scale reading is obtained. Assuming that the meter is scaled 0–10, then with S1 set for 10kHz, the scale reading is read as kilohertz deviation.

Change the signal generator to 10kHz deviation and note the meter reading. It should read full-scale – if not adjust RV3 slightly. Reduce the deviation in steps of 1kHz on the signal generator to confirm the true linearity of the indicating meter circuit.

While the signal generator is still connected it is prudent to determine the upper frequency limit of the meter. Turn off the deviation on the signal generator and set S2 to TUNE.

Table 11.12. Components list for the HF/UHF deviation meter

R1	2k7	R61	39k	C58	1µ electrolytic
R2	100k	R64	3k9	C59, 65	470µ electrolytic
R3	27k	R70	18k	L1	100µH
R4, 9, 18,		R71–73	10k, 0.5W	T1	Pulse transformer,
57	10k	RV1	10k lin,1W cermet		10mm ferrite ring, 4t
R5	1k5	RV2	5k lin, min cermet		bifilar ECW
R6, 24, 30	1k2	RV3	20k lin, min cermet	D1	BB105, BB405B, BB809
R7	680R, ½W	RV4	200k lin, min cermet		varicap
R8	33k	RV5	50k log carbon pot with	D2	6V8, 400mW
R10, 56, 63	2k2		S3	D3, 4	1N4148
R11	1k8	C1, 6, 8–13,		D5, 6	BAT85
R12	220R	15, 22,		D7	OA90
R13	680R	28–30, 34,		TR1-3, 5	BC109, 2N3904 or
R14	100R	36, 41, 44,			similar
R15	470R	62, 66	100n ceramic	TR4	BC479, 2N3906 or
R16	68R	C2, 48	1n ceramic		similar
R17,19, 27,		C3	100p SM/polystyrene	TR6	2N3906
45	1k	C4, 5, 52,		TR7	2N3904
R20, 23, 26,		53	2n2 polystyrene	IC1, 3	MC33174P
28, 29, 35	82R	C7,14, 20	10n ceramic	IC2	NE565
R21	3k3	C16, 18	220 ceramic	IC4	LM380
R22, 25, 31	270R	C17, 19, 21,		REG1	12V, eg 7812
R32, 33, 34	56R	23, 33, 47,		LS1	8Ω miniature
R36, 38, 39,		50, 51, 64	10µ electrolytic	M1	Meter, 100µA, scaled 0–
46,47	5k6	C24, 25	18p SM/ceramic		10
R37, 53, 54,		C26, 27	10p SM/ceramic	S1,2	SPDT min toggle
58	4k7	C31, 32	100p ceramic	S3	Push-button, NO (part
R40, 44, 67,		C35	150p SM/ceramic		of RV5)
69	5k6	C37	136p (2 × 68p)	Enclosure: ABS, RF shielded, 190 ×	
R41	2M (2 × 1M)	C38	68p SM/ceramic	110 × 60mm	
R42	120k	C39, 40	100p SM	Socket (DC): 3.5mm chassis mount-	
R43	56k	C42, 43, 45,		ing	
R48, 66	11k	60, 61	22µ electrolytic	Socket (RF): 50Ω BNC panel mount-	
R49, 62, 65,		C46	470p SM/ceramic	ing	
68	22k	C49	4n7 ceramic	Socket (pulse): 50Ω BNC panel	
R50–52, 55	10k, 0.5W	C54, 67	47µ electrolytic	mounting	
R59, 60	15k	C55–57, 63	100µ electrolytic		

Resistors 0.25W, ±5% metal film unless stated otherwise.

Progressively increase the carrier frequency in sensible increments, retuning at each step, until it is no longer possible to obtain a suitable maximum on the meter. If required, the frequency tuning range of the VFO may be conveniently measured at the test pulses output socket.

The instrument is now ready for use.

Use

Apply the RF signal to be measured to the input socket via a coaxial cable or by plugging into the socket an elementary pick-up antenna of some 100–200mm length. In either case the instrument will behave correctly with an input as low as 5µV but a higher signal is preferred, eg 50µV.

With no modulation of the RF carrier and S2 set to TUNE, rotate RV1 for maximum deflection on the meter. Switch S2 to DEV and read the meter, altering S1 if necessary.

NOISE MEASUREMENTS

Noise can be defined as any unwanted disturbance that is superimposed on a wanted signal. It will interfere with the information contained within the wanted signal and in the limit will prevent it being decoded.

In TV reception it can result in a grainy picture with possible white and black spots, and in the limit loss of picture. In radio reception it can produce crackling or hissing which in the limit will mask the speech or music. In data transmission it will affect the reliability with which the data is decoded, a poor signal with a high noise level providing a much higher error rate.

Where does noise come from? It can be generated externally to any equipment and can be classified as *man-made* (ie from electric motors, ignition systems etc) or *natural* (such as that from lightning discharges or stellar sources). In addition to these, there is what is known as *thermal noise*. At frequencies up to around 21MHz, the external noise is generally greater than any noise generated in a receiver. Above this frequency and up into microwaves the receiver-generated noise is generally dominant, especially at 144MHz and above.

Thermal noise is generated within components by the random agitation of atoms and results in a random voltage. At absolute zero this voltage is zero, increasing as temperature rises. It consists of frequencies that start virtually at DC and rise well into the gigahertz region. Some components generate more noise than others and, if the semiconductor literature is scanned, devices classified as 'low noise' will be noticed.

If a group of components in the front-end of a receiver generate noise in the microvolt region then this can well mask received signals of the same order. It is therefore important that receiver front-ends are well designed and set up in order to minimise the effect of noise. The following sections deal with equipment for this and how to perform these measurements.

Noise figures

In any amplifier, noise is added to the signal so that the signal-noise ratio at the output of the amplifier is worse than at the input even though the signal has been amplified. This is especially important in receiver RF amplifiers which deal with low-level signals. The ratio:

$$\frac{\text{Signal} / \text{noise in}}{\text{Signal} / \text{noise out}}$$

is defined as the *noise factor* but, as this ratio can have a wide range of values, it is convenient to express it in decibels (dB). The above ratio then becomes:

$$\text{Noise figure} = 10 \log_{10} \frac{s / n \text{ in}}{s / n \text{ out}} \text{ decibels}$$

In a receiver, there are a number of cascaded stages which will each contribute noise but the effect of the noise contribution of each successive stage is reduced by the power gain of the preceding stage. Thus if F_1, F_2 and F_3 are the respective noise figures of each successive stage and P_1, P_2 and P_3 are the stage gains, then the overall receiver noise factor F will be given by:

$$F = F_1 + \frac{F_2 - 1}{P_1} + \frac{F_2 - 1}{P_1 \times P_2}$$

In most cases only the first and second terms are significant.

Noise performance is measured by noting the noise output of the receiver when its input terminals are terminated with the value of source resistance for which it is designed and then adding a known amount of noise at the input such that the value of output noise is doubled. It is then obvious that the added noise is equal to the noise generated by the receiver, although two assumptions are made for this to be true:

1. All of the known output from the noise source is, in fact, coupled into the receiver; and
2. the receiver output doubles when the effective input is doubled (ie the receiver is linear over this range of inputs).

The first point will be met provided that:

(a) none of the noise is shunted;
(b) transit time effects are negligible; and
(c) the output of the noise source is coupled into the receiver by a very short length of low-loss cable of the correct characteristic impedance.

The linearity of the receiver can be established by providing two identical noise sources and shunting the output of the receiver by a 3dB attenuator when the second source is switched on, but for amateur use this is scarcely worthwhile.

Noise figure measurements [12]

If the radio amateur can get hold of a calibrated noise source then it is possible to obtain accurate noise figures for a piece of equipment. Fig 11.63 shows a typical arrangement of equipment. The noise source should be matched to the receiver and the impedance across which the audio output power is measured must be known.

The first reading is taken with the noise generator turned off. The receiver audio gain is adjusted for a convenient noise reading in decibels as observed on the audio power meter.

The noise generator is next turned on and its output is increased until a convenient power ratio, expressed by N_2/N_1, is observed. The ratio N_2/N_1 is referred to as the *Y factor*, and

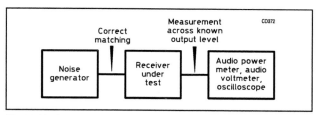

Fig 11.63. Arrangement for performing noise measurements

this noise figure measurement is commonly called the *Y-factor method*. From the Y factor and output power of the noise generator, the noise figure can be calculated, ie:

$$\text{NF} = \text{ENR} - 10 \log_{10}(Y - 1)$$

where NF is the noise figure in decibels, ENR is the excess noise ratio of the noise generator in decibels and Y is the output noise ratio N_2/N_1. The excess noise ratio of the generator is:

$$\text{ENR} = 10 \log_{10}(P_2/P_1 - 1)$$

where P_2 is the noise power of the generator and P_1 is the noise power from a resistor at 290K.

Most manufacturers of amateur communication receivers rate the noise characteristics with respect to signal input, and a common expression is:

$$\frac{\text{Signal} + \text{Noise}}{\text{Noise}}$$

or the *signal-to-noise ratio*. Usually the sensitivity is given as the number of microvolts for a signal-to-noise ratio of 10dB.

Typically, the noise figure for a good receiver operating below 30MHz is about 5 to 10dB. Lower noise figures can be obtained but they are of no real value due to the external noise arriving from the antenna. It is important to remember also that optimum noise figure in an RF amplifier does not always coincide with maximum stage gain, especially at VHF and higher. This is why actual noise measurements must be used to peak for best noise performance.

Noise sources

In the past various devices have been used as noise generators such as saturated thermionic diodes or the argon-filled fluorescent discharge tube. However, these devices have now become obsolete and semiconductor devices must be considered.

One noise source has been the reverse-biased germanium diode. Unfortunately the law relating noise with diode current varies for each diode and cases have been observed where the noise actually decreases for an increase of current over a limited range. Although individual diodes whose characteristics have been determined can be useful to optimise the noise performance of a receiver, they cannot be regarded as a measuring instrument. Fig 11.64 shows a typical circuit.

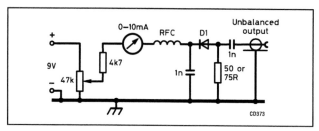

Fig 11.64. Noise generator using reverse-biased diode

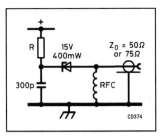

Fig 11.65. Zener diode reference noise source. Note that R should be selected for 5mA diode current from a supply of somewhat more than 15V: the components may conveniently be built into a coaxial plug

Silicon diodes in the avalanche region often produce wide-band noise. Zener diodes (especially those exhibiting avalanche breakdown) also provide a simple source of consistent noise over a wide frequency range. The noise output is not completely dependent on the current and they are not suitable as adjustable noise sources. A simple reference noise source may be made using the circuit of Fig 11.65, it being possible to mount the components all within a coaxial plug.

A zener/transistor noise source

This design is taken from reference [13] and the circuit diagram shown in Fig 11.66. The major noise source is zener diode D1 which is used to bias the first amplifier TR1. As there is no bypassing of the zener diode at the base of the transistor and the current in the diode is small, the excessive noise currents in the diode will flow through the base of the transistor. The resulting amplified output is applied to a second stage of gain, TR2. The second amplifier has a 51Ω resistor (R3) in the collector in order to provide a controlled output impedance.

The noise output of this circuit has been measured on a spectrum analyser. The detailed distribution of noise with frequency will not be presented since it will vary considerably with zener diode and transistor characteristics. Generally noise in the HF region was quite robust, reaching levels of 80dB higher than the noise output from a room-temperature resistor. The noise output is still 20dB above a 290K resistor at 432MHz.

The constructor should not attempt to estimate noise figure with a device as crude as this. It may be used, however, as a source for tuning receivers or amplifiers. If one were to build a free-running multivibrator using a 555 timer, with a total period of one to two seconds, it could be used to automatically turn the generator on and off. The system could then be used in conjunction with a step attenuator to adjust a

Table 11.13. Components list for the zener/transistor noise source

R1, 2, 5	330R
R3	51R
R4	100R
C1–4	10n, ceramic
D1, 2	6V2, 400mW zener, eg 1N753A
TR1, 2	2N5179

Resistors are 0.25/0.5W, ±5% unless stated otherwise.

VHF preamplifier for low noise figure. The output detector would be the constructor's ears, although refined circuitry could be built for this purpose.

A gated noise source

The circuit [12] described in this section may be used to construct a simple low-cost device to optimise a converter/receiver for best noise figure. The simplicity of this system makes effective alignment possible without a lot of test equipment.

The circuit diagram is given in Fig 11.67. TR1 and TR2 form an astable multivibrator operating at about 700Hz. The value of C1 is chosen to be greater than C2 so that the duty cycle is deliberately not 50%. The output from TR2 is capacitively coupled via C3 to the base of TR3, which acts as the current source for D1 via R7 and R8.

The diode generates broad-band noise which is output to a socket via R9. R7, C4 and C5 form a low-pass filter to prevent high-order harmonics of the switching pulses from appearing at the output. It should be noted that an absolute value of noise figure is not obtainable with this unit.

The circuit uses readily available components and may be easily duplicated. The lead placement in and around the diode should follow good VHF practice with short leads and direct placement. The influence of stray RF signals entering the device under test through the generator may be minimised by shielding the components shown. The unit can be housed in a metal box or one made from PCB scraps.

For best match, this source should be connected directly to the input of the equipment under test; therefore the unit should be equipped with a male connector. This matching becomes a greater consideration as the frequency of interest increases.

The gated noise source does not require a special detector, or any detector other than one's ear. By turning the noise

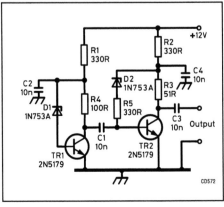

Fig 11.66. Circuit diagram of a noise generator (ARRL)

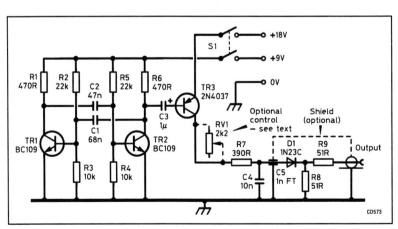

Fig 11.67. Circuit diagram of gated noise source (ARRL)

Table 11.14. Components list for the gated noise source	
R1, 6	470R
R2, 5	22k
R3, 4	10k
R7	390R
R8, 9	51R
RV1	2k2 pot (see text)
C1	68n
C2	47n
C3	1µ, 50V
C4	10n
C5	1n feedthrough
D1	1N23C or equivalent
TR1, 2	BC109 or equivalent
TR3	2N4037 or equivalent
S1	DPDT switch

Resistors are 0.25/0.5W, ±5% unless stated otherwise.

source on and off at an audio rate, the ratio of noise contributed by the system to noise of the system plus excess noise appears as an audio note. The louder the note, the greater the differential in levels. Hence, the greater the influence of the excess noise, the better the noise figure.

If greater precision is desired than that obtained by subjectively listening to the signal, an oscilloscope may be used. Connect the vertical (Y) input to any point in the audio system of the receiver, eg loudspeaker terminals. Adjust the oscilloscope for a display of several multiples of the train of rectangular pulses. Proceed by adjusting the device being tested for greatest vertical deflection.

In some cases the available noise generated by this unit may be too great. The output may be reduced by inserting attenuators between the generator output and the equipment under test. Alternatively a potentiometer (RV1) may be added as indicated in Fig 11.67. The use of an attenuator is preferred because it reduces the apparent output VSWR of the generator by increasing the return loss. If a control is used it must be returned to its minimum insertion loss position when starting a test or no signal may be heard.

Some contemporary receivers and transceivers cannot be operated in the AM mode and consequently the noise source seems unusable. The detection of noise is the process by which the noise source operates; therefore it will not work through an FM detector, nor will it work through a product detector since one of the terms of the detection (the noise) is not coherent.

The oscilloscope jack on many receivers is loosely coupled to the IF amplifier preceding the detector. A wide-band oscilloscope connected to this point will show the train of pulses and eliminate the need for aural detection. The alignment of the later IF stages of a system should have the least impact on the noise performance and maximum signal response will always occur at the same setting. Therefore the simple detector of Fig 11.68 will generally work for aural AM detection. Connect point A to the last IF amplifier anode, collector or drain. Connect point B to the audio amplifier at or near the volume control and ground point C. With this arrangement the normal output detector is turned down with the volume control and the temporary detector provide AM detection.

The gated noise source has been used for literally hundreds of applications and has proved to be a powerful yet simple addition to the test bench. While no guarantee of duplication

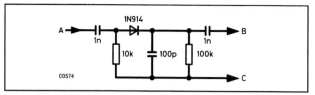

Fig 11.68. A simple detector that can be used when aligning SSB and FM receivers *(ARRL Radio Amateur's Handbook)*

may be made, these units develop approximately 18dB of excess noise in the region 50–300MHz. This unit was originally described by Hartsen in *QST* January 1977.

MEASUREMENTS ON MODERN VHF/UHF FRONT-ENDS

This section is taken from an article by G3SEK in *Radio Communication* [14] and expands on the principles of the previous sections. Power gains and losses are the basic currency of front-end system design. It is important to be able to measure them reasonably accurately.

The gain or loss of a device is the power level at its output relative to the signal level fed into the input – strictly speaking it is the insertion gains and losses that are being measured. To measure gain and loss a signal source is required together with an instrument for measuring relative power and calibrated in decibels. Although the absolute power level in watts need not be known, measurements must be made at the right sort of power levels. To make valid measurements on receiver front ends, the power levels must be well below the gain compression point [15], ie at levels of tens to hundreds of microwatts. At this low level accurate power measurements require a special instrument – see later.

RF amplifier gain

Set up the measuring system as shown in Fig 11.69 but with a coaxial adaptor instead of the amplifier. The two 20dB attenuator pads are used to establish 50Ω source and load impedances for the amplifier under test. Adjust the meter so that it reads 0dB, then remove the adapter and insert the amplifier. The meter reading should increase and the amount which it rises is the amplifier gain in decibels. If a long length of 50Ω coaxial cable had been inserted instead the meter would have fallen below the 0dB setting – this would then represent the cable loss in decibels. As well as simple losses and gains, this technique can be used for practically any other measurement that involves relative RF power levels, from HF to microwaves. For instance one can measure filter responses, crosstalk in diplexers and coaxial relays, antenna gains and radiation patterns and the VSWR of anything that has got a VSWR!

Stage-by-stage measurements of gains and losses is an extremely powerful technique for checking out a newly-built RF system such as a receiver front-end. If the system has been designed correctly [14] one knows already what to expect. This is one of the big rewards for spending time on the design before picking up a soldering iron: if there are problems they will hopefully be spotted. It's always useful to design a system with 50Ω interconnections so that each stage can be tested separately. This does not mean that each stage has to be built in separate boxes with plug and socket connections. Even a single-board layout can be designed to include interstage

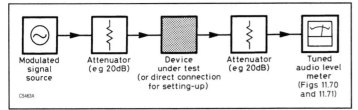

Fig 11.69. Typical set-up for gain or loss measurement

connections of 50Ω stripline with in-line coupling capacitors. By removing a capacitor, a coaxial test lead can be connected to the output of one stage or the input of the next. Thus, an entire system can be stepped through stage by stage, checking that all the gains and losses agree with design values.

Attenuators

One way to calibrate relative power measurements is by comparison with fixed resistive attenuators. These should be of good design for use in a 50Ω system (see 'Attenuator' section earlier). They should include a switched set giving any combination of 1, 2, 3, 4, 10 and 10dB) to allow 1 to 30dB to be selected in 1dB steps), plus fixed attenuators such as 3, 6, 10 and 20dB. It is also useful to own or have access to a few attenuators of known high quality to check the others against.

Almost all the measurements will be made on 50Ω systems, feeding the device from a 50Ω source impedance and terminating it in a 50Ω load. This can be ensured by placing the device under test between two 50Ω attenuators of 20dB or so. Any power reflected from a mismatch at the far side of an attenuator will itself be attenuated on the way back, hence the VSWR seen by the device under test will not vary very much from 1:1. For example, the VSWR looking into a 20dB attenuator theoretically cannot exceed 1.02, no matter what is connected at the other end. (In practice the VSWR would probably be rather higher owing to errors in the attenuator itself.) If all the gain and loss measurements are made with impedance-stabilising attenuators at the input and output of the device under test, the results should be well defined. If the practice is not followed then confusing and misleading results may ensue. For example, even the so-called standard attenuators will not perform as designed unless they themselves are in a 50Ω system.

Tuned AF level meters

As mentioned earlier, gain and loss measurements on receiver front-ends need to be made at power levels of tens to hundreds

of microwatts. Conventional power meters using diode detectors (as mentioned elsewhere in this chapter) and DC voltmeters either are not sensitive enough or tend to suffer from noise and drift. A better solution is to use a test signal which is amplitude modulated by a steady audio tone and to measure the relative level of the tone instead of the carrier. The signal is detected by a diode in the usual way, but instead of trying to dredge the DC component out of the hum and noise, the audio tone signal is amplified. AC-coupled amplifiers neatly side-step the DC drift problem, and hum and noise are reduced by a sharp audio filter tuned to the tone frequency. The level of the tone is finally measured on a meter calibrated directly in decibels, those being the units of relative power level.

Test gear for the modulated signal technique is very easy to build. The only special instrument is the meter which measures the level of the audio modulating tone. Fig 11.70 shows a partial circuit diagram [16]. It is simply a tuned AF amplifier with adjustable gain, followed by an active rectifier which drives a meter. Gain is adjustable by both a switched attenuator and a continuously variable control. The switched attenuation is in 10dB steps; the total of 60dB is split into two separate 30dB attenuators to maintain a good signal/noise ratio without overdriving any stage. The amplifiers should be a modern low-noise type such as ZN459CP, OP-27G, NE5534N, TL071/2 or similar. Construction should follow standard hi-fi preamplifier practice. The first 20dB (×10 voltage) gain block is a low-noise audio preamplifier and requires careful shielding and grounding around the input. The two 40dB gain blocks (×100 voltage) are much less critical. Any frequency around 1kHz will do for the two tuned circuits as long as they are both tuned to the same frequency. The two inductors L1 and L2 should be about 80–100mH and are resonated by capacitors C4 and C6 which should each be about 220nF. Capacitors C3 and C5 are chosen to match the low output impedances of the gain blocks to the high-impedance tuned circuits; the values shown should be satisfactory, though some adjustment maybe necessary. Transformer T1 should be a typical interstage type with a step-up ratio of about 1:5. The active rectifier will typically be an op-amp with diodes in the feedback circuit in order to minimise the effect of the diode forward voltage drop. The resistors should be metal film types.

Fig 11.71 shows an alternative instrument [17] which uses 88mH inductors for selectivity. (Note: 88mH inductors used

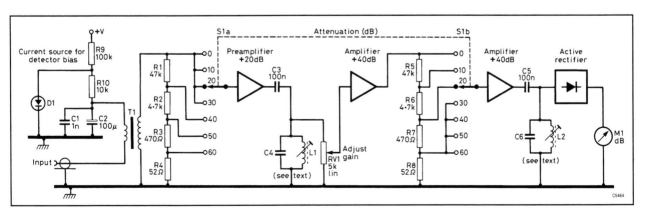

Fig 11.70. Partial circuit of a tuned audio level meter for modulated-signal measurements

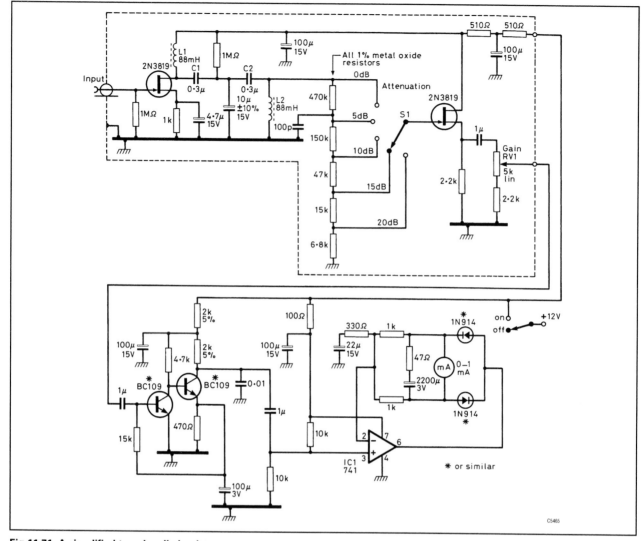

Fig 11.71. A simplified tuned audio level meter

to be readily available but it may be necessary to substitute the more easily available 82mH type or alternatively to wind them).

To get the best from either instrument, a large and accurate analogue meter is required with some existing form of linear calibration. The instrument should preferably be battery powered in order to avoid direct pick-up of the modulating signal via ground loops instead of via the device under test.

Detectors and VSWR bridges

A variety of diode detectors can be used for the modulated-signal technique. The most convenient are ordinary Schottky diodes fed with a few microamps of DC forward bias provided by the level meter of Fig 11.71. At or below the milliwatt RF level, these diodes are in their square-law region, which means that the rectified audio level is accurately proportional to the RF power (*not the voltage*). If the meter scale already has an accurate linear calibration, a decibel scale can be added using nothing more than a calculator. Detectors usually need to provide a 50Ω RF termination, and this can be made with a Schottky diode in a BNC tee adapter – see Fig 11.72. The RF impedance is not exactly 50Ω

but this can be preceded by an attenuator to 'flatten' the VSWR.

Since the modulated-signal technique basically measures power ratios, it can also measure VSWRs. Although VSWR is defined as a ratio of impedances, it is more often measured as a ratio of the 'forward' and 'reverse' power levels, as detected by directional sensors. An ordinary VSWR meter contains these directional couplers but typically requires at least

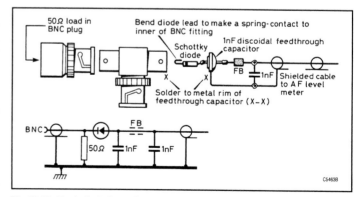

Fig 11.72. Exploded view of a detector and 50Ω load using a BNC T-fitting

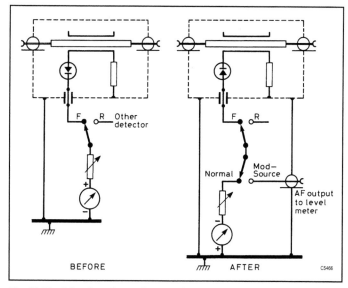

Fig 11.73. Adapting the ordinary VSWR bridge for modulated-signal measurements. The two detector diodes in the bridge are reversed, as are the meter connections

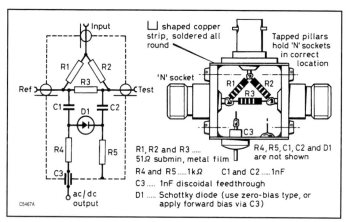

R1, R2 and R3 .....
51Ω submin, metal film
R4 and R5 .....1kΩ
C3 ..... 1nF discoidal feedthrough
D1 ..... Schottky diode (use zero-bias type, or apply forward bias via C3)

R4, R5, C1, C2 and D1 are not shown
C1 and C2 .....1nF

Fig 11.74. Circuit and sketch of a return loss bridge

1W of RF to give a good indication on the DC meter display. Simply reversing the diode detectors allows you to use the modulated-signal technique to measure the VSWR of delicate circuits at very low power levels – Fig 11.73. For example, it is possible to measure the input or output VSWRs of preamplifiers, mixers and other allegedly 50Ω devices (prepare for nasty surprises!).

Other kinds of VSWR sensors can also be used. Fig 11.74 shows a home-made VHF/UHF return loss bridge. Return loss is an alternative way of expressing VSWR and can be read directly in decibels from the meter scale [18]. W7ZOI has recently described many uses for an HF/VHF test set based on an HF-type return loss bridge and unmodulated RF sources [19]. By using the modulated-signal technique and the bridge of Fig 11.74, the same measurements can be extended to UHF. For microwaves you can use a slotted coaxial line or waveguide to observe and measure standing waves more directly [20].

Modulated signal sources

A wide variety of modulated signal sources can be used with the same detectors and level meter. For example, on 432MHz a crystal-controlled source, modified from a converter local oscillator strip, which provides a few milliwatts of RF can be used. An RSGB Microwave Committee board [21] would serve equally well if throttled back to the same power level. Since any signal source will always need a 50Ω output attenuator to establish the correct source impedance, a suitable pad can be permanently built-in. Modulation can be very simple; almost any waveform will do, so long as the frequency is adjustable to match the tuned circuits in the level meter. Typically a 432MHz source can be modulated by an AF oscillator using a 555 timer IC, which chops the RF output by supplying square-wave forward bias to the base of the final transistor – a bit brutal but effective! Whatever kind of modulated source is used, it should be very well screened, with supply leads decoupled to avoid stray pick-up into the detector. The RF output should also be spectrally pure, because the device under test may have significant – and misleading – responses to spurious frequencies from the signal source.

Modulated-signal sources can be made for all the VHF/UHF amateur bands of interest following the above guidelines. The modulated-signal technique can also be used outside the amateur bands, and is equally useful at HF. For example, a suitable general-coverage AM signal generator could be used with its internal modulation adjusted to the peak audio response of the meter. This would allow measurements of gains and losses in the IF stages of a front-end, and to manually sweep the frequency response of filters. If sweeping over a wide frequency range or measuring the gain or loss of a frequency-translating device (eg a mixer, transverter or complete front-end) you are also relying on the detector having a flat frequency response. It would be wise to check the detector first, using a good signal generator.

Accuracy

The modulated-signal technique can measure gains and losses with excellent accuracy. From the 0dB reference at full scale on the meter, the first 1dB of loss is spread over 21% of the meter scale, so changes of less than 0.1dB can be resolved. Changes of 10 or 20dB are taken care of by the range switch, while larger changes require external RF attenuators. Since calibration of the instrument relies only on resistor values and the linearity of the 0–10 meter scale, you can use it to cross-check the calibration of attenuators. Take care to make all measurements at power levels within the square-law region of the detector diode. This can be checked by increasing the applied power by a known amount and observing that the meter reading increases by exactly the same amount. All the calibrations – the meter scale, the 10dB range switches and all fixed and variable RF attenuators – are capable of being consistent within a small fraction of a decibel at frequencies up to at least 432MHz.

Noise measurements

Measurements related to noise are another stock-in-trade of front-end performance testing. In the test methods described the test signal itself is a known amount of broad-band RF noise, and you are interested in measuring the relative difference in noise levels when the test signal is applied. Noise

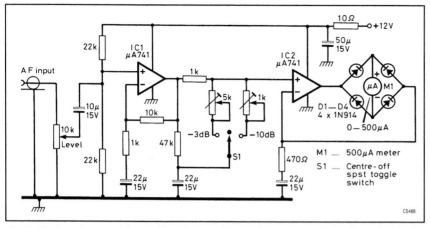

Fig 11.75. A peak-responding audio voltmeter for use in measuring (signal + noise)/noise ratio. For further details see [13]

levels are most conveniently measured at the audio output of the receiver. When this is done, you are relying on the audio output being strictly proportional to the noise or signal level, and hence the receiver's AGC must be switched off for all the tests to be described. Care must also be taken to avoid limiting or distortion in any RF or AF stage. Always repeat the measurements, especially where random noise is involved. Repeat the measurements under the same conditions to get some idea of the random errors. Then alter the RF and AF gain settings and repeat the measurements. If the results change, find out why.

A suitable instrument for relative AF noise power measurements is a rectifying meter as shown in Fig 11.75, which can be pre-calibrated in decibels by calculation [13]. This is essentially a peak-detecting instrument, so be careful that noise peaks are not being significantly clipped by overloading of

any stage in the receiver. More complex RMS-detecting audio noise level meters are less prone to this error, but with care the simple meter of Fig 11.75 is quite adequate. With such a meter, (signal + noise)/noise ratios can be measured accurately as required in any of the following techniques for sensitivity measurement.

Sensitivity measurements

VHF/UHF receivers are extremely sensitive, as mentioned in [15]. A good 144MHz front-end would have a noise figure of about 2dB and would be able to detect signals as weak as 20 nanovolts. At those levels, accurate sensitivity measurements using an attenuated signal generator are extremely difficult. The signal-generator technique is still satisfactory for HF receivers and relics from the older generation of 'deaf' VHF/UHF receivers; but accurate measurements on low-noise systems require an extremely well-screened signal generator and meticulous attention to both practical and theoretical details. For modern VHF/UHF front-ends, better techniques for sensitivity measurement are those that stay as close as possible to the fundamental concept of noise temperature [15]. Best of all measure the noise temperature itself.

Noise temperature measurement techniques are based on supplying a known amount of excess noise to the RF input of the receiver and measuring the change in noise output. If the receiver noise temperature to be measured is T_{RX} and the noise source has a noise temperature T_{ON} when switched on and T_{OFF} when switched off, the system noise temperatures are:

$$T_{SYS} = T_{RX} + T_{ON} - \text{noise source on}$$
$$T_{SYS} = T_{RX} + T_{OFF} - \text{noise source off}$$

The noise power from the receiver is proportional to the system noise temperature, so the on/off power ratio Y is given by:

$$Y = (T_{RX} + T_{ON})/(T_{RX} + T_{OFF})$$

If T_{ON} and T_{OFF} are known and Y is measured, T_{RX} can be calculated from:

$$T_{RX} = (T_{ON} - YT_{OFF})/(Y - 1)$$

The hot/cold method

The main problem is to generate RF noise at two different known noise temperatures T_{ON} and T_{OFF}. The simplest way is to use the thermal noise from a 50Ω resistor at two known physical temperatures – Fig 11.76(a). This is called the *hot/cold method* and is the closest you can get to a fundamental measurement of noise temperature. For the best accuracy you need a large difference between the two temperatures. Resistors do not like being 'roasted', so the hot end of the range cannot go too high. The cold end can be extended down to 77K if liquid nitrogen can be obtained from your friendly local laboratory (in rural areas ask the AI man!), or to about 196K in crushed solid CO_2.

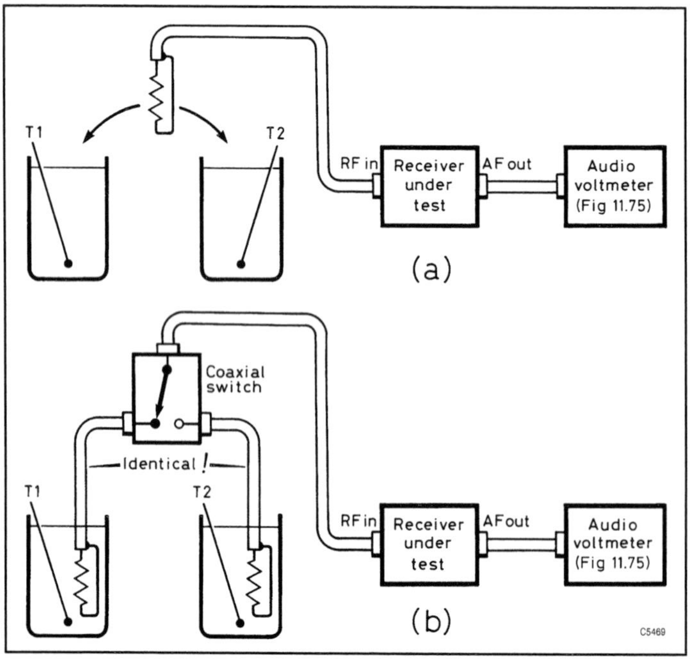

Fig 11.76. The hot/cold method for measuring noise temperature. The basic method (a) involves transferring one resistor between two temperature baths. The two-resistor method (b) is more convenient but requires even more care in setting up

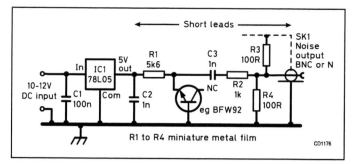

Fig 11.77. A diode noise generator with low VSWR in on and off states. The circuit from C2 to the output socket SK1 is built with the shortest possible leads on a copper groundplane (PCB) soldered directly to the back of SK1. R1 may be altered to maximise noise output

Note: the use of liquid nitrogen and solid CO_2 can be dangerous and unless it is known how to handle these potentially hazardous materials properly, it is safer to use a shorter temperature baseline, eg between melting ice and hot water. With care and a good laboratory thermometer, it is still possible to obtain quite accurate results.

Even the fundamental and basically simple hot/cold method has pitfalls for the unwary. To present an accurate 50Ω termination at both temperatures, the resistor must have good RF characteristics and a low temperature coefficient. Corrections need to be made for losses and thermal noise from connecting cables. There may be errors owing to drift in system gain while the resistor is being warmed up or cooled down, and measurements can become very tedious and slow. It is far quicker to compare noise powers from two 50Ω resistors at different temperatures – Fig 11.76(b), but then the two resistors and all their associated connections need to be identical in all respects (except temperature) so the test system itself requires careful preliminary checking before the results can be trusted.

Non-thermal noise sources

Another way of generating noise is to use a non-thermal source such as the noise generated in certain kinds of diode. The traditional method was to use a thermionic diode or a silicon microwave detector diode in forward conduction.

Nowadays a better and cheaper method for amateurs is to use a diode in reverse breakdown, eg a zener or the base-emitter junction of a silicon transistor. With careful control of the diode current, the long-term noise characteristics can be quite repeatable.

It is absolutely vital to make sure that the noise generator represents an accurate 50Ω source, and the impedance must not change when the generator is switched on or off – many published noise generator circuits ignore this precaution. The noise temperatures of many modern preamplifiers (especially GaAsFET types) are extremely sensitive to source impedance, and measurements can be totally falsified by changes in the on/off impedance of the noise source.

A suitable diode noise generator is shown in Fig 11.77. The diode is a transistor base-emitter junction operated in reverse breakdown, the resistor in series with the regulated 5V supply having been selected to maximise the noise output. The on/off impedance change is stabilised by over 30dB of RF attenuation; the RF attenuator arrangement in Fig 11.77 was optimised at 432MHz with the aid of a home-made return loss bridge (Fig

11.74) and its performance was subsequently verified using commercial equipment.

Regardless of whether the DC supply is on or off, the noise generator presents a good 50Ω termination up to 432MHz, and is still passable at 1.3GHz. Although its noise temperature is not calibrated, the generator can be used in comparative measurements and for checking system performance. It can also be used with the G4COM noise figure comparator [22] (see p11.41) which is highly recommended for aligning front-ends to give the best possible noise figure.

The problem with all semiconductor noise generators is that they cannot be used for absolute measurements until their noise temperatures have been calibrated against some other standard, preferably a hot resistor. Even so, their convenience and repeatability has made semiconductor noise sources the norm in commercial noise generators for VHF, UHF and at least the lower microwave region.

To summarise, relative measurements of noise temperature with uncalibrated noise sources are quite straightforward, given a certain amount of care and basic understanding. But there are no simple methods for absolute measurements. The hot/cold method is probably the most promising for use at home, though even this needs a great deal of care.

Strong-signal (dynamic range) measurements

As explained in [15], strong off-frequency signals can have several possible effects on receivers. The following tests evaluate the three effects that are of most concern to amateur VHF/UHF operators because of their potential to interfere with weak signals. The three effects are:

- *Third-order intermodulation* – mixing between at least two strong in-band signals, to give products which are also in-band and can interfere with the wanted signal.
- *Reciprocal mixing* – raising of the receiver's apparent noise level, due to the noise sidebands of the receiver's own local oscillator.
- *Gain compression* – when a strong off-frequency signal causes one of the stages in the receiver to limit, suppressing all other signals including the wanted one.

Different levels of strong signals are needed to provoke each of these effects. These levels can each be expressed in decibels above the receiver's noise floor, giving the dynamic range for the overload effect in question [15]. Remember, there is no single definition of dynamic range: a receiver has a separate dynamic range for each overload effect, and thus needs a separate test. Even slight overload could interfere severely with a barely copyable weak signal. When testing receivers meant for amateur DX working, the so-called 'spurious-free dynamic ranges' are measured, which relate to the situation where the particular overload effect just begins to be noticeable.

Strong-signal sources

Strong-signal tests require signal sources capable of delivering CW carriers at known power levels of several milliwatts, with low levels of spurious signals including noise sidebands. For gain compression measurements on modern front-ends

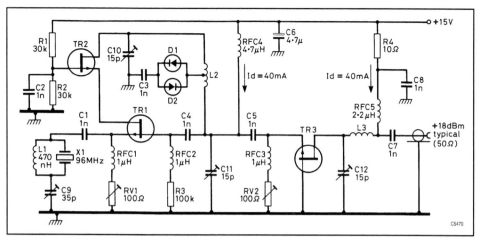

Fig 11.78. A low-noise crystal oscillator for 96MHz. The circuit is adaptable to 72MHz (×2 = 144MHz) or 108MHz (×4 = 432MHz). For details see [23]. D1, D2: Schottky diodes; TR1-3: P8000 power FETs (or U310 at I_d = 20mA); X1: 96MHz; L1: to resonate at 96MHz with X1; L2: 6t, 1mm dia wire on 6mm dia former, centre-tapped; L3: as L2 but no tap

the level of the single-tone test signal needs to be variable up to about 0dBm (1mW). A power level of about −30dBm is required to test for reciprocal mixing – and many present-day commercial VHF/UHF receivers are in deep trouble with test signals of much lower power!

Home-built signal sources for VHF and above need to be crystal controlled, and designs for low-noise crystal oscillators are available. Fig 11.78 is a typical example of a low-noise oscillator [23] for the frequencies of interest. The oscillator is based on a FET cascode amplifier with positive feedback through the pi-network C10, L2 and C11. The overtone crystal bypasses the source of TR1 to ground at its series-resonant frequency, producing sufficient loop gain to permit crystal-controlled oscillation. The active devices in most oscillator circuits not only provide gain but also limit the amplitude of the oscillation, so the devices have to operate in a non-linear mode. This can lead to increased levels of noise sidebands. In the circuit of Fig 11.78 the amplifying and limiting functions are separated; D1 and D2 provide the limiting, allowing TR1 and TR2 to run in linear Class A for lower noise. Other low-noise features include the use of power FETs at high bias currents, and the generally high signal levels maintained around the oscillator loop. Note the RF chokes RFC1 and RFC3 in series with RV1 and RV2, the source bias resistors of TR1 and TR3. Without these chokes, RV1 and RV2 would become sources of thermal noise because their resistances are quite well matched to the circuit impedances prevailing at these points.

A low-noise oscillator deserves low-noise amplifiers and frequency multipliers. Amplifier TR3 is a power FET running at high current in Class A. Higher-level amplifiers can also use power FETs or bipolar VHF/UHF power transistors, which should be operated in Class A and considerably below their normal RF output ratings. Strong signal sources for 50MHz and 70MHz can use overtone oscillators directly on those frequencies, while sources for the higher bands require frequency multipliers. Multipliers have to be non-linear or else they would not work, but the operating conditions of ordinary transistor multipliers are very vague indeed, making it hard to design for low-noise performance as well as reasonable efficiency. Avoid high-order multiplication in a single stage;

frequency double if you can, treble if you must, but nothing higher. Thus a 144MHz source requires an oscillator on 72MHz followed by a doubler (overall, this will probably be easier, cheaper and better than going for an oscillator on 144MHz direct), and 432MHz requires an 108MHz oscillator and two doublers. Following this logic, a 1.296GHz source requires an 81MHz oscillator and four doublers but it may be worthwhile trying a solution with one trebler in it.

A frequency-doubling technique worth exploring is the balanced diode circuit of Fig 11.79. If this circuit does look similar to a power supply, that is because it is a full-wave rectifier. (Remember how a 50Hz mains input produces a 100Hz ripple on the smoothed but unregulated DC?). In Fig 11.79 an input RF signal of frequency f is applied through a suitable centre-tapped transformer T1. In this application one is after the ripple at $2f$ and so smoothing is minimal. The output therefore is mostly at $2f$ because the balanced arrangement tends to cancel out the neighbouring frequencies, f and $3f$. A single tuned circuit is enough to give a very pure output at $2f$. The diodes should be fast Schottky switching types for VHF/UHF, and for low noise and good doubling efficiency they need to be driven hard so they cannot dither in partial conduction. Diode multipliers are passive, so they need a Class A amplifier at the output frequency to make up the loss in the diode circuit. Comparing a diode multiplier chain with a conventional chain using transistor multipliers, about the same number of transistors are required but also the diodes and their transformers. But diode multipliers do not require double-tuned circuits and they give a far better chance of obtaining low noise and good spectral purity without special setting up.

Intermodulation measurements

Intermodulation requires at least two strong signals, so a test for intermodulation performance requires two separate signals fed into the receiver input. For accurate results, the only source of intermodulation between these two signals must be the actual receiver under test. This can be tricky! Somehow the two signals must be brought together without letting them

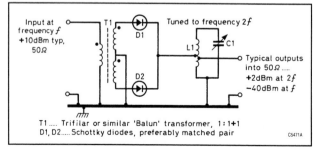

Fig 11.79. Balanced-diode frequency multiplier for VHF/UHF [13]

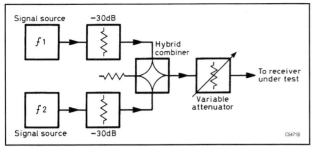

Fig 11.80. Intermodulation test set-up. Note the precautions to isolate the two signal sources from each other

intermodulate. Intermodulation could occur in any non-linear components outside the receiver – most likely in the output amplifiers of the signal generators themselves, where signal levels are the highest. So the two signal generators need to be isolated from each other by in-line attenuators plus a special hybrid combiner to add the two signals while keeping the sources isolated. Another attenuator after the combiner varies the level of the two-tone test signal. The basic set-up is shown in Fig 11.80 and more details are given in the references [24, 25].

For measurements on modern VHF/UHF front-ends, the level of the two-tone test signal needs to be variable up to about −40dBm, with incidental intermodulation products suppressed by more than 60dB. (It is conventional to quote the levels of intermodulation products against the power level of *one* of the two equal test signals, rather than the sum). Since the output of each signal generator has to pass through a high-value attenuator plus another variable attenuator after the combiner, each generator must provide an initial output of at least +10dBm. This means making *two* high-level low-noise signal sources following the guidelines outline earlier. The direct RF signal paths are not the only source of intermodulation between the two generators. One RF source can modulate the other via leakage along the *outside* of coaxial cables, or by RF getting on to the DC supply lines. Each signal source must be very carefully screened and all DC supplies must be fanatically filtered and shielded; typical precautions include boxes within boxes, each with soldered-up lids, double filtering of DC supplies through screened compartments and permanently soldered connections of solid-wall coaxial cable for the high-level signals [24, 25].

Having assembled the whole test set-up, try to get it tested on a spectrum analyser to check for unwanted intermodulation and to get an absolute calibration of the RF levels. You *can* calibrate it, but why not let it be done on professional equipment?

Conclusion

With the home-built test equipment described in this section, you can make all the necessary tests and measurements on modern VHF/UHF receiver front-ends. Simple relative measurements may be all that is needed to optimise front-end performance and to check that it stays that way. Beyond that, absolute measurements *can* be made with all the accuracy needed in amateur radio. It will take longer than the person using professional gear but with care and understanding good results can be obtained.

What really matters is getting the best possible on-the-air performance from your receiver. Any measurement, no matter how simple, is better than guesswork and wishful thinking!

RECEIVER ALIGNMENT AID

By far the most common method of aligning amateur low-noise receivers relies upon listening to a weak signal from a distant station, such as a beacon, and adjusting the matching components of the receiver input stage for maximum signal-to-noise ratio [7].

Signals from distant sources are notoriously unreliable, varying rapidly in strength over a range of many decibels. This makes it necessary to repeatedly check the strength of the beacon to ensure that an improvement in signal-to-noise ratio has been achieved.

A locally generated signal which can be adjusted in level down to barely detectable would appear to be ideal, since it would not suffer from the vagaries of propagation. In practice it can be very difficult to attenuate the test signal to the required level because of the amount of screening needed.

A second, and not often considered, problem with this approach is matching between the source and the receiver. A well-attenuated signal generator output will provide a good 50Ω match, whereas the antenna may not provide the same degree of matching. The result can be less than optimum.

A better approach to aligning low-noise receivers is to use a noise generator in place of the signal generator [22]. With this technique, broad-band noise is injected into the receiver input. The noise source is turned on and off and the receiver matching adjusted until the ratio of *noise on* to *noise off* at the receiver output is at a maximum. It can be very difficult to judge aurally when the ratio is maximum, so that some form of visual indicator becomes desirable.

Such an instrument is known as *an automatic noise figure meter* when it indicates directly the true noise figure of the item under test. It is, however, necessary to use a source with an accurately known noise output in order to make an accurate measurement. If the noise output of the source is not accurately known the instrument can still be used to adjust the receiver for best signal-to-noise performance, although the actual noise figure will not be known.

The instrument described in the following sections can be used to adjust receivers operating at any frequency for optimum sensitivity. It provides a continuous readout of the difference between the audio output of a receiver with no RF input and the output when a wide-band noise generator is connected to the receiver's antenna socket. The meter indicates the ratio between the outputs under these two conditions.

By design the meter reading is not affected by changes in audio level over a wide range of volume settings. The circuit has a logarithmic response so that the meter scale can be linearly calibrated in signal-to-noise ratio in decibels. Unless the absolute level of noise output from the noise source is known, the scale cannot be marked in noise figure.

The unit uses a reverse-biased diode as a noise source.

Circuit description

The circuit diagram is shown in Fig 11.81. Audio input from the loudspeaker socket of the receiver under test is connected to a small speaker (LS1) at the instrument input. This speaker provides a means of monitoring the receiver output which would otherwise be inaudible due to the muting action of most

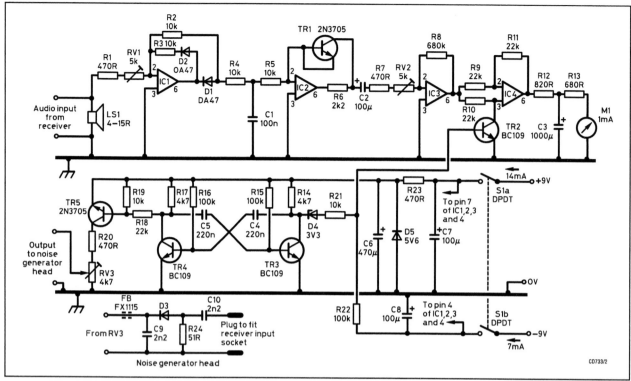

Fig 11.81. Circuit diagram of the alignment aid

loudspeaker external connection sockets. The AC across the speaker is rectified by the precision rectifier formed around IC1. This arrangement effectively overcomes the forward voltage diode drop of a rectifier and thus very-low-level AC signals can be accommodated. The voltage gain of this circuit is given by:

$$\frac{R_2}{R_1 + RV_1}$$

while D2 and R3 prevent the operational amplifier saturating on the negative half-cycles of the input. R4/C1 act as a low-pass filter to the input of IC2.

IC2 is formed into a logarithmic amplifier by the use of TR1 in the feedback loop. *Note:* the voltage across the base/emitter junction of a transistor with its base connected to its collector is proportional to the logarithm of the current through the transistor.

Because the receiver is fed with two signals then IC1 and hence IC2 are also fed with them. The difference (in the millivolt range) between the output voltages under these two conditions is a function of the ratio between the two input voltages and this ratio is independent of the average input level. Provided that the various stages of the receiver and the circuit around IC1 are working within their linear range, the AC output from the circuit formed around IC2 at the pulse frequency used will be dependent only on the overall signal-to-noise ratio. As the output from IC2 is only a fraction of a volt peak to peak it is amplified by the following stage formed around IC3 which has a voltage gain given by:

$$\frac{R_8}{R_7 + RV_2}$$

The output of IC3 is fed to a unity gain phase-sensitive

detector (PSD) based on IC4. The reference signal is fed via TR2 from the pulse generator (or multivibrator) TR3 and TR4. A PSD is ideally suited to applications such as this, where an indication is required of the magnitude of an AC signal which has a known frequency and phase but a high accompanying noise level. In this application the PSD gives a usable output when the signal is accompanied by so much noise that it is undetectable by ear.

IC4, which has a relatively low output impedance, can drive a 1mA meter. Full-scale deflection of the meter in the prototype was set at approximately 10dB signal to noise with the scale reading linearly in decibels. R12 and R13 limit the current through the meter with C3 providing smoothing of the detected signal, otherwise the meter would show an erratic response due to the nature of the noise inputs.

The pulse generator is formed from a conventional astable multivibrator (TR3 and TR4) operating at about 30Hz, the output of this being fed to amplifier TR5 which is used to pulse the noise source.

The noise generator uses a reverse-biased diode mounted in a separate enclosure with matching and decoupling components. An ideal arrangement would be to mount this within a coaxial plug. The diode D3 used in the prototype was a CV364 microwave mixer, but alternatives are 1N21, 1N23, 1N25 and 1N32. A possible, but not tried, alternative is a BAT31 silicon avalanche device which is intended as a noise source from 10Hz to 18GHz.

Construction

Construction of the receiver alignment aid is not critical and audio techniques can be used with the exception of the noise head which must be built using VHF techniques if it is to operate reliably at the highest frequencies. The circuit requires

Table 11.15. Components list for the receiver alignment aid

R1, 7	470R
R2–5, 19, 21	10k
R6	2k2
R8	680k
R9–11, 18	22k
R12	820R
R13	680R
R14, 17	4k7
R15, 16, 22	100k
R20, 23	470R
R24	51R or 75R
RV1, 2	5k skel preset, 0.1W
RV3	4k7 lin carbon pot
C1	100n polystyrene
C2	100μ, 6V3 tantalum
C3	1000μ, 10V electrolytic
C4, 5	220n polystyrene
C6	470μ, 16V electrolytic
C7, 8	100μ, 16V electrolytic
C9, 10	2n2 ceramic disc
D1, 2	OA47, OA79, OA90, BAT85
D3	See text
D4	3V3, 400mW zener
D5	5V6, 400mW zener
TR1, 5	2N3705, 2N3703, 2N4126
TR2–4	BC109, 2N2926
IC1–4	741, 8-pin
FB	FX1115 or equivalent
LS1	4–15Ω min speaker
S1	DPDT switch
M1	1mA FSD meter

Resistors are 0.25W/0.5W, 5% unless specified otherwise.

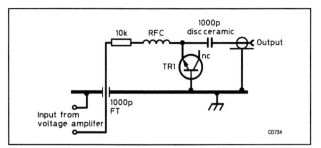

Fig 11.82. HF-to-UHF noise head. TR1: 2N2369, BFY90 etc – see text; RFC: 3t of the 10kΩ resistor lead, 2mm inside dia

a symmetrical ±9V DC supply at about 20mA. A PCB and component layout are given in Appendix 1.

Alignment

The unit requires little alignment and no test equipment is needed. Plug the noise head into a receiver and gradually increase the diode current until an audible 'purring' sound is heard in the receiver loudspeaker. Connect the audio output of the receiver to the input of the unit. The 'purring' should now transfer to the unit's loudspeaker and the meter should show a fairly steady reading which can be varied by adjusting the noise diode current (using RV3). Set RV1 so that the meter reading is constant over a wide range of receiver volume settings. Set RV2 to give a full-scale deflection of the meter at maximum diode current on the highest frequency band of interest. The unit is now ready for use.

Operation

Connect the unit and noise head to the receiver under test and adjust RV3 for about half-scale deflection on the meter. Any adjustment to the receiver that results in an improved signal gain with no change in the noise figure, or a reduced noise figure with no change in signal gain, or both simultaneously, will result in an increased meter reading. By noting the reading of the meter before and after any circuit adjustments, improvements in performance can readily be seen.

Although the unit is not especially sensitive to small temperature changes, it is best to switch the unit on at least 10 minutes before use and to ensure that the ambient temperature is reasonably constant.

Additional notes on use

Use of the receiver alignment aid assumes reasonable linearity of the receiver, therefore care must be taken when aligning FM receivers to ensure that the receiver does not limit with the noise source on. With most receivers this will mean that the level of noise injected must be as small as possible, consistent with still exceeding the FM threshold. With AM/SSB receivers the noise blanker and AGC must be disabled if meaningful results are to be obtained.

Care must be taken if the alignment aid is to be used for initial alignment of a converter or receiver. Noise output from the unit is constant over a wide range and it is therefore possible to inadvertently align on a spurious or image frequency, especially if the receiver has a low intermediate frequency. A signal generator or similar should therefore be used for initial alignment to avoid the problem.

Some receivers have been encountered that have a small DC voltage appearing at the loudspeaker socket. When connected to the alignment aid this voltage can bias IC1 beyond its linear range, thus resulting in false readings on the meter. Connecting an electrolytic capacitor of about 47μF in series with the input overcomes this problem. The negative terminal of this capacitor should be connected to the junction of R1 and the monitor loudspeaker.

Additional improvements

Considerable development work has been carried out to the receiver alignment aid since it was first published and this has resulted in several very useful improvements [26].

The original noise head was designed primarily for VHF operation. An alternative design that can be used throughout the HF range and up to at least 1.3GHz is shown in Fig 11.82. Useful output may still be available at 2.3GHz when a suitable transistor is used for TR1. It is best to select a transistor with a high f_T for TR1. It may be necessary to try several transistors before one with enough output is found.

Better phase detector performance is achieved at low levels with an FET (eg 2N3819) in place of the bipolar transistor TR2. Sometimes difficulties have been encountered with the meter reading not being independent of audio drive level. This can be just a matter of incorrect use or it can arise when the comparator is used in conjunction with receivers possessing an odd audio frequency response. This can be cured by replacing the components R4, C1 and R5 by the circuit shown in Fig 11.83.

Fluctuating meter readings can also be a problem at times. Changing the meter to one of 50μA FSD and altering the time constant of the meter circuit can noticeably improve matters.

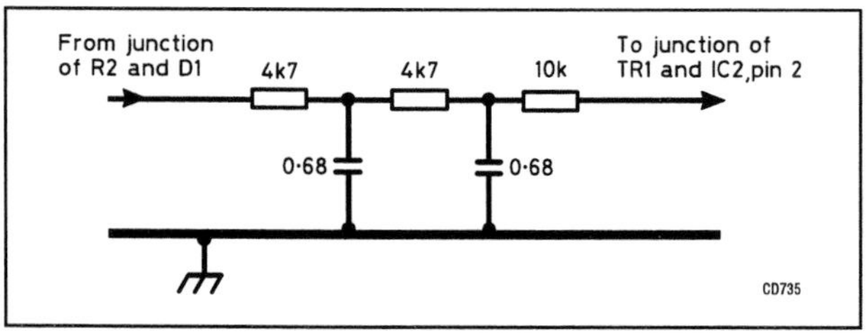

Fig 11.83. An improved interstage coupling network between IC1 and IC2

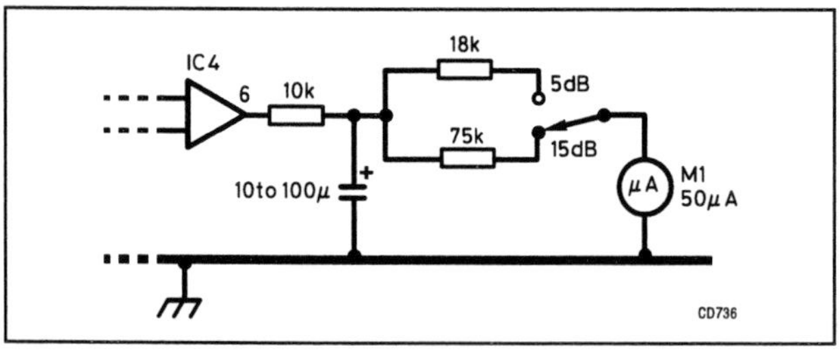

Fig 11.84. Modified meter circuitry

Fig 11.84 incorporates these modifications as well as including a switch to give different full scale readings of signal-to-noise ratio.

STATION MONITOR FOR FM TRANSMISSIONS

The unit described here [27] is designed to enable an amateur with some constructional experience to build a simple FM monitor, capable of monitoring FM transmissions from his or her station from HF to UHF. The use of a sampling mixer allows a very wide frequency coverage with a simple low frequency oscillator.

Principle of operation

The sampling mixer essentially consists of a switch which is opened and closed by short pulses derived from the local oscillator signal (Fig 11.85). When the switch is closed, the input signal is fed to the hold capacitor so that, when it opens again, the capacitor holds a charge proportional to the value of the input signal during the sampling interval. Operation is shown in somewhat idealised form in Fig 11.86. The low-frequency (LF) signal which appears on the hold capacitor is filtered and forms the intermediate frequency (IF).

There are several assumptions implicit in Fig 11.86.

1. The sampling pulse is short compared with the period of the input signal.
2. The switch resistance is small so as to allow the input signal to charge C to the correct value during the short period

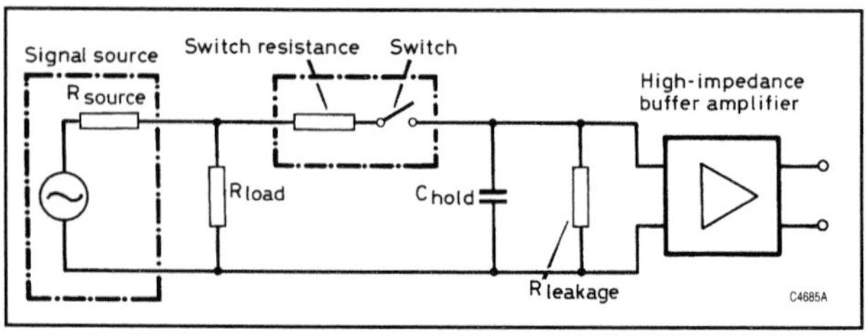

Fig 11.85. Simple model of a sampling gate

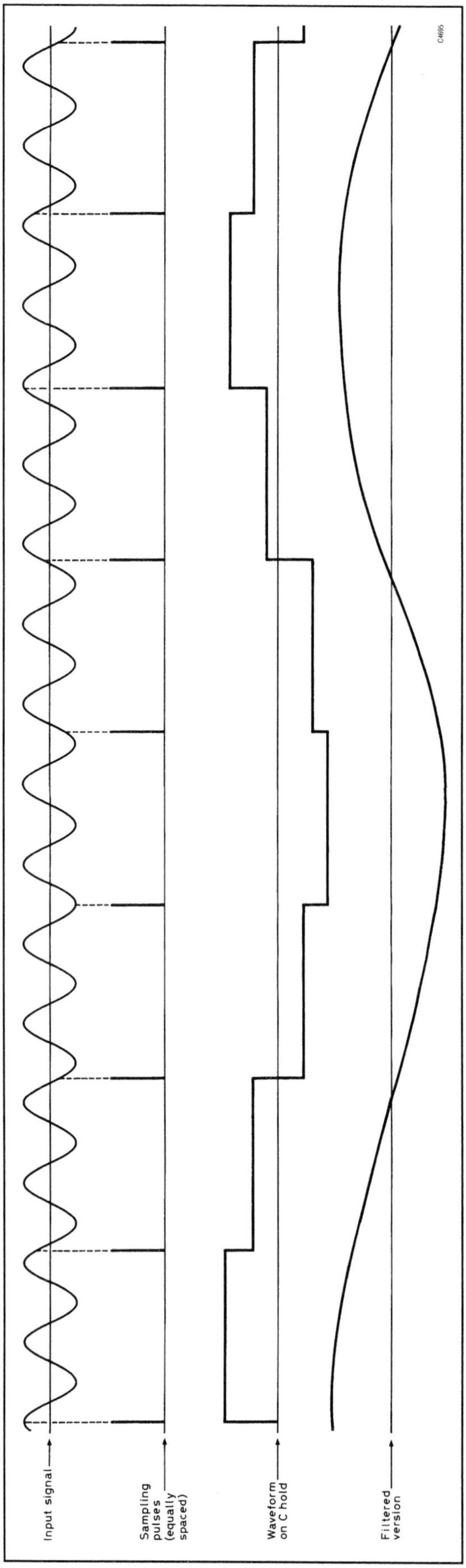

Fig 11.86. Idealised sampling action

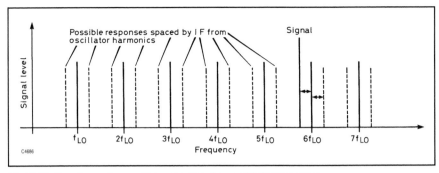

Fig 11.87. Spectrum of sampling gate showing multiple responses

when the switch is closed. Finite resistance of the switch means that the hold capacitor is not charged to the peak of the input signal and manifests itself as loss in the mixer which increases as the intermediate frequency is raised.

3. The leakage resistance must be sufficiently large that the capacitor voltage does not fall appreciably inbetween samples, causing mixer loss.

The sampling mixer can also be considered in the frequency domain (Fig 11.87). The local oscillator (LO) pulse, if infinitely short in duration, would have a spectrum extending out to infinity, a so-called harmonic 'comb', with a 'tooth' spacing equal to the LO frequency. Practical pulses of finite duration have a comb which is not flat but falls at high frequencies. The wider the pulses, the lower the roll-off frequency.

Also depicted in Fig 11.87 is the fact that each LO harmonic can produce an IF with any signal spaced an IF away on either side. The sampling mixer thus has a multitude of responses and is not therefore recommended as a receiver front-end. For transmitter monitoring, there will (it is hoped) be only a single frequency present and this is then of no concern. The sampling mixer described enables transmitter monitoring of frequencies beyond the 432MHz band.

Monitor block diagram

The block diagram is shown in Fig 11.88. The sampling mixer, consisting of a diode gate fed by an LO pulse generator, is followed by a high-impedance FET buffer amplifier. The IF signal is selected by a low-pass filter and then amplitude limited. The FM signal is rendered intelligible by a pulse-counting discriminator. This form of discriminator is used because it is wide band and removes the need for excessively tight tolerance on the LO frequency. For example, a LO operating

in the region of 4MHz will produce an IF with a 432MHz signal on around its hundredth harmonic. A narrow-tuned discriminator would require very careful setting of the LO.

Circuit description

Economy was a major design consideration and the unit uses relatively cheap components throughout. The circuits are shown in Fig 11.89 and Fig 11.90. A diode gate (D1 to D4) acts as the switch, with C4 the 'hold' capacitor. The diodes should be either germanium or of the Schottky type. A FET amplifier (TR1) buffers the sampling gate. IC1, an ECL triple line receiver, forms a somewhat unorthodox pulse generator. The first two sections square up the oscillator signal, and the resulting square wave feeds the third section (with a delay to one input caused by the insertion of a short length of coaxial cable, eg 300mm). The square-wave edge at pin 7 causes the output at pin 14 to go *high*. After the very short cable delay, the delayed edge returns pin 14 to the *low* state, giving a very narrow pulse. An anti-phase signal is available at pin 15. The two outputs are very convenient for driving the sampling gate and the symmetrical drive to some extent balances out the LO and reduces breakthrough into the IF.

The LO is not shown. Frequencies from 4 to 100MHz have been used, with levels above about 20mV being suitable. Hence, the LO may be based on a large number of designs appropriate to the frequency chosen. A crystal source is recommended.

The IF at TR1 is low-pass filtered to remove any LO signal and applied to a limiter, IC2. The limited IF signal is then fed to a pulse-counting discriminator based on the design by G3JGO [28].

The value of C20 shown on the circuit allows operation with an IF up to 500kHz. The sampling gate, however, is capable of operating with an IF of more than 1MHz. If this extended range is required, the capacitor value should be reduced in proportion to the maximum IF; eg if 1MHz maximum IF is used, C20 should be reduced to 90pF.

The penalty paid for this is that the discriminator then produces a smaller output for a given deviation and more audio gain must be used to restore the level. IC5 provides audio gain with the gain set to 48. This is given by (R30 + R31)/R30 and should be adjusted if C20 is changed.

With component values as in the circuit, the audio output will be approximately 1V peak for 1kHz deviation. A signal with ±2.5kHz deviation will therefore give an audio output of 5V peak to peak. The op-amp (IC5) will clip outputs some way under 12V peak to peak which (fortunately) limits the amount of noise when the input signal is disconnected.

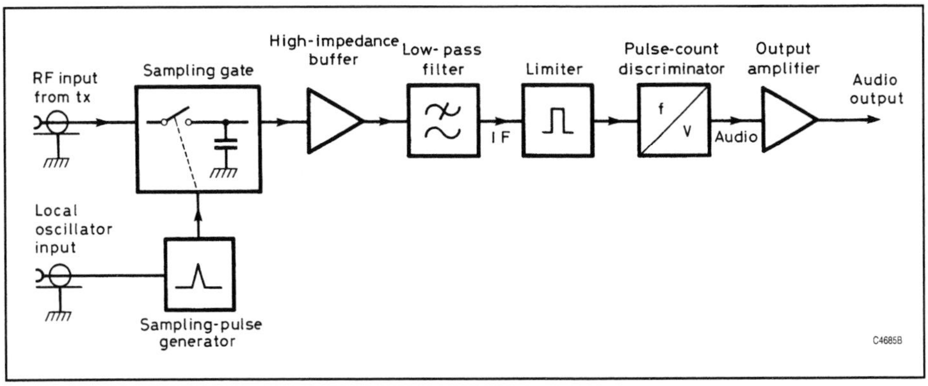

Fig 11.88. Block diagram

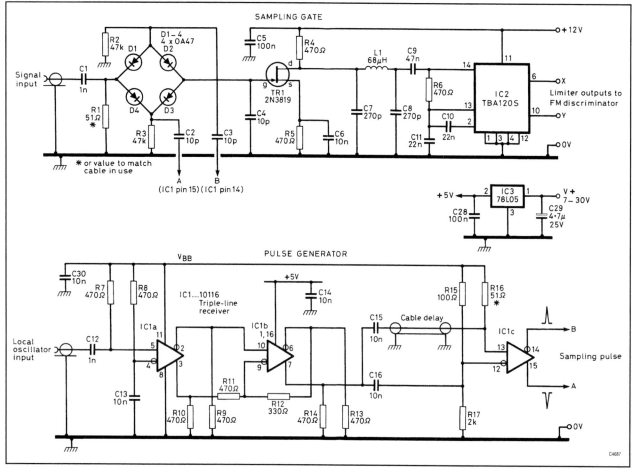

Fig 11.89. Circuits of the sampling gate and pulse generator

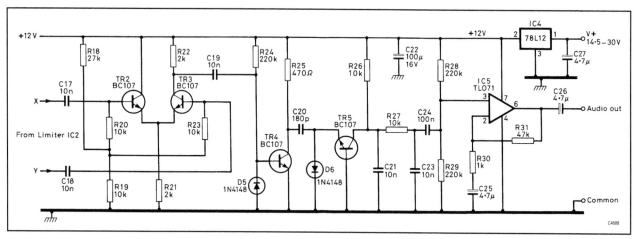

Fig 11.90. Pulse-count discriminator circuit

Construction

Several prototypes have been built. The quickest, surest method of construction of the high-frequency circuitry of the sampling gate and pulse generator is to build them on an earth plain of plain copper-clad glassfibre board, with components soldered together using minimum lead lengths, and decoupling capacitors and other earthed parts soldered directly to the board. IC1 should be mounted upside down and connections made direct to the pins – unfortunately this leads to an ugly-looking circuit. The braid at each end of the delay cable should

be soldered direct to the copper (see Fig 11.91). The input and LO leads can be soldered similarly. If 75Ω cable is used,

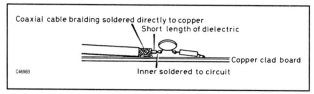

Fig 11.91. Soldering coaxial cable to earth plane

Table 11.16. Component list for sampling monitor

R1, 16	51R
R2, 3, 31	47k
R5–11, 13, 14, 25	470R
R12	330R
R4, 15	100R
R17, 21, 22	2k
R18	27k
R19, 20, 23, 26, 27	10k
R24, 28, 29	220k
R30	1k
C1, 12	1n ceramic disc
C2, 3, 4	10p ceramic
C5, 24, 28	100n ceramic disc
C7, 8	270p ceramic
C9	4n7 ceramic disc
C6, 13–21, 23, 30	10n ceramic disc
C10, 11	2n2 ceramic disc
C20	180p polystyrene
C22	100µ, 16V electrolytic
C25–27, 29	4µ7, 25V electrolytic
L1	68µ RF choke
D1–4	OA47 or similar – see text
D5, 6	1N4148
TR1	2N3819
TR2–5	BC107, 2N2369 or similar
IC1	10116
IC2	TBA120S
IC3	78L05
IC4	78L12
IC5	TL071

Resistors are 0.25/0.5W, ±5% unless stated otherwise.

R16 should strictly be increased to 75Ω or a close value to provide a match, but this is not critical. No advantage is gained by shortening the cable.

Providing good RF layout is used for the high-frequency circuits, performance of the unit should be satisfactory. Following the FET buffer stage, construction becomes non-critical and any of the large range of constructional techniques available may be used.

Choosing the local oscillator frequency

Using a single LO frequency, the availability of a range of several hundred kilohertz of IF allows a similar range of frequencies within an amateur band to be used. For example, suppose that the discriminator capacitor is set for a maximum IF of 500kHz. An attempt should be made to find a local oscillator frequency which gives an IF from about 100 to 500kHz and thus a 400kHz band coverage. Of course, the image response will give another 400kHz on the other side of the local oscillator harmonic if this is useful. The relation between the various frequencies is:

$$\text{Input frequency} = N.f_{LO} \pm f_{IF}$$

where N is the harmonic number in use. Taking a realistic case:

$$f_{LO} = 12.0333\text{MHz (crystal)}$$
$$36f_{LO} = 433.1988\text{MHz}$$

Thus FM simplex channels 433.375 to 433.500MHz can be covered with an IF of 176.2 to 301.2kHz and discriminator values shown would be suitable. The 12th harmonic of the same oscillator frequency is 144.3996MHz. An IF up to 1MHz would then give coverage up to 145.400MHz. A 8.0222MHz input gives the same results with $N = 54$ and 18 respectively.

As the IF is lowered below 100kHz, more IF signal appears in the audio output and the application determines whether this is tolerable.

Operating the unit

Having chosen the LO frequency, apply this signal to the unit at a level exceeding 20mV EMF. If a fast oscilloscope is available, the pulses should just be seen at pins 14 and 15 of IC1. Arrange for a signal of 30mV to 300mV RMS (PD, −13 to +3dBm) from the transmitter. Excessive drive will cause conduction of the gate diodes and degrade performance. The limiter should now provide square waves from the IF and audio should be available at the output. The audio can be used in a number of ways:

1. The audio can simply be used for listening to the modulation.

2. An oscilloscope can be used to check on the peak deviation.

3. A peak detector can be used (suggested circuit in Fig 11.92) to give readings proportional to peak deviation. If the recommendations in the text are followed, the 1kHz/V of peak deviation will be maintained.

Conclusion

It is hoped that the unit described will be taken as the basis for further experimentation and used by amateurs to ensure that the quality of modulation and efficient spectrum use are kept to a high standard.

TWO-STUB TRANSFORMER

For impedance matching, a two-stub transformer (tuner) provides a satisfactory method. It is effectively a coaxial or VHF pi-coupler.

The general arrangement is shown in Fig 11.93 and

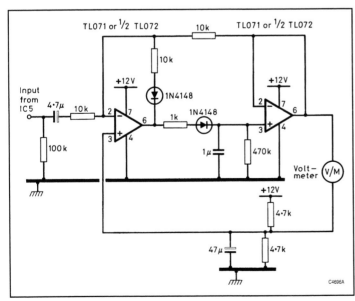

Fig 11.92. Suggested circuit for peak detector

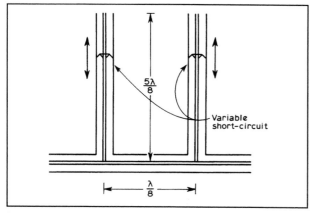

Fig 11.93. General arrangement of the two-stub transformer

this is made using 3.2mm diameter centre conductor and 12.7mm outer. The transformer will have a useful range of $Z_0/2$ to $2Z_0$.

If the section of line between the two stubs is made adjustable and the stubs themselves are long enough for the lowest frequency required, then a unit for use on more than one band can be made.

COAXIAL SWITCH

Although manually operated coaxial switches are available, these are generally fitted with SO239/PL259 UHF-type connectors which are a variable-impedance type. Many stations use N-, BNC- or TNC-type connectors which have superior performance and are of a constant impedance.

Of course, adapters may be added to a commercial unit with UHF-type connectors but this is both expensive and cumbersome. It is relatively simple to construct a unit in a small die-cast box using a two-way single wafer switch or a slider switch. In such a unit the preferred connector can be used to fit into the existing system.

The unit illustrated (Fig 11.94) is fitted with N-type connectors. The two slide connectors are positioned as close to the end of the box as possible and are soldered directly to the switch terminations. The centre connector, mounted on the box end, is connected by a short piece of copper strip (lower inductance than wire unless rod with 'turned down' ends is used).

An additional connector has been included at the other end of the box, to which a coupling loop is connected so that a DFM or other monitor may be attached without having to 'break in' to the main circuit. The coupling loop is tuned by a small piston capacitor.

A switch of this type is useful for switching two different antennas or from antenna to dummy load. The performance of the prototype, with all ports matched to 50Ω and the switch set to connect ports 1 and 2, is shown in Table 11.17.

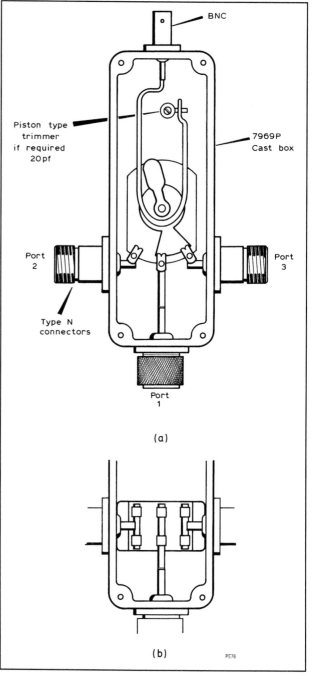

(a)

(b)   PE76

Fig 11.94. Coaxial switch using (a) rotary switch or alternatively (b) a slide switch

REFERENCES

[1] *Test Equipment for the Radio Amateur*, 3rd edn, Clive Smith, G4FZH, RSGB, 1995.

[2] *Amateur Radio Licence (A) or (B): Terms, Provisions and Limitations Booklet BR68*, Radiocommunications Agency.

[3] *Amateur Radio Software*, J Morris, GM4ANB, RSGB, 1985.

[4] 'Absorption Wavemeters for 144MHz', G R Jessop, G6JP, *Radio Communication* September 1982.

[5] 'A VHF dip oscillator', A L Mynett, *Radio Communication* September 1970.

Table 11.17. Performance of prototype coaxial switch

Frequency (MHz)	Insertion loss ports 1 to 2 (dB)	Isolation ports 2 to 3 (dB)	VSWR
70	<0.1	44	1.15
144	0.2	38	1.3
432	0.85	26	2.1

[6] 'Simple Spectrum Analyser', R Blackwell, G4PMK, *Radio Communication* November 1989.

[7] *Microwave Handbook*, Vol 2, Ed M W Dixon, G3PFR, RSGB, 1991.

[8] 'A frequency counter for a 144MHz transmitter', N B Pritchard, *Radio Communication* May 1979.

[9] *Data sheet for ICM7216A/B/D*, Harris Semiconductors.

[10] *Data Sheet for 8680B*, Plessey Semiconductors.

[11] 'HF/UHF deviation meter', E Chicken, G3BIK, *Radio Communication* May 1989.

[12] *The ARRL Handbook for the Radio Amateur*, ARRL.

[13] *Solid State Design for the Radio Amateur*, Wes Hayward, W7ZOI, and Doug DeMaw, W1FB, ARRL.

[14] 'Measurements on modern VHF/UHF front ends', I F White, G3SEK, *Radio Communication* October and November 1986.

[15] 'Modern VHF/UHF front-end design, I F White, G3SEK, *Radio Communication* April-July 1985.

[16] From an article by W6SVS in a pre-1970 edition of *Ham Radio*.

[17] 'Antenna gain measurements', Fred Brown, W6HPH, *QST* December 1982.

[18] 'More about return loss bridges', Ian White, G3SEK, *The Lunar Letter* May 1983.

[19] 'Beyond the dipper', Wes Hayward, W7ZOI, *QST* May 1986.

[20] 'How to use an SWR indicator', Bob Stein, W6NBI, *Ham Radio* January 1977.

[21] *Microwave Newsletter Technical Collection,* RSGB.

[22] 'An alignment aid for VHF receivers', J R Compton, G4COM, *Radio Communication* June 1976.

[23] 'An extremely low-noise 96MHz crystal oscillator for UHF/SHF applications', B Neubig, DK1AG, *VHF Communications* Winter 1981.

[24] 'A two-tone test generator for the two-metre band', M Ploetz, DL7YC, *VHF/UHF Technik* (Berliner DUBUS Gruppe 1978). *UHF-Unterlage*, Teil 3, Ed K Weiner, DJ9HO, contains designs for 144MHz and 432MHz (in German).

[25] 'Intermodulation measurement techniques in mixers and amplifiers', P E Chadwick, Application Note AN1009, Plessey Semiconductors Ltd.

[26] 'Microwaves', C Suckling, G3WDG, *Radio Communication* October 1979 and March 1980.

[27] 'A sampling FM monitor', I Braithwaite, G4COL, *Radio Communication* October 1983.

[28] 'A pulse count discriminator unit', B Priestley, G3JGO, *Radio Communication* Sept 1971.

12 General data

Capacitance
The capacitance of a parallel-plate capacitor is:

$$C = \frac{0.224\,KA}{d} \quad \text{picofarads}$$

where K is the dielectric constant (air = 1.0), A is the area of dielectric (sq in), and d is the thickness of dielectric (in). If A is expressed in centimetres squared and d in centimetres, then:

$$C = \frac{0.0885\,KA}{d} \quad \text{picofarads}$$

For multi-plate capacitors, multiply by the number of dielectric thicknesses.

The capacitance of a coaxial cylinder is:

$$C = \frac{0.242\,K}{\log_{10}(D/d)} \quad \text{picofarads per centimetre length}$$

where D is the inside diameter of the outer and d is the outside diameter of the inner.

Capacitors in series or parallel
The effective capacitance of a number of capacitors in *series* is:

$$C = \frac{1}{\dfrac{1}{C_1} + \dfrac{1}{C_2} + \dfrac{1}{C_3} + \text{etc}}$$

The effective capacitance of a number of capacitors in *parallel* is:

$$C = C_1 + C_2 + C_3 + \text{etc}$$

Characteristic impedance
The characteristic impedance Z_0 of a feeder or transmission line depends on its cross-sectional dimensions.

(i) *Open-wire line*:

$$Z_0 = 276 \log_{10}\frac{2D}{d} \quad \text{ohms}$$

where D is the centre-to-centre spacing of wires (in) and d is the wire diameter (in).

(ii) *Coaxial line*:

$$Z_0 = \frac{138}{\sqrt{K}} \log_{10}\frac{d_o}{d_i} \quad \text{ohms}$$

where K is the dielectric constant of insulation between the conductors (eg 2.3 for polythene, 1.0 for air), d_o is the inside diameter of the outer conductor and d_i is the diameter of the inner conductor.

Decibel
The *decibel* is the unit commonly used for expressing the relationship between two power levels (or between two voltages or two currents). A decibel (dB) is one-tenth of a *bel* (B). The number of decibels N representing the ratio of two power levels P_1 and P_2 is 10 times the common logarithm of the power ratio, thus:

$$\text{The } ratio\ N = 10 \log_{10}\frac{P_2}{P_1} \quad \text{decibels}$$

If it is required to express *voltage* (or *current*) ratios in this way, they must relate to identical impedance values, ie the two different voltages must appear across equal impedances (or the two different currents must flow through equal impedances). Under such conditions the *power* ratio is proportional to the square of the *voltage* (or the *current*) ratio, and hence:

$$N = 20 \log_{10}\frac{V_2}{V_1} \quad \text{decibels}$$

$$N = 20 \log_{10}\frac{I_2}{I_1} \quad \text{decibels}$$

Dynamic resistance
In a parallel-tuned circuit at resonance the dynamic resistance is:

$$R_D = \frac{L}{Cr} = Q\omega L = \frac{Q}{\omega C} \quad \text{ohms}$$

where L is the inductance (henrys), C is the capacitance (farads), r is the effective series resistance (ohms), Q is the Q-value of the coil and $\omega = 2\pi \times$ frequency (hertz).

Frequency – wavelength – velocity
The velocity of propagation of a wave is:

$$v = f\lambda \quad \text{centimetres per second}$$

where f is the frequency (hertz) and λ is the wavelength (centimetres).

For electromagnetic waves in free space the velocity of propagation v is approximately 3×10^8 m/s and, if f is expressed in kilohertz and λ in metres:

$$f = \frac{300{,}000}{\lambda} \quad \text{kilohertz}$$

$$\lambda = \frac{300{,}000}{f} \quad \text{metres}$$

$$\text{Free space } \frac{\lambda}{2} = \frac{492}{\text{MHz}} \quad \text{feet}$$

$$\text{Free space } \frac{\lambda}{4} = \frac{246}{\text{MHz}} \quad \text{feet}$$

Note that the true value of v is 2.99776×10^8 m/s.

Impedance

The impedance of a circuit comprising inductance, capacitance and resistance in series is:

$$Z = \sqrt{R^2 + \left(\omega L - \frac{1}{\omega C}\right)^2}$$

where R is the resistance (ohms), L the inductance (henrys), C the capacitance (farads) and $\omega = 2\pi \times$ frequency (hertz).

Inductors in series or parallel

The total effective value of a number of inductors connected in *series* (assuming no mutual coupling) is given by:

$$L = L_1 + L_2 + L_3 + \text{etc}$$

If they are connected in *parallel*, the total effective value is:

$$L = \frac{1}{\dfrac{1}{L_1} + \dfrac{1}{L_2} + \dfrac{1}{L_3} + \text{etc}}$$

When there is mutual coupling M, the total effective value of two inductors connected in series is:

$$L = L_1 + L_2 + 2M \text{ (windings aiding)}$$

$$\text{or } L = L_1 + L_2 - 2M \text{ (windings opposing)}$$

Ohm's Law

For a unidirectional current of constant magnitude flowing in a metallic conductor:

$$I = \frac{E}{R} \qquad E = I\,R \qquad R = \frac{E}{I}$$

where I is the current (amperes), E is the voltage (volts) and R is the resistance (ohms).

Power

In a DC circuit, the power developed is given by:

$$W = E\,I = \frac{E^2}{R} = I^2 R \text{ watts}$$

where E is the voltage (volts), I is the current (amperes) and R is the resistance (ohms).

Q

The Q-value of an inductance is given by:

$$Q = \frac{\omega L}{R}$$

where L is the inductance (henrys), R is the effective resistance (ohms) and $\omega = 2\pi \times$ frequency (hertz).

Reactance

The reactance of an inductance and a capacitance respectively is given by:

$$X_L = \omega L \text{ ohms}$$

$$X_C = \frac{1}{\omega C} \text{ ohms}$$

where L is the inductance in henrys, C is the capacitance in farads and $\omega = 2\pi \times$ frequency (hertz).

The total reactance of an inductance and a capacitance in series is $X_L - X_C$.

Resistors in series or parallel

The effective value of several resistors connected in *series* is:

$$R = R_1 + R_2 + R_3 + \text{etc}$$

When several resistors are connected in *parallel* the effective total resistance is:

$$R = \frac{1}{\dfrac{1}{R_1} + \dfrac{1}{R_2} + \dfrac{1}{R_3} + \text{etc}}$$

Resonance

The resonant frequency of a tuned circuit is given by:

$$f = \frac{1}{2\pi\sqrt{LC}} \text{ hertz}$$

where L is the inductance (henrys) and C is the capacitance (farads).

If L is in microhenrys (μH) and C is picofarads (pF), this formula becomes:

$$f = \frac{10^3}{2\pi\sqrt{LC}} \text{ megahertz}$$

The basic formula can be rearranged thus:

$$L = \frac{1}{4\pi^2 f^2 C} \text{ henrys}$$

$$C = \frac{1}{4\pi^2 f^2 L} \text{ farads}$$

Since $2\pi f$ is commonly represented by ω, these expressions can be written as:

$$L = \frac{1}{\omega^2 C} \text{ henrys}$$

$$C = \frac{1}{\omega^2 L} \text{ farads}$$

See Fig 12.1.

Time constant

For a combination of inductance and resistance in series the time constant (ie the time required for the current to reach $1/\varepsilon$ or 63% of its final value) is given by:

$$t = \frac{L}{R} \text{ seconds}$$

where L is the inductance (henrys) and R the resistance (ohms).

For a combination of capacitance and resistance in series, the time constant (ie the time required for the voltage across the capacitance to reach $1/\varepsilon$ or 63% of its final value) is given by:

$$t = C\,R \text{ seconds}$$

where C is the capacitance (farads) and R is the resistance (ohms).

Transformer ratios

The ratio of a transformer refers to the ratio of the number of turns in one winding to the number of turns in the other winding. To avoid confusion it is always desirable to state in which sense the ratio is being expressed, eg the 'primary-to-secondary' ratio n_p/n_s. The turns ratio is related to the impedance ratio thus:

$$\frac{n_p}{n_s} = \sqrt{\frac{Z_p}{Z_s}}$$

where n_p is the number of primary turns, n_s is the number of secondary turns, Z_p the impedance of the primary circuit (ohms) and Z_s the impedance of the secondary circuit (ohms).

COIL WINDING

Most inductors for tuning in the HF bands are single-layer coils and they are designed as follows. Multilayer coils will not be dealt with here.

The inductance of a single-layer coil is given by:

$$L(\mu H) = \frac{D^2 \times T^2}{457.2 \times D + 1016 \times L}$$

where D is the diameter of the coil (millimetres), T the number of turns and L the length (millimetres). Alternatively:

$$L(\mu H) = \frac{R^2 \times T^2}{9 \times R + 10 \times L}$$

where R is the radius of the coil (inches), T is the number of turns and L is the length (inches).

Note that when a ferrite or iron dust core is used, the inductance will be increased by up to twice the value without the core. The choice of which to use depends on frequency. Generally, ferrite cores are used at the lower HF bands and iron dust cores at the higher. At VHF, the iron dust cores are usually coloured purple. Cores need to be moveable for tuning but fixed thereafter and this can be done with a variety of fixatives. A strip of flexible polyurethane foam will do.

Table 12.1. Wire data

Diameter	Approx SWG	Turns/cm	Turns/in
1.5	16–17	6.6	16.8
1.25	18	7.9	20.7
1.0	19	9.9	25
0.8	21	12.3	31
0.71	22	13.9	35
0.56	24	17.5	45
0.50	25	19.6	50
0.40	27	24.4	62
0.315	30	30.8	78
0.25	33	38.5	97
0.224	34–35	42.7	108
0.20	35–36	47.6	121

Note: SWG is Imperial standard wire gauge. The diameters listed are those which appear to be most popular; ie they are listed in distributor's catalogues. The 'turns/cm' and 'turns/in' are for enamelled wire.

Designing inductors with ferrite pot cores

This is a simple matter of taking the *factor* given by the makers and multiplying it by the square of the number of turns. For example, an RM6-S pot core in 3H1 grade ferrite has a 'factor' of 1900 nanohenrys for one turn. Therefore 100 turns will give an inductance of:

$$100^2 \times 1900nH = 10000 \times 1900nH = 19mH$$

There are a large number of different grades of ferrite; for example, the same pot as above is also available in grade 3E4 with a 'factor' of 3300. Manufacturers' literature should be consulted to find these 'factors'.

Table 12.2. Coaxial cables

Type	Nominal impedance (Ω)	Outside diameter (mm)	Velocity factor	Capacitance (pF/m)	Maximum RF voltage (kV)	Attenuation per 10m of cable 10MHz (dB)	100MHz (dB)	1000MHz (dB)
CT100	75	6.65	0.84	56	—	0.2	0.6	2.1
H100 [1]	50	—	—	—	—	—	0.44	1.35
LDF4-50A [2]	50	16.0	0.88	75.8	8.0	0.07	0.224	0.77
LDF5-50A [3]	50	28.0	0.89	75	8.0	0.037	0.121	0.43
RA519 [1]	50	10.3	0.80	84	5.0	0.10	0.35	1.25
RG58BU	50	4.95	0.66	100	3.5	0.5	1.7	5.6
RG58CU	50*	4.95	0.66	100	2.5	0.5	1.7	5.6
RG59BU	75	6.15	0.66	68	3.5	0.5	1.5	4.6
Min RG59	75	3.7	0.84	51	—	0.4	1.2	3.9
RG62AU	95	6.15	0.84	44	—	0.3	0.9	2.9
Min RG62	95	3.8	0.84	41	—	0.4	1.4	4.5
RG174AU	50*	2.8	0.66	101	2.1	0.3	0.9	2.9
RG178PE	50*	1.83	0.85	99	—	1.5	4.8	16
RG179PE	75*	2.54	0.85	69	—	1.2	4.0	13
RG213/URM67 [1]	50	10.3	0.66	100	6.5	0.2	0.7	2.7
RG402U	50	3.58†	—	—	—	—	—	—
RG405U	50	2.20†	—	—	—	—	—	—
UR43	50	5.0	0.66	100	2.6	0.4	1.3	4.5
UR67	50*	10.3	0.66	100	6.5	0.2	0.68	2.5
UR70	75*	5.8	0.66	67	1.8	0.5	1.5	5.2
UR76	50*	5.0	0.66	100	2.6	0.5	1.6	5.3
UR95	50	2.3	0.66	100	1.3	0.9	2.7	6.9
UR202	75*	5.1	0.84	56	—	0.4	1.1	4.2
UR203	75	7.25	0.84	56	—	0.2	0.8	2.7
WF103 [1]	50	10.3	0.85	78	5.0	0.09	0.32	1.30

* Indicates cable with flexible core. † Indicates cable with solid drawn outer, ie rigid.

[1] Minimum bending radius is 60mm. Obtainable in the UK from W H Westlake Electronics, West Park, Clawton, Holdsworthy, Devon, EH22 6QN.
[2] Minimum bend radius is 125mm. Obtainable in the UK from Andrew Ltd, Lochgelly, Fife, KY5 9HG. This needs special coaxial fittings.
[3] Minimum bend radius is 250mm. Obtainable from Andrew Ltd. This needs special coaxial fittings.

There are many further types of coaxial cable but these are the most popular ones; ie those listed in distributors' catalogues. The characteristics of others are listed in earlier editions of the *VHF/UHF Manual*.

Table 12.3. Colour coding for glass fuses

Colour	Rating (mA)	Colour	Rating (A)
Green/yellow	10	Green	0.75
Red/turquoise	15	Blue	1.0
Eau-de-Nil	25	Light blue	1.5
Salmon pink	50	Purple	2.0
Black	60	Yellow and purple	2.5
Grey	100	White	3.0
Red	150	Black and white	5.0
Brown	250	Orange	10.0
Yellow	500		

Note that this coding does not apply to the ceramic-bodied fuse commonly found in 13A plugs etc.

Table 12.4. Useful twist drill sizes

Screw size	2	3	4	5	6
Clearance drill	2.10	3.10	4.10	5.10	6.10
Tapping drill	1.55	2.65	3.50	4.50	5.20

All sizes are in millimetres.

Twist drill no	¼in 0.250 in	1 0.228 in	9 0.196 in	17 0.173 in	24 0.152 in	32 0.116 in	43 0.089 in	50 0.070 in
Clearance for woodscrew no	14	12	10	8	6	4	2	0
Clearance for BA	0	1	2	3	4	6	8	10
Tapping size for BA	—	—	0	1	2	4	6	8

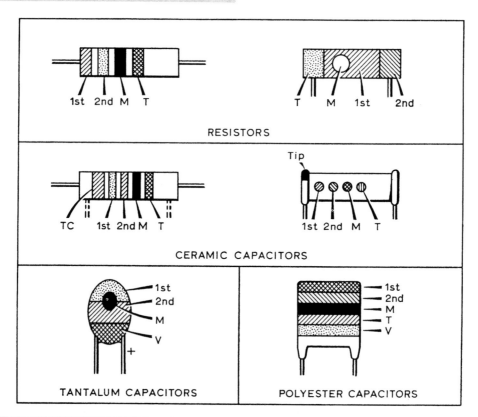

RESISTORS

CERAMIC CAPACITORS

TANTALUM CAPACITORS

POLYESTER CAPACITORS

Table 12.5. Component colour codes

Colour	Significant figure (1st, 2nd)*	Decimal multiplier (M)	Tolerance (T) (per cent)	Temp coeff (TC) (parts/10^6/°C)	Voltage (V) (tantalum cap)	Voltage (V) (polyester cap)
Black	0	1	±20	0	10	—
Brown	1	10	±1	−30	—	100
Red	2	100	±2	−80	—	250
Orange	3	1000	±3	−150	—	—
Yellow	4	10,000	+100, −0	−220	6.3	400
Green	5	100,000	±5	−330	16	—
Blue	6	1,000,000	±6	−470	20	—
Violet	7	10,000,000	—	−750	—	—
Grey	8	100,000,000	—	+30	25	—
White	9	1,000,000,000	±10	+100 to −750	3	—
Gold	—	0.1	±5	—	—	—
Silver	—	0.01	±10	—	—	—
Pink†	—	—	—	—	35	—
No colour	—	—	±20	—	—	—

Units used are ohms for resistors, picofarads for ceramic and polyester capacitors, and microfarads for tantalum capacitors.
* Some close-tolerance resistors have *three* significant figures followed by a multiplier. These are usually metal-film types and have a tolerance of ±1% or less.
† A pink fourth ring on a resistor indicates 'high stability'.

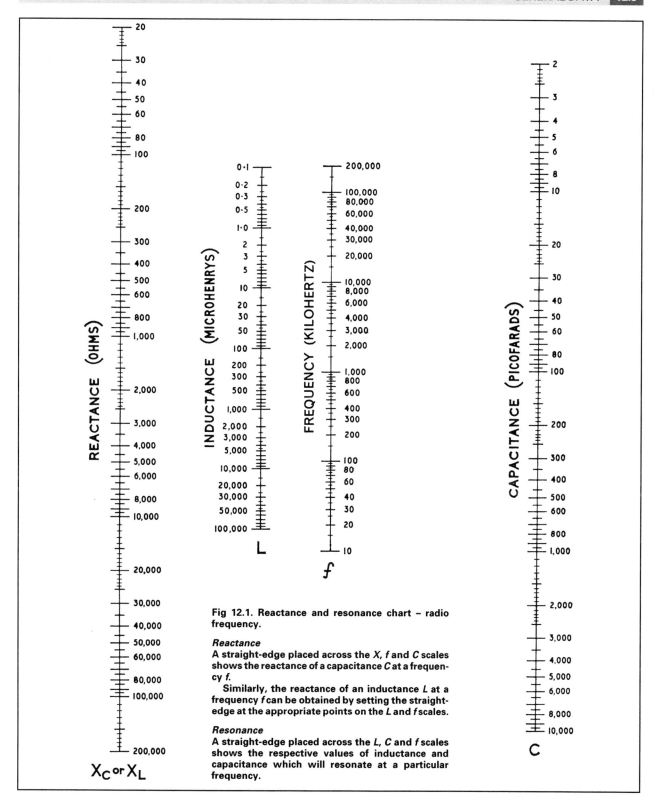

REACTANCE (OHMS)

INDUCTANCE (MICROHENRYS)

FREQUENCY (KILOHERTZ)

CAPACITANCE (PICOFARADS)

X_C or X_L

L

f

C

Fig 12.1. Reactance and resonance chart – radio frequency.

Reactance
A straight-edge placed across the X, f and C scales shows the reactance of a capacitance C at a frequency f.
  Similarly, the reactance of an inductance L at a frequency f can be obtained by setting the straight-edge at the appropriate points on the L and f scales.

Resonance
A straight-edge placed across the L, C and f scales shows the respective values of inductance and capacitance which will resonate at a particular frequency.

1 PCB layouts

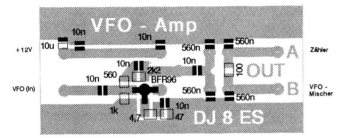

Fig 4.54. Component layout with the surface-mount parts on the track side of the PCB

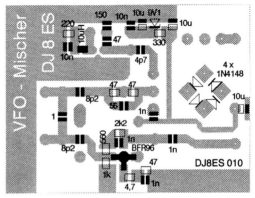

Fig 4.59. Layout of the mixer PCB (ground-plane side)

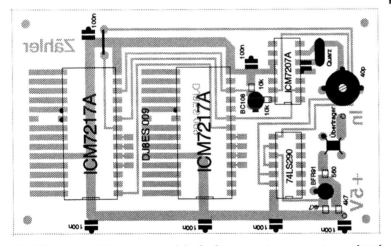

Fig 4.57. Layout of the counter module. Surface-mount components are placed on the track side of the PCB

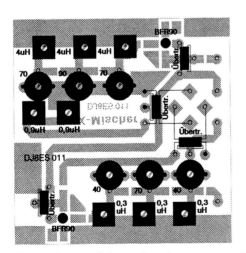
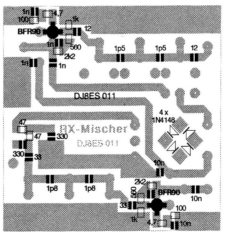

Fig 4.61. Layout of the receive mixer: component side and track side

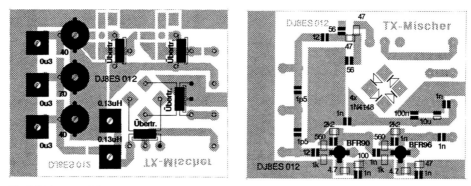

Fig 4.63. Layout of the transmit mixer. Left: component side, right: SMD component layout on track side

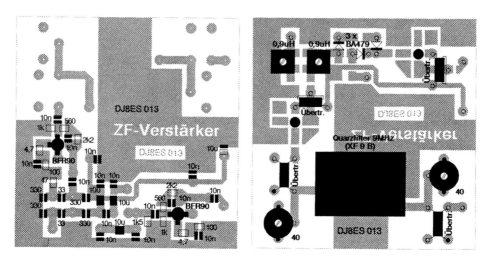

Fig 4.65. Layout of the IF amplifier. Left: component side; right: track side with SMDs

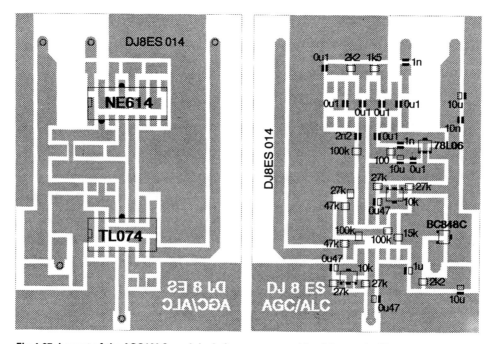

Fig 4.67. Layout of the AGC/ALC module. Left: component side; right: track side

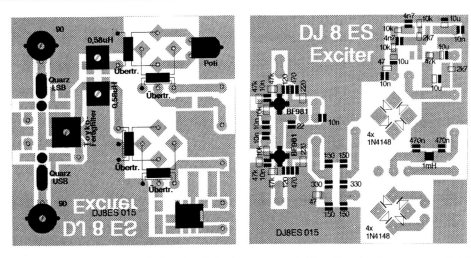

Fig 4.69. Layout of the SSB/CW exciter. Left: the component side with only a few components on the earth plane; right: the track side

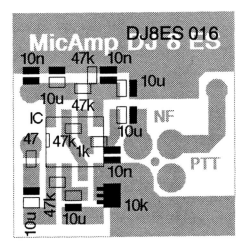

Fig 4.71. The layout of the microphone amplifier (components side)

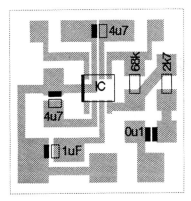

Fig 4.73. Layout of the AF amplifier

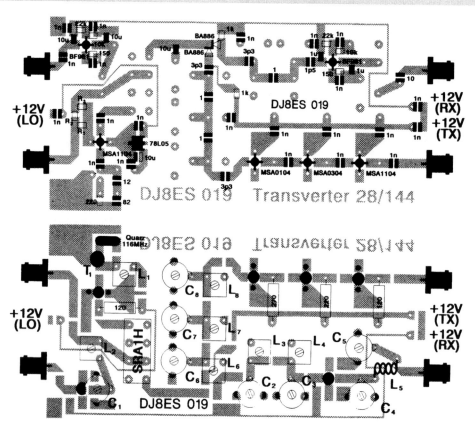

Fig 4.78. Transverter component layout. Top: track side with semiconductors and SMD components; bottom: components side

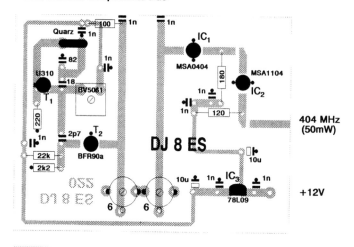

Fig 4.81. Layout of frequency synthesiser. Top: component side; bottom: track side

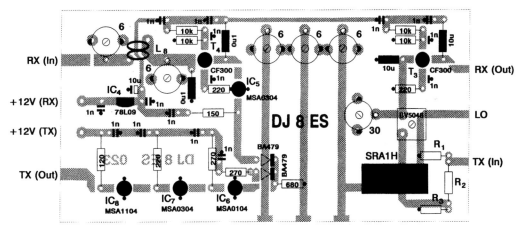

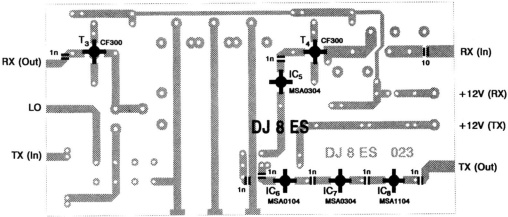

Fig 4.82. Layout of main board of transverter. Top: component side; bottom: track side with semiconductors and coupling capacitors

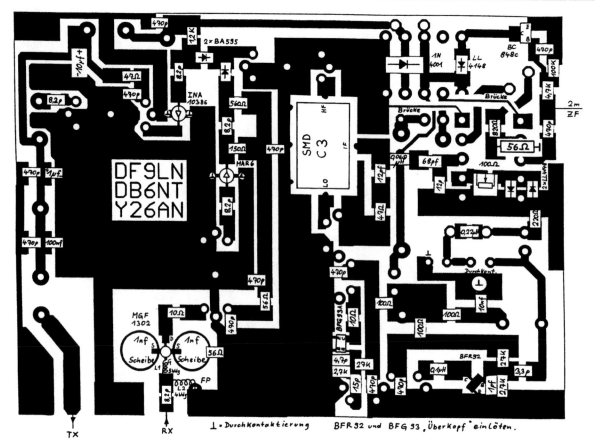

Fig 4.84. PCB track-side layout *(DUBUS Technik IV)*

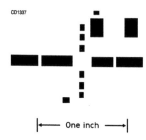

Fig 4.136. Etching pattern for the driver amplifier. The board should be 1/16in G-10 or FR-4 double-sided glass-epoxy circuit board. One side is unetched to act as a ground plane *(QEX)*

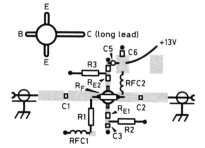

● Connection to reverse side of PCB – 0.8mm hole with wire link (see Fig 4.105(c))

Fig 4.137. Layout diagram for the driver amplifier. Six 0.8mm holes are drilled to allow connecting ground pads with copper foil to the ground plane *(QEX)*

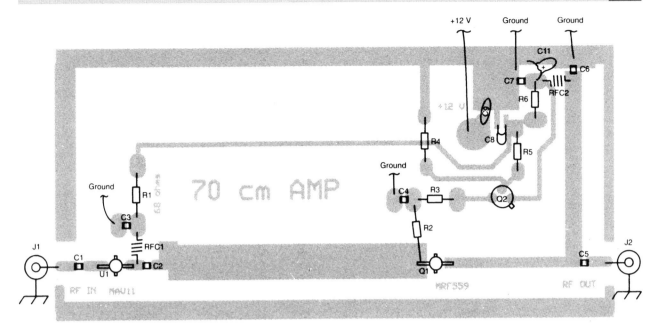

Fig 4.139. Component layout diagram for the amplifier *(QEX)*

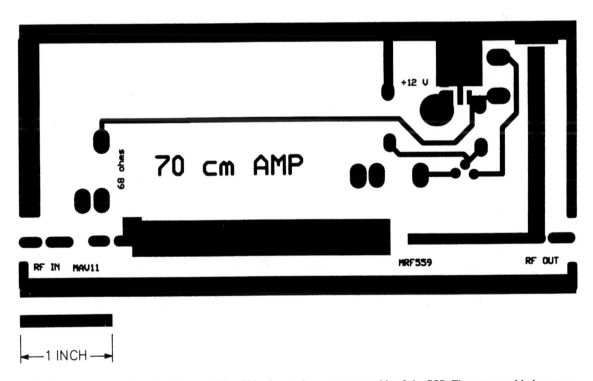

Fig 4.140. Circuit board layout of the amplifier. This shows the component side of the PCB. The reverse side is copper ground plane with links to the component side ground connections with wires/pins (copper foil for U1 and Q1) *(QEX)*

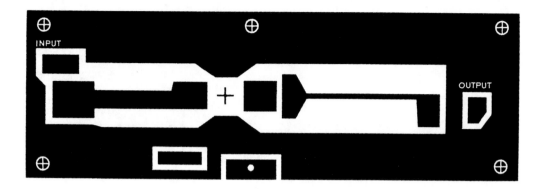

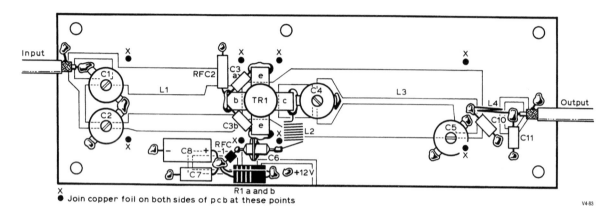

X
● Join copper foil on both sides of pcb at these points

V4-83

Fig 4.155. Transmitter PA board, actual size, and component layout. This board is double-sided (see text)

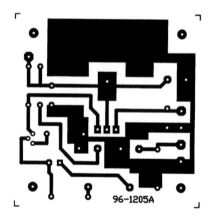

Fig 8.15. PCB for 70cm ATV modulator

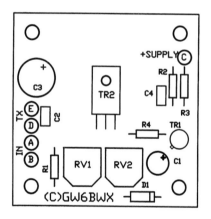

Fig 8.16. Component layout for 70cm ATV modulator

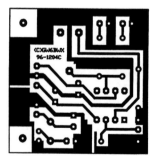

Fig 8.17. PCB for video amplifier

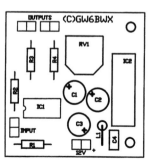

Fig 8.18. Component layout for video amplifier

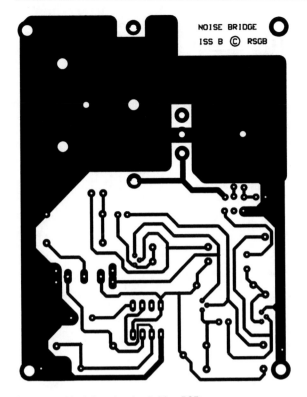

Fig 11.95. Modulated noise bridge PCB

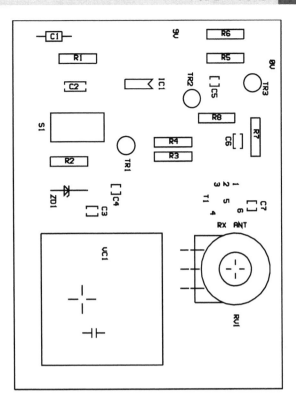

Fig 11.96. Modulated RF noise bridge layout

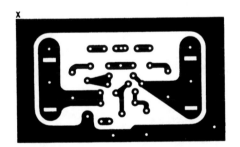

Fig 11.97. VHF dip oscillator PCB

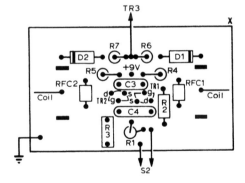

Fig 11.98. VHF dip oscillator layout

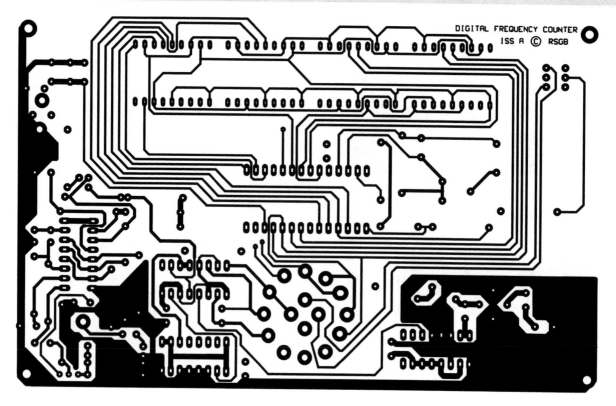

Fig 11.99. 600MHz frequency counter PCB (bottom layer)

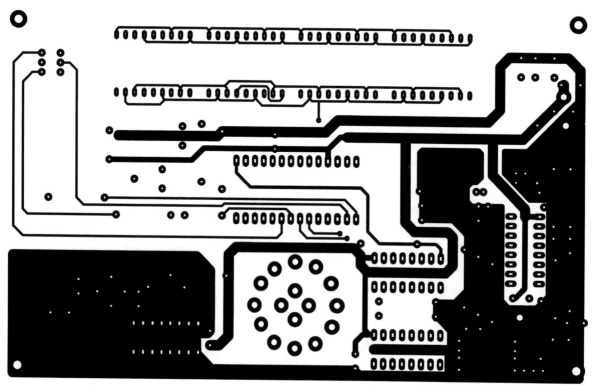

Fig 11.100. 600MHz frequency counter PCB (upper layer)

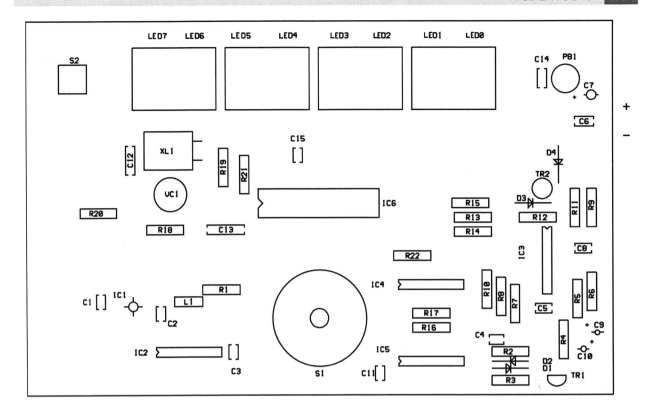

Fig 11.101. 600MHz frequency counter layout

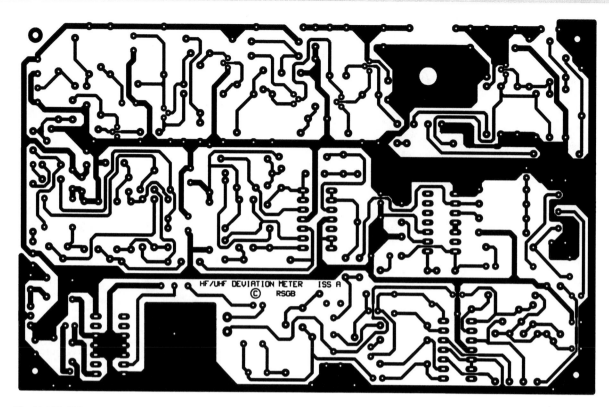

Fig 11.102. HF/UHF deviation meter PCB

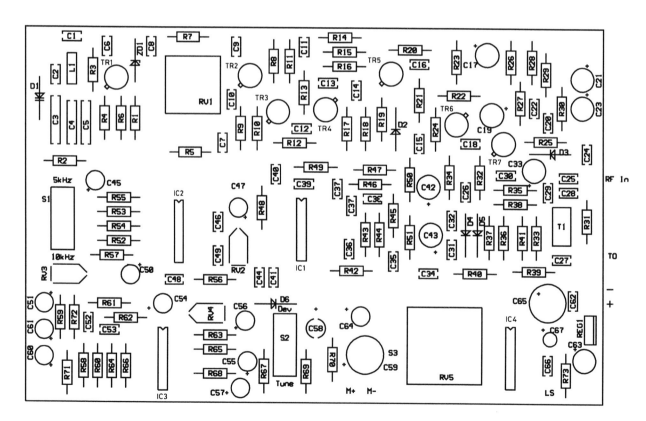

Fig 11.103. HF/UHF devaition meter layout

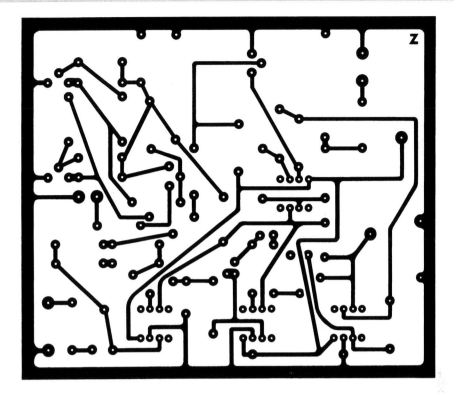

Fig 11.104. Receiver alignment aid PCB

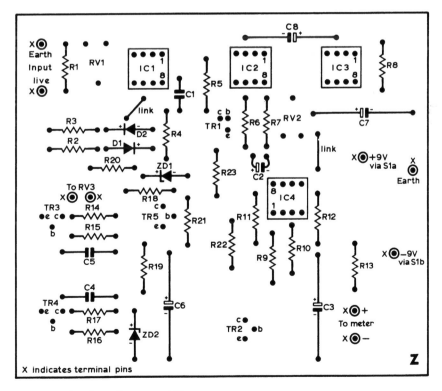

Fig 11.105. Receiver alignment aid layout

2 Fitting coaxial connectors

FITTING coaxial connectors to cable is something we all have to do, and like most things there are probably more wrong ways of fitting connectors than right ones. The methods I'm going to describe are not necessarily the right ones, but they work. Although specific styles of connector and cable are mentioned, the methods are applicable to many others.

CABLES AND CONNECTORS

The main secret of success is using the right cable with the right connector. If you're buying connectors, it is important to be able to recognise good and bad types, and know what cables the good ones are for. Using the wrong connector and cable combination is sure to lead to disaster. Any information you can get, such as old catalogues, is likely to prove useful, especially if you can get the cable cutting dimensions and equivalents lists. Two further sources of dimensions and techniques are [1] and [2]. Some excellent general advice on cable and connector selection is contained in [3].

Cables commonly are of one of two families, the American 'RG' (RadioGuide MIL specification) types and the English 'UR' (UniRadio) series. For details of the most-popular types, see Chapter 12. URM67 is equivalent to RG213, is 10.5mm in diameter and is the most common cable used with type N and PL259 connectors. URM43 (5mm OD) is one usually used with BNC connectors, although these also fit RG58 cable since both have similar dimensions. If there is any doubt about the quality of the cable, have a look at the braid. It should cover the inner completely. If it doesn't it is unlikely to be worth buying.

Having obtained your cable, the easy bit is over. Now to select the connector. The three most popular connector types are the UHF, BNC and N ranges. I'll cover these in some detail, and mention a few others later. If you can, buy connectors from a reputable manufacturer. Some names that spring to mind are RS Components, Greenpar, Suhner, Radiall, Transradio, Kings and Amphenol, among many. There are some good surplus bargains about at rallies.

It cannot be too widely known that the iniquitous UHF connector is no good much beyond 200MHz, because the impedance through the plug-socket junction is not 50Ω. The suitability of N and BNC connectors for use at UHF and beyond is due to them maintaining the system impedance (50Ω) through the connector. PL259 plugs, like the RG8 cable they were intended for, have a lot of nasty imitations. Beware of any that don't have PTFE insulation. They might be OK, but many cheap types are lossy and badly made. The plating should be good quality (silver solders best, although some proprietary plated finishes are just about as good), and there should be two or more solder holes in the body for soldering to the braid. There should be two small tangs on the outer mating edge of the plug which locate in the serrated ring of the socket and stop the body rotating. If you are going to use small-diameter cable with these plugs, get the correct reducer. Often two types are available, one being for 75Ω cable. The 50Ω type is often called 'UG175'. Using the wrong one is certain disaster. Incidentally, buy your reducers at the same time, as some manufacturers use different reducer threads.

With BNC, TNC (like the BNC but threaded) N and C (like N but bayonet) types, life can be more complicated. All these connectors are available in 50 and 75Ω versions. Be sure that you get the right one! To help those of you who are hunting for bargains at rallies, Table A2.1 shows some common manufacturers' designations. All of these connectors have evolved over the years, and consequently you will meet a number of different types. The variations are mostly to do with the cable clamping and centre pin securing method. The original cable clamp is usually called 'unimproved MIL', the later modification the 'improved' and the best for most uses is the 'pressure-sleeve' type. If you are buying new then for normal use go for the pressure-sleeve type. It is much easier to fit. If you are fortunate enough to have some of the double-braided PTFE dielectric cable such as RG142, you may find it easier to use the older clamp types, although the pressure-sleeve type will fit properly with care.

All original clamp types use a free centre pin that is held in place by its solder joint onto the inner conductor. Captive

Table A2.1. Some common connectors and equivalents

Type	Pin	Clamp	Fits cable	MIL No	Part numbers RS Components	Greenpar
BNC types						
Plug	C	P	URM43	UG88D/U	455-624	GE35070C10
Plug	F	I	URM43	UG88C/U	—	GE35018-10
Plug	F	O	URM43	UG83	—	GE35001-10
Angle plug	C	P	URM43	—	455-646	GE35002C10
Line skt	C	P	URM43	UG89C/U	455-652	GE35060C10
N types						
Plug	C	P	URM43	UG536B/U	455 949	GE15055C10
Plug	C	P	URM67	—	455-753	GE15015C1
Plug	F	I	URM67	UG21E/U	—	—
Angle plug	C	P	URM67	UG594/U	455-393	GE15003C1
Line skt	C	P	URM67	UG23D/U	455-775	GE15022C1

Pin types are: C, captive, and F, free. Clamp types are: P, pressure sleeve, I, improved and O, original.

The Greenpar part numbering system

Greenpar connectors are numbered systematically in a way that should enable you to quickly identify connectors suitable for your use, and to check through those rally ' bargains'. The part number is 'GE' followed by a five-digit number, a letter, another number and lastly some more letters. The first digit is the connector series (N, BNC etc) which is already apparent from looking at the connector. The second digit is vital – it is '5' for 50Ω connectors, and '7' for 70 or 75Ω types. The next three numbers are the connector style. The letter refers to the cable clamp method – it is 'C' for pressure sleeve types, 'A' for modified MIL clamp with captive contact, 'D' for crimp types and '-' for MIL clamps with non-captive pins. The next group of numbers is the cable series. Useful ones are '1' for URM67 and RG213, '4' for RG214 *and* URM67 and RG213, '10' for URM43, URM76, RG58 and 142, and '22' for URM95 and RG174. There are many others for less common cables. The final group of one or more letters refers to the panel mounting holes and optional finish (if any). So a connector numbered GE3507C22 is a BNC plug suitable for RG174 or URM95 50Ω cable with a pressure sleeve clamp.

contact types have a two-part centre insulator between which fits the shoulder on the centre pin. Improved MIL clamp types may have either free or captive contacts. Pressure-sleeve types have a captive centre pin. As an aid to identification, Fig A2.1 shows these types. Pressure-clamp captive-pin types are easy to spot; they have a ferrule or 'top hat' that assists in terminating the braid, a two-piece insulator and a centre pin with a shoulder. Unimproved clamp types have a washer, a plain gasket, a cone-ended braid clamp and a single insulator, often fixing inside the body. Improved types have a washer, a thin ring gasket with a V-groove and usually a conical braid clamp with more of a shoulder. There are variations, so if you can get the catalogue description it helps!

TOOLS FOR THE JOB

To tackle this successfully, you really need a few special tools: while they may not be absolutely essential, they certainly help. First and foremost is a good soldering iron. If you never intend to use a PL259, then a small instrument type iron is sufficient. If you use PL259s, or intend to use some of the 'dirty tricks' described later, something with a lot more heat output is required. Ideally a thermostatically-controlled iron is best; as with most tools, a little extra spent repays itself handsomely in the future.

A *sharp* knife is another must. A Stanley-type is essential for larger cables, provided that the blade is sharp. For smaller cables, you can use a craft knife or a very sharp penknife. I use a scalpel. A word or two of warning is in order, however. Scalpels excel at the job they were designed for – cutting flesh. Make sure it isn't yours! Use sharp blades, cut away from you, and keep the object you're cutting on the bench, *not in your hand*. Although sharp, the steel blades are brittle and will shatter if you apply excessive force or bend them. Dispose of used blades in a box or plastic jar. Model shops have a good range of craft knives which will also do an excellent job.

A pair of sharp small scissors is needed for cutting braids, and a blunt darning needle (mount it in a handle made from a piece of wood dowelling) is useful for unweaving the braid: so

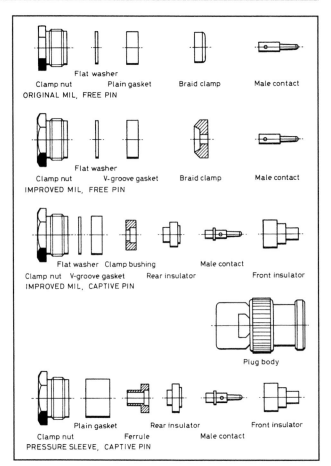

Fig A2.1.Types of BNC/N cable clamps

too is a scriber. You will find a small vice a great help as well. For BNC, TNC and N type connectors, some spanners are essential to tighten the gland nuts. The BNC/TNC spanners should be thin $^7/_{16}$in AF. Those for type N need to be $^{11}/_{16} \times$ $^5/_8$in AF. BNC spanners are sold in pairs by RS Components (available via Electromail in the UK) and are $^7/_{16} \times \frac{1}{2}$in AF – the other end suitable for BNC line sockets. A junior hacksaw is needed to cut larger cables such as URM67. Finally, if you intend to put heatshrink sleeves over the ends of plugs for outdoor use, some form of heat gun helps, although the shaft of a soldering iron may work. (You probably have a heat gun already, thinly disguised as a hot-air paint stripper).

PREPARING CABLES

Fitting a plug requires you to remove various bits of outer sheath, braid and inner dielectric. The important knack to acquire is that of removing one at a time, without damaging what lies underneath. To remove the outer sheath, use a sharp knife or scalpel. Place the knife across the cable and rotate the cable while applying gentle pressure. The object of doing this is to score right round the cable sheath. Now score a line from the ring you just made up to the cable end. If you have cut it just enough, it should be possible to peel away the outer sheath leaving braid intact underneath. If this is not something you've tried before, practise on a piece of cable first. For some connectors, it is important that this edge of the sheath is a smooth edge at right-angles to the cable, so it really is worth getting right.

Braid removal usually just requires a bit of combing out and a pair of scissors. Removal of the inner dielectric is most difficult with large-diameter cables with laid multi-strand inner conductors like URM67. Again, it is important that the end is a clean, smooth cut at right-angles to the cable. This is best achieved by removing the bulk of the dielectric first, if necessary in several stages, and finally trimming the dielectric to length. There is a limit to how much dielectric you can remove at one go: 1–2cm is about as much as can be attempted with the larger sizes without damaging the lay of the inner. For the larger cables, it is worthwhile to pare down the bulk of the unwanted material before trying to pull the remainder off the inner. If you can, fit one plug on short cables before you cut the cable to length (or off the reel if you are so lucky). This will help to prevent the inner sliding about when you are stripping the inner dielectric.

FITTING PL259 PLUGS
Without reducer, URM67-type cable

First make a clean end. For this large cable, the only satisfactory way I have found is to use a junior hacksaw. Chopping with cutters or a knife just spoils the whole thing. Having got a clean end, refer to Fig A2.2 for the stripping dimensions. First remove the sheath braid and dielectric, revealing the length of inner conductor required. Do this by cutting right through the sheath and braid, scoring the dielectric, then removing the dielectric afterwards. Next carefully remove the sheath back to the dimension indicated, *without disturbing the braid.* Examine the braid: it should be shiny and smooth. If you have disturbed it or it looks tarnished, start again a little further down. Now the tricky bit. With a hot iron, tin the braid carefully. The idea is to do it with as little solder as possible. Lightly tin the inner conductor also at this stage. Take a breather while the cable cools.

Now slide the coupling piece onto the cable (threaded end towards the free end). Examine the plug body. If it isn't silver plated, and you think it might not solder easily, apply a file around and through the solder holes. Now screw the body onto the cable, hard. When you've finished, the sheath should have gone into the threaded end of the connector, the inner should be poking out through the hollow pin, and the end of the exposed dielectric should be hard up against the inside shoulder of the plug. Look at the braid through the solder holes. It should not have broken up into a mass of strands; that's why it was tinned. If it has, it's best to start again.

If all is well, lightly clamp the cable in the vice, then apply the iron to the solder holes. Heat it up and then apply solder. It should flow into the holes: if it stays there as a sullen blob, the body isn't hot enough. Now leave it undisturbed to cool before soldering the inner by heating the pin and feeding solder down the inner. Finally, when it's all cool, cut any excess protruding inner conductor and file flush with the pin, then screw down the coupling ring. Merely as a confidence check, of course, test for continuity on both inner and outer from one end of the cable to the other, and check that the inner isn't shorted to the braid.

With reducer, URM43 type cable

First, slide the outer coupler and the reducer on to the cable. Next, referring to Fig A2.2, remove the outer sheath without nicking the braid. Now, using a blunt needle, gently unweave

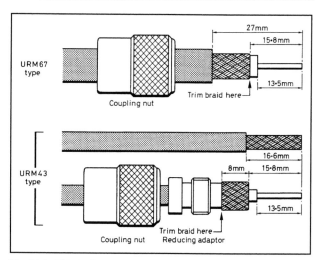

Fig A2.2. PL259 plug assembly

the braid a bit at a time until it is all straight and sticking out like a ruff around the cable. Remove the inner dielectric without nicking the inner conductor, so as to leave the specified amount of dielectric. Tin the inner conductor. Bring up the reducer until the end of it is flush with the end of the outer sheath. Fold the braid back so it lies evenly over the shank of the reducer, then cut off the excess braid with scissors so that it is not in danger of getting trapped in the threads. Smooth it down once more, then offer up the plug body and, *while holding the reducer and cable still,* screw on the plug body until it is fully home. The only really good way of doing this is with two pairs of pliers. Now hold the assembly in the vice and ready the soldering iron. There has been a spirited discussion from time to time about the advisability of soldering the braid through the holes: the best information that I have is that you should. If you don't, the cable will sooner or later fail. So, *with a big iron,* solder the braid through the holes. See the section above for advice. Finally, solder and trim the inner conductor and test the assembly as described earlier.

FITTING BNC AND TYPE N PLUGS

These are 'constant impedance' connectors: that is, when correctly made up, the system impedance of 50Ω is maintained right through the connector. It is vital that the cable fits the connector correctly, therefore check that each part fits the cable properly after you prepare it. Refer to Fig A2.3 for BNC dimensions and Fig A2.4 for N types.

Original or unmodified clamp types

Slide the nut, washer and gasket onto the cable in that order. With the sharp knife, score through the outer sheath by holding the knife and rotating the cable, without nicking the braid. Run the knife along the cable from the score to the end, then peel off the outer sheath. Using a blunt needle, for example, start to unweave the braid enough to enable the correct length of dielectric to be removed. Now slip the braid clamp on, pushing it firmly down to the end of the outer sheath. Finish unweaving the braid, comb it smooth, then trim it with scissors so that it just comes back to the end of the conical section of the clamp. Be sure that the braid wires aren't twisted. Now fit the inner pin and make sure that the open end of the pin will fit up against the dielectric. Take the pin off and lightly tin the exposed inner conductor. Re-fit the pin and solder it in

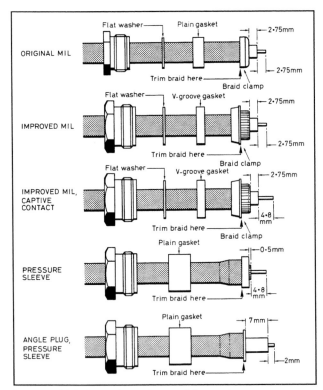

Fig A2.3. BNC dimensions, plugs and line sockets

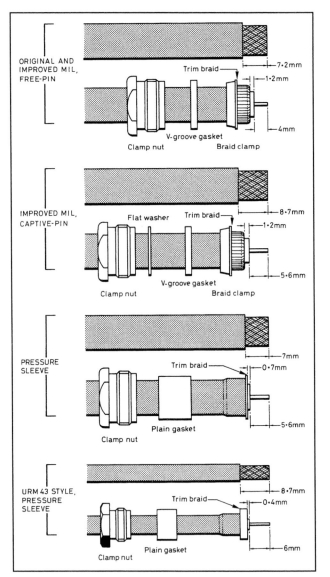

Fig A2.4. N-type dimensions, plugs, angle plugs and line sockets

place by placing the soldering iron bit (tinned but with the solder wiped off) on the side of the pin opposite the solder hole. Feed a small quantity of solder (22 SWG or so works best) into the hole. Allow to cool and examine. If you've been careful enough, the dielectric should not have melted. Usually it does, and swells up, so with the sharp knife trim it back to size. This is essential as otherwise the plug will not assemble properly. Remove any excess solder from around the pin with a fine file. Now push the gasket and washer up against the clamp nut, check the braid dressing on the clamp, then push the assembly into the plug body. Gently firm home the gasket with a small screwdriver or rod and then start the clamp nut by hand. Tighten the clamp nut by a spanner, using a second spanner to hold the plug body still; it *must not rotate*. Finally, check the completed job with the shack ohmmeter.

Modified or improved clamp types

In general, this is similar to the technique for unmodified clamp types described above. There are some important differences, however.

The gasket has a V-shaped groove in it, which must face the cable clamp. The clamp has a corresponding V-shaped profile on one side: the other side may be conical or straight sided, depending on the manufacturer. If the clamp end has straight sides, then the braid is fanned out and cut to the edge of the clamp only, not pushed down the sides. Some types have a small PTFE insulator which is fitted before the pin is put on (common on plugs for the small RG174 cable).

You now appreciate why having the assembly instructions for your particular plug is a good idea! Still, by using these instructions as a guide, it shouldn't be too difficult to get it right, even if it does not fit the first time.

One important point – if the plug has been assembled correctly and tightened up properly, the clamp will have

(intentionally) cut the gasket. It is then rather difficult to re-use it as the gasket, being thin, will not stand a second attempt. The thicker gasket types will often allow careful re-use.

Captive-contact types

These have a small shoulder on the pin and a rear insulator which fits between the pin and the cable. Most types use a thick gasket and a ferrule, although some use a V-grooved braid clamp and thin gasket. I shall describe the ferrule type, as these are the most commonly available and the easiest to fit.

First, slip the nut and gasket on to the cable. Refer to Fig A2.3 or Fig A2.4 for cutting dimensions, then strip off the correct amount of outer sheath by rotating the cable, producing a neat scored circle. Score back to the end of the cable and peel off the unwanted sheath. Comb out the braid, and with it fanned out evenly around the cable, slide the ferrule (small end first) on to the dielectric-covered inner conductor. Push it home so that the narrow portion of the ferrule slides *under* the braid, and the end of the outer sheath rests against the ferrule shoulder. Trim the braid with scissors to the edge of the ferrule. Slide up the gasket so that it rests gently against the ferrule shoulder, which will prevent the braid from being disturbed. Using the sharp knife, trim the dielectric back to the indicated dimension without nicking the inner conductor. Fit the rear insulator, which will have a recess on one side to accommodate the protruding dielectric. Incidentally, if you don't have the size for your particular plug, trim the dielectric until it fits but don't overdo it! Now trim the exposed inner conductor to length and check by fitting the pin, whose shoulder should rest on the rear insulator unless the inner has been cut too long. Tin the inner lightly, then fit the pin and solder it by applying the iron tip (cleaned of excess solder) to the side of the pin opposite from the solder hole and feed a small amount of solder into the hole. Allow to cool and remove excess solder with a fine file. Now fit the front insulator (usually separate from the body) and push the whole assembly into the body. Push down the gasket gently into the plug body with a small rod or screwdriver. Start the nut by hand, then tighten fully with one spanner, using the other to prevent the body from rotating. Check with the ohmmeter, then start on the other end, remembering to put the nut and gasket on first!

VARIATIONS

Angle plugs generally follow a similar pattern to the straight types, except that connection to the inner is via a slotted pin, accessed via a removable cap screw. Tighten the connector nut before soldering the inner. Line sockets are fitted in the same way as plugs.

DIRTY TRICKS

Most of these were originally described in 'The Golden Treasury of Connector Abuse' in the December 1985 issue of the VOWHARS newsletter. The author gratefully acknowledges the contributions by a number of connector abusers, who wish to remain anonymous, and also including G3SEK.

We would like to use new connectors every time, but often a pressure-sleeve type can be re-used if the gasket is not too deformed. Get all the solder you can out of the pin and then carefully ream out the rest with a small drill, held in a pin chuck. The sizes to use are 1mm for URM43-style pins, and 2.6mm for URM67 ones.

Tarnished silver-plated connectors can be made to shine by dipping the metal parts in Goddards 'Silver Dip' silver cleaner. Rinse carefully afterwards, then bake in a slow oven.

BNC connectors for URM67 cable can be rather hard to find. A standard captive-contact BNC plug can be fitted to URM67 in the following way. First discard the nut, gasket and ferrule, and prepare the rear insulator by removing the ridge from it with a sharp knife. Now prepare the cable by cutting with a knife, right through the jacket, braid and insulator about

5mm back from the end. Cut sufficiently deep so that you notch the inner conductor strands, and remove the remains. Carefully bend the six individual outer strands of the inner so they break off flush with the end of the dielectric, leaving one straight inner strand. Now remove sufficient outer jacket (about 2cm) such that when the body is pushed on the cable, some braid is still visible. Tin the braid and inner conductor lightly, then fit the rear insulator, pin and front insulator and push home the assembly into the plug body. With the big iron, heat the plug body and feed solder down the joint with the braid. After it has cooled, put some heatshrink adhesive-lined sleeving over the plug and cable join to protect it. Testing of this trick with a TDR has shown it to be almost as good as the real plug, and certainly better than an adapter. This assembly will happily stand 100W of 1296MHz.

An N plug can be *carefully* pushed on to a BNC socket; OK for quick test equipment lash-ups, but don't do it too often or too hard as you will eventually damage the socket. In a similar vein, the pin of a PL259 is about the same diameter as a 4mm wander plug; after all, what is a PL259 but a screened wander plug?

To make a PL259 to BNC adapter, solder a length of copper wire to the back of a BNC single-hole socket. Drop it (without the nut) on to the top of a PL259 so that the wire pokes through the pin of the plug. With a big iron or a careful blowtorch, solder the body of the socket and plug together. After it has cooled, solder the inner wire to the pin. Not exactly a precision job, but good enough for a PL259!

Finally, to waterproof a connector-cable joint and to provide added strength where flexing of the cable will occur, heatshrink a piece of adhesive-lined heatshrink sleeving over the plug body and cable. For N connectors, a 19mm diameter variety (that shrinks to a minimum of 6mm, such as RS399-748) can be slid on to the cable and connector after assembly.

CONCLUSIONS

With a little practice, care and patience, I hope that these notes make the fitting of connectors a little less of a chancy business. Practice on some short leads (there is no such thing as too many spare short coaxial leads in any shack) and remember that the best time to put new connectors on the feeder isn't two minutes before the start of the contest!

REFERENCES
[1] *The Radio Amateur's Handbook* (any edition), ARRL.
[2] *Microwave Measurements and Techniques,* T S Laverghetta, Artech House, 1976. (Good advice on cable, connectors and how to fit them. Much useful practical advice on many subjects, not just for microwavers!)
[3] *The Buyer's Guide to Amateur Radio,* Angus McKenzie, MBE, G3OSS, RSGB, 1986.

Index

A

ABAC – reactance and resonance, 12.5
Absorption wavemeters, 11.18
Active components, 4.7
AD600 IF amplifier, 4.16
Adiabatic changes in the atmosphere, 3.8
AF amplifier, 4.27
AF level meters, 11.35
AGC, 4.15, 4.15
Air flow measurement, 4.57
Amateur research projects, 3.34
Amateur television, 8.1
    kits, 8.8
    receivers, 8.6
    repeaters, 8.3
    transmitters, 8.3
Amplifiers
    AF, 4.27
    power, 4.37
    RF, 4.9, 4.20
AMTOR, 7.8
Antennas, 5.1
    arrays, 5.3
    choosing, 2.2
    directivity, 5.2
    EMC, 6.1
    gain, 5.2
    impedance, 5.3
    installation, 5.11
    materials, 5.15
    satellite operation, 5.45, 9.1
Atmospheric absorption, 3.3
Atmospheric pressure, 3.5
Atmospheric temperature, 3.5
Attenuation of coaxial lines, 5.7
Attenuators, 11.15, 11.35
ATV – see Amateur television
Audio systems and EMC, 6.6
Auroras
    boundary fence, 3.23
    monitor, 3.26
    propagation, 3.3, 3.21
    warning networks, 3.26
AX25 packet radio, 7.1
Axial mode helical antenna, 5.30

B

Baby alarms and EMC, 6.7
Baluns, 5.10
Band-pass filter, 4.8
BATC, 8.8
BBSs, 7.5
Beamwidth, antenna, 5.1
Bessel functions, 4.34
Biasing of PAs, 4.40

Block diagram, multimode receiver, 4.10
Block diagram, transceiver, 4.33
Block diagram, transmitters, 4.33
Blocking, 4.3
Blowers, 4.57
BNC connectors, A2.3
Boundary layer, 3.17
Breakthrough, EMC, 6.3
British Amateur Television Club, 8.8
Broad-band 300W FET amplifier, 4.55
Broadside arrays, 5.3
Buffer amplifier, 4.12
Bulletin boards, 7.5

C

Cable TV and EMC, 6.5
Capacitors
    calculations, 12.1
    chip, 4.3
Cavity tuned circuits, 4.4
Cavity wavemeter, 11.19
Characteristic impedance, 4.5, 4.6, 12.1
Chimney mounting, 5.14
Chip capacitors, 4.3
Choice of equipment, 2.1
Choosing an antenna, 2.2
Clover, 7.8
Coaxial balun, 5.11
Coaxial cables, 5.6
    properties, 12.3
    switch, 11.48
Coaxial connectors, A2.1
Coaxial lines, 5.6
Code of practice, satellite use, 9.2
Coil winding, 12.3
Collinear antennas, 5.35
Colour codes, 12.4
Colour TV, 8.1
Colpitts oscillator, 4.11
Combiners, 4.46
Computers and EMC, 6.9
Contests, 2.6
Continuous tone coded squelch
        system, 10.2
Cooling
    transistor amplifiers, 4.37
    valve amplifiers, 4.56
Corner reflector, 5.24
'Cot' transformer, 5.9
Crossed Yagi antenna, 5.26
Crystal filter, 4.25
CTCSS, 10.2

D

Data modes, 1.8, 7.1

hardware, 7.2
    interface, 7.6
Decibel, 12.1
Demodulators, 4.15
Detectors, 4.15
Deviation, 4.34
    meter, 11.28
Dew point, 3.5
Dielectric constant, 4.6
Diffraction, 3.4
Digipeaters, 7.4
Digital frequency counters, 11.25
Dip oscillators, 11.21
Direct digital synthesis, 4.13
Directivity, antenna, 5.2
Discone, 5.34
Dummy loads, 11.8
Duplexers, 10.4
DX cluster, 7.5
Dynamic range, 4.3, 11.39

E

Earthing PAs, 4.39
Electromagnetic spectrum, 1.1
EMC, 6.1
    regulations, 6.12
    satellite TV, 6.3
EME, 3.3, 3.18
Endfire arrays, 5.4
European meteorological bulletin, 3.12

F

F2 layer, 3.3
FAI, 3.3
Fans, 4.57
Fax, 7.8
Feeders, 2.4
Ferrite rings and cores, 6.6
Field aligned irregularities, 3.3
Field strengths and EMC, 6.2
Filter method for SSB, 4.36
Filters
    audio, 4.34
    ladder, 4.8
    for radio and TV receivers, 6.5
    RF, 4.8
Fitting coaxial connectors, A2.1
Fixed frequency oscillators, 4.14
FM, 4.16, 4.34
Franklin antenna, 5.37
Franklin oscillator, 4.11
Free space attenuation, 3.18
Frequency measurement, 4.14
Frequency synthesisers and EMC, 6.8
Frequency-wavelength, 12.1

Front-end measurements, 11.34

G

G3SEK/G4PMK amplifier, 4.78
G3WZT 100W amplifier for 50MHz, 4.44
GaAsFETs, 4.7
Gain compression, 4.3
Gain of Yagi antennas, 5.16
GB3ER collinear, 5.39
General data, 12.1
Geomagnetic data , 3.32
Getting started, 2.1
Grounded-grid amplifier, 4.58
GW3XYW amplifier , 4.52

H

H-plane, 5.1
Halo antenna, 5.44
Harmonic generators, 4.33
Harmonics and EMC, 6.7
Hartley oscillator, 4.11
HB9CV minibeam, 5.25
HDLC, 7.1
Heater supplies, 4.62
Heatsinks, 4.37, 4.49
Height gain, antenna, 5.12
Helical resonators, 4.5
High-level data link, 7.1
High-power amplifiers, 4.68
High-pass audio filter, 4.34
History of VHF/UHF, 1.2
Huff and puff oscillator, 4.13
Hybrid modules, 4.48

I

IARU locator, 3.2
IF amplifier, 4.25
Image modes., 1.9
Impedance, 12.2
Impedance matching, 5.7
Inductor calculations, 12.2
Input circuits, 4.7
Intermediate frequency, 4.14
Intermodulation, 4.2
    measurements, 11.40
Internal antennas, 5.14
Ionospheric propagation, 3.19
Isopleths, 3.9

J

J antenna, 5.38

K

K value, 3.16
KA-node, 7.4
Klystron oscillator, 1.5

L

Ladder filter, 4.18
Licence classes, 1.7
Local oscillators, 4.11
Locators, 3.2
Log-periodic antenna, 5.22, 5.24
Logging, 2.8
Long Yagis, 5.17
Low-power devices and EMC, 6.7
Low-profile antennas, 5.43

Low-pass filters
    audio, 4.34
    RF, 4.8
Lumped-constant circuits, 4.4

M

Magnetron, 1.5
Masthead TV amplifiers and EMC, 6.4
Masts, antenna, 5.14
Matching circuits, 4.42
Matching in PAs, 4.40, 4.59
Maxwell bridge, 11.2
Meteor scatter, 3.3, 3.28
Meteor showers, 3.30
Meteorological units, 3.5
Microphone amplifier, 4.27, 4.34
Microstrip circuits, 4.5
Mixer oscillator, 4.12
Mixers, 4.10, 4.25
Mobile and portable antennas, 5.39
Modulation index, 4.34
Morse keying, 4.34
Morse/CW, 4.15
MOSFETs, 4.7
MSF, 3.33
Multimedia data communication, 7.6

N

N connector, A2.3
N value, 3.6
Neighbours and EMC, 6.11
Network BBS, 7.5
Nodes, 7.4
Noise, 4.1
    bridge, 11.13
    factor, 4.1
    figure, 4.1
    filter, 4.18
    measurements, 11.31
    sources, 11.32
    temperature, 11.38
Non-linearity, 4.2
Normal-mode helical antenna, 5.43

O

Ohm's Law, 12.2
Omnidirectional antennas, 5.31
Open-wire lines, 5.6

P

Packet radio, 7.1
    digipeaters, 7.4
    nodes, 7.4
Pactor, 7.8
Parasitic components, 4.3
Pawsey stub, 5.11
PCB layouts, A1.1
Phase-locked loop, 4.13
Phase modulation, 4.34
Phase noise, 4.2
Phasing, antennas, 5.5
Phasing method for SSB, 4.37
Pi-network, 4.59
PL259 plugs, A2.3
Polar diagrams, 5.1, 5.19
    E-plane, 5.1
Polarisation, 5.1, 5.12

Potential refractive index, 3.14
Power
    amplifiers, 4.37
    calculations, 12.2
    dividers, 5.5, 5.10
    measurement, 11.7 11.11
    supplies, valve amplifiers, 4.61
    supplies, for 2m linear, 4.66
Prescalers, 11.26
Propagation, 3.1
    modes, 3.2

Q

Q value, 12.2, 4.59
QSL cards, 2.7
QSOs, 2.5
Quad antennas and arrays, 5.18
    quadruple, 5.21
Quarter-wave transformer, 5.9
Quarter-wave whip, 5.40

R

Radiation patterns, 2.3, 5.1
Radio refractive index, historical, 3.16
Radiosondes, 3.4
Reactance, 12.2
Receivers, 4.1, 4.21
    alignment aid, 11.41
    building blocks, 4.3, 4.7
Reflection, 3.4
Reflectometer, 11.1
Refractive index, 3.4
Relative humidity, 3.5
Repeaters, 1.8, 2.7, 10.1
    logic control, 10.3
Resistor calculations, 12.2
Resonance, 12.2
Resonant lines, 4.4
RF amplifiers, 4.9, 4.20
RF bridge, 11.12
RF emission standards, 6.9
RF filters, 4.9
RF gain, 11.34
RF immunity standards, 6.2
RF leakage, 6.9
RF noise bridge, 11.13
RF power measurement, 11.7
RF probes, 11.9
RF voltmeters, 11.9
Ring antenna, 5.43
RTTY, 7.8

S

S-meter, 4.19
Safety, antenna, 5.15
Satellite communications, 1.9, 9.1
    modes, 9.1
    propagation, 3.29
    users' code of practice, 9.2
Selectivity, 4.15
Sensitivity measurements, 11.38
Signal interference, 5.12
Signal sources, 11.17
Simplex operation, 2.5
Skeleton-slot Yagis, 5.18
Skirted antenna, 5.34
Sleeve dipole, 5.34

Snell's Law, 3.4
Soft switching, 4.62
Solar effects, 3.30
Solar rotation table, 3.31
Sources of data, 3.10
Spectrum analysis, 11.25
Sporadic-E, 3.20
Spurious signals and EMC, 6.7
SSB, 4.15
   exciter, 4.26, 4.36
SSTV, 7.8
Stability of PAs, 4.39
Stacked arrays, 5.4
Static electricity, 4.7
Station monitor, FM, 11.44
Strong-signal sources, 11.39
Stubs for matching, 5.8
Super turnstile antenna, 5.44
Synthesised oscillator, 4.13

T
TCP/IP, 7.1
Telephones and EMC, 6.6
TEP, 3.3, 3.27
Tephigram, 3.13
Terminal node controller, 7.1
Test gear, 11.1
Third method for SSB, 4.37
Third-order products, 4.2
Time constant, 12.2
Time recording, 3.33
TNC, 7.1
Towers, antenna, 5.14
Trans-equatorial propagation, 3.3, 3.27
Transceivers, 4.1

Transformer ratios, 12.2
Transmission lines, 4.5, 5.6
   filters, 5.11
   transformers, 5.9
Transmitters, 4.1, 4.32
Transverters, 4.1
Tropo DX, 3.3, 3.7
Tropospheric scatter, 3.3, 3.18
Trough-line tuned circuits, 4.4
Tuned circuits, 4.4
Tuning valve PAs, 4.63
Turnstile antenna, 5.44
TV AM modulator, 8.4
TV distribution amplifiers and EMC, 6.4
TV transmitter design, 8.5
Two-stub transformer, 11.47

V
Vackar oscillator, 4.11
Valve amplifiers, 4.55
   circuits, 4.64
Valve bases, 4.60
Vapour pressure, 3.6
Variable polarisation antenna, 5.26
Vehicle keys and EMC, 6.7
VFOs, 4.11
VHF/UHF amateur bands, 1.1
Video amplifiers, 8.7
Video equipment, 8.3
Volute antennas, 5.46
VSWR bridge, 11.6

W
W2GN amplifier, 4.73

Wavemeters, 11.18
Weak-signal modes, 7.8
Weather, 3.2
Wilkinson divider, 4.24
Wind loading, antenna, 5.14
Wire gauges, 12.3

Y
Yagi antennas, 5.16
   crossed, 5.26
   dimensions, 5.17

Numbers
2m transverter, 4.28
2m valve linear amplifier, 4.64
2m 25W amplifier, 4.50
2m 10W amplifier, 4.53
2m 100W amplifier, 4.53
23cm transverter, 4.30
23cm TV transmitter, 8.5
23cm valve amplifier, 4.77
4m 100W amplifier, 4.52
4m 200W amplifier, 4.54
4CX250 amplifiers, 4.55
6m 2W amplifier, 4.52
600MHz frequency counter, 11.26
70cm 4W amplifier, 4.54
70cm high-power amplifier, 4.77
70cm transverter, 4.29
9600 baud FM modulator, 7.4

Symbols
$\lambda/2$ and $5\lambda/8$ antennas, 5.41
$\lambda/4$ ground-plane antenna, 5.33
$7\lambda/8$ whip, 5.42

Get more out of amateur radio . . . as an RSGB member!

Radio Communication

A magazine which covers a wide range of interests and which features the best and latest amateur radio news. The Society's journal has acquired a worldwide reputation for its content. With 100 pages, many in colour, 'RadCom' strives to maintain its reputation as the best available and is circulated free of charge to members throughout the world.

The regular columns in the magazine include those for HF, VHF/UHF, microwave, SWL, clubs, satellite, data and contests. In addition to the many technical articles, the highly regarded 'Technical Topics' feature caters for those wishing to keep themselves briefed on recent developments in technical matters.

The 'Last Word' is a lively feature in which members can put forward their views and opinions and be sure of receiving a wide audience. To keep members in touch with what's going on in the hobby, events diaries are published each month.

Advertisements for the equipment you wish to sell can be placed in the magazine, with the advantages of short deadlines and large circulation.

QSL Bureau

Members enjoy the use of the QSL Bureau free of charge for both outgoing and incoming cards. This can save you a good deal of postage.

Special Event Callsigns

Special event callsigns in the GB series are handled by RSGB on behalf of the RA. They give amateurs special facilities for displaying amateur radio to the general public.

Specialised News Sheets

The RSGB publishes the DX News-sheet for HF enthusiasts and the Microwave Newsletter for those operating above 1GHz.

Specialised Equipment Insurance

Insurance for your valuable equipment which has been arranged specially for members. The rates are very advantageous.

Audio Visual Library

Films, audio and video tapes are available from RSGB HQ for all affiliated groups and clubs.

Reciprocal Licensing Information

Details are available for most countries on the RSGB computer database.

Government Liaison

One of the most vital features of the work of the RSGB is the ongoing liaison with the UK Licensing Authority – presently the Radiocommunications Agency (RA) of the Department of Trade and Industry. Setting and maintaining the proper framework in which amateur radio can thrive and develop is essential to the well-being of amateur radio. For example, the Novice Licence was introduced by the RA after long discussions with the RSGB. The Society also spares no effort in defence of amateur radio's most precious assets – the amateur bands.

Beacons and Repeaters

The RSGB supports financially all beacons which are looked after by the appropriate committee of the Society, ie 1.8–30MHz by the HF Committee, 30–1000MHz (1GHz) by the VHF Committee and frequencies above 1GHz by the Microwave Committee. For repeaters, the Society's Repeater Management Committee has played a major role. Society books such as the RSGB Yearbook give further details, and computer-based lists giving operational status can be obtained from HQ.

Operating Awards

A wide range of operating awards is available via the responsible officers: their names can be found in the front pages of Radio Communication and in the RSGB Yearbook. Details of these awards can be found in the latter and also the Amateur Radio Operating Manual published by the Society.

Contests (HF/VHF/Microwave)

The Society has two contest committees which carry out all work associated with the running of contests. The HF Contests Committee deals with contests below 30MHz, whilst events on frequencies above 30MHz are dealt with by the VHF Contests Committee.

Morse Testing

The Society has responsibility for Morse testing of radio amateurs in the UK. If you wish to take a Morse test, write direct to RSGB HQ (Morse tests) for an application form.

Slow Morse

Many volunteers all over the country give up their time to send slow Morse over the air to those who are preparing for the 5 and 12 words per minute Morse tests. The Society also produces Morse practice tapes.

RSGB Books

The Society publishes a range of books for the radio amateur and imports many others. Members are entitled to a discount on all books purchased from the Society – this discount can offset the cost of membership.

Propagation

The Society's Propagation Studies Committee is highly respected – both within the amateur community and professionally – for its work. Predictions are given in the weekly GB2RS news bulletins and the Society's monthly magazine *Radio Communication*.

Technical and EMC Advice

Although the role of the Society's Technical and Publications Advisory Committee is largely to vet material intended for publication, its members and HQ staff are always willing to help with any technical matters.

Breakthrough in domestic entertainment equipment can be a difficult problem to solve as well as having licensing implications. The Society's EMC Committee is able to offer practical assistance in many cases. The Society also publishes a special book to assist you. Additional advice can be obtained from the EMC Committee Chairman via RSGB HQ.

Planning Permission

There is a special booklet and expert help available to members seeking assistance with planning matters.

GB2RS

A special radio news bulletin transmitted each week and aimed especially at the UK radio amateur and short wave listener. The script is prepared each week by the Society's HQ staff. The transmission schedule appears in the *RSGB Yearbook*. The GB2RS bulletin is also available via the packet radio network, the RSGB website and a premium-rate telephone number.

RSGB Exhibitions and Mobile Rallies

The Society's Exhibition and Rally Committee organises an annual exhibition and an annual mobile rally. Full details and a rally calendar can be found in *Radio Communication*.

RSGB Conventions

The Society's diary in *Radio Communication* contains details of all special conventions which are open to all radio amateurs. The Society holds several major conventions each year.

Observation Service

A number of leading national radio societies have volunteers who monitor the amateur bands as a service to the amateur community. Their task is to spot licence infringements and defective transmissions, and report them in a friendly way to the originating station.

Intruder Watch

This helps to protect the exclusive amateur bands by monitoring for stations not authorised to use them.

Send for our Membership Information Pack today and discover how you too can benefit from these services. Write to:

RADIO SOCIETY OF GREAT BRITAIN, Lambda House, Cranborne Road, Potters Bar, Herts EN6 3JE, England Tel: 01707 659015

Visit our website – www.rsgb.org

Some other RSGB publications...

• Amateur Radio Operating Manual

Covers the essential operating techniques for most aspects of amateur radio including DX, contests and mobile operation, and features a comprehensive set of operating aids.

• Microwave Handbook

A major publication in three volumes. Volume I covers operating techniques, system analysis and propagation, antennas, transmission lines and components, semiconductors and valves. Volume 2 continues with construction techniques, common equipment, beacons and repeaters, test equipment, safety, filters and data. Volume 3 concludes with practical equipment designs for each band.

• Packet Radio Primer

A light-hearted introduction to the exciting world of packet radio which will help any beginner to get started with the minimum of fuss. Detailed practical advice on connecting up equipment is followed by a guide through the maze of configurations possible. This second edition has been completely revised and greatly expanded.

• The Radio Amateur's Guide to EMC

Helps you avoid electromagnetic compatibility (EMC) problems by practising good radio housekeeping, and assists you in the diagnosis and cure of any which do occur. The social dimension is not forgotten, and a whole chapter is devoted to dealing with neighbours. If trouble ever does come to your door, you can reach confidently for this book.

• Radio Communication Handbook

First published in 1938 and a favourite ever since, this large and comprehensive guide to the theory and practice of amateur radio takes the reader from first principles right through to such specialised fields as packet radio, slow-scan television and amateur satellite communication.

• Space Radio Handbook

Space exploration by radio is exciting and it's open to everyone! This book shows you how it is done and the equipment you will need. It covers the whole field of space communication and experimentation, including meteor scatter, moonbounce, satellites and simple radio astronomy. A particularly valuable feature is a collection of experiments which will be of interest to schools wishing to explore the many educational possibilities of this fascinating subject.

• Technical Topics Scrapbook 1985–89

Contains the complete 'Technical Topics' columns from 1985 to 1989 inclusive, reprinted from *Radio Communication* magazine, together with a new index. No amateur experimenter or constructor should be without this information at his or her fingertips.

• Test Equipment for the Radio Amateur

Describes a range of test instruments and measurement methods which should satisfy the requirements of most amateur stations. The theory behind the methods is given, and complete constructional details are included for the majority of the test instruments described.

 ## RADIO SOCIETY OF GREAT BRITAIN

Lambda House, Cranborne Road, Potters Bar, Herts EN6 3JE, England
Tel: 01707 659015

Visit our website – www.rsgb.org